VAN LOON'S
LIVES

Being a true and faithful account
of a number of highly interesting meetings
with certain historical personages, from
CONFUCIUS and PLATO to VOLTAIRE
and THOMAS JEFFERSON, about whom
we had always felt a great deal of
curiosity and who came to us
as our dinner guests in a bygone year.
Written and illustrated by

Hendrik Willem van Loon

1942
SIMON AND SCHUSTER
NEW YORK

MANUFACTURED IN THE UNITED STATES OF AMERICA
BY THE AMERICAN BOOK—STRATFORD PRESS, NEW YORK, N. Y.

In dedicating these pages to
JULIANA
Heir to the Throne of the Free and Independent
Kingdom of the Netherlands
I know that I give expression to the sentiments that are
foremost in her own heart
if I inscribe these chapters to
the memory of
those valiant men of our beloved Zeeland
who died
while trying to preserve and maintain
that most cherished of their possessions
their LIBERTY

TABLE OF CONTENTS

Table of Contents

Table of Contents

Table of Contents

ILLUSTRATIONS

Illustrations

Illustrations

Illustrations

Illustrations

FOREWORD WRITTEN FOR
MY GRANDCHILDREN

OF COURSE *you never knew your Uncle Frits, for he died long before you were born. I am sorry. You would have loved him. He was like one of those elderly gentlemen in Central Park who go around feeding birds and squirrels. Their pockets are filled with everything these small creatures may like to eat. The birds and the squirrels sense this and they perch on the shoulders of their benefactors and climb all over them in quest of what they consider their legitimate belongings.*

In the case of Frits, who would have been your "honorary" uncle if he had lived, gaiety and kindness and tolerance and understanding were the gifts he bestowed upon the world. Wherever he went, he squandered these rare possessions in a most magnificent and bountiful manner, for he knew (what all wise people have realized since the beginning of time) that the only treasures which are truly ours are those we lay up in the hearts of our friends.

In the country of my birth, still suffering from the aftereffects of the great Calvinistic ice age of the sixteenth century, a personality like his was as welcome as it was unexpected, and, in spite of a considerable difference in years, we had become fast friends just five minutes after we had met in the dining room of the beloved old abbey of Middelburg.

That period of intimacy lasted only a few years, but those were the happiest years of my life, for they were spent in Veere, and the magic of that delectable ruin (a veritable city and the capital of a regular marquisate), consisting of a few hundred decrepit houses, a number of gardens, and endless memories— the enchantment of that queer little paradise was such that we rarely felt the need of any contact with the rest of the world and we thought with infinite pity of our poor contemporaries, doomed to spend their days in such dull and unimaginative hamlets as London, Paris, New York, or Rio.

Having decided that this was the place for us (at least until our money should run out), Jimmie and I had bought ourselves a pleasant house, constructed in the year 1572 and therefore considered a bit too new and glittering and not quite in keeping with the rest of the neighborhood, which still showed decided influence of its Gothic origin.

Soon afterward Frits also made up his mind to join the small band of the truly wise ones who, having inspected all other Elysian premises from Tahiti to Bermuda, had come to the conclusion that Veere was the only completely satisfactory answer to the question: "Where can a civilized human being spend his days with the least possible minimum of irritation and the greatest possible maximum of inner satisfaction?"

And in this way commenced that very brief period of absolute contentment during which both Frits and I probably learned more about ourselves and our fellow men than we had done in all the schools, academies, and universities we had graced with our physical attendance if not always with our intellectual and spiritual presence.

Now it so happened (another fortunate coincidence) that neither Frits nor I was really very seriously addicted to any kind of physical exercise, although we agreed that it was a good thing for most other people, and as a result we used to sit for hours at a time in his small parlor with the high window (light is at a premium in that foggy part of the Low Countries) and we used to indulge in that pastime, which has never quite ceased to surprise the excellent Jimmie, who, like all true Americans, never ceases to wonder what possible pleasure two people may consciously derive from just sitting and talking—doing nothing at all but just sitting and talking.

That, however, was all we wanted. We wanted to sit and talk God out of his heaven and the Devil back into his hell. We found delight in juggling with the solar system, and we used to turn the Milky Way into a bowling alley down which we rolled Betelgeuse to see how many signs of the Zodiac (which we used as our pins) we could knock down with one single ball.

The tower of the ancient town hall dominated the landscape.

Foreword

And there was not a name in the whole card catalogue of the past which we did not feel at liberty to take out of its little drawer and put aside for special examination; and then (the crime of crimes of all good librarians!) if we did not really feel that it belonged in that collection of the great and near-great, we were just as apt as not to tear it up and throw it into the harbor and good riddance!

And now I want to tell you about a certain morning—it was during the Christmas holidays—when I had dropped in on Frits for an eleven-o'clock cup of coffee. We were sitting in front of the window of his dining room and we looked at the town-hall tower opposite us and we talked of some people Jimmie and I had invited for dinner that evening, and Frits said, "What a pity we can't ask that old tower some day to drop in for a plate of pea soup! It has been there such a long time, it has seen so much! It ought to be able to tell us lots of amusing things about all sorts of people it would have been fun to meet."

"Listen, my dear Frits," I answered, "why are you and Lucie and all the rest of us in Veere? Because there really is no longer such a place. It only exists in our imagination—it is 'memory turned flesh.' We had grown sick and tired of a life of gadgets and tangibles and activities that were a waste of effort and we had come to hate all the rest of our beloved modern civilization which made us yawn and reach for a bottle of beer. And so we came here, for since there is nothing concrete in Veere, we can deal with facts."

"A most noble speech," Frits said, "but what does that have to do with my idea that it would be nice to have the tower drop in for dinner and tell us about all sorts of people we would have liked to meet?"

Here it was my turn to interrupt. "Why go in for the second best," I asked, "when we can have first best and at no greater expense of effort or money? If we can make a Gothic tower come and sit down at your dining-room table, it must be just as easy to invite some Babylonian potentate who has been in his grave these last fifty centuries!"

Frits agreed. "There is something to what you say."

"Well," I suggested, "suppose we go ahead and do. it! There is nobody to tell us no." And then and there we began to work on a general list of the people we would have liked to meet and whom we now intended to invite.

This took us quite a long time. Not because there was a lack of suitable candidates, but what were to be the qualifications according to which we would proceed in asking them to our dinner parties? At first we were very serious about it, and we began to divide mankind into different categories, the good ones and the evil ones and those who had said yea unto life and those who had said nay and those who had liked boiled mutton (very few, we were delighted to discover) and those who had hated boiled mutton. Until one day Frits said to me, "I am afraid we are on the wrong track. It seems a hopeless task to try and divide the human race into definite categories. They are all of them such hopeless mixtures of good and bad and indifferent. Suppose we drop all our philosophic considerations and ask those whom we would like to meet and for no other reason than that, for the moment at least, we happen to feel that it would be interesting to find out what they looked like and what they had to say."

This seemed an eminently intelligent decision, and it was so decided.

Next we had to choose the day of the week on which it would be most convenient to have our parties. Frits, who did not have to take business very seriously (it was during the happy days when anybody could make all the money he wanted by going through the motions of running an office), thought that he could almost always drive from Amsterdam to Veere late Friday night or take the Saturday-morning mail train to Flushing. And so the dinners were set for Saturday evenings at seven, for we kept early hours in our little village.

Came the question of what to give our guests for dinner. After some deliberation we thought it would be best to offer them (as nearly as we could) the same sort of food and drink to which they had been accustomed during their own lifetime. This would mean a great deal of serious study in old cookbooks, but Henri Meijer (who knew everything about everything that had ever been printed) would find us these long-forgotten volumes, and we were near enough to Paris and London to order anything else we might want.

Should we have music with our meals? Yes and no. Music can of course be a great hindrance to conversation but, if applied with care and circumspection, it can break the ice while you are meeting strangers and it might put our guests into the right mood and make them all the more willing to talk.

Frits had an excellent phonograph, and there were records to be had for every time and occasion. He told me that he would leave that part to me, and we would put the phonograph upstairs in one of the bedrooms so that it would not sound too loud and it might perhaps make some of our guests believe that we had hired an entire orchestra in their honor.

Then our final problem. "You know these people," Frits said, "at least you know something about them, for that happens to be your job. But to me, most of them are only names. So why don't you write them up for me—just a short account of who they are and what they have done? I don't want to make any clumsy breaks and talk about daggers when we have Mary of Scotland—it might be somewhat of a faux pas—*and William the Conqueror would probably not like to hear too much about bastards."*

As long as Frits was going to take care of all the practical details of the entertainment (or, to put it a little more correctly, as long as he was going to pay the bills), I felt that such an arrangement was only fair and I promised him that every Wednesday evening, by special delivery, he would have what the diplomats used to call "a piece" about our next guests—a short and concise summing up of their antecedents and accomplishments and a statement about the most important facts and dates in their worldly careers.

But, you will ask, how in the name of heaven did we get in contact with these people whose bones lay spread all over the surface of the globe and who had been dead and gone for hundreds and sometimes thousands of years? Of that I hope to tell you some other time. It was really very simple, but for the moment it must remain our secret, a secret, by the way, which belongs to the happiest recollection of my life—the memory of a perfect friendship.

—HENDRIK WILLEM VAN LOON

Nieuw Veere
Old Greenwich, Connecticut
May 8, 1942

VAN LOON'S
LIVES

NOTE TO THE CRITICAL READER

THE READER may have come upon a few statements within the pages of this book which strike him as anachronisms. The author is fully aware of their existence. But what else was to be expected in a volume in which people dead and buried for thousands of years discuss their preference for veal chops over stuffed carp and try to murder each other on obscure points of theology which the rest of the world had forgotten twenty generations before?

CHAPTER I

DESIDERIUS ERASMUS, Our First Guest, Arrives
Punctually on Time and Gives Us a Most
Delightful Evening

WE HAD been promised that our plan would work, but when we
found out how simple it was going to be, both Frits and I were
a bit perplexed and we looked at each other and said, "This is
almost too good to be true!" and we crossed our fingers and held
our breath and we decided to wait and see how our next party
would come off before we committed ourselves definitely.

Our negotiations had been rather complex, but after we had
made it quite clear what we intended to do and that we meant
to be very, very discreet, we had experienced no further difficulties and had never even been asked for any kind of guarantee
that we would live up to our promises. We had merely let it
be known that from our side everything would be done "in
order and decency"—for in the beginning of our discussions
we instinctively stuck to a sort of semi-Biblical vernacular and
we used to rack our brains for odds and ends of long-forgotten
texts whenever we approached what was to remain the Great
Mystery. And in addition, we most solemnly promised that,
from our side, we would do everything to make our guests as
comfortable as possible, and be at hand to make them feel
thoroughly at home. We had given our word that we would not
bother any of them with questions which might possibly embarrass them, no matter how curious we might feel about certain unrevealed secrets in their private lives, and that we would

not delve too deeply into the hidden motives underlying some of their actions that never, as far as we were concerned, had quite made sense.

If they themselves should bring up such subjects, then we might make a few very discreet inquiries, but we must remember that most of our future companions had lived very strenuous existences and were apt to be people with rather sensitively balanced nervous systems. What they had suffered at the hands of their fellow men had given most of them a desire to be allowed to spend the rest of eternity removed from all further contact with the human race, and there was to be no coercion in case they sent their regrets.

It was explained that a great many would be quite eager to accept our invitation. A short glimpse of the old familiar scenes might make them all the more resigned to their present mode of existence. But we must never take the initiative in any of our conversations and we must leave it to them to bring up whatever subjects they wished to discuss and they must have complete freedom of coming and going.

For the rest, there were to be no restrictions. All we would have to do was to write the names of those persons we wanted to meet on a slip of paper and leave this document underneath one of the stone lions that guarded the ceremonial staircase of the old Veere town hall. After that, we must wait and see.

To be quite honest, until Erasmus was actually there, sitting in his chair at the head of the table and smiling at us from behind his queer-looking old glasses, we had felt sure that it was all a dream and that nothing would happen. But we had decided that we would go on with the plan as it had been outlined to us and would not reveal any of the doubts which still beset us. At the worst, so we told each other, we would have ordered a rather elaborate meal and we would have spent a few guilders on a few bottles of wine and a few hard-to-get phonograph records, and if our first guest failed to show up, we would walk across the street and ask one of our neighbors to come and take his place, and so we could not possibly go very far wrong.

All that had remained to be done was to decide whom we would choose as our first guest.

Quite naturally, the name of Erasmus had suggested itself to us before that of any others. In the first place, he was a native of the same city in which I myself had seen the light of day, and certain outward physical resemblances had always made me suspect that somehow or other, in that little medieval town, we must have had a common ancestor. Of course, as poor Erasmus had been born out of wedlock, it would have been rather indelicate to inquire too closely into his origins, and I realized that even a personal meeting would not shed much light upon a subject that has puzzled historians for so many centuries. All the same, a chance to make a quiet study and comparison of the hands of our guest and my own (the hands of Erasmus, as revealed to us by Dürer, and mine as shown by von Bree's photograph)—that in itself was something to be most cordially welcomed. And furthermore, Erasmus might easily be prevailed upon to come to Veere, as at one time of his career our little town had played quite a role in his life.

Erasmus was by nature a sociable kind of person. Much against his own will he had been forced to take holy orders. This had been done because the relatives and executors of his mother (who had died of the plague while her sons were still quite young), wishing above all things to rid themselves of their unwelcome charges (two bastard boys with no particular financial assets), had practically taken these poor infants by the scruff of their necks and had thrown them into a cloister. In their case it was the cloister called Steyn. It was situated near the city of Gouda, and Erasmus, all his livelong days, was to remember the spot with the same kind of cold-blooded detestation with which I myself remember the town of Ter Gouw, where I spent the four most miserable years of a by no means happy childhood.

But these monastic vows, once taken, had been final and definite and they had excluded the famous humanist from any kind of normal friendship with the feminine half of the human race. There are evidences that this was a source of great annoyance to him. Not because he was interested in women as such. But conscious of his brilliant powers as a conversationalist, he liked to enter into the normal social life of his day and he soon found that the Augustinian habit that he was forced to wear was hardly the right kind of introduction to a merry party. As a result, Erasmus, during the threescore and ten years he spent upon this earth, rarely came in direct contact with what we sometimes and quite irrationally call "the gentler sex."

But among the statues which adorned and which even today (unless Mr. Hitler has suddenly decided differently) continue to adorn the façade of Veere's ancient town hall, there is one of a certain Anna van Borselen. This charming lady (who was a *grande dame* in every respect of the word), had she not fallen in love with the wrong man and (infinitely worse) married him, might have become one of the great figures of history. She could (had she remained.solvent) have qualified as the patroness of her unfortunate fellow countryman, who, in spite of all his most persuasive begging letters, never quite achieved what could be called "an established position in life" until he was much too old and much too famous to care either one way or the other.

My lady of Borselen's father, Wolferd van Borselen, had been the richest and most powerful nobleman of the province of Zeeland. He was lord of Flushing, lord of Veere, and owner of almost as many farms and estates as the abbots of Middelburg, who were the greatest capitalists of the whole of southern Holland. But Wolferd was a bad manager. Competition with the Burgundian dukes, who were just then establishing themselves in the southern Netherlands, had made him indulge in a too-grandiose display of his own opulence. And when he died, Wolferd left his daughter a fine escutcheon with all the necessary quarterings but not by any means as rich as she was supposed to be.

She fortunately understood her position and when during her late twenties she was left a widow, she decided to do the wise thing and retire to her estate on the island of Noord Beveland (opposite our own town of Veere) that she might devote

herself to the education of her children and bring some semblance of order into the chaos of her private finances.

In those days the Low Countries were far removed from the

The Lady Anna of Borselen.

center of civilization, and Anna of Borselen realized that if she
wanted to turn her oldest son into a true gentleman, able to
hold his own at the court of the Duke of Burgundy and to
shine among the brightest spirits of the Renaissance, she must

give him an education far above anything that could be provided by the simple schoolmen of the little cities along the North Sea. And so she asked a few questions about the possibilities of hiring a really competent teacher, and it was then that one of her good friends suggested a certain Gerrit Gerritszoon (beginning to be known to the learned world as Desiderius Erasmus) who, it is true, was a native of Rotterdam but who was recognized far and wide as being possessed of a most elegant Latin style and a vast amount of erudition.

Furthermore, although of humble and uncertain birth, this Desiderius Erasmus was a young man of genteel manners and in holy orders, so that the problem of a suitable chaperon would not rear its disturbing head. As he was free just then and was looking for a suitable position, he would undoubtedly be delighted to consider associating himself with so noble a house as that of the Borselens.

A correspondence followed, and everything seemed beautifully arranged, including a salary, which to poor Erasmus, who had always lived a hand-to-mouth existence, must have looked like the perfect answer to a poor scholar's prayer. Alas, at that very moment the Lady Anna decided to fall in love with a handsome but useless young nobleman from Holland and expressed her intention of marrying him.

This alliance was far from welcome to her many relatives. They somehow had come to regard her as a permanent widow and in their anger they hired all the lawyers of their lawyer-ridden age and proceeded to persecute their unfortunate cousin with such unceasing and endless fury that when it was all over, both she and the heirs were well-nigh ruined. But at the moment when Erasmus hopefully traveled northward to meet his future employer at her castle of Kortgene, these unhappy developments were still hidden by a merciful future, and he was full of hope that this beautiful and generous patron of the arts and letters would not only engage him as the private tutor for her small son but also would listen to his modest suggestion that a visit on his part to the universities of Italy (at her expense, of course) would make his services even more valuable than they could be at present when he had merely picked up a few odds and ends of learning at Paris and Cambridge.

And so he had happily clambered on the horse that Anna van Borselen had kindly sent him and, accompanied by his servant (for he could not possibly travel without someone to look after him), he had set out for the land of his birth and of a new future.

He was soon to be most sadly disappointed. That noble Latin poem which he had addressed to his benefactress and in which he had compared his Anna to Anna the sister of Queen Dido, to Anna the grandmother of Jesus, and to Anna the mother of the prophet Samuel—it had been a complete waste of time, ink, effort, and parchment, for the Lady seemed to have had no idea who those famous namesakes might have been. She could read and write better than most of her female contemporaries, but she did not intend to become a bluestocking. And she remained completely aloof when the great humanist informed her that he intended to dedicate his *Adagia* to her little son Adolf, and merely asked: "What are adagia?"

This shocked Erasmus. He considered these *Adagia* his magnum opus. They consisted of eight hundred Greek and Latin proverbs which he had collected most carefully that they might serve as the harmless pegs upon which to string those far-from-harmless and exceedingly pungent observations upon the affairs of the day which made him the founder of our tribe of modern columnists.

In his innocence—or his pride in being considered the most promising young humanist of his day—he had felt that Anna van Borselen would be greatly flattered by the idea of her little Adolf's name appearing on the dedicatory page of a volume for which the world was waiting as eagerly as today it is waiting for the Ninth Symphony of Sibelius. But Greek and Latin proverbs were entirely beyond the Lady's intellectual reach, and so this curious relationship remained in a state of profound uncertainty and suspense until the two met. And then Erasmus was to discover that his rich benefactress, while nominally the ruler of thousands of fertile acres, depended upon the bounty of some of her more loyal farmers for her daily sustenance.

She therefore was out of the question as that enlightened and opulent patroness of whom Erasmus had dreamed all his live-long days, the good fairy who, by an order on some well-known banking house in Antwerp or Paris or Rome, would enable him to devote himself exclusively to his serious literary pursuits without being forced to waste his energies upon those everlasting potboilers which took up so much of his time and were such a very doubtful source of revenue.

This sad incident in the life of one who seems to have proceeded from one disappointment to the next has never attracted the serious interest of most of the old fellow's biographers. But to Frits and to me it meant a great deal. For it was during this ill-fated visit to Noord Beveland that Erasmus had lived through an adventure that was still clearly remembered by several of our fellow citizens, who had got it from their grandfathers, who had got it from their great-grandfathers, and so on, back to the end of the fifteenth century.

Early in February Erasmus had reached Veere, from where he was to be ferried to his new Zion in Noord Beveland. The winter had been more severe than usual. As a result, all communications between Walcheren and the other islands had for quite a long time been suspended, for the broad expanse of water separating Walcheren from Noord Beveland was covered with a solid floor of ice through which no vessel could hope to pass. A few days before Erasmus arrived in Veere, a sudden thaw accompanied by heavy rains had set in, and then, quite as unexpectedly, the wind had changed from east to west and a sleet storm had done the rest. Now both the water and the land were covered with a heavy layer of slippery ice. There was only one way in which he could hope to reach his destination. He must go on foot.

"Behold us therefore," as Erasmus wrote shortly afterward to his friend, Lord William Mountjoy, "with Anna's castle right before our eyes but a sea of solid ice separating us from our destination. Such a terrific wind was blowing that two men from the other island, who had tried to come across to our shore that morning, had been forced to return. That, however, meant that we had this howling hurricane right in our own back. And so I crouched down on the dike and I slid across the ice and, as I had expected, the wind caught me and blew me right to my destination while I sat on my haunches and steered my course with the help of a long stick which served me as a rudder. Surely this was a novel kind of navigation!

"That is a true account of my voyage—one long succession of miserable adventures—but what followed was an equally uninterrupted succession of pleasurable experiences.

"In good health I reached the home of my Lady Anna of Veere. How shall I describe unto you the civility and the kindness and the generosity of this most noble woman? A more modest, more intelligent, and more charming creature than she surely never was born. Etc., etc."

Those flattering observations had of course been made before the true state of the Lady's insolvency and her indifference about the real life of the mind had revealed themselves unto the eager pilgrim. However, the fact that Erasmus had actually been in Veere, that he must have spent some time there, living in the house of one of its merchants or artisans, that perhaps he had been struck with the loveliness of the town hall, then in the final stages of its construction—all these considerations had made us feel that Erasmus was the ideal person to be invited to our first, and therefore experimental, dinner party.

And we had guessed right. For no sooner had the chimes of the tower, just across from Frits' house, begun to play the opening bars of Valerius' lovely old *Hymn of Thanksgiving* than we heard a commotion in the street. We hastened to the window and saw coming around the corner from the harbor a small, slightly bent old man, leaning heavily on a cane but marching with great assurance straight toward our front door. The strange-looking figure was followed by a tall and skinny fellow who undoubtedly must be his famous servant, his eternal famulus, and the noise we had heard was that of the wooden shoes belonging to a dozen or so little boys and girls who, attracted by this unfamiliar sight, had hastened to find out what queer folk the American and his friend from Amsterdam might, this time, have brought into their midst.

At the very moment the tinkly bells finished their stately tune, the small dark figure stood in front of our house. Then it turned around and faced the town hall, and a long bony finger pointed tremblingly at one of the seven stone figures which are the pride of this noble old edifice. We realized what was happening. Erasmus was showing his companion the portrait of Anna of Veere, who might have meant so much in his life and who had only sent him on a wild-goose chase in the heart of winter to discover that once more he had to give up all hope for a "safe future."

In the matter of getting up the menu for our guest, we had experienced little difficulty. Erasmus was known to have been a good deal of a hypochondriac. In his letters he was forever worrying about his health, but there was something to be said on his side. As a child he had been very delicate. In the cloister of Steyn he had never had enough to eat. Afterward, as a charity student in the Paris college of Montaigu, he had contracted that horrible disease which was to make him a chronic patient for practically all the remaining days of his life.

At the same time, like most people who lead a sedentary and contemplative existence, Erasmus had a tendency to exaggerate those discomforts which were inseparable from existence in the early Renaissance. In the epistles to his friends he was forever complaining about a cold or a cough he had caught in an inn with a damp bed while traveling from London to Cambridge or was predicting his forthcoming demise as the result of a fever which had been the result of drinking the sour beer of Flanders while going from Antwerp to Brussels and which had laid him low for almost three weeks.

The bells of the town hall used to toll the hour of departure.

And it was his rule, before he honored a stranger's house with a visit, to make sure that his host would not feed him the wrong dishes or let him sleep in a bed that had not been aired thoroughly or let him study in a room with a draft. As a result, I had so much material upon this subject that it was quite easy to order a meal that would come up to all the finicky requirements and specifications of the distinguished old humanist.

First of all I ordered a vegetable soup with sausage from Guelders, for I knew that he considered Guelders sausages to be one of the few true delicacies which his native land had contributed to the culinary treasures of the Continent. Next I intended to serve veal, but as Erasmus had lived just when the world was progressing from fingers to forks, I had somewhat hesitated whether to serve him roast veal or a veal stew. I remembered, however, that somewhere (I think it was in Basel) I had seen a leather case containing a knife and fork that a Polish abbot had sent him. Therefore it was safe to assume that Erasmus would know how to handle a fork, and so we decided upon veal cutlets with a sauce made of sour cream mixed with horse-radish. He would undoubtedly complain afterward that the horse-radish had carried him to the brink of the grave, but as he was to leave immediately after dinner we felt that we need not worry about this detail. We supposed that heaven provided bicarbonate of soda, and Saint Peter would know how to give him the right mixture. Potatoes, of course, he would never have eaten (he would have disliked them as a tasteless sort of vegetable), but we had both beans and carrots, being very careful, however, to avoid any of the cabbage family, for his gastric ulcers would have objected seriously to *Rothkohl*, or sprouts.

For dessert I meant to provide that fresh fruit of which he had been so fond and in the matter of wines (his kidney stones forced him to be very careful about what he drank) I had chosen some of his dearly beloved Moselle vintages, a bottle of Berncasteler Doktor, *Auslese* 1921, and for good measure a magnificent Hochheimer *Spätlese*, also dating back to 1921, which had been the last year for German wines of more than ordinary excellence.

In honor of his visit Frits had got hold of an excellent reproduction of the old gentleman's portrait painted by Hans Holbein in the year 1523. This had been a happy choice, for Erasmus noticed it at once and he spoke of it, though afterward he
confessed that he himself preferred the picture made by
Quentin Matsys and painted when he was in his early fifties.
"It does not make me quite as venerable as the Holbein picture," he explained, "and I wish that people would sometimes
remember that I too was young once upon a time and was not
born a hundred years old." And then he added some criticism
(a well-taken criticism, it seemed to us too) of the way Holbein
had handled his mouth.

I realized that this was a rather delicate subject with him.
During his earlier years he himself had given evidence of a
very distinct gift for the pictorial arts. But it had been deemed
incompatible with his position, both as a cleric and the leading
Latin and Greek scholar, that he should devote himself to a
craft whose members were then still supposed to register with
the guild of the wooden shoemakers. This sounds rather
curious, but it was not until more than a century after the
death of Erasmus that the painters of the Low Countries had
at last acquired sufficient social prestige to be allowed to organize a guild of their own and to call it after the Apostle Luke,
the gentle physician who was said to have spent his leisure
hours painting pictures of the Blessed Virgin.

And so Erasmus had given up his brush, but his interest in
some kind of pictorial self-expression had remained as strong
as ever, as we know from the endless dingbats and doodads he
scribbled all over his letters and manuscripts and which would
fill a small volume if anyone would ever take the trouble to
lift them out of their original texts. If this were done, I am
sure that our psychologists, carefully studying these tiny monsters, these misshapen proletarians and dwarfish devils, would

be able to reveal certain angles of the Erasmian philosophy of life that have never yet been suspected.

But for that very reason we intended to avoid the entire subject of the graphic arts and instead we tried to imagine what kind of reaction we would obtain to the music we had selected. I remembered that Erasmus had never been as happy as when he was staying with his old friend, Sir Thomas More. England, incidentally, was the country he preferred above all others. He complained, of course (as who has not, these last four hundred years?), about the damp beds in the inns and the abominable food served to him everywhere except in a few private homes, but for the rest he adored this delightful country where young girls were in the habit of kissing the older gentlemen who frequented their parents' homes.

And in those days before the unfortunate advent of the Puritan, England was indeed a merry country, and, in spite of its being ruled by a lecherous madman and in spite of the gallows and racks which exposed their hideous burdens at almost every crossroad, there was a genuine atmosphere of unaffected gaiety and good living and surprisingly high thinking which made itself manifest in every part of the land. That, of course, meant that there was a lot of music. Most of that music was of the amateur variety, for the Englishman, with his hard common sense, had never taken much interest in mere virtuosity.

We therefore had searched the gramophone catalogues for the seemingly simple songs which had been so popular in England during the sixteenth century, and we had ordered records of Orlando Gibbons' *Ah, Dear Heart,* of John Bull's *The King's Hunt,* of Thomas Morley's *Go from My Window* and *It Was a Lover and His Lass,* of William Byrd's *The Bells* and of two of his motets, and Francis Pilkington's *Rest, Sweet Nymphs.* We played Henry Purcell's Chaconne when he came in and served William Byrd's Pavanne and Galliards with the soup.

He seemed pleased and a little puzzled as to where the music came from. But we soon discovered that conversation was the old gentleman's real passion. He liked the music, but when it came to an end, he did not ask for more. And small wonder! He was a brilliant talker and he knew it, and he seemed like one starved for a bright and amusing exchange of ideas. Indeed, from some casual remark of his, we rather came to the conclusion that while he was contented enough with his present status, he occasionally found the atmosphere just a little too solemn and oppressive and then wished that he might return to an existence slightly more—well, shall we say, slightly more active? —than that which he had enjoyed for the last four centuries.

He seemed pathetically eager to catch up with the affairs of the day and he was forever drawing parallels between the political and religious situations of the early half of the sixteenth century and those of the twentieth. As we soon discovered, he was not at all well informed about the things that had happened after his own death. In a general way, however, his logical mind had allowed him to keep surprisingly well informed about the main outlines of what had been really important within the field of letters and politics and religion. But his knowledge was spotty, and today I would say that he reminded me of a fugitive Norwegian or Hollander who, after years of German tyranny, finally reaches the United States and then tries to catch up with the news which has either not reached him at all or has come to him hopelessly mangled by the local censors or in too abbreviated a form, as it was sent out by the English or American short-wave stations.

The old gentleman, however, had a mind as quick and agile as a hartebeest and, jumping from one spot to the next with an absolute sureness of foot, he covered a terrific amount of territory. And when, shortly after eleven (for he still kept early hours), he looked at the clock and remarked that it was about time for him to retire, he tried to sum up the whole of the evening's conversation in these not very helpful words:

"What poor, deluded fools these human beings are! Won't they ever learn? Of course, today they seem to do everything at a much faster rate of speed than we did in our day. They get born faster. They live faster. They eat faster. They burn out faster. But what do they gain? And you tell me that all of them can now read and write! But what do they read and what do they write? And are they any better at living in peace with each other than we were? Do they love each other any the better? Let me put it even more simply. Do they treat each other with any greater decency and tolerance than we did in our time, when we were forever slaughtering each other for some opinion which was mere guesswork and probably always would remain so, and yet caused one half of humanity to send the other half to the gallows and the stake—and for what? . . . I am sorry, but even today, I don't quite know for what!"

As to the exact details of our dinner conversation, I was too excited about this first strange encounter to remember many of them. Of course, after he left, Frits and I still spent considerable time discussing the strange adventure of that strange evening. But before I report our little *post cenam* (why not?—it is a pleasanter expression than the more familiar *post mortem!*), I must give you the short account of Erasmus' life as I had written it down for Frits' private information as soon as we had decided that he was to be our first guest of the historical dinners.

Here it is, my report, as I had sent it to Frits' office in Amsterdam, three days before our meeting.

I first met Desiderius Erasmus when I was six years old. Every morning at half-past eight, Hein, our old man of all work, used to take me sternly by the hand to guide me (or rather, to drag me) to school, for school, in that terrifying old house on the river front, was not very amusing, whereas the streets and docks of Rotterdam were full of fascinating sights, sounds, and smells. And every morning I begged and implored old Hein to let me tarry before that graven image until the clock of St. Lawrence struck the hour, for I had been told that when Erasmus heard the hour strike, he would turn a leaf of the book he held in his left hand. And every morning old Hein would grab me a little more firmly and would pull me a little faster past this fascinating spot. Never did he explain what I only learned later—that there was a catch in this story, because Erasmus, being made of iron and not of ordinary flesh and blood, could not possibly hear the clock strike.

That is how I first got in touch with my famous fellow towns-man, but who he had been or what he had ever done to deserve a statue in a country which was not very much addicted to hon-oring its famous men—that was something I never quite discov-ered until a great many years afterward. And I doubt whether most of my fellow Rotterdamers were much better informed upon this subject than I. When they thought of Erasmus at all, they vaguely associated him with the Reformation, which was still an actuality to these pious folk, and they suspected that he had had something to do with the so-called "House of the Thousand Fears," which stood directly opposite his statue. In this ancient edifice, during the sack of Rotterdam by the Span-ish troops, when all the Protestants had been murdered, a num-ber of men and women had found a safe refuge because they had cleverly smeared the door and the windows of the building with the blood of a little pet goat. As a result, the mercenaries of King Philip, noticing these bloody crosses, had decided that the occupants of the house had already been "attended to" and had gone their way, leaving the poor wretches shivering in the cellar and the attic until they were able to escape under the cover of darkness.

I remember that I always felt terribly sorry for that little goat which had been obliged to give its blood that others might live, and I too shared the belief that the iron man with the book in his hand had had something to do with that ghastly in-cident in our glorious struggle for freedom. Perhaps it was he himself who had cut the throat of that unfortunate little beast, although he looked quite amiable, had a long and amusing nose and a smiling mouth, and carried neither sword nor dagger nor any other instruments of violence.

The next time I came in contact with my hero was some half-dozen years later. I had, without realizing it, followed in the old gentleman's footsteps and was conjugating Greek and Latin verbs (both regular and irregular, but all of them very bewildering and upsetting) in the little city of Gouda, which will be more familiar to readers of Charles Reade's *The Cloister and the Hearth* under the name of Ter Gouw.

It was not a happy experience. The men who were supposed to reveal unto us the mysteries and beauties of the ancient world were pretty hopeless barbarians. They were supposed to have qualified for their jobs by learning a couple of grammars by heart and getting a Ph.D. by means of writing a short, dull treatise upon some obscure point of syntax or grammar. But they were totally devoid of any feeling for style or literary charm. Homer, as far as they were concerned, had merely sung his magnificent songs to catch little Dutch boys in irregularities of construction and erroneous accents. Cicero was the only ancient author who came up to their pedantic expectations, and this uninspired corporation lawyer was forever held up to us as an example after which we should strive with might and main in order that we too might become what they used to call "pure Latinists."

Alas, even at the tender age of eleven, I was already affected by that passion which has been the driving force of my whole life. I was incurably curious about my fellow men. I instinctively wanted to understand what made them behave the way they did and I felt that I might get a key to this mystery by learning everything I could about the people of the past. For that purpose I wanted to know enough Latin and Greek to read the ancient authors, but my teachers merely insisted that I learn whole chunks of grammar by heart and they greatly resented my everlasting questions about the real meaning of those texts which were thrown at us, not for the purpose of teaching us something about the true spirit of the old world, but merely to catch us in obscure conjugational irregularities and to find out whether we knew that a certain word which occurred only once in the whole of Greek literature suffered from ablative trouble.

These doleful lamentations about the inadequate pedagogical methods of my youth sound exactly like those of Erasmus, as you can find out for yourself by reading the letters he wrote while he wandered hopelessly from one school and university to the other, trying to find a really intelligent and inspiring teacher. The only difference is this: Erasmus was a good deal more vituperative in his denunciations of his professors and the indifference of his fellow scholars than I can ever hope to be. He called them "ignorant boors," "dumb churls," "hopeless clods," "miscast plowboys," and "ill-mannered louts," and I am quite sure that they were all of that and even more. But Erasmus was spared one indignity that we had to suffer in silence, for when I was young, the teacher was always right, and there was therefore no use bringing the matter to the attention of our parents. His teachers did not smoke. They did not come into the classroom with a grammar and a marking book in one hand and three cigars in a paper bag in the other. Out of the grammar they would ask us their questions. In their little marking books they would meticulously note down all our wrong answers, and they would smoke the three cigars while gloating happily over our helpless bewilderment.

It is not a pleasant picture I am drawing here of the days of my childhood in the old country. But it is an almost exact replica of the existence of little Desiderius, when he was a pupil in the school of the cloister Steyn. One day in Gouda I discovered that not far away from the city there still stood a farm which bore the name of Steyn and which was said to occupy the same site as the old cloister had done. The buildings were mostly gone, except for a few scraps of the original walls. Also, according to my information, there were a few chairs and desks left from the days of Erasmus, all of them in a sad state of repair.

I decided to investigate. Wednesday and Saturday afternoons were my own. I was supposed to spend them playing football "to develop my physical health." I was not greatly interested in my physical health and I hated football. So I walked along the dikes of the river Ysel and felt that I had started upon quite an expedition.

It was a lovely day early in May. The clouds were way up in the sky. The leaves of the willow trees rustled gently in the wind. The birds were very busy with those architectural pursuits which were to provide homes for new crops of their squeaking progeny. And after an hour and a half I reached the spot where I had been told I must find a gate with the name Steyn on it.

The gate was there. It was part of a rather dilapidated wooden fence. A few hundred yards from the gate was a farmhouse, quite run-down in appearance and surrounded by stables which looked as if they too could stand a considerable amount of paint. A slovenly maiden in a dirty dress, the usual blue denim of all Dutch farm help, was pushing a wheelbarrow filled with fresh and fragrant cow manure. She stood still when she saw me coming, dropped her wheelbarrow, and asked me curtly what I wanted. This, so she reminded me, was private property, and strangers were not wanted. I asked her whether this was the placed called the Steyn. She said yes, it was. I told her that I had heard that there was some old furniture in the house. Would I be allowed to see it?

She wanted to know why I wanted to see it. I told her that this used to be a famous monastery. She told me that she had never heard of it. When had it been here?

"Long ago," I answered. "Several hundred years ago."

She shook her head. There was no old furniture, and she knew nothing about a monastery. She was not a Catholic and was not interested in monasteries. That was where monks lived, and she hated all monks, for they did not mean well by honest farm girls. Her grandmother had told her so, and therefore it must be true.

I was young in those days and very shy and I did not quite know how to handle the situation. All I could do was to tell her that I was sorry. I had probably made a mistake. I hoped she did not mind. I wished her a good afternoon. She did not return this slight civility. She picked up her wheelbarrow and continued to push her manure in the general direction of the fields.

A man came out of the door and, shouting, asked her what that little boy had wanted. She called back that he had asked her whether there was some old furniture there.

"Just another nut," the man in the door of the farmhouse bellowed, ostensibly for my benefit. "The next time one of those fools asks for that old furniture here, I shall turn the dog loose on him."

I have never liked dogs that are turned loose on people and I was glad when I had once more closed the gate behind me and was back on the road to Gouda.

When Erasmus came to dinner, I told him about my experience. He was amused.

24

All that remained of the old cloister Steyn.

"They have not changed much since my time," he said. "It was a loathsome place. I tried all my life to forget it, but I never quite succeeded. The memory of all I had suffered there at the hands of those savages in their dirty cowls and with their vulgar minds still haunts me. Even now, after all these hundreds of years, I shudder when I think of them."

That little personal recollection is a suitable introduction to the story of Erasmus.

I think that I have already told you we do not know the exact year in which the great humanist was born. It may have been 1466, but then again it may have been 1465 or 1467. The only information upon the subject that has come down to us is a short autobiographical paragraph in one of his own letters. He was quite fond of dramatizing his unfortunate birth and of elaborating upon the hardships his illegitimate status had wrought upon the whole of his subsequent career. But he knew only what he himself had been told, and that apparently was very little.

About his father, too, there are only a few details. His name apparently had been Roger Gerard, and so his little bastard boy became known as Gerrit Gerritszoon, or Gerard, the son of Gerard. When he went into the writing business he was obliged, according to the custom of his time, to Latinize his name. He then indulged in fabricating one of those philological puzzles which were so popular among the men of learning of the Renaissance. He associated his Dutch name Gerrit with the verb *geeren* or *begeeren,* which means to desire. In Latin, "to desire" was *desiderare* and in Greek it was *eraomai.* The rest was simple. Out of *desiderare* and *eraomai* he distilled the strange concoction of Desiderius Erasmus. On official occasions he added the name of the town in which he had seen the light of day and in the end, when he became quite famous, he became known simply as Erasmus Rotterodamus, or Roterodamus with only one *t,* although Rotterdam had got its name from the river Rotte with two *t*'s.

He had as little love for his birthplace as I have. He never went back there if he could help it, and he never received the slightest recognition from his townsfolk until much later when, to their surprise, they discovered that his world-wide reputation could be turned into a profitable asset and could be used to impress distinguished visitors with the love these sturdy burghers (as materialistic a crew as ever went after the almighty rijksdaalder) had always felt toward both the letters and the arts.

His father, according to rather irrefutable circumstantial evidence, had been some sort of cleric, but we do not know quite what kind of cleric, and there were all kinds of clerics during the latter part of the Middle Ages, when the Church and the world at large were so hopelessly intertwined and interwoven that it took nothing less than a full-fledged revolution (known afterward as the Reformation) to untangle them.

If his father had been a regular priest (as is sometimes maintained), some slight sexual irregularities would hardly have attracted the public's attention, for in spite of the strict rules about celibacy, a great many of the priests of the fifteenth century lived in a semiofficial state of concubinage. Those were the days when a cardinal (Alexander Borgia by name) could be known as the father of four children, yet be elected to the papacy, and when the mendicant orders, which originally had done so much to regain the world for a purer form of Christianity, had long since degenerated into something far different from what they were intended to be. The noble ideals of Saint Francis and his fellow reformers, who had worked so valiantly to bring the Church back to the days of an earlier and simpler form of Christianity, had long since been discarded as too hopelessly unpractical and impracticable for a world of common, ordinary human beings who knew on which side their bread was buttered and meant to get their share—with a little extra meat and cheese.

Quite naturally, those who took their faith seriously greatly objected to this state of affairs and loudly clamored for reform and purification. Had they had their way, the popes would have ceased to be the richest princes in Christendom, the bishops would have been obliged to eat dry bread instead of living on the fat of the land, and the village priests would have been restrained from letting their eyes rove a little too lustily among the womenfolk of their congregations, while all the thousand and one hangers-on of the Church, the lawyers and overseers and the tradesmen and even the Jews who dealt in the agricultural products of the cloisters, would have been deprived of those easy and comfortable revenues which they had come to regard as their due.

But all these highly necessary reforms did not come until Erasmus himself was well past the prime of life, and so the "moral lapse" of poor Roger Gerard of Gouda (for that seems to have been the birthplace of Erasmus' father) was really not a matter of grave importance to anyone except the unfortunate issue of this irregular union—Desiderius himself and his elder brother Pieter, for whom Erasmus seems to have had a sincere affection and who shared many of his own miseries during the impressionable days of their common childhood.

We have never been able to reconstruct this period of Erasmus' life with any great degree of accuracy. Charles Reade went to considerable trouble and to far lengths to try and explain why Roger Gerard had not been able to marry the mother of his children. He was, of course, guessing. That is the good right of all novelists, whose duty it is to put their heroes into the best possible light, and I should be the last one to criticize him. But to me, the episode has a familiar touch.

Here we had a small Dutch town in which everybody knew everybody else. In that overgrown village, there lived a young couple very much in love with each other, but unable to marry for one of those innumerable reasons which now seem about as farfetched to us as the plot of Goethe's *Faust,* but which meant unsurpassable barriers in an age when Mrs. Grundy still had the full backing of the Church. Next we behold two respectable middle-class families deeply upset by the disgrace that has overtaken their respective children and so blinded by fear of what the community might say that they quickly and most thoroughly forget whatever little they have ever learned about common decency and kindness.

And so next we find them quietly wishing the two unfortunate children upon some relatives in the near-by city of Gouda, where they will at least be out of sight and will no longer be the cause of raised eyebrows among their respectable Rotterdam neighbors.

To Gouda, therefore, the two boys go (a good day's walk) and there they are sent to school that they may absorb enough grammar to be able to enter some monastic establishment where they can be conveniently forgotten and will cease to be (by their mere presence) a perpetual cause of shame and mortification.

But there must have been other influences at work. There must have been an uncle or an aunt who felt sorry for these neglected waifs, for we can also trace certain efforts that were made to give the boys at least as sound an education as then could be obtained in this remote part of the world, still so far removed from the true center of European civilization.

During the Middle Ages it used to be said that the degree of the true Christian virtues in any given community was in direct ratio to its distance from Rome. How could it have been otherwise? In the fifteenth century, the papacy had become what the crown of Poland was to be three hundred years later. It was an investment, pure and simple, not only for the person who actually got elected, but also for all his relatives, his friends, and his hangers-on. This was so well understood and so generally accepted by the people of Rome that the mob was allowed to plunder the palace of whatever cardinal was elevated to the seat of Saint Peter. And why not? Did not every child in the Eternal City know that the new incumbent was now in a position to recoup himself for his losses by bestowing all the best-paying sinecures upon his nephews and cousins and, in some notorious cases, upon his own children?

All this sounds incredible to our modern ears, when the occupant of the Vatican (even if he now has a few country houses, his own post office, and a radio station) lives a life as frugal as that of a village priest in some remote hamlet in Wyoming. But the world was very big in those days before the re-establishment of proper roads, and stories of the hopeless corruption and degradation of the papal office did not travel across the Alps faster than any other news. The benighted people of the north therefore continued to take their Christianity in a spirit of such utter confidence and simplicity that they had long since become somewhat of a joke in the eyes of their more sophisticated Italian masters. That joke, however, was most carefully guarded within the walls of the Eternal City, for the faithful northerners, who actually believed every word their Saviour had uttered upon the subjects of honesty, charity, and poverty, were hardworking merchants and artisans who were not only willing but were actually eager to contribute to the utmost of their abilities toward the support and maintenance of their beloved Father in the City of the Seven Hills. It was a far-wiser policy to humor them than to be humorous about them, for they suddenly might grow suspicious and pull tight the cords of their wellfilled leather purses. At times one even had to close a discreet eye when they went so far as to proclaim that the word of Christ had more weight with them than that of any mere man and that, in case of a conflict between the two, they intended to stand upon the side of Christ rather than upon that of his representative on earth.

This desire on the part of the Church authorities not to kill the geese that laid the golden eggs probably accounts for many of the successful experiments that the northerners as practicing Christians were allowed to make.

In Italy, the followers of Saint Francis, who also believed in sharing all wealth, were to discover, even while their master was still alive, that such a doctrine was far from popular at headquarters and might even lead to death at the hands of the executioner. But beyond the Alps there was a chance for the development of many things that would have been a matter of grave concern had they happened a little closer to the center of

31

authority. That is why it had been possible for entirely new kinds of semiclerical organizations of a suspiciously communistic brand not only to gain great popularity among the masses of people of the Low Countries, but also to maintain themselves for well-nigh three hundred years.

In saying this, I realize that communism was nothing new inside the body of the Church. All monastic orders were based upon those collectivist principles which had caused so much concern among the more respectable Romans of the second and third centuries, when the words *Christian* and *communist* had been practically identical. But these experiments in sharing both wealth and poverty had been comparatively harmless, for they had remained restricted to the small space of ground that lay inside the high walls of the monastic retreats. And a monk, as all the world knew, was a man set apart from the rest of the world. He had sworn an oath of allegiance. He was a soldier subject to the strict discipline of his order and was bound to obey the commands of his immediate superior, the abbot. This abbot in turn was responsible for everything that happened within his own bailiwick to his commander in chief, who in turn was responsible to his chief executive, the Pope. And so the practical world of affairs ran but small risks from those strange and undesirable experiments in communal co-operation and applied Christianity which from time to time might be tried by small groups of those earnest but sadly misguided enthusiasts who took Christ's story about the rich young man's slender chances of entering into the kingdom of heaven as gospel truth and meant to be guided by it in their own daily existence. Should they go a little too far, the long arm of the Lateran Palace and, afterward, of the Vatican would quietly reach out toward the danger spot, and there would be a change in the bylaws of the offending institute or a purge of its board of directors. In case of a serious emergency, a few heads would fall, and all would be well again in the best of all possible worlds.

These new Brotherhoods of the Common Life, however, which were being established in the Low Countries during the last twenty years of the fourteenth century and which were to play such a great role in the lives of Erasmus' contemporaries, were in one very important respect quite different from ordinary monasteries. Their members took no direct monastic vows and therefore they remained private citizens and as such were not immediately subject to the laws of the Church.

These curious institutions had been the invention of a certain Geert Groet, or Groot, who became known to the rest of the world as Gerardus Magnus. He was a native of the city of Deventer, situated in the eastern half of the Low Countries. After studying at the University of Paris and visiting the papal court of Avignon, Geert Groot, with every prospect of a brilliant clerical career, had undergone a sudden and deep-going conversion. For reasons unknown to us, he had turned his back upon this sinful vale of tears, had lost himself for three years in a monastic retreat, and, when once more he had joined his fellow men, had been turned into a full-fledged evangelist—one of the most popular and successful ones the world had ever seen.

He was, however, a vastly superior type of evangelist. He had brains and common sense and was devoid of all personal ambition. During his period of retirement he had done a great deal of hard thinking, and now he was ready with a plan that would allow the average citizen to live the life of a true Christian, yet remain a member of the community in which he worked and had his daily being. It was not only a lofty ideal, but it was so practical that it worked. The Bishop of Utrecht, Groot's immediate superior, understood this so well that he immediately raised a cry of heresy.

That holy man (from his own angle) was entirely right. The latter half of the fourteenth century with its widespread economic discontent was hardly the time to inform the people at large that among the original Christians there had been neither rich nor poor, that all of the faithful had then shared equally such wealth as was at the disposal of their congregations, and that such a happy state of affairs could be brought back again to this earth if only the faithful would listen to the words of

Geert Groot, the popular preacher who was traveling up and down the land, preaching and explaining his ideas to all those who cared to listen.

The Black Death, which raged throughout the life of Geert Groot and which in less than twenty years destroyed almost two thirds of the entire population of both Asia and Europe, had also played havoc with that fairly equal distribution of wealth which had been typical of the earlier part of the Middle Ages. Quite unexpectedly, it had made the few survivors very rich, while it had caused such a scarcity of labor that the honest farm hand, now having the employment market practically at his mercy, could ask for the most preposterous wages (often as much as three cents a day) and could join the survivors of this holocaust in their absurd display of "ostentatious wealth," which in the end made them wear silver bells on their shoes and hats just to show that they could afford this deplorable waste of ready cash.

In England, the cloisters (and who in that pious age did not think of insuring his future blessedness with at least some small gift to the keepers of his soul?) were as full of uninvestable funds as our own banks were during the first few years of our recent depression. They did not know it—those haughty abbots who were so sure of themselves and their position in the world —but it was the presence of all that gold in their vaults which a century later would provoke Henry VIII to make his far-reaching raids upon their accumulated treasures, that he might use this welcome plunder to enrich himself and his own henchmen. And therefore, as the good Bishop of Utrecht rightly argued, it was not exactly the most welcome moment for a prophet of a "direct and aggressive Christianity" to appear among the multitudes and to ask them, in a language so simple that even the humblest of spirit could understand him, what it would avail a man if he had all things but had not the true love of Christ in his heart.

The eloquence of the Middle Ages is very much like its music. It no longer appeals to us, for we are accustomed to something a little less simple. But when we take the trouble to read these sermons of that courageous Carthusian, Brother Groot, we still feel what a profound impression they must have made upon those multitudes who had profited neither as heirs of their departed relatives nor as members of the much-needed and highly paid "labor gangs," but who had been caught between the two and had been so completely ruined by the unexpected rise in prices that they were forever on the brink of starvation and ran an almost daily chance of losing their small farms and of being thrown upon a world in which there was no longer any room for them.

Thomas à Kempis was a small child when Geert Groot died and therefore he can only have heard about the great man's success from others. Yet, Thomas, who was as sincerely indifferent to worldly success as Groot had been, has left us a detailed description of these gatherings to which men and women and children from miles around would come, often walking for many days without food or sleep that they might be on hand when their beloved preacher was scheduled to make a personal appearance at some distant church. Once having come under his spell, as the good Thomas tells us, they would follow him to his next destination that they might not lose a single drop of the spiritual balsam which he poured into their souls with such profound and reassuring eloquence.

Needless for me to point out that the victims of Geert Groot's denunciations—the rich bishops, the moneylenders, and the members of the café society of that day (with rings on their fingers and bells on their toes)—felt quite differently about this wandering menace to their own comfort and safety. And it was not long before rumors began to reach Rome about a new and very dangerous heretic somewhere in the far north, a fellow who actually mixed religion with life and who should not only be thoroughly investigated but should also be promptly repressed in case he was found to have expressed ideas not in keeping with the tenets of the Church.

It was a ticklish problem, as the authorities clearly understood. Groot was known to be much too well versed in the doctrines of the Church ever to expose himself to a direct accusation of spiritual irregularity. The Church, which then as now always preferred a pleasant and plausible "way out" to a noisy altercation and an open breach with someone who enjoyed the favor of the multitudes, soon discovered a way in which this popular evangelist could be removed from the scene without bringing up the question of his orthodoxy or lack thereof. The Bishop of Utrecht quietly issued an order which forbade all those who were not regularly ordained priests to preach within the limits of his diocese. Geert Groot appealed to Rome and asked that this edict be declared null and void—at least, in his own case.

The papacy, accustomed to deal with problems involving eternity, had never been in any hurry to answer letters. It knew that letters which are not answered at all really answer themselves in a most efficient way, and Geert Groot was allowed to twiddle his thumbs (but in silence) until he grew tired of waiting and decided to pay a visit to the monastery of Groenendael, not far from the village of Waterloo in Flanders, where there lived one Jan van Ruysbroeck, as curious a character as you will find anywhere within the realm of the Middle Ages.

Ruysbroeck was the perfect mystic on a Flemish basis of piety and common sense—of prayer mixed with soap. Not that anyone born in 1293 can have been exposed to a great deal of soap, even if, like Ruysbroeck, he lived to be almost ninety years old. But whereas the Oriental or Mediterranean mystic was very apt to develop into an unappetizing anchorite, spending his days and nights on the top of a pillar or hidden in a cave, his Flemish counterpart remembered First Corinthians xiv:40 and, even when he withdrew from the world, continued to insist that all things pertaining to his daily existence be done decently and in order. Therefore, there was an almost complete absence of the more revolting kind of sainthood in the Low Countries at a time when even an otherwise sensible person like Francis of Assisi could be guilty of such nauseating acts of self-debasement that the more sober-minded folk from the north were repelled rather than attracted and never quite got over a feeling of ab-horrence and of a rather futile waste of time and energy.

I have already told you that the cloister in which Erasmus spent the greater part of his childhood days had been no par-adise. The monks had been recruited from the peasantry of the immediate neighborhood, and the institution was only too often used as a harbor of refuge for those farmers' sons who were either too weak or too indolent or too dumb to make good field hands. But at least a few of the amenities of life had been ob-served, and those survivals of medieval days—the Beguines of Flanders and Holland—show us that, with the exception of an occasional backslider (I vaguely remember a saintly female from the town of Schiedam—of all places!—who was reputed not to have washed or changed her clothes for more than forty years!), the majority of those men and women, no matter how completely they had lost themselves in mystical speculations, never quite forgot that they also owed certain duties to a body supposedly created after God's own image.

The same held true for the ideas of those northern mystics. I shudder every time I look at the picture of Ignatius of Loyola. There is a cruelty in those eyes and in that mouth which I fear almost as much as the sneering contempt which is the most noticeable characteristic of the physiognomy of Adolf Hitler. Had I lived four hundred years ago, I would as instinctively have fought Loyola as I now am fighting the Führer. Don't ask me to explain why a mere mouth or a pair of eyes should cause an otherwise easygoing and peace-loving citizen like myself to burst forth into such a fury of unreasoning hatred. I could not possibly tell you. It may be due to that all-overpowering passion for personal liberty which was part of my birthright as a Hol-lander. It may be an unconscious recollection of acts of cruelty and torture committed in my native land (and God knows in how many other countries!) by a nation which seems to derive an intense personal satisfaction from sticking steel spikes into a drowsy bull or whipping hell out of a half-starved donkey

which can no longer stand on its feet. Then again, it may be
that during my childhood days I was still so intimately surrounded by memories of men and women who had been quar-
tered, hanged, decapitated, drowned, or burned for the sake of
their beliefs that I could never forget.

I have long since given up trying to find out why all this
should still affect me so personally and so directly, but there it
is, and it is too late now for me to change or to rid myself of the
urge to kill anyone who tortures a child or an animal. Nor
would I have brought this up if I had not discovered during
the evening he spent with us that Erasmus had fully shared my
sentiments in this respect.

Somehow or other, the name of the Emperor Charles V had
come up. "It was a pity," our guest said, "that he could not
have stayed right here where he was born and where he really
belonged. He was at heart as good a Fleming as they come. He
was much happier here in the Low Countries than anywhere
else. He liked our food. He liked our beer. He liked our women
and our way of living. He liked that young secretary of his, the
young Prince of Orange, as much as he detested his own misbegotten son. But he had to leave us and follow his crazy mother
to her own country. Flanders, the richest part of Europe, was
too small to hold him. He must needs rule the whole world.
But what a pity! The poor man would have been so much happier right here.

"My own relations with the Emperor were never very intimate, but I knew many people who were very close to him.
They told me that during the first half of his days he was physically ill whenever he had to sign the death warrant of a heretic
who had to be burned at the stake. And he only did so for political expediency. But I suppose those German princes who
supported Luther were little better than he was, although they
hanged or decapitated their victims instead of burning them."

Silence again. Then: "Burning a living human being is a
dreadful thing! A most dreadful thing!"

Frits asked, somewhat embarrassedly, "I suppose you never saw it happen?"

Erasmus slowly looked up from the bit of silver paper that he had been rolling up into a little ball after having tried the chocolate inside, which he had found greatly to his liking. "Yes," he answered, "just once. In Paris while I was at college. I could not help it. A young woman, quite fair-looking, but her hair was all ablaze and she was shrieking hideously in the midst of the flames. I shall never forget it."

Silence again. Then: "They accused me, after I broke with Luther, of being a coward, of having made and kept my peace with the Church from fear of being myself burned at the stake. Perhaps they were right, for I never could forget that woman with her hair ablaze—a red halo of flames—and so I just did whatever I could to bring about the necessary reforms, but in my own way."

But I was talking of Geert Groot, and I must not wander too far afield. This is what Geert Groot did after his visit to his friend Ruysbroeck in Groenendael. It was very typical of both the man and the society in which he lived. He humbly obeyed his Bishop and the Holy See, went back to his native city of Deventer, and there founded that curious religious community which was to become known as the Society of the Brothers of the Common Life.

Headquarters were established in the house that Groot's life-long friend, Florentius Radewyn, had donated for the purpose. Then he let it be known that all men and women who wished to withdraw from the world without actually taking monastic vows would, by moving into this new communal house and sharing each other's existence, be allowed to live the kind of life that was supposed to have been practiced by Christian communities of the first four centuries after the death of the Master. The fourth chapter of the Acts of the Apostles was the model after which he intended to organize this community of true Christians.

The Brethren of the Common Life, although they retained full civil liberties and could go back to their old mode of living any time they desired, promised that while they were members of Groot's establishment they would practice obedience and charity, humility and self-denial and piety, and furthermore that they would give up all hope of personal gain and would put their worldly possessions and their future earnings into one common treasury.

That was a sufficiently startling point of departure in an age of such crass materialism, but the Brethren went even farther with their experiments in applied democracy. They elected their own head, their own rector, and this personage did not have to be a priest. That, however, did not indicate a desire on their part to break away from the Church, for the Brethren of the Common Life were most obedient and loyal children of the Church and they were careful to see to it that in every one of their houses there should be at least two priests and a number of minor clerics. But they wanted to maintain a very careful balance between heavenly aspirations and earthly needs, for they were recruited from all kinds and varieties of plain, ordinary people. Occasionally there was a small sprinkling of nobles and day laborers among them, but for the greater part they took their members from the better-class merchants and artisans and scholars, with here and there a few poor students in search of a free education.

These good folk started the day with common prayers, and after that every member of the community went quietly about his or her own daily tasks, returning late in the evening for more prayers and an exceedingly frugal meal. If they decided to withdraw even more completely from the world than they could do while still running their shops or offices, they learned the trade of a copyist or of an illuminator of manuscripts and worked on the premises. Those who had no artistic gifts were trained in some humbler craft or hired out as servants, for every one of them was under the obligation to engage in some kind of practical labor. Geert Groot had seen what mendicancy would invariably lead to. There must be no professional beggars among his followers. The community houses of the Brothers of the Common Life had to be entirely self-supporting or they were not allowed to exist.

It is very difficult for us today to reconstruct the atmosphere in which these contemporaries of Erasmus lived. For the Church, even to the faithful, is no longer the whole of life, as it was to the men and women of the late Middle Ages and the Renaissance. They got up at the crack of dawn and the first thing they did was to say their prayers. Next they hastened to Mass before they had had anything to eat. Their working day was entirely regulated by the ringing of church bells. Every meal was preceded by a short appeal for a divine blessing, and they only went to bed after they had once more expressed their allegiance to their Heavenly Lord and Master.

But that was not all. The Church took hold of them even before they were born. To assure them their ultimate salvation, they might, under certain circumstances, be baptized while still inside their mother's womb. They were married by the Church, for there was no civil ceremony that could make such a union legal. The Church took care of their earthly remains after they had bade farewell to their terrestrial home, and having confided them to that dust out of which their original ancestor had been formed, it undertook to guide the departed soul as quickly as possible through the unhappy years of purgatory.

Even that was not the whole of the story. The Church provided its children with everything that made life interesting. It gave them their art, their music, their theater, and most of their literature. It taught them their letters, if they were considered bright enough to acquire the art of reading and writing. It controlled their morals and sometimes actually undertook to give them a rudimentary conception of manners, but as most priests were recruited from among the lower ranks of society, this was not done so very successfully.

In short, every living creature (except the beasts of the fields, which, being without immortal souls, were never an object of the Church's immediate interest) was at practically every moment of his existence reminded of the fact that he was not merely a citizen of such and such a village or such and such a country, but first of all an inseparable part of the vast superstate which by divine ordinance could lay claim to everything a mere mortal called his own—his house, his horses and cows, his wife, his children, and his life and soul.

To defy this power was closely akin to defying Almighty God Himself, and to do so took an amount of courage for which we have no exact equivalent in our present age. I realize that during the last four hundred years many nations have successfully rebelled against oppression and tyranny. A handful of colonists along the western shore of the Atlantic declared themselves independent of Great Britain. A few hundred thousand Dutchmen successfully defied a king who ruled over half the world. Less than a century ago, the Italians threw off their Austrian yoke, and the Swiss had done the same thing, five hundred years before.

Those rebels, however, while undoubtedly they took serious risks, knew that they could suffer only a certain amount of physical harm. They might lose their homes, their goods and chattels, their wives and children. But the ability of their enemies to inflict sorrow or pain ceased this side of the grave. It did not reach beyond the cemetery, whereas the Church had a lien on eternity and could influence man's happiness even in the hereafter. And that was a terrible fate to contemplate in an age when people were certain of the existence of an actual hell, full of hideous devils with horns and long black tails and with pig snouts that exhaled clouds of stinking vapors, all of them gleefully engaged in pitching unrepentent sinners from vast kettles of boiling pitch into equally generous caldrons of molten brimstone.

These images mean nothing to us because we have never seen people being cooked alive in hot tar or being roasted alive on a pyre of fresh green wood. Few of us have even seen people being hanged or shot. But such scenes were only too familiar to the people of the Middle Ages, who, every time they left or entered a city, were forced to pass underneath a gallows on which the strangled bodies of some of their fellow men were swaying slowly in the breeze, while on near-by wheels the vultures were gorging themselves on the remnants of other human beings, recently hacked to pieces for no other crime than having questioned the "orthodox" explanation of some obscure passage in Revelation or the Second Epistle to the Thessalonians. Not to mention those terrible afternoons in front of the town hall, when some half-demented old women, shrieking in holy terror, were thrown into vats of boiling water because they had been guilty of witchcraft and had sold their souls to the Devil.

Therefore, those scenes of Satanic torture which were depicted every Sunday by the eloquent "hell evokers" (for there were preachers specially trained in dramatizing the abode of the damned) were an actuality to the contemporaries of Erasmus, something they knew from personal experience, just as most Europeans today know from actual experience what it means to be bombed. That, in spite of these horrible deterrents, they dared to protest against what they held to be evil in their Church shows that these men and women were possessed of a courage that is not often matched in our world of today. Yet, in this world of fear and oppression, when no one could quite call his soul or body his own, Geert Groot and his followers undertook to set up an organization which, by its very adherence to the true principles of the original form of Christianity, was to be a constant reproach to the Church as it actually existed.

About the time Erasmus was born, the movement of the Brethren of the Common Life had reached its highest point of success. Quite naturally, he too was influenced by it, and unmistakable evidences of that influence were to make themselves manifest in everything he afterward thought or wrote.

It has been said that during the sixteenth century the religion

43

of the people of the Low Countries was that of Erasmus. I feel inclined to answer that the religion of Erasmus was the religion of the common people of the Low Countries.

Soon afterward both Luther and Calvin were to make such a loud noise that the gentler tones of Erasmus were shouted out of existence and were no longer heard except here and there by ears carefully attuned to the more delicate sounds of a well-tempered reasonableness. Fortunately, no word that once has been spoken is ever quite lost, and a world set free from its present political, economic, and religious passions and furies may some day again listen to the amiable disciple of Geert Groot.

I had got this far when I suddenly remembered that I was merely writing what was supposed to be a short résumé for the benefit of Frits, who, busy with his own affairs at the Amsterdam Exchange, wanted to have his memory refreshed, but who could hardly be expected to spend a whole week reading about his prospective guests. And so I saved further time and space by giving him a mere outline of Erasmus' further career.

I don't know whether (after the fashion of Mr. Kipps and all ambitious young men who some day hope to make a success of life in a practical world) Erasmus ever noted down a list of his future ambitions. The people of the early Renaissance were not quite as self-conscious as we are. Being more interested in God than in themselves, they were not forever analyzing their chances of salvation, as we modern hypochondriacs watch the vitamins we consume with our morning's breakfast food.

But quite unconsciously, Erasmus throughout his life endeavored to play the role of the Gentleman of the Goose Quill, as Franz Liszt, three hundred years later, would try to become the Gentleman at the Keyboard. The fact that he had started life under a cloud, that as an illegitimate child he had been forced to atone for a sin he had never committed, may have been the driving force of all his ambitions. For it is a well-known fact, clearly demonstrated by history (though only rarely stressed by our moralists), that most people who have achieved great things in this world have done so because they wanted to avenge themselves for the way in which, at one time or another in their careers, they had been treated by God or man.

Napoleon, the son of an out-at-the-elbows Corsican gentleman, a funny-looking little pip-squeak and the butt of endless jokes on the part of his classmates at the military school of Brienne, cannot rest until he is the son-in-law of the Emperor of Austria. Robespierre, the child of a good-for-nothing father, unattractive, halitotic, and awkward to such a degree that no woman will ever look at him twice, can find no rest until he has destroyed that society of fine-looking ladies and gentlemen who have humiliated him in the days of his youth. Mohammed, the man of God from Mecca, finding that his fellow townsmen refuse to listen to him, hastens to the rival city of Medina and shows the Meccans what they missed when they failed to take him seriously. Adolf Hitler, a fifth-rate artist and a most unattractive personality, told by all his teachers that he would never amount to anything, is just now setting the whole world on fire to prove (to his own, if to no one else's, satisfaction) that he is really a great man and was not properly understood when he was compelled to live in Vienna's flophouses and get his meals from a soup kitchen maintained by a charitable Austrian Jew.

I could write a book upon the subject. Some day I may do so, and I shall call it *The Inferiority Complex as a Motive of Success.* Of course, this inferiority complex can work in more ways than one. In the case of truly inferior characters, it will provoke them into acts of cruelty and malevolence and inhumanity. In the case of superior characters, it may lead to manifestations of great benevolence, kindliness, and deep compassion for suffering humanity. Among this latter class of human beings I count Erasmus.

He himself, when young, had suffered so much from the selfishness and suspicion and bigotry of his fellow men that he meant to save other youngsters from a similar fate and as he could do this only by preaching a cheerful gospel of tolerance, forbearance, and human compassion, he became the leading pamphleteer and editorial writer of his day and devoted the forty active years of his life to this one and only purpose.

Meanwhile, of course, he had to make a living. Books as yet did not pay. As a rule, their publication left the author poorer than he had been before. So the unfortunate author depended upon the good will of rich princes and commoners for his daily sustenance. Indeed, much of Erasmus' career can be summed up by the Pirandelloesque title of *An Author in Search of a Dozen Patrons*. From our modern angle, it was a rather undignified way of making both ends meet. But Erasmus (and, for that matter, all his contemporaries) did not feel it that way. Had they argued the point, they would have answered that it was less humiliating to have to please the taste of some highly cultivated prince or churchman than to cater to the doubtful taste of Mrs. Schmalz and her friends who "do not know what art is but who know what they like."

I rather feel that there was something to be said for such an attitude. Indeed, I suspect that most composers, conductors, and fiddlers of our own times (were they to be entirely honest with themselves) would confess that a couple of intelligent and rich patrons of the Esterházy variety would be a veritable godsend in this age of a triumphant democracy.

But all this, while not uninteresting, is once more getting us nowhere in particular, and so I shall jot down the main lines of Erasmus' life while in search of those patrons who either died just when he needed them most or who went bankrupt the day he had arranged to go and live with them or who in some other way disappointed him and forced him once more to pack his books and his writing apparatus on his spare mule and to go forth in search of still another kindly disposed Maecenas.

Desperately unhappy in the cloister Steyn, Erasmus looked far and wide for someone in need of a competent Latin secretary. That someone was found in the year 1494, when he left Gouda for Cambrai (Kortryk to him) to become the confidential secretary of the Bishop of that city in the southern part of Flanders.

But the Bishop of Cambrai was a very worldly person and maintained a miniature court of his own—not exactly the place for a scholar in search of peace and quiet. So the young secretary cast about for another job, and when an English friend offered him a chance to go to the University of Paris, he eagerly accepted. His funds, however, were negligible, and he was obliged to enroll among the charity students at one of the colleges. There he had a dreadful time, almost starved to death, never was sufficiently warm, and contracted a contagious disease which was to make the rest of his days miserable. But he learned what he wanted to learn. He improved his Latin style and got a thorough training in the Scriptures. He felt that clearing up the very corrupt text of many of the holy books (and the translation of the Bible by Saint Jerome was then more than eleven hundred years old) would be the best mode of attack if he wanted to make an outstanding name for himself in the field of literature.

However, in order to perform this task thoroughly, Erasmus had first of all to learn Greek, and the next six years of his life were spent in an effort to find a competent Greek teacher.

It may at first strike us as somewhat curious that there was such a dearth of good Greek professors. But that was only natural. Originally, the Greek teachers had been Byzantine refugees who had seen the handwriting on the wall and had escaped from Constantinople while the roads toward the west were still open. When Erasmus appeared upon the scene, that generation of fugitives from Turkish violence, to whom Greek had been an actual and living tongue, had died out before they had had time to train a sufficient number of successors. Hence, there was such a scarcity of first-rate Greek preceptors that the few who could qualify for the better-paid positions were in great demand. The rich English universities could offer higher salaries than the French and Italian ones. And as scholarship as well as art has always tended to follow the full dinner pail, it was in

England that Erasmus hoped to find what he was looking for.

Erasmus hated the sea, but there was no choice, and as soon as an obliging English patron appeared to subsidize his stay at Oxford, he crossed the Channel and took horse for that famous city on the Isles. This was the first of several visits to England, during which Erasmus gradually rose from a mere student to the rank of full professor, for a dozen years later, the former Oxford pupil was called to teach at Cambridge, where he then finished his epoch-making labors on the New Testament. And somehow or other, English life seemed to suit him better than that of his own country or of France. Indeed, he never seems to have gone back to his native land unless he was taken sick, which happened quite often, but even then, he complained about its barbaric customs and manners.

It may strike us as curious that this highly outspoken and often very caustic commentator upon life in general never came in contact with the law. But during his stay on British soil he most carefully refrained from getting mixed up with politics. Yet it was the period when bluff King Hal (Henry VIII to history) was butchering his wives and ministers, was robbing the monasteries of their wealth (in spite of his title of Defender of the Faith, bestowed upon him by the Pope for his pamphlet against Luther), and was plundering everybody except those among his subjects who were too poor to be worthy of his attention.

Erasmus now showed that he was not only a man of great learning, but also a personage of profound caution. His evident desire to steer a safe course between two extremes, his unwillingness to come out openly for either the Pope or Luther, has often been held up against him. The liberal who sticks to the middle of the road is apt to be denounced not only by those who eat rich viands in the mansions on the right, but also by the others who partake of their daily cabbage in the hovels on the left. They denounce him as a coward and reproach him for his lack of principles. "Be it so," Erasmus answered to these accusations, "but I intend to live. I intend to preach reason and mutual forbearance, and when you have finished cutting each other's throats for theories which neither of you can prove to be right or wrong, you will perhaps come and listen to me, and I shall be there to show you how you can live happily with each other instead of forever carting your opponents to the gallows and the wheel."

Did he succeed? Yes and no. On the whole, I think he did, for though his voice was rarely listened to in the midst of the violent din of battle which followed in the wake of Luther's open defiance of Church discipline, the more intelligent part of the world paid careful attention to everything he said. And this much is certain—all through the next four hundred years we can follow the tracks of the shrewd and sensible Erasmian philosophy of life. I realize that few people could now be hired to read a line of what Luther and his adherents and enemies wrote about and against each other, but some of the work of the old Rotterdam scholar can still be perused for the sheer pleasure of spending a few hours in the pleasant company of a thoroughly civilized human being who realized that a difference in theological opinions is about the last thing in the world for which anybody should be deprived of his livelihood or publicly disemboweled.

In proof whereof I recommend his tiny little volume entitled *Moriae encomium,* or *In Praise of Folly.* He wrote it right at the beginning of the sixteenth century and while staying at the home of his dearly beloved friend, Sir Thomas More.

In this tiny opus (of not more than a hundred pages), Erasmus did what Voltaire was to do a few centuries later in his famous *Candide.* "Since the human race," so he argued, "insists upon being completely crazy—since everybody from the Pope down to the humblest of village priests—from the richest of men to the most miserable of paupers—from the fine lady in her silks and satins down to the slut in her calico dressing gown—since the whole world has firmly set its heart against using its God-given brain but insists upon letting itself be entirely guided by its greed, its vanity, and its ignorance, why in the name of a reasonable Deity should the few truly intelligent people waste so much of their time and their effort in trying to change the human race into something it never wanted to be?

"Let them be happy in their follies," he boldly proclaimed. "Don't deprive them of that which gives them more satisfaction than anything else—their sovereign power to make fools of themselves."

This was the only direct broadside Erasmus ever fired at the hopeless conditions into which Europe was plunged by a Church which was unable to reform itself from the inside and by the men who were equally unable to reform it from the outside. He labored at his self-imposed task of "a reasonable revolution" during all the rest of his days, but he had no taste for martyrdom, and he therefore refrained from frontal attacks and did his best to corrupt the garrisons which occupied the citadels of his enemies, and in this laudable effort he was eminently successful.

He wanted to make himself the champion of tolerance, but as he was born in an age that had neither newspapers nor magazines, his activities as a publicist had to be highly original.

Erasmus, like all true ironists, was a master of innuendo and hidden meanings. So he published respectable-looking collections of Greek proverbs and equally harmless-looking volumes of conversations, but in every one of these books he concealed a number of offhand commentaries upon the affairs of the day which undoubtedly would have brought him into conflict with the authorities if only they had been bright enough to read between the lines. But not unlike those Austrian police officers of a century or so ago who failed to hear the strains of the forbidden *Marseillaise* in Schumann's *Faschingsschwank aus Wien*, the censors approved of everything this famous cleric wrote and did not in the least understand that those seemingly innocent assortments of popular Greek proverbs contained dynamite enough to blow all of them sky-high the moment enough people should have got hold of these little chunks of the truth and had learned to use them for their own explosive activities.

Even in Rome, nobody seemed to have suspected that this long-nosed Dutchman with the dangerous twinkle in his eyes was something more than just a very bright Augustinian monk who happened to write an excellent Latin style and who had done most valuable work in purging the Scriptures of their manifold impurities. For when Erasmus finally cajoled an unusually generous patron, a cartain Baptista Boerio, physician to His Majesty King Henry VIII, into entrusting him with his two sons that they might visit the universities of Italy, and dragged them all the way down to the Holy City, he was there received with great honor and might even have been attached to the household of the Pope if he had only been willing to accept such an honor. Quite wisely, he preferred to remain footloose and, instead of staying at the Vatican, went to Venice that he might find out what Aldus Manutius, the famous printer, was doing with his new presses and whether that greatest of all contemporary publishers would perhaps feel inclined to accept him as one of his authors.

The learned Manutius had started out with high hopes of becoming a famous writer but, finding that his fellow scholars were greatly hindered in their studies by a lack of reliable and cheap texts, he had turned printer and was now turning out those books which were so highly esteemed for their minute proofreading and for their exquisite physical beauty. He was more than willing to add Erasmus to his "list" (as we would say today) and at once set to work on a revised edition of the Dutchman's *Adagia,* that well-known collection of proverbs with many learned elucidations and lots of clever little quips concealed in the footnotes.

This Venetian interlude was a happy one. Hard work meant nothing to Erasmus, for he only enjoyed himself when fishing little words out of his inkhorn or talking to others about what he intended to do next. He had no immediate cares. His publisher looked after his daily needs, and the magistrates left him alone, realizing that the presence in their city of the world's most illustrious publicist and commentator was an excellent advertisement for their city's love of learning. And when the job of rewriting and recasting his *Adagia* was coming to an end, Erasmus enjoyed another stroke of luck. A new, and this time a very rich, young patron asked to be allowed to place himself in his care. His name was Alexander Stewart and, like his teacher, he was of illegitimate origin. But being the bastard son of a Scotch king—James IV—was something different again from being the unwanted offspring of a humble Dutch cleric and his equally obscure housekeeper. Richly provided with spending money, young Stewart now attached himself to his brilliant mentor, and together the two visited the University of Siena and from there proceeded to Rome.

In the capital city Erasmus found a letter from his old friend, Lord Mountjoy, begging him to return to England. After a great deal of hesitation, he accepted. Rome offered him a much more lucrative existence than England, but much less personal freedom. Erasmus proved that his so-called love of liberty was something more than a hollow phrase. He saw his pupil off to Scotland, followed him at a leisurely distance, and finally settled down in Cambridge.

Alas, England was no longer the paradise it had been before, for Henry VIII had now started upon his true career. But on the Continent things were just as bad. Only half a dozen years were to go by before Luther was to break definitely with the Church. The pot of religious controversy was merrily cooking on the furnace of unreasoning fanaticism. Soon—so Erasmus felt—it would boil over, and then God help the poor scholars who refused to take sides!

Erasmus was not without powerful friends. He had been asked to be one of the teachers of the young Emperor, Charles V—then a boy of sixteen and preparing himself among his fellow countrymen of the Low Countries for his future career. This request that he become one of the imperial tutors he owed to a former classmate in Deventer, a certain Adriaan Dedel of Utrecht, who for the last five years had been Charles' private instructor and who, not so very long afterward, was to be known

The road toward Rome was long and difficult.

as Adrian VI, the last foreigner, by the way, to be elected to the papal chair.

Sure of such high protection, Erasmus had every reason to feel safe. Yet, he hesitated to accept any definite positions that were offered him and preferred to continue making his living as a free lance. The only spot in which he could hope to do this, during the first quarter of the sixteenth century, was the city of Basel, in Switzerland.

Just recently we have heard a great deal of agitation about abolishing the smaller European nations. They no longer serve any practical purpose, so we are told. I am of a very different opinion. Their record shows that they have played a most important role in the development of what until only yesterday was known as "the common culture of Europe." For they were the only spots where scholars and scientists could catch a breath of that free air which is absolutely indispensable to them if they want to function to the best of their abilities.

Remove Switzerland and the Netherlands from the map, and the list of those cities which have truly served the greatest of all mankind's needs (freedom of the soul and of the mind) will shrink to very meager proportions. Names that have become household words to all of us would never have been heard of.

The little city of Basel has the honor of being way at the top of the list of those noble citadels of personal liberty. Founded in the fourth century by the Emperor Valentinian, this little Swiss town had rapidly grown into an important center of the commerce between northern and southern Europe, for it was situated on the spot where the Rhine ceased to be a mountain stream and became a river and one of the main arteries of trade of western Europe. During the first thousand years of its existence, the city had been ruled over by its bishops, but, with the return of trade during the fourteenth century, the authority of these churchmen had waned considerably. The rich burghers, with their well-filled strongboxes, grew conscious of their power and resented having to take orders from outsiders. They had turned Basel into a stronghold of the New Dispensation—of those forces which were no longer willing to submit to the will of Rome.

Finally, in the year 1501, the sovereign city of Basel had joined the Swiss Confederation, that ancient and curious experiment in self-government in the very heart of Europe, which has outlived almost all of its neighbors as an independent nation. And as soon as Luther had posted his declaration of defiance on the doors of the court church in Wittenberg, the honest Baselers had sent their bishops a-packing and had joined the Reformation. From that moment on they intended to be masters of their own fate.

A printing press, then as now, was an indispensable part of any revolutionary movement, and the Baselers were delighted when one of their Bavarian neighbors, and a very famous publisher, decided to make their city his permanent home. Like so many of the leading craftsmen of the golden age of the book, Johannes Froben had originally prepared himself for a professional career, but, like Aldus, he had given up the writing of books for the pleasure of printing them. It was he who in 1516 had put through the press Erasmus' revised and corrected Greek Testament, the book which, incidentally, was used by Luther when he spent his voluntary confinement in the Wartburg, translating the Bible into the German vernacular.

Froben was not only a most excellent printer, but he was also a first-rate businessman. Like Alice, he asked, "What is the use of a book without pictures?" and he had persuaded Hans Holbein to leave his native Augsburg and settle down in Basel, where he could offer him permanent employment as an illustrator. In the year 1521, after endless years of wandering, Erasmus, who was beginning to feel the burden of his years (he was only fifty-five, but that was pretty old for a man of the sixteenth century), now decided to make his permanent home in this ancient Swiss city. And in order not to lose any valuable time, he moved right into his publisher's home. With the exception of a few years spent in the near-by city of Freiburg (a move made on account of his health) he was to remain in Basel until the day of his death—July 12, 1536.

The amount of work Erasmus achieved during this period was stupendous. How a man constantly plagued by so many afflictions—both real and imagined—could find the opportunity to do all the things he did is quite a puzzle to us moderns who have all the timesaving devices at our disposal—typewriters, dictating machines (both animate and inanimate), carbon paper, fountain pens, Roget's *Thesaurus,* endless handbooks covering the whole realms of history and science—and who, in spite of all these short cuts, accomplish so pitiably little. But of course Erasmus enjoyed one enormous advantage over us. He did not have to be a public performer. He did not have to attend cocktail parties. He did not have to make after-dinner speeches. He did not have to endorse the bad books of unknown authors. He did not have to address women's clubs, and he was in his latter years so famous that he could even pick and choose whom he wanted to admit into his presence.

For the world did not forget Erasmus. More than ever he had become a center of public interest. Every courier who reached Basel brought letters addressed to the learned doctor. The Pope wrote to him. Emperors asked his advice. Kings offered him tokens of their deep regard. As the uncrowned head of the Republic of Letters, Erasmus received the homage of his devoted subjects.

Many of those missives were not quite as innocent as they looked. They had a purpose, ofttimes ill-concealed and not infrequently couched in the terms of a bold challenge. "What side do you intend to take?" his correspondents would ask. "Are you a Luther man or do you still support the Pope of Rome?"

Erasmus, however, remained adamant. He refused to take sides. He insisted that the man of true wisdom can render no better service to mankind at large than by remaining above the battle. Should he be foolish enough to enter into the arena he might be forced to do things of which afterward he would be ashamed. Dr. Martin Luther urging the German princes to go after their rebellious peasants with fire and sword—to burn them, hang them, hack them to pieces, break them on the wheel, drown them and their children like vermin—does not show up in a very pleasant light. Perhaps these manifestations of Hitlerian fury were an unavoidable part of his character, and Luther may have had to react that way in order to make himself understood by his neighbors. But his outbreaks of a berserk fury proved nothing. They settled nothing. They only led up to that hideous violence which a century later, during the Thirty Years' War, was to affect the German mentality in such a way that, ever since, the Teutonic people have been a menace to the safety of Europe.

The peace-loving Erasmus was of a different breed. He was horrified by the dreadful things that were happening all around him. He intended to devote his last years to a supreme effort to make his fellow men understand that a philosophy of reason alone could save them from that wholesale moral and physical suicide toward which they were rushing at such alarming speed. Like an avalanche his books began to pour from the Froben presses. He tried every form of literary approach. He was in constant epistolary contact with all the most important people of his time, and with them he discussed every subject between heaven and hell, but mostly those connected with their ·common efforts to save the world from any further outbreaks of religious violence.

The liberty and dignity of the human soul meant more to Erasmus than all those religious arguments which (whether they were offered by the followers of Luther or the other side) had but one single purpose—the continued enslavement of the spirit. And he clearly foresaw that the triumph of the Protestant cause would merely substitute the rule of a Book for that of a Man—that is to say, the Pope—and in that case he felt that the Man would be preferable. One could at least argue with the Man, but one could not argue with the Book. So why change from one system to another when there was really nothing to be gained and much perhaps to be lost? Why not try to reform the Man and the system he represented rather than discard him and make the road free for the advent of a score of little men, each with his own version of the truth and each trying to do, on the scale of a small German principality, what the Pope had failed to do on the scale of the whole civilized world?

What Erasmus failed to understand was this: once an ordinary human being, like an overabused horse, has taken the bit into his teeth, he is no longer able to listen to reason, but he will run his course until he is stopped by either his own exhaustion or an act of brute force from the outside. Some day, when we shall know a lot more about the inner workings of the human mind than we do today, we may learn to handle the situation, and then we may be able to prevent whole nations from running amok. But that can only be accomplished after we have substituted professional psychologists for professional politicians. And the latter know on which side their bread is buttered and that they are totally unfit for any other kind of job that guarantees them such lavish rewards for so small a display of talent and effort. These politicasters will try and prevent such a change with their very last breaths. They will even denounce a serious scientific investigation of this problem as a dangerous revolutionary effort meant to upset the "existing order of things." And since in this respect the first half of the sixteenth century was exactly like the first half of the twentieth, Erasmus ere he died must have realized that though he had indicated the road we should follow, there were powerful forces at work which intended to prevent people from doing just that. His last years cannot have been very happy. On all sides there was unrest. There were quarrels and fights, and a general outbreak of war was only prevented by a system of compromises which satisfied no one and only increased the general feeling of suspicion and distrust. Soon there would be an incident, for invariably, when everybody goes around armed to the teeth, a gun is somewhere apt to go off by itself, and the first shot leads to a salvo, and a wholesale massacre then becomes almost unavoidable. Erasmus departed this life before that point had been reached, but already there was so much strife that he—the most peaceful of men—must have felt quite contented to call it a day and bid this world a final farewell.

Erasmus had one consolation. During his last years he had at last found that economic security for which he had so earnestly longed when he was still young. Pope Paul III had made him the nominal head of a deanery in the city of Deventer, where he had gone to school. And His Holiness, with his fine Italian hand (was he not a member of the famous old house of the Farnese?), who meant to save the Church by means of his diplomatic agility and not by brute force, now appealed to all those intellectuals who had remained loyal to their ancient mother and whose literary efforts might persuade the wandering children to come back into the fold. And the same pontiff, who employed Michelangelo to decorate the Sistine Chapel and who patronized and protected Ignatius of Loyola and his newly founded Society of Jesus, now tried to gain the good will of Erasmus by offering him, as an out-and-out gift, those three thousand ducats which were necessary if a person aspired to be created a cardinal.

Erasmus as always went through the motions of being deeply grateful, but he respectfully declined. He must remain free. During the winter of 1535–36 he was confined to his room in his publisher's house. Soon afterward he was unable to leave his bed, and on July 12 of the year 1536 he quietly dropped off into his last sleep.

Just before he died, his mind wandered back to the scenes of his childhood days. And this Dutchman, who, without knowing it, had presented the world with a philosophy of life as typical of his native land as rain or a love of neatness, but who had never written a single line in the language he had learned at his mother's knee, suddenly slipped back into the familiar tongue of his youth. Just before he ceased to breathe he was seen to smile and was heard to utter the words, *"Lieve God."* The next moment he stood before his "dear God" to give an account of all those many years he had spent in His service. And then he may have discovered that he had been mistaken when, during his last years, he had so often complained of having merely wasted his time, for no word that has been uttered for the purpose of making man the master of his own fate has been spoken in vain.

The first of our dinners passed off very successfully. We found that we could easily understand our guest if he did not talk too rapidly. His English and German and French were as antiquated as his Dutch, but it was no trouble at all to follow him in our native tongue, the words of which he pronounced with a decidedly Flemish accent, or at least so it seemed to us. After about ten minutes, the conversation was in full swing. It covered every subject under the sun, from such modern inventions as radio and airplanes (in which, by the way, he showed very little interest, being doubtful of their ability to make people much happier) to the threat of Bolshevism, Fascism, and Hitlerism, which these last years had become a subject of grave concern to all of us. He had never heard of them before, but his quick mind easily grasped the situation.

"The Italian," he said, "as you describe him to me, bears a very close resemblance to the Colleonis of my own day and to all those other soldiers of fortune who infested Italy when I visited there. In every city—even in Rome—I found that the old free form of government had disappeared, or what they used to call their 'free form of government,' which was often enough a very unpleasant sort of demagoguery—an irresponsible rule by the masters of the guilds and the workingmen's corporation. When I was in Italy, every village, every hamlet, had a little tyrant of its own. I met quite a number of them. Most of them were a very crude type of citizen of low origin and even lower taste. Often they had not even been born in the cities over which they ruled, being strong-armed peasants who had made a name for themselves as the leaders of some band of professional cutthroats. Few of them could write their own name, though they loved to pose as the protectors of the arts, and several of them tried to persuade me to stay with them, though they had never read a single one of my books. They apparently thought I was some kind of foreign version of their own Mirandola, though I am sure I never laid any claim to be considered a paragon of good looks and social elegance.

"Others got me confused with another young man—I think his name was Aretino—who was just then beginning to make a name for himself as a writer of blackmail poetry, though of course he did not call it by that name. In the end, I used to carry copies of my Greek New Testament with me and send them those with my compliments as soon as I reached their territory, so that there would be no mistake as to the sort of work I did. Taking them by and large, they were a miserable pack of lazzaroni, and now their type seems to have spread all over the world. But they had better be on their guard, for *hoi kuboi Dios aei eupiptousi,* and they will go the way of all their kind."

Frits and I hastily looked at each other. Apparently the old gentleman, who for so many years had been a walking collection of proverbs, was quoting from his own works.

"Would you mind writing that down for us?" Frits asked. "It is Greek, isn't it? Perhaps we don't pronounce it today as you did four hundred years ago."

Erasmus reached for one of my sketching pads. I offered him my fountain pen. "I would rather not use that," he said. "I am accustomed to a goose quill, but if you will kindly give me one of your pencils—they seem so much better than the ones we had —I will spell it out for you." And in his precise handwriting, which looked as if it had been printed, he wrote down, οἱ χύβοι Διὸς ἀεὶ εὐπιπτουϛι.

"There it is," he said, "and here is the translation. 'The dice of the gods are always loaded.'" And then, looking at me: "I thought you told me a little while ago that you had studied Greek?"

"Only six years," said Frits, who was a bright fellow. "Only seven years," said I, who had not been quite so bright and had been obliged to repeat one year.

"I don't quite understand that," Erasmus replied. "In my day, we learned a language like Latin or Greek in about three years. Of course, we were not perfect. Our Greek especially was

rather poor, and I am afraid that we wrote it as Luther wrote
Latin, though they tell me that his German is most excellent. I
don't know—I always hated that tongue—but then I was probably prejudiced. But tell me—for that greatly puzzles me—why
did it take you so long to learn those languages?"

"Perhaps because we *had* to learn them. You, my dear Doctor,
learned Greek because you *wanted* to."

"Of course I did! It was the only way I could ever hope to do
some really good work on the New Testament."

"Yes," said Frits, "and after you got through with your New
Testament, you went on reading Greek, while we never looked
at another line of it as soon as we had left school."

"Why not?"

"Because there are so many other things to read besides Latin
and Greek, and to us those other things seem much more interesting."

"Yes," Erasmus answered, helping himself to another piece of
that chocolate for which by this time he had developed quite a
passion, "I hear that today even in English and Dutch there are
books now that are worth studying. In my day it was different.
There was a volume by a certain Chaucer which my dear friend,
Sir Thomas, was forever urging me to read. I tried it once or
twice, but it rather bored me. So I stuck to my old Romans."

"And to Homer?" asked Frits.

"Yes," Erasmus answered. "But I could never find a text that
quite satisfied me. Now, so they tell me, the texts are perfect,
but you no longer bother to read them! This is a curious world.
First we spend our lives trying to get something. Then we get
it, but we no longer want it. I am afraid that we shall always
remain like children, and children, alas! are savages."

This remark was neither particularly brilliant nor very new.
But it was getting late, and, as both of us noticed, Erasmus was
really a very old gentleman and he was getting tired. After
dinner I had offered him a glass of an excellent but rather over-
sirupy Tokay. But I knew that the people of the Middle Ages
had had a much sweeter tooth than we have and I had felt that

I could take the risk. He had tasted it and had expressed his sincere approval. *"Vinum bonum laetificat cor hominis,"* he had said, quoting from the hundred and fourth psalm. A few minutes later he quietly dozed off. Apparently he was no longer accustomed to such good fare. I beckoned to Frits, and we slipped out of our chairs and sat down on a bench in front of the fire.

"Well," I said, "the plan worked, didn't it?"

"Yes," he answered, "but I still can't quite believe it. And it rather frightens me. For what shall we do next? To tell you the truth, I feel rather lost."

"I have thought of that too," I answered, "but I have had an idea. Suppose we ask the old gentleman over there to be our guide, philosopher, and friend, so to speak! He will know much better than we what to do and he can help us out with our other guests."

"That's a splendid idea," said Frits, "and perhaps he would enjoy a little vacation, for he seems a bit bored with his present existence. You remember the other day in the town hall, when the city treasurer showed us that big Gothic room with the high ceiling, and so full of light, and told us that it was going to pieces because they had no use for it? Suppose we fix it up for him as some kind of study? I'm sure he would love it. We could furnish it so that it would look like his old workshops in Cambridge or Basel. We have a great many Dürer drawings and reproductions. Lucie would help us. She is marvelous at that sort of thing. Suppose you suggest it to him when he wakes up?"

"Suppose you do?"

"Suppose we both do?"

And so, as soon as Erasmus woke up (he was only indulging in a little cat nap) we very carefully approached him on the subject. At first he seemed greatly surprised and rather bewildered at our offer. But after talking it over from every possible angle, he said that nothing would please him more than to come back to earth for a while.

"Of course," he warned us, "you must remember that it is

not quite my time for a sabbatical leave. As a rule, we get permission to return to this earth for a short while every seven hundred years, and, as you know, it is only some four centuries since I left it. But I think that it can be arranged. The good Lord has always been very nice to me. I hear that He has even read some of my books!

"One day I overheard Him quoting something from my *Praise of Folly*. He was talking to Saint Peter, just after he had interviewed a man by the name of Napoléon or Napoleone —it was an Italian name, though I could not possibly tell you how it was spelled. The little fellow had been very noisy and had insisted, with a great many Italian oaths, that he must be allowed to come right in after Peter had told him that he must not come back for another ten thousand years, when they might reconsider his case. There had been quite a scandal, for the Italian, brandishing his foolish little sword, had threatened Saint Peter that he would appeal directly to the Almighty Himself, and at that moment the good Lord, Who does not like to hear His name used in vain, came down from His throne to find out what this unseemly noise might mean and as soon as He understood the situation, He patted Saint Peter on the back in that friendly way of His and told him not to worry, for he had done exactly the right thing. And it was then that He quoted a few words from my *Praise of Folly* about tyrants and so-called conquerors. So I knew that He is not quite ignorant about what I tried to do and is rather well disposed toward me. Therefore, I think that it can be arranged if I go about it in the right way."

"That would be wonderful for us," I assured him and then, returning to Frits, I asked him how long he thought it would take to fix up that room in the town hall.

"I don't know, of course," Frits answered, "but I don't think it would take more than four or five days."

"I would really love it," Erasmus told us, "but will you allow me to make one observation? You will see to it, of course, that the room is kept warm?"

"Don't worry about that," we assured him. "We shall give

you one of our own stoves—a good sheet-iron stove that is guaranteed to burn day and night."

"Marvelous! And another little item. You will promise me that there will be no drafts?"

"We'll tell the village carpenter to fix all the windows in such a way that not a single drop of fresh air will come dribbling in through the cracks."

"Nothing could please me better! And finally, will there be any cooking on the premises?"

"No, sir. Your study will be in the town hall, and in the town hall, no cooking is allowed."

"How about the neighbors? Will they be cooking all day long?"

"Well, of course, they will have to feed their families, but we'll ask them to be very careful."

Erasmus looked at us with an apologetic smile. "You must think that I am terribly fussy," he said, "but there is one thing in this world I just can't stand. That is the smell of fish. I simply loathe fish! I'm afraid I had too much of it at the cloister Steyn. And ever since, the smell of fish, whether frying or boiling, makes me sick."

"We promise you on our word of honor there will be no smell of fish, either fried fish or boiled fish, if we have to put the whole of the village on a meat diet."

"And one more item. You will be very careful about my wine? As you may know, I suffer from the stone, and therefore I have to be most careful. But I loved the Moselle you gave me tonight. I do not want to cause you any unnecessary expense, but I would be sincerely obliged to you if you could give me some light beverage like that, for water does not agree with me."

I hastened to assure him that we would attend to all those details. "How about a light Burgundy?" I asked him. "A Chevalier Montrachet or a Bâtard Montrachet?" I realized too late that that had not been the happiest word to use in the presence of a man who was so conscious of his illegitimate origin.

"The Chevalier Montrachet would be wonderful," he answered, stressing the "Chevalier." "Or some Goutte d'Or. I would be very grateful for some Goutte d'Or. And now," he said, wiping his clumsy, old-fashioned glasses, "I notice that it is very late, and I wonder whether you would let me hear some more of that music your little hidden orchestra played earlier in the evening?"

"Do you remember how the tune went?" I asked.

Erasmus hummed a few bars, and we recognized Orlando Gibbons. We found that we had several more of his records, and we first played *The Silver Swan* and next Thomas Morley's *Sing We and Chant It*.

During this last madrigal, the first notes of Valerius' *Hymn of Thanksgiving* played by the town-hall chimes began to trickle in through the closed blinds. Some familiar strain in this ancient hymn seemed to strike a reminiscent note in our guest's memory. His slender right hand, the hand bearing that well-known blue ring given him by his pupil, Alexander Stewart, and showing the picture of Dionysus, was slowly beating time, and he hummed the words of a song he must have remembered from his days at school. He seemed as happy as a child who has come home at last and recognizes the familiar scenes of his own nursery. He looked at us and smiled.

"This has been a perfect evening," he said, "and I am grateful to both of you, not to forget that most excellent cook."

Then the candles on the table began to flicker. Suddenly they went out. The hour was midnight and our guest was gone.

Erasmus indulges in his usual forty winks.

CHAPTER II

We Arrange a Room for ERASMUS in the Veere Town Hall and Entertain Our Next Two Guests, WILLIAM THE SILENT and GENERAL GEORGE WASHINGTON

FRITS LEFT on Sunday evening, and I therefore asked Lucie van Dam and Jimmie to look after the business of fixing up that room in the old town hall where Erasmus meant to spend part of the holiday he so quaintly called his "sabbatical year." My wife could take care of the practical details and talk to the carpenter and the painter and the glazier, while Lucie, with her fine artistic sense, would re-create it into something resembling the old gentleman's familiar study in Cambridge. She used the pictures of both Hans Holbein (that of 1530) and of Albrecht Dürer (dated 1526), and at Bal's in Middelburg she even found a chair (late Gothic and pretty badly shopworn) that looked exactly like the chair in the woodcut an unknown Basel artist had engraved in the year 1530 and which showed Erasmus dictating to his secretary in his house at Freiburg.

In the meantime we had to make arrangements for the entertainment of our next guests. On Sunday morning we had decided whom we meant to ask. It seemed to us that we owed it to Veere to try and get a famous historical personage connected not only with the history of our own little city, but of the country at large. There was only one name that suggested itself to us.

William of Orange had not merely been Marquis of Veere, but more than that, he had been the Prince, for he was the man who had founded the Dutch nation and had sealed its independence with his own blood. But whom would we ask to meet him? The moment our first visitor had left us, Frits and I had come to the conclusion that if we meant to be really successful, we must always try to have at least two guests at the same time. It made for a more animated kind of conversation.

"But who," Frits asked, "is there who would fit in with our Prince?"

Suddenly I had an idea. "Look here," I told him, "I'm a sort of amphibious creature when it comes to nationality. Here in Zeeland everybody takes me for a perfectly good Hollander. Most of our neighbors hardly know that I have ever left the island. But in America, in spite of my accent, I am never thought of as anything else but American. The Prince gave me my original nationality. Why not invite the man responsible for my other country?"

"Whom do you mean?" Frits asked. "George Washington?"

"Of course. Whom else?"

"Would the two understand each other?"

"They would get along like old friends, for they had a lot in common."

"Well then, let us go ahead. We will write the name of George Washington down on our slip of paper together with that of the Prince, and you can hide it underneath the stone lion of the town hall when you go home tonight."

We then discussed the menu for next Saturday's meal. In these matters I usually took the lead, leaving it to Frits to get the necessary raw materials from Amsterdam, for Middelburg did not have some of the strange articles of food we were obliged to order.

"First of all," I suggested, "let us have a good *pot-au-feu*. I found an ancient recipe in *Le Cuisinier français* of the year 1674. Then a boiled turbot with oyster sauce (we can always get oysters from Ierseke, though they are rather expensive for cooking purposes). The General, as I seem to remember, liked his victuals. So a fish course alone is not enough, and I would be in favor of some turkey afterward—let us say *dindon aux marrons* and *petites saucisses à la broche*—and fresh string beans done in the English style, for these will remind General Washington of Virginia and will make him feel at home and will show him that we mean to do well by him. For dessert, why not an *omelette aux confitures flambée?* We have some good cognac for that purpose, and it will burn brightly. With the fish we can have a white Bordeaux—a bottle of Yquem 1921—and with the turkey a red Burgundy—a Clos Vougeot I found in Middelburg the other day, and a very good brandy with the coffee, but I also shall order some punch, for the General will like that— Jamaica punch—it'll take him back to the days of his youth, when he went to the Caribbean with his brother."

Most of those dishes were not exactly part of the daily Dutch kitchen routine, but all of the recipes were to be found in the new edition of *Le Cuisinier français* of Bertrand Guégan (Paris: Émile-Paul Frères), and I translated them, but that was hardly necessary, for the excellent Jo Verlinde was a born cook and had such an instinct for the culinary arts that a mere hint was sufficient to make her do the right thing. And no matter what outlandish concoctions we put before her, the result was always perfect, though she herself (and, for that matter, we too) preferred a simple Dutch beefsteak with lots of gravy and fresh bread to dunk in it.

The next three days I was busy all day long fixing up Erasmus' study in the town hall. For it was not enough to give him the necessary tables and chairs. He also had to have something to keep his mind occupied, for one who has worked hard all his life can't just sit down and stare out of the window. So I telephoned Henri Meyer at Nijhoff's in The Hague and arranged that quite a number of old books should be sent us by the first mail. I explained vaguely what I wanted and left the rest to him, as I knew that I could safely do. As I had expected, the books arrived within twenty-four hours.

The invitations were discreetly placed underneath the old stone lion which guarded the entrance to the town hall.

There were a few curiosities among them. There was a Horace, printed in Venice in 1471, and I hoped that nothing would happen to it, for it cost a barrel of money! Then, a very early French edition of the comedies of Terence, a fine *Speculum humanae salvationis* (1473), Wynkyn de Worde's *Polychronicon* (1495), Caxton's *Historyes of Troyes,* printed in Bruges in 1471, and all the Aldine editions Henri had been able to find: a complete Virgil, Horace, Plutarch, Sophocles, Aristotle, Plato, Herodotus, Thucydides, Xenophon, Euripides, most of them reminiscent of that New Academy which the learned printer had founded in Venice and where no one had been allowed to speak anything but classical Greek—or as classical as he could make it.

And then suddenly I had a stroke of great good luck. I had gone to Middelburg to buy some parchment and some old van Gelder rag paper, and I had dropped in on my friend van Benthem, the bookseller, and I had said, "Where in heaven's name am I going to find a few goose quills?" and he had answered, "You came to the right place. The other day I was cleaning up the attic, and I came across some goose quills my grandfather must have sold in the twenties and thirties of the last century. They were still in their old packings and as good as the day they were cut. I will gladly give you a bundle." So we had everything, except that the ink was Higgins' India ink, and I am sure Erasmus never had had any writing fluid quite as good as that.

Everything therefore was set for Erasmus' arrival. I thanked Jimmie and Lucie for their faithful labors, and we locked the door and awaited what would happen.

On Friday, shortly after eleven, Repko, the village treasurer, banker, cigar dealer, and barber (a delightful combination of occupations, for while you were having your hair cut you could smoke a cigar, cash a check, and pay your taxes), came to me in such a hurry that he almost lost his slippers when he jumped off his bicycle. Jimmie and I were sitting on the stoop, and we asked what had happened.

"That friend of yours, the old gentleman with the long nose, has just arrived. I thought that the door of that room was locked, but it stood wide open and there he was, sitting at his little desk and looking at the pictures in one of the old books. I asked him how he had got in, but all he answered was, 'You have given me a perfectly lovely room here, and I am sure that I shall be very comfortable.' Now, what I want to know is this—how did he get in when he had no key?"

"My dear friend," I said, "we may have a few rather strange visitors here during the next few months. Please ask no questions, but just take them for granted. They will be quite harmless."

"I'm not afraid of spooks, but what I want to know is this. Is this old gentleman going to be a permanent resident of Veere and if he is and has to pay taxes, where do I send the bill?"

"Send it to me," I told him, "and I will see to it that the village gets every cent to which it is entitled."

"Fine, that's really all I wanted to know. Otherwise, I would get in trouble. For the rest I think all this is a wonderful idea. Veere always needed a few more tourists, and perhaps these visitors of yours will tell the folks at home, and they will come, too. Come to think of it, I had better lay in an extra stock of picture post cards and cigars, and spruce up the barbershop a little."

I urged him to do so. I could already see old Erasmus sending his friends "at home" a picture post card of the town hall with an "X marks my room, wish you were here." Saint Peter, I am afraid, would have been somewhat puzzled.

This is a copy of the report about the Prince of Orange I had sent Frits by the last mail on Thursday. With most of the facts he would already be familiar. It was what the diplomats of the old school used to call an *aide-mémoire*—something to guide his memory.

It was the twenty-fifth of October of the year 1555. The place

Erasmus in his native city of Rotterdam.

was Brussels. More than a thousand people had gathered together in the Hall of the Golden Fleece to bid their ruler farewell. They were delegates to the Estates of the seventeen different provinces which went to make up what was known as the Netherlands.

These counties and duchies and bishoprics had passed through many hands. For a while, the House of Bavaria had played quite a role in their affairs—a role which had given one particular princess, Jacqueline of Bavaria, a chance to distinguish herself as a woman of great determination, who might have come out on top if her career had not been so seriously interfered with by her sex. Like Mary of Scotland, she had married a succession of weak but handsome young men, and she had spent her last years drinking away her sorrows, a prisoner in a castle whose walls still arise in lonely grandeur amid the flat meadows of the old province of Holland.

Next there had been the House of Burgundy, during whose sway the southern part of the Low Countries had become the richest manufacturing center of the whole Continent, turning the wool of England into those finished garments which the rustic English had not known how to prepare for themselves.

Bruges and Ghent and Ypres had accumulated such riches that the rising royal dynasties of central Europe had fought for their possession. But as these communities, forever at the mercy of their undisciplined labor leaders, had been in a state of constant rivalry and strife, they had been unable to maintain their independence and had been incorporated into the more efficiently run monarchies of the south.

Finally, Mary, the daughter of Charles the Bold of Burgundy, had married Maximilian of Austria. Her father had been killed in a quarrel with that prize scoundrel of the early Renaissance, Louis XI of France, and in that way the House of Austria had fallen heir to the Netherlands.

The grandson of Maximilian and Mary—that famous Charles of the protruding jaw (which in due course of time was to become the trade-mark of all true Austrian princes)—had therefore been born a Fleming, for he had seen the light of day in Ghent. Before he died, he was to become the owner of so vast an empire that it covered more territory than the British Empire of today. Let us give the Devil his due and say of Charles that he had done his best, but that circumstances had been too much for him. One cannot very well hope to govern a hundred different peoples, all the way from the Straits of Magellan to the Baltic Sea, if at the same time one is obliged to settle a religious quarrel in which every one of a hundred million subjects has taken definite sides for either the Pope or Martin Luther. And at heart, Charles, a pupil of Erasmus, was too intelligent to care.

"A plague upon both your houses!" had been his feelings during the first twenty years of his life. And even after he had been forced to move to Spain, he had tried to observe some moderation in dealing with these people of the Low Countries, whom he understood so well. But all this came to an end after he had withdrawn from the actual management of affairs and had left his realm to the care of his son Philip. For Philip was as much of a Spaniard as his father had been Flemish, and the day Philip succeeded his father as ruler over the Low Countries the real trouble had begun.

In Spain, in Italy, in Austria, in Peru, and on the plains along the Río de la Plata, Philip could successfully play the role of "I, the King," and order whatever he pleased, with every chance of being obeyed. But in the Netherlands, the piece of paper with the latest royal edict was apt to be torn from the wall on which it had been pasted the moment it had been put there, and a caricature of His Majesty was likely to take its place.

In the end, I am glad to say, Dutch cussedness was to win out over Hapsburg obstinacy, but all that was still mercifully hidden by the future on the sad day when Charles bade a last and affectionate farewell to the people among whom he had spent the only happy days of his life.

The big hall of Brussels was filled with all that was noblest and best within His Majesty's realm of the Low Countries.

In his new study Erasmus was as happy as a clam.

After a short wait, Charles himself appeared. He was, as he had so often described himself, an old and worn-out man. He leaned heavily on the shoulder of one of his pages. People knew that young man and they knew him well. They whispered that he was the Emperor's favorite—that old Charles liked this eager-looking stranger much better than his own son, the morose and sulky Philip. They hoped that William might assume the leadership of that opposition to the "rule of the foreigners" which was sure to make itself felt as soon as old Charles (God bless him!) was succeeded by Philip. They were not sure, but they prayed that it might come that way.

The name of this young secretary was William, and he was one of the five sons of William, Count of Nassau-Dillenburg, and his wife, Juliana, Countess of Stolberg. Countess Juliana seems to have been a woman of parts—a sort of late medieval Abigail Adams. For she gave the world a brood of sons, practically all of whom played a very decided role in the affairs of the latter half of the sixteenth century. And of these, William, her eldest, was predestined to become one of those historical figures who, for one reason or another and in spite of the comparatively limited scope of their activities, are able to impress themselves so thoroughly upon their environment that they rank among history's "immortals."

It is always difficult to put one's finger upon a simple, outstanding characteristic which accounts for that kind of success. William had no gift whatsoever for military leadership. He had never won a single battle and he often ran the risk of being either captured or killed. Nor was he inspired by that fanatical belief in some particular mission which has carried many mediocre men to the peak of fame. He lived in an age when all the world was sharply divided upon points of religious doctrine, and several of his brothers became zealous, even bigoted, adherents of the new doctrines. But William always kept himself carefully aloof from such disputes. He had been brought up a Protestant. When he had an opportunity to inherit the rich possessions of a French cousin who had died without issue, he went through the outward formality of returning to the Catholic faith that he might be recognized as the head of the principality of Orange. Yet, a few years later, we find him in supreme command of the rebellious forces of the Netherlands, composed entirely of rabid Protestants.

William never pretended that he had been subject to a great conversion and had seen the light. He merely ceased going to Mass and once more listened with perfect equanimity to the sermons of those Calvinistic ministers who had replaced their Lutheran colleagues, who had been found a little too mild for the dour taste of the good Hollanders. And during his last few moments on this earth, when he lay dying on the stairs of his house in Delft, William thought of the people entrusted to his care, but none of those who were near by heard him whisper a request that he be attended by either priest or minister.

William, while not exactly an intellectual, was possessed of an excellent and quick brain. He had had a good education. He had never worked for his Ph.D., so to speak, but why should he? He expected to fall heir to the estate of his father, William the Rich. In addition, and while still quite young, he suddenly had obtained the very considerable revenues from the estates of his cousin, the Prince of Orange, and as one of the most opulent young princes of northern Europe, he could look forward to a career in which the world would expect very little of him except that he should be a fairly just and not oversevere ruler when he succeeded to the estates of his father.

But being far above the average in intelligence and industry of the gilded young men of his age, William had not spent his days in idleness and had devoted his time to the practice of those arts of statecraft and diplomacy which would some day allow him to play a role as a leader of men within the realm of international politics. The Emperor's court in Brussels had given him full opportunity to develop his particular talents, and he had learned how to manipulate his brain with the dexterity of a first-rate fencer who can hold his own even when called upon to defend himself with a small rapier against an

Erasmus was our first guest.

opponent who is clad in full armor and who swings a battle-ax.

This stood him in good stead when he espoused the cause of the rebellious Netherlands in their quarrel with the King of Spain. During a quarter of a century, all of Europe watched the duel between this leader of a supposedly lost cause and the mightiest of all European potentates, and when the latter descended to assassination to win the bout, there were a great number of people who agreed that, on points, the Prince had most certainly carried away the victory. Posterity has fully agreed with this verdict.

How and why had this young German prince ever decided to leave his ancestral estates in Germany and why had he moved to the Netherlands? The change had been entirely practical. Old William the Rich, his father, had invested a great deal of his money in Low Country real estate. The Emperor Charles, suspecting the father's Lutheran leanings (the mother had long since gone over to Wittenberg), had hinted rather broadly that these possessions would run less risk of possible confiscation if the eldest son of the house were to be educated in Brussels as one of his pages (read *hostages*). And so this handsome and amiable young man had been sent to Brussels, there to learn all that could be learned within the realm of applied government, and there he had kept open house and had spent money like water and incidentally had married some more money. If he had lived today, his name and his wife's would have appeared every day in the society columns of all the big dailies, and the sob sisters would have thrilled over the cost and splendor of the dear Prince's latest entertainment in honor of the illustrious Principe degli Ughi-Bughi, ambassador from the court of Milan, and the Sunday supplements would have shown pictures of the wonderful whippets the couple were raising on their estates near Breda.

That this idle young man of fashion would, within a few years, develop into the serious and highly competent leader of an almost desperate cause shows that there was more in him than had thus far appeared on the surface. As a matter of fact, a few of his contemporaries had already become very much aware of his extraordinary gifts as a courtier and political scene shifter. The viceregal court at Brussels was a hotbed of intrigue, and there were by far too many foreign hangers-on present to please the native element. Both the Dutch and the Flemings wanted all the lucrative posts for their own children and they hated to see fat bishoprics and well-paid governorships in their native provinces go to Italians or Spaniards or Frenchmen.

William, on the other hand, on account of his holdings in the Low Countries, was considered a Dutchman, and, as he had much more common sense and polish and business acumen than most of the other nobles (who very rarely rose above the mediocre cultural level of country squires), his colleagues were quite willing to let him look after their interests. Meanwhile they could continue to live quietly in their castles, hunt all day long, drink beer or wine all night long, lay bets on the next bear-baiting, and quarrel in a most unseemly manner for the few young heiresses whose marriage to one of their loutish sons might enable them to lift at least part of their uncomfortable burden of loans and mortgages.

That was the way the stage was set when the Emperor Charles resigned, and the Spanish and Italian fortune hunters at court soon found out that most of the opposition to their plans (for they, too, wanted these heiresses and jobs) came from the side of this well-mannered but tight-lipped young German. And they sarcastically dubbed him the "silent one"—the fellow who wasted no needless words, who worked in silence, but who invariably got what he wanted.

Actually, William was not at all a silent person. He was a man of the world—in the best sense of that oft-misused expression. He loved to go out among his fellow men. He could carry on any kind of conversation with any kind of people in any kind of place. He had the rare gift of making everyone with whom he came in contact feel at ease. He even knew how to handle the wild-eyed fanatics who invariably come to the surface during a great emotional and religious crisis. But he also understood how to hold his tongue when such a course suited his own best interests, and he would have gone far as the leading executive in a modern business enterprise.

That, then, was the young man on whose shoulder the old Emperor leaned when he bade farewell to the Estates of his beloved Netherlands, to whom he excused himself for the halting way in which he read his message, saying, "Gentlemen, you must not be surprised if, old and feeble as I am and also from the love I bear you, I shed a few tears." It may have been the aching in his rheumatic bones and the affection for his dear Flemish and Dutch subjects which made him mumble his words so badly that hardly anyone understood him. Or it may have been the loss of all his teeth, as the result of a disease that had struck him during his famous African campaign. But the result was that everybody present felt a great deal of sympathy for their pathetic old master and wished him well.

Charles had three more years in which to enjoy that rest to which he was most assuredly entitled by the forty years he had spent in the field or at the council table, but toward the end of that period he was once more obliged to take a personal interest in the affairs of his former possessions. For under Philip there at once arose that confusion from which Spain was never afterward able to rid itself and which was to bring about the eventual downfall of the Spanish Empire.

No sooner had Charles withdrawn to his lonely retreat in the south than the great duel began. On the one hand, Philip with his totalitarian ideas, and, on the other hand, William with his insistence upon personal liberty, both of action and of thought. In the end, it led to an open break, and a punitive expeditionary force under the ruthless Duke of Alva marched northward through France, convinced that in a few short months it would be able to crush this rabble of butter manufacturers and cheese-mongers which had dared to defy its legitimate master.

In open battle, these veterans quite easily disposed of their opponents, but when the rebels withdrew to the sea and opened the dikes and let their lands be drowned rather than surrender them to the hated enemy, the butter began to slip through the steel-clad fingers of the great Duke of Alva and his foreign hirelings.

In the end, Alva had to give up. Having, like all of Philip's most faithful servants, been obliged to maintain his armies on credit (Philip never paid anybody if he could possibly help himself), he had got himself so hopelessly into debt that he was obliged to escape from Brussels in the middle of the night, lest in the morning he be arrested by his outraged creditors and dragged before a civil court, for in this damnable land of tradesmen and artisans, the civil courts functioned even in the midst of war.

After this first failure, Philip tried a new approach. This time he sent a Man of Peace and Moderation. At least outwardly so, for at heart Philip never changed in his attitude toward the enemies of the True Faith. Every one of the new proposals of the rebels was listened to with polite attention. Then the same stony silence. "Will the hated foreigners be recalled and will King Philip please deal with his Dutch subjects through the regular established channels of the courts and refrain from forcing the Inquisition upon an unwilling people who are accustomed to freedom of thought?"

Upon the first of these two points, the King in faraway Madrid (always half a year behind with his correspondence) pretended to be willing to compromise. But heresy, he insisted, must be stamped out once and for all, and if the Netherlanders were either unwilling or unable to return to the bosom of the Church of their own volition, the King intended to give the Inquisition a free hand.

The people of the Low Countries, conscious of their economic strength, replied by sabotaging all the royal taxes, and without money the regent could hire no soldiers. Soon conditions grew so bad that no Spaniard was safe unless he went about with an armed guard. And all this cleverly organized op-

position, as the King knew and as his sister knew, was the work
of just one person—that little German princeling who, without
support from abroad, had regularly checkmated His Most
Catholic Majesty on every point.

Philip, like a good Spaniard, then bethought himself of another effective way to rid the world of this obstinate enemy. A
price was put upon the head of the Prince. There were quite a
number of candidates for this generous sum of blood money,
for it was known that in this case Philip intended to pay with
a certified check. Fortunately for the cause of the Hollanders,
the assassins were either caught before they had had a chance to
pull their triggers or they fumbled the job, and the Prince recovered from his wounds. In the end, he was even able to strike
a counterblow so staggering in its effects upon the established
order of things that the whole world was to feel the recoil of his
attack upon royal authority.

Already in the year 1579 the Prince's brother John (the
founder of that line of Orange-Nassau from whom the present
royal family is descended) had persuaded the Protestant provinces to join together in some sort of defensive alliance, which
came to be known as the Union of Utrecht. Two years later, a
more important step was decided upon. Delegates from the
United Provinces, in congress assembled at The Hague on July
26, 1581, signed a document which is not very well known outside the confines of the Netherlands, but which in a way is even
more significant than Magna Charta, for it recognized certain
definite principles of government which, two hundred years
later, were to be incorporated into our own Declaration of
Independence.

Here are a few excerpts from this famous Act of Abjuration,
which was at once translated into almost every European language and was distributed all over the Continent so that all the
world might know that the people of the United Netherlands
had not acted in a moment of unreasoning passion but had most
carefully weighed all the pros and cons in this very serious case
of "The People vs. Their Legitimate Sovereign."

The general principle underlying this solemn Act of Abjuration was summed up in the preamble:

"As everybody knows," it read, "a ruler has been called by God to rule over his subjects, even as a shepherd is called to take care of his flocks, and, as has been held true from the beginning of time, a people does not exist for the benefit of its prince, but the prince exists to protect and cherish the interests of his people."

The man who probably had drawn up this challenging document was a certain Marnix van Sint Aldegonde, a Zeeland noble whose estate was situated not far from our own Veere and who gained lasting renown as the author of the song known as the *Wilhelmus van Nassauwe,* which was to become the battle hymn of the Republic and the national anthem of the Kingdom of the Netherlands. At odd moments he had also acted as William's ghost writer, an office for which he was eminently fitted by reason of his knowledge of the classics and his thorough familiarity with the general political setup of his day.

In this Act of Abjuration, Sint Aldegonde dug deep into ancient history and by many eloquent examples he proved that ever since the beginning of time a people has had the right to rid itself of any kind of tyranny which threatened to interfere with the natural rights of its free citizenry. Here was a new sound within the realm of practical politics or, rather, an almost forgotten sound, for even during the Middle Ages the peoples of Europe had always remained conscious of certain "natural and inalienable rights" that belonged not only to themselves but also to their wives and their children, their grandchildren, and all their future progeny until the end of time.

Sint Aldegonde's declaration of independence makes inspiring reading even after these many centuries, and I am sure that Thomas Jefferson, in his most eloquent moments, could not have done better. And I have always rather wondered how familiar Sam Adams of Boston was with this document when in 1743 he qualified for his master's degree at Harvard with a thesis entitled: "Whether it be Lawful to resist the Supreme Magistrate if the Commonwealth cannot otherwise be preserved." I rather think he knew about it. It also seems certain that Thomas Jefferson, as well as most of the other men connected with our own Declaration of Independence, had read it. Why it is so little known in the America of today and is so rarely mentioned in our schoolbooks, which carefully stress Magna Charta, is somewhat of a mystery, but the Dutch Act of Abjuration of the year 1581 is well worth our attention as "source material" for our Declaration of Independence of almost two centuries later.

The author, having delivered himself of a short historical review of the events of the previous thirty years, thereupon, and in the most formal of terms, declared that, in view of his many acts against the constitutional privileges of the different provinces, the King of Spain had now *ipso jure* forfeited his rights to the sovereignty over the people of the Netherlands and that therefor these subjects were now set free of their former oath of allegiance.

And so the deed had been done, and the world gasped, as well it might. For here, and for the first time in modern history, one of the Lord's anointed—a sovereign by the grace of God—had been thrown out on his ear, so to speak, and had been sent packing like an incompetent and dishonest servant. Not even his baggage had been sent after him, for the revenues of these rich provinces now went directly to the Estates-General. And they, as representatives of the people, spent it hiring those armies and equipping those navies with which they intended to attack their former liege lord in every part of the globe and by means of which they were to ruin his dynasty until the last members of it were glad to find employment as automobile salesmen in our modern New York.

Philip now was out of the way, and William, by his shrewd sense of politics and by his instinctive feeling for what he could induce his fellow citizens to do and what he had better leave alone, had won out. His position as the generally recognized leader of the forces that were working for independence had by now been so firmly established that he was the logical candidate for the vacancy. Alas, the petty jealousies among the political leaders of the different provinces (a breed that never learns anything!), as well as the inherent respect for "legitimate authority" so typical of the people of that era, still made the Estates-General hesitate and forced them to look once more for a ruler of the blood royal. They tried a brother of the King of France, but he proved to be wholly undependable and almost sold the country to its enemies. Until the Estates, despairing of ever finding a real prince of some reigning house who did not merely regard the Netherlands as a welcome source of revenue, decided to do the sensible thing and to ask William of Orange to become the legitimate ruler of the United Netherlands.

Alas, ere the final step could be taken, old Dame Fortune, who ever since the beginning of time has been the decisive factor in all human relationships, had taken a hand in the proceedings and by her most unwelcome interference had completely spoiled the prospects of that normal development which would have given the country a definitely established form of government and would not have left it to the mercies of self-interested factions and ambitious functionaries.

For many years now the Prince had lived under the terror of death. The royal edict, outlawing him as an enemy of mankind, had not gone unobserved, and hardly a month went by without some eager zealot trying his hand at a little private murdering. None of these candidates for fame and riches had been successful until the year 1582, when William had gone to Antwerp to make still another effort to bring the northern and southern provinces together.

A poor, half-witted clerk of Basque origin, employed by a bankrupt Spanish merchant and a hopeless fanatic, had taken a shot at the Prince. The bullet had entered through the right ear and had passed out by the left side of the jaw. At first it seemed that it must be fatal, and in Spain the demise of this "archenemy and corrupter of the true Christian faith" had been celebrated by several holy *Te Deums*.

The medical science of that time did not know how to cope with such a complicated wound except by constantly pressing a piece of lint against the gap so as to stop the bleeding. For weeks the Prince's wife, Charlotte of Bourbon, just recovering from having given birth to a child, had sat by the side of her husband, refusing to let anyone else perform this act of mercy. She had saved the Prince's life but she had died from exhaustion on the very day her patient was able to attend a service of thanksgiving for his recovery.

Being the father of a whole brood of children, the Prince had needed a woman to act as the head of his household, and his choice, after Charlotte's death, had fallen upon a person of remarkable ability and outstanding nobility of character. This was Louise de Coligny, the daughter of the gallant French admiral who, as leader of the French Protestants, had been one of the first victims of the Massacre of St. Bartholomew.

After this almost disastrous attempt upon his life, the Prince had deemed it wise to leave Antwerp and move to Delft. The city of Delft, although small, was the most heavily fortified town of the province of Holland. Not only could it be defended easily, but strangers within its gates would easily attract attention and could then be asked to explain exactly why they had come to this particular spot and whether they had any right to be where they were.

It was early in the month of July of the year 1584. During the last few days, a stranger had been observed hanging around the former monastery that had been converted into a home for the Prince and his family. He had, of course, been detained and had been strictly interrogated. But he had offered an entirely acceptable excuse for his presence. His name, so he said, was Balthazar Gérard, and he was a Frenchman, the only surviving son of a family massacred during an anti-Calvinistic riot in his native city.

This plausible story he had learned by heart from a Jesuit priest in Trier, who at Easter had not only confessed him but had at the same time absolved him of the sin he was so soon afterward to commit and which, in the eyes of his spiritual adviser, would not be a sin but a highly virtuous act and one deserving of every honest Christian's praise.

Monsieur Gérard must have been an excellent actor, for the Prince's court preacher, who examined him in the matter of the Calvinistic faith, had only good things to report and felt absolutely convinced that the shabby-looking visitor was indeed the unfortunate victim of papist fury. As for the reason for his living in Delft, he reported that Gérard had been asked to proceed to Delft by the Prince's own representatives in Paris that he might enlighten His Highness about the last hours of the Prince's great and good friend, the Duke of Anjou, who had recently succumbed to that tuberculosis which was so sadly prevalent among his mother's people, the members of the House of Medici.

The story clicked in all respects, and the supposed messenger deceived the Dutch officials so cunningly that he was allowed to visit the Prince in his bedroom and there give him all the details about Anjou's last hours. As a matter of fact, he knew nothing about those last hours, but neither did anybody else, and who was to tell him that he was a liar?

On July 8 the young man was once more discovered roaming through the hallways of the Prince's residence. Asked what he might be doing there at so early an hour, he answered that he was on his way to the church where the Prince was supposed to attend services that morning. As that church happened to stand right across the canal from the Prince's home, this explanation was accepted without further ado. But why, some curious person suggested, hadn't he come in through the front door? Why use the back door? He replied that he would never have dared to do this. Look at his clothes! They were so old and disreputable that he was ashamed to show himself in public, let alone in the residence of a prince.

William was told about all this. Generous as always, he sent the French refugee enough money to buy himself a new outfit for his return to France. The poor refugee expressed his deep gratitude and promptly used the money of his benefactor to buy two pistols from one of the guards. Then he begged that someone kindly ask the Prince for a letter of safe-conduct, so that he could return to his native country without being molested by the Dutch officials. This request was sent to the Prince's secretary, and the safe-conduct was promised for the afternoon of the next day, July 9.

At the appointed hour, the murderer once more presented himself at the Prince's door. William's wife noticed him as she passed through the hall and she was frightened by the man's looks. "A most despicable character," she said. "I would not trust him." Her husband reassured her. "Merely a poor devil of a French refugee. An honest Calvinist and one who has suffered much for his faith."

The Prince that day had a guest. His name was van Uylenborch. He was burgomaster of the city of Leeuwarden in Friesland. Incidentally, he also was the future father-in-law of the painter Rembrandt. During their midday meal the two men discussed the political conditions in Friesland and then made ready to return to the living room. At that moment the assassin, who had been waiting there for several hours, jumped out of his hiding place. He pulled the triggers of both his guns. One of his bullets passed through the Prince's lung, the other pierced the stomach.

William dropped down on the stairs. He realized that this time his enemy had been successful. Falling back into the arms of his master of horse, he commended his soul to God and as his last prayer he whispered, "O Lord, have pity upon my soul and upon these poor people." After that a few mumbled words, a gasping "Yes" when his wife asked him whether he died in Christ—and it was over.

King Philip had gained his immediate point. His enemy was

dead, but the ultimate victory was to be with his opponent. During the next three hundred years, that nation which William had founded was to become the haven of refuge for all those who, in other parts of the world, suffered persecution on account of their beliefs. Some of them were dreamers and fanatics. But a great many others were practical men of affairs. When they set foot on Dutch soil, they brought with them not only the clothes on their backs but also that knowledge and experience which had accounted for their rise in the countries of their birth. They eagerly entered into the life of their new fatherland and they were among the first to found those great foreign trading companies which in the end were to drive the Spanish flag from every sea and reduce Spain to the rank of a fifth-rate country.

The reward for delivering Christianity of its worst enemy was actually paid. Not, I am happy to say, to the assassin himself. He had been duly apprehended. It was then discovered that Monsieur Gérard was a highly methodical sort of person, for it was found that he had carefully provided himself with two pig's bladders. These were to have supported him while swimming across the canal, so that he could safely reach the other side, where he had hidden a horse, also bought with the money the Prince had given him.

After a very careful trial (during which the Dutch authorities did their best to find out who had been Gérard's accomplices), the assassin was executed with all the cruelty of which the people of that age were capable and on this occasion they rather outdid themselves. I shall save you the details. It was the last thing William himself would have tolerated, but he was no longer there to speak words of mercy.

The treatment which Gérard received has often been held up for serious criticism by people who tried to prove that the Calvinists were no better than their opponents, but it was no worse than that meted out almost three quarters of a century later to the regicide judges in England and surely with much less cause. Charles I, unlike William, had quite generously deserved the

*The Prince was coming down the stairs. The murderer was still
waiting for his chance.*

fate that overtook him. Indeed, he had worked for it from the day he came to the throne. And in one respect, the misbegotten Frenchman was much more fortunate than his English fellow sufferers. Their heads had been left on the gallows until the birds had picked out the eyes and the rest had rotted away. Whereas the head of this French terrorist was at once stolen by some zealous local Catholics and was carefully removed to Cologne, where for quite a long time it was revered as a precious relic.

Even more incredible, a movement was started to have the assassin elevated to the rank of a saint. After a short while, however, the more intelligent Catholics began to realize that they were doing their own cause little good by taking the side of this contemptible character and that it would serve a better purpose to forget about him.

I have already told you that the blood money was paid. It went to the murderer's mother and to his brothers. Their patent of nobility survived for more than two centuries. It was rescinded during the French Revolution. Robespierre and his companions were not exactly squeamish when it came to spilling a little blood, but they drew the line somewhere. As for the subsequent events in the Netherlands, there had been no one else who had enjoyed such universal esteem as the Prince, and the moment he was gone, the old provincial rivalries once more broke forth in all their old fury and, though all official documents of the Dutch Republic of that era stressed the fact that "In union alone lies our strength," the rich merchants, who were thereupon entrusted with the care of the nation, were much too jealous of each other to overcome their mutual ill will and to work wholeheartedly for their common cause.

And so the United Netherlands went the way of all democracies. As time went by, it degenerated into a debating society in which the controlling interests grabbed whatever they could for themselves, leaving the public weal to the Devil. On such occasions, the Devil is never very far away and is always most ready to oblige.

And now a few words about General George Washington, but so much has been written about him that I can be very short.

Within the realm of geology it sometimes happens that one layer of rock will push itself across another layer, and then it takes an expert to determine exactly what has taken place. The same holds good for history. Not infrequently it occurs that some particular cultural or economic or social layer shifts from one part of the world to another, but as a rule this takes place so quietly and so gradually that hardly anybody notices the change. Then the denuded soil at home develops a new civilization entirely different from the old one, but that too comes about so slowly that it attracts few people's attention. Until the fatal day when the people wake up to a realization that, though nominally they still speak the same language, are still loyal to the same flag, and are still supposed to worship the same God, they have no longer anything in common with each other. After that the more they try to explain themselves and their motives to their former neighbors, the less they succeed in doing so.

Take our own case. We are only beginning to suspect what happened during the seventeenth century in regard to the old England and the new one. The peace which had finally made an end to the great Lutheran-Catholic controversy had decreed that every prince should have the right to decide what form of religious worship his subjects must accept. That, of course, had been one of those "compromises of desperation" which are the result of an intolerable situation. Europe could not possibly survive if the people continued to destroy each other on account of their religious convictions. Any kind of arrangement, guaranteeing at least a momentary respite from the everlasting slaughter, was better than a continuation of the war, and the disastrous principle of "whose rule I accept, his God I also worship" was greeted as a very clever solution, worthy of the support of all good citizens and not to be questioned or debated any longer.

But in reality, the compromise was just another Trojan horse, filled with the partisans of totalitarianism, and after they had clambered out of their uncomfortable hiding place and had stretched their arms and legs, they descended upon the peaceful denizens of every town and hamlet in Europe and put before them the choice either of accepting the tyranny of their new masters or of being hanged in their own doorways.

It was then that the old Continent was delivered over to the mercies of a dozen competing dynasties, and it was then that the last remnants of medieval self-government were threatened with complete destruction. Here and there, in a few of the Swiss cantons and a few of the Dutch provinces, people continued to rule themselves (to a certain extent, for money, as it has always done, counted heavily in politics), and it was then that England made her noble and glorious effort to establish the supremacy of Parliament over the pretensions of the crown.

I am expressing myself perhaps a little too modernly. The medieval belief in an omnipotent God and in an equally omnipotent source of worldly authority was still part of the spiritual and intellectual make-up of most people. The King was still revered as the God-anointed embodiment of all terrestrial authority and therefore above criticism. Even the Act of Abjuration, which had curtly dismissed King Philip of Spain as ruler over the Low Countries because he had been an unfaithful shepherd unto his flocks, continued to be regarded by many people as something that interfered much too boldly with the orderly progress of a universe in which it stood decreed that a few were predestined to command while the rest must obey.

However, there now were definite precedents for a different approach to this subject, and the people of England were the first to make use of them. Hence, a prolonged struggle between the crown and its subjects. Good Queen Bess may have been just as much of a tyrant at heart as her dear cousin, Mary of Scotland, but she was too shrewd to reveal her true feelings. She knew how to temper her authoritative instincts with acts of good-humored bonhomie (is there a feminine equivalent for this expression?), and if occasionally she spanked her children, they accepted it good-naturedly enough. What was the use of having such a sweet and loving mother if now and then she could not lose her temper with her brood and treat them to a few slaps and cuffs?

But after the old lady had departed this life and had been succeeded by the son of Cousin Mary, a great change came over this Merrie England. The Stuarts now moved from Edinburgh to. London, but being Scotchmen they never quite understood their English subjects, and, with their arrival in the British capital, there came a change over the land that led up to that half a century of constant friction which in turn was to lay the foundations for the free and independent United States of America. For those elements in England's life which foresaw what was coming despaired of maintaining the liberties and prerogatives they needed in order to function properly and happily and, as there seemed to be no chance of getting rid of their imported Scots monarchs, they began to look for another place of abode where they might continue to live their own kinds of lives without being constantly exposed to a visit from the local sheriff and a polite invitation to hie themselves to the Tower, there to await His Majesty's pleasure and (most likely) his executioner.

When an exasperated nation at last grew tired of their rulers and sent for Dutch William to put their house in order, there seemed to be a chance that all would now be well. Unfortunately, headachy William did not even live as long as Oliver Cromwell, and a dozen years after his death the British crown fell into the hands of a minor German dynasty that had to spend two centuries in its adopted country before it finally lost its guttural Teutonic accent and could express itself more or less adequately in the tongue of William Shakespeare. From a merely political point of view, therefore, little was gained when the House of Hanover succeeded that of Stuart, and gradually there came about such a hopeless cleavage between the England of the Old World and that of the New that only a war could decide the issue. That war became known as the American Revolution, and it gave us our own republic.

William the Silent and George Washington

The ancestors of George Washington came from Northamptonshire. They moved to the New World in 1658, when George's great-grandfather bade farewell to England's white cliffs and settled down near Bridges Creek, in Virginia. We know little about him, except that he continued to follow the sort of career he would have chosen in the Old World and became a member of the Virginia House of Burgesses. He died in 1676, leaving his meager estates to his son Lawrence.

Lawrence's second son, Augustine, having been born on this side of the ocean, felt more at home among his new surroundings than his father had done. He caught the spirit of the new country and saw more profit in running an iron mine and an iron smelter than in doing what all the members of his tribe had done. Thus far they had contented themselves with raising tobacco for the London market—a rather hazardous venture, as it placed them completely at the mercies of their British agents.

Digging iron out of the soil was, of course, not quite as genteel a profession as supervising lazy and unwilling Negro slaves, but it was much more profitable, and after he had returned from his schooling in England, Augustine had settled down near Fredericksburg and in due course of time had married two wives (one after the other, of course), by the second of whom, Mary Ball, he had six children, the oldest of whom was baptized George.

The boy grew up in the normal way of that period. The local sexton taught him his letters, and afterward a schoolmaster was hired to give the young gentleman a smattering of Latin. Mathematics, for which Master George felt a great liking, was not on the regular curriculum of the Virginia educational system of the middle of the eighteenth century (George was born in 1732), and so he was obliged to go after it on his own account. He later extended his scientific researches into the realm of practical surveying, and this knowledge of how to make and read maps was of the greatest value to him when he was called upon to lead the armies of the rebellious colonists.

It was a time when boys of fourteen were supposed to be able to shift for themselves. In consequence, his half brother Augustine, who had been the head of the family ever since their father's death and who recognized that George had the makings of an excellent manager, entrusted him with the care of several plantations at an age when a modern youngster has not even thought of choosing a career. George liked his new life, for it meant action. He was forever on the move, examining accounts, hiring and firing overseers, buying and selling crops and slaves, learning all about tobacco, experimenting with new kinds of cattle, and in a general way making himself useful until, at the ripe old age of seventeen, he was deemed fit for public office and was appointed assistant public surveyor of Fairfax County. This favor was bestowed upon him by the amiable Thomas, Lord Fairfax, who, having acquired a trifling five million acres in the Shenandoah Valley, had at last decided to cross the ocean and inspect his property in person. He was now living on a fine estate along the Potomac, not far away from that plantation where John, the first Washington in America, had started the family's fortunes.

It was during this period as a public surveyor that Washington became thoroughly familiar with life in the wilderness and got some conception of the vastness of this new world in which the colonists, until then, had stuck anxiously to the narrow strip of land along the seaboard. But these carefree years, which he probably enjoyed as well as any other part of his career, came abruptly to an end in 1752, when his half-brother Lawrence died.

The Washingtons as a family were apt to have weak chests, and Lawrence had never recovered from the hardships of his campaign against the Spanish city of Cartagena, in what is now the republic of Colombia, in South America. There he had served with the fleet, and the fleet had been commanded by that Admiral Edward Vernon who as "Old Grog" won everlasting detestation in the British navy by ordering that the sailors should not get their rum straight but mixed with water so that they should not be incapacitated quite as much of the time as they used to be, when the stuff was poured raw down their throats.

This expedition against Cartagena had not accomplished much toward making England mistress of the Caribbean (through no fault of Vernon's, but because of the incompetence of most of his colleagues), but out of it had grown that friendship between Lawrence Washington and his commander in chief which made Lawrence change the name of Little Hunting Creek plantation to Mount Vernon.

As I just said, Lawrence died in 1752. He left Mount Vernon to his widow, Anne Fairfax, who within the same year married into the Lee family. She sold the estate to her brother-in-law George, who, then at the age of thirty, began that career of a sound marriage and shrewd investments which eventually was to make him one of the richest young men of Virginia.

But in the meantime, George had done several other things which were to prepare him still further for the role he would soon afterward be called upon to play.

In the year 1753 Governor Dinwiddie had appointed him a major and had sent him into the wild West with orders to find the commander of the French forces, who, after an overland voyage from Canada, had occupied the greater part of the Ohio Valley. Major Washington was to remind his French colleague that he was poaching on British territory and to suggest that he leave as soon as possible.

Whether on this occasion Washington was guided by his own woodcraft, by divine Providence, or by his interpreter, Jacob Vanbraam, I could not tell you, but Washington did find the man he was looking for and delivered his message. The Frenchman courteously invited him to dinner in a fort which is now the town of Waterford, in Pennsylvania, but added that for the present, at least, he and his French troops intended to remain where they were.

This refusal on the part of the French to withdraw their forces led to skirmishes, and these skirmishes in turn led to war. During this conflict Washington, badly supported by the undisciplined colonial troops, was taken prisoner by the French and was only released after he had signed a promise that the British would not try to build any other fortifications in the Ohio Valley for at least a year.

After the failure of their irregular troops, the London authorities hoped to have better luck with their regulars. In February, 1755, General Edward Braddock arrived in Virginia. Washington, like most of the other native officers, had withdrawn from army life. The reason for such a step? These American-born fighters resented being treated as "colonials." No "colonial" officer could receive the same pay as one born in the old country, and any colonial officer, no matter what rank he held, was supposed to be inferior to a mere youngster who held a direct commission from the King.

It was that sort of thing—that irrepressible habit of all good Britishers to act in a superior manner toward all non-Britishers —which had more to do with the outbreak of the American Revolution than all the taxes on tea and all the stamps on official documents. But England was not to learn this until more than a century and a half later.

Heaven knows, these colonials had no reason to feel inferior toward their London superiors. General Braddock, in spite of his personal bravery, was as ignorant of wilderness warfare as the commander of the Horse Guards, a hundred years later, was to be unfamiliar with the topography of the territory around Balaklava. And if it had not been for George Washington (who at the last moment had once more taken to the field, probably anticipating what was going to happen), hardly a man of that British expeditionary force would have come back alive.

In consequence whereof, Colonel Washington was appointed to the post of commander in chief of all the Virginia troops. Did all this teach the British regulars their lesson? It did not. For when George Washington, holder of a colonial appointment, told a mere captain with a royal commission to do something he wanted done, the captain told him to go jump into the lake. And Washington was obliged to travel all the way to Boson, where the British commander in chief was stationed, to get redress for this insult.

This time he won out, but it was that sort of inexcusable stupidity and arrogance which kept the colonials in a constant state of irritation. It is quite understandable that the Virginian, whose health had been greatly impaired by his campaign in the wilderness, used the first possible opportunity to resign his commission and refused to have anything further to do with British officialdom. From then on he was going to enjoy the quiet life of a plantation owner, and the world, whether sober or drunk, could pass by his door—it was to be no concern of his what happened to it. A military lean-to in the forest was at best a pretty poor sort of makeshift, whereas a home of his own in his beloved Virginia would allow him to forget the hardships and discomforts of his earlier days in the field.

Of course, one could not very well administer a plantation without a wife. But suitable wives were hard to find, and furthermore, George Washington had never been very successful with the ladies. This, in spite of his six feet and his perfect willingness to adapt himself completely to the customs and habits of the society into which he happened to have been born and to partake of all the fashionable pleasures of that day, such as dancing, hunting, riding, drinking, and going to Sunday service in the nearest Episcopal church.

But, as most of us six-footers know only too well, women, being what they are, prefer the little fellows whom they can pick up when they fall and hurt themselves and whom they can carry away in their arms and fondle until they smile again and are able to say, "I am feeling much better, and now I will go and pluck you a daisy."

George Washington was no daisy plucker. A young man who before his twenty-fourth year had gone through a couple of wilderness campaigns, who had fought in half a dozen battles, and who had experienced a great deal of sickness was apt to be a rather serious person, and that, of course, did not help him very much either while trying to win the favor of some Virginia belle. Finally, in sheer exasperation he decided to be practical rather than romantic, and he married the widow of a fellow planter, one Colonel Daniel Parke Custis. Martha Dandridge Custis was the mother of two children and the owner of fifteen thousand acres of land near Williamsburg, sixty-five thousand dollars in cash in the bank, and one hundred and fifty slaves. Martha Custis also was (and was to prove herself even more so in the years to come) a very kindhearted and understanding companion, an excellent housekeeper, and a discreet and faithful wife to a man who was to occupy the highest position in the land. Best of all (the only real consideration in such matters), she gave her husband everything he most cared for. She provided him with a well-run home, where at any time he could entertain all the friends he wanted to bring, and she saved him from all those fussy details which are so exasperating to a man who has got a real job to do.

Fifteen years after their marriage, George Washington came at last into his own. For he was given the task of reorganizing the new England on our side of the ocean into a nation that would be able to take over when the older England overseas should have failed.

The rest is history. It has been told so often and so well that I shall not waste your time repeating what all of us know. In England no one connected with the government seemed to have grasped the fact that the crown was dealing with a people who were·the spiritual descendants of those Englishmen who, a century and a half before, had already rid themselves of one head bearing a crown. There is a story current in many parts of New England of how, during a threatened Indian massacre, there suddenly appeared an old, white-haired fellow, coming from nowhere in particular but wearing an outmoded Cromwellian uniform and wearily but efficiently swinging an old Cromwellian sword with which he promptly slew so many of the savages that the others fled in panic and were never again seen. Having saved his fellow settlers by his unexpected arrival, the white-haired, white-bearded hero silently withdrew into the dark fringe of the near-by forest and never again showed himself to mortal eye.

There was more truth to this bit of folklore than most people suspected. The number of regicide judges and other fugitives from Charles Stuart's revenge who had actually lost themselves in the American wilderness to find safety was probably very small. But their spirit was everywhere, and it lay hidden in the souls of a great many people who were completely unconscious of being anything but good, loyal subjects of His Majesty the King. Had a clever man ruled over England just before our Revolution, or even a merely mediocre one, capable at least of surrounding himself with wise counselors, all might have yet been saved, and the Revolution could probably have been avoided. But by this time the real rulers of England had been petrified into an aristocracy—into a rigid caste—and the country squire had so completely lost touch with the realities of daily existence that the world for him did not really begin except at five hundred pounds a year. How could those insular port drinkers and fox hunters, who only went abroad for the purpose of returning home infinitely more self-satisfied than they had left, ever have been made to understand that old Oliver Cromwell's ideas were still stirring among the spiritual descendants of those preposterous dissenters who had dared to lift their blasphemous hands against the sacred person of their anointed Majesty and who—serve them right!—had been taught a lesson when the body of their abominable leader had been dug out of its grave and had been thrown to the dogs.

That much was true. The remains of the great Oliver no longer rested in the chapel of Henry VII in Westminster Abbey, but his soul had gone marching on. It continued to march on for six long and desperate years, until that ever-fateful nineteenth of October of the year 1781, when General George Washington of Mount Vernon in Virginia, commander in chief of the armies of the United States of America, courteously bowed to Major General Charles Cornwallis, commander in chief of His Majesty's forces in South Carolina, and told that dejected gentleman to keep his sword, for he had been a brave foeman, and the code of honor of their common heritage demanded that one behave generously toward a conquered enemy who had fought the good fight squarely and decently and who had behaved as modestly and decorously in victory as in defeat.

With this little anecdote, I think I can bid the General farewell, for you will now understand what kind of person he was. And now that all the evidence is available, we can sum him up in a very few words, for there really was nothing very complicated about this greatest of all Americans.

George Washington was not a great military leader. He was careful and methodical, but he lacked the genius of an Alexander or a Napoleon. He was not a creative statesman like Jefferson, and old Ben Franklin was his undisputed master when it came to diplomatic negotiations that required shrewdness and patience and a gift for horse trading. As an orator he was deplorably lacking in all those tricks by which an experienced speaker can sway his audiences. Nor did he ever indulge in what we would now call original and creative thinking. He was by nature a conservative and deeply distrusted the bright boys who tried to sell him the ideal of the French Revolution. Indeed, if he had had his way, all radicals would have been sent back right away to where they had come from. They upset his notions about a well-regulated commonwealth in which every man, woman, child, horse, and dog should know his, or her, or its place in society. He wanted freedom, but it was the freedom that had prevailed in the England of his ancestors. The conception of liberty which was to arise soon afterward among the disinherited masses of the future republic he did not understand at all, and it is doubtful whether it would have been very much to his liking.

Yet, it was he who founded our republic; it was this Virginian planter who set us free from foreign domination; it was this Southern aristocrat who started us off on our noble experiment in self-government, and he was able to do this because he was far ahead of his contemporaries in that one particular respect which counts more heavily in the scales of the gods than all other qualifications for glory and success put together.

George Washington was the embodiment of character.

Webster defines character as follows: "Highly developed or strongly marked moral qualities; individuality, esp. as distinguished by moral excellence; moral vigor or firmness, esp. as acquired through self-discipline; inhibitory control of one's instinctive impulses. . . ."

I think that I can let it go at that. For my final comment upon both William of Orange and George Washington need consist of but one single word: CHARACTER.

As soon as I had finished these short biographical notes, I put a special-delivery stamp on the envelope and walked to the post office to mail it to Frits in Amsterdam. But on the way home, I remembered that we had done nothing as yet about our music. So I went back to my desk and got up a little program that I thought would be suitable for the occasion.

The Prince was easy, but I felt a little uncertain about the sort of tunes that would appeal to George Washington. Since he had lived in the same social atmosphere as Thomas Jefferson, I decided that he would most likely prefer some of the English ballads which had so delighted the heart of the master of Monticello. I therefore decided upon several arias from Henry Purcell's opera *Dido and Aeneas,* and I got records of *If Music Be the Food of Love* and *How Long, Great God,* and also his so-called "Golden" Sonata for two violins and harpsichord, together with his Chaconne in G minor, and from Handel I took *Where'er You Walk,* from *Semele.*

This proved to be a good enough selection, though it seemed that the General preferred the simpler tunes, for he asked us to repeat Purcell's *If Music Be the Food of Love* and *How Long, Great God.*

As for the Prince, I thought that he had probably heard

enough hymns to last him through eternity, and I ordered some of the older German tunes, such as Heinrich Isaak's *Innsbruck, ich muss dich lassen* (forever associated with the name of the Emperor Maximilian, the grandfather of his friend and benefactor, Charles V). I also asked for a number of arias from Monteverdi's first opera, and for *Lasciatemi morire* and a canzonetta for two voices, *Chiome d'oro, bel tesoro,* together with Jacopo Peri's *Gioite al canto mio,* Orpheus' song.

Having thus settled this rather important matter, I went to bed, got up, worked all day, and the next afternoon, at about seven, decided to take a short walk before I went to Frits' house on the Markt. Frits had called me up as soon as he arrived, for we were very modern and had two of the five telephones in Veere. The others belonged to the doctor, to the post office, and to Hubrecht Castel, who ran the bus to Middelburg.

As always when I merely wanted a breath of fresh air, I went to the old ramparts that Napoleon, some hundred and twenty years before, had ordered to be erected when he decided to make the island of Walcheren the spearhead of the expedition he intended to launch against England. They were heavy earthen walls surrounding our village on all sides. Two or three old cannon had been left for, I suppose, the sake of a romantic effect, for they no longer served any practical purpose.

When I approached the biggest of these cannon, the one nearest the mouth of the harbor, I noticed an unfamiliar figure. I thought that I recognized the General, and when I came a little closer I realized that I had come into the presence of the first President of our country. He wore the full-dress uniform of the commander of the Continental army. With one arm he was leaning on the gun. When I came nearer, I honored him with my best European bow—a mixture of that polite gesture with which Lafayette would have greeted him and a click of the heels in the manner of von Steuben. The General looked up, and the first thing that struck me was how badly his face had been marked by the smallpox he had caught in the West Indies at the time he had visited those islands, trying to help his

Frits' house on Veere's Market Place.

brother Lawrence regain his health. But I forgot all about this when I looked at his eyes. Those eyes smiled at me with that unconscious friendliness which is the main characteristic of all well-bred Americans.

"General," I said, borrowing a familiar phrase from his correspondence, "I am your very humble servant."

"And I am yours, sir," he answered, "and I suppose you are the young man who has so kindly invited me for dinner tonight and who is now looking for his guest."

I forgot that I was addressing a man who had been famous for his truthfulness and answered that he had guessed correctly.

"Well," the General replied, "I am ready to follow you, but I noticed these pieces of ordnance and I thought I would inspect them. They are ugly things—these cannon—and I detest them, but in the history of every nation there are moments when they become an absolute necessity. They are, indeed, the 'ultimate ratio' when all other arguments have failed." And then, with a final look at the landscape, he indicated that he was at my disposal.

On our way to Frits' house, I noticed that the General moved with that somewhat painful stiffness I had sometimes observed in people who have spent most of their lives on horseback. At one moment, while going down the steep little iron ladder that led to the top of the ramparts, I was even obliged to assist him in getting his feet on the rungs. He noticed it and apologized. "I am not what I was when I marched with Braddock," he said. "Poor old Braddock! He was very kind to me. I shall always remember him as the perfect gentleman of the old school, but hopelessly lost when it came to fighting in the American wilderness. Well, he paid with his life for his refusal to take our advice. Too bad! Too bad! And now, tell me, this seems quite a small village. Yet that church over there looks big enough to hold all the people in Philadelphia, and I notice by the way your harbor has been dug that it must once have been very much larger than it is now. And how do people still manage to live here when all commerce is gone?"

I gave him a short outline of Veere's history. I told him how originally it had been merely the ferryhead from which people crossed from the island of Walcheren to the island of Noord Beveland, how we thought that even before then the Romans had chosen this spot to cross from the mainland to England, and how, on account of its favorable location on the western branch of the Scheldt, Veere had developed as a trading port with Flanders and the British Isles. I went into some detail about the curious way in which it had become a "free port" for the wool trade with Scotland. One of the Borselens, who also happened to be lords of Veere, had married a daughter of James I of Scotland, and, as a wedding present, an arrangement had been made by which all Scottish wool could be imported free of charge into the Netherlands, provided that it came in by way of Veere. This had brought quite a large Scots colony to the little city, and everything had gone along in fine shape until the collapse of the Netherlands during the second half of the eighteenth century.

I showed the General the old house in which the headquarters of the Scots staple had been established and the dormitories and dining room of the visiting skippers and businessmen. I told him of the strict regulations for those visitors, who were not allowed to carry the steaks they had bought at the butcher's home on the point of their swords, for that sort of thing was not done in a respectable Dutch city. They had to take them home in a bundle underneath their arms.

And next to the Scots' House I pointed to the house called the Ostrich, because there was a large stone with the picture of an ostrich in the façade. That is to say, people had always called it an ostrich until a professor, who knew all about birds, had happened to come to Veere and had exclaimed, "Lord help us all if that is not a picture of a dodo!" And it was—the only image of a dodo probably ever made from an original model, brought home by a Veere sailor and done by the not very experienced hand of the local stonecutter, but a dodo nevertheless.

General Washington was leaning with one hand on one of our old cannon.

Curiously enough, no one had noticed it until that bird professor visited us.

This greatly interested the General, for he too had wondered what had become of the dodo, and he said we ought to know a lot about it in Holland because the Dutch were the first to have settled down on the island of Mauritius. But when I asked him, hadn't he noticed that pioneers never had the slightest interest in their physical surroundings, he said yes, and it was perfectly deplorable, but when immigrants from Europe settled in the wilderness, they had apparently only one idea—to destroy and hack and maim and in general to kill off every living creature that came within reach of their guns. He had a theory about it. It might have been because in the Old World these people never had had guns, had not been allowed by the government to have guns. Then, when they came to a part of the world where they were left to their own devices and where the laws against firearms could not be enforced and where there was no danger of being hanged for the dreadful sin of poaching, their newly found sense of liberty had gone to their heads and they had indulged in those frenzies of killing which in America had developed into a serious menace to all wild-animal life. He, himself, had often observed this while surveying in Virginia and Pennsylvania, and he had often expressed the fear that eventually such a course might lead to the complete extermination of all sorts of useful and interesting birds and mammals.

I hastily changed the subject (it was a very painful one to me) and drew his attention to a few baskets of native shrimps that had just been carried on shore from the boat of an Arnemuiden fisherman. He remarked upon their tiny size—so different from the American shrimps—veritable giants compared to their Dutch cousins. I agreed, but said that the Scheldt shrimps had more taste, and, in order to prove it, I told the Arnemuider to bring fifty cents' worth of his shrimps to Frits' house. "We will serve them to you, sir," I said, "with a little oil and vinegar, and you will have a new and very pleasant experience."

"Too bad," he answered, "that I only discover them now. We

might have tried them in Virginia." And then it was almost seven o'clock and time for dinner.

Inside Frits' house we found the Prince sitting in front of a small wood fire—not that it was exactly cold in the room, but His Highness seemed in need of a little extra warmth. He looked like his last picture, which shows him just after he had recovered from the attack upon his life in Antwerp. I compared the face of this tired old man with that of the handsome fellow painted by Antonio Moro, when he was still a rich and noble young gentleman, clad in magnificent armor and with the whole of the world before him. Now, in his small black skullcap and fur-lined coat, he looked as if he were seventy, though he had been murdered when barely in his fifty-second year. Life had been hard on him, but he had borne all his misadventures with great and good courage.

When we entered, Erasmus, also warming his aching fingers before the fire, was telling the Prince some of his recollections of Charles V, whom he had known as a young man. "The Emperor was by no means deprived of intellect," he was just beginning his sentence, when the Prince noticed General Washington and rose to greet him. But the General would have none of this. Dropping his coat to me (he was a gentleman and accustomed to such small services), he hastily stepped forward to prevent the Prince from leaving his chair.

"*Je vous prie, monseigneur,*" he said in excellent French, though with a strong accent, using the title by which he had addressed the Marquis de Lafayette. "*Je vous prie, monseigneur, ne vous dérangez pas.*" And, with a gesture of the hand, he waved him back into his seat.

As for Erasmus, the General at first was not quite certain where to place this fellow guest, but he soon realized that he had to deal with someone of outstanding ability and, although he always spoke to him as "*monsieur le professeur,*" there was none of the contempt in the expression he had felt for the learned divines of Harvard and Yale who had so often made his life miserable after he had assumed command over the American army.

Washington and the Prince were entirely congenial from the moment they set eyes on each other. They were almost two centuries apart, but they had gone through exactly the same kinds of experiences, and, as the human race does not really change in the deeper essentials of its character, these two men had suffered equally from the misunderstanding with which their noblest efforts had so often been greeted by their fellow men.

Fortunately, both of them had absorbed some slight admixture of the old Roman and Greek philosophies with their more formal Christian training. They had therefore learned how to take their neighbors with many spoonfuls of salt (large soupspoons, too) and had trained themselves to accept what could not be helped. Not in that humility of spirit of which the Scriptures spoke when they advocated a life of meek subjugation. Far from it! Both men had often fallen into fits of uncontrollable fury at some new outrage perpetrated upon them by those whom they were trying to help. But after a short while, their sense of the inevitable (the most valuable thing we can learn from the classics) had shown them the folly of such a course (which could only lead to high blood pressure and sudden death), and they had returned to their former equanimity of soul.

We had an example of this early during the meal. "Yes," the General remarked with the fish (about which he was very polite, excusing himself for his lack of interest in it by telling us that during Valley Forge he had got an aversion to fish, as it was about the only thing he had got to eat), "I hear that I am now called the Father of my Country and that I have a statue at every crossroad, so to speak, that cities have been called after me and even a whole state, and that in all the schoolbooks I am held up as a paragon of every human virtue. I myself lay no claim to such superhuman qualities. All my livelong days I wanted to do just one thing. I wanted to live peacefully in my own house with my good Martha and perhaps have a few neighbors in for dinner and a bowl of punch, and own enough land to support me.

"None of us Washingtons were very strong. My poor brother should never have gone on that foolish expedition against Cartagena. He never recovered from it, and think of the life I myself was forced to lead! For six whole years I hardly ever spent a night underneath my own roof. Those miserable Philadelphia hucksters and moneygrubbers let me and my men starve one whole winter in that dreadful hole of Valley Forge. My men died of hunger and disease or they ran away and had to be caught and shot. Those German drillmasters surely taught us how to turn our farm boys into an army, but their methods were pretty harsh. I wish I could have turned them loose on the dear neighbors of old Ben Franklin! They absolutely refused to touch our continental money. They would only do business with us when we were able to pay them in English gold. Just like the farmers in Jersey who would not sell us anything unless we paid them in English money. And where were we to get hold of sovereigns unless we first took them away from the English, and how could we take them away from the redcoats unless we had money with which to buy guns?"

That was about the longest speech the General made that evening, and it greatly surprised us, though we were delighted to notice that all we had heard about the General's eloquent use of the English language had been true. Indeed, he swore like a trooper and seemed totally unconscious of the impression this might make upon people who had been brought up on the fairy tales of Parson Weems. But perhaps he felt that he was among friends and could let himself go. Hence, out of decent respect for public opinion, I am giving a slightly censored version of his actual utterances.

After his outburst, the General dropped into a profound silence (the turkey had been served in the meantime), and it was then the turn of the Prince. He seemed to feel quite as deeply upon the subject as the General had done.

"Yes," he said, "I too feel that if I had never left that old castle of Dillenburg where I was born, I probably would have been a great deal happier. I even might have lived a few years longer. And what I received in return—I don't know. I really don't know—but what I got, was it worth all the endless suffering and the endless troubles of that hopeless fight? I was not really much of a military man. I hated to be thrown in with those dirty, hairy Swiss mercenaries I had to hire and who were forever asking for money I did not have to give. The stench of their camps and their bodies is still in my nostrils. They were either drunk or plundering. And when they were not paid on the dot, they would go wild and burn down a couple of villages or they would run away and hire out to the enemy.

"And then I had to deal with those Calvinist preachers, forever ranting and canting, quarreling among each other and forcing themselves into my presence when I was busy with a dozen much more important things. And once I had let them come in, they had nothing better to do than tell me that the kingdom of God was now at hand and I must repent (repent of what?)—and then, and this is the actual truth, they would denounce me in my own house for the sin of not listening to them as the chosen vessels of God to save this wicked world from perdition.

"That was only half of the story. There was that everlasting problem of getting hold of enough money to pay my troops. Every one of those little cities that called on me to defend them was only thinking of its own interests. *Mon Dieu!* how they hated each other! in spite of all their fine speeches about Unity and their Common Cause!

"And what did I ever see of my own family? My oldest son was kidnaped by the Spaniards and he was taught by Philip to loathe and despise me. He was even obliged (so they told me) to be present at that thanksgiving service they held at the Escorial when they thought that I was dead—the time that man in Antwerp shot me in the jaw—the time I lost my beloved Charlotte. As for my other sons, they had to learn their father's business, but I am glad to say that they, at least, became first-class soldiers. They would have been a great help to me, but when at last I thought that I would be able to carry my plans to completion, Philip struck his final blow, and I was murdered on my own doorstep."

The conversation was taking a somewhat pathetic turn. In trying to change the subject, I am afraid that I was guilty of asking a rather trite question.

"Your Highness," I said, "and Your Excellency, if you will pardon me, but if you were given the chance, would you do what you had done before, or would you really prefer to spend your days peacefully in your Dillenburg Castle and your house in Mount Vernon? And would you have been content if today there were no independent nation of the Netherlands and no independent republic of the United States?"

Neither the Prince nor the General answered me right away. They both sat in silence. Then they replied at the same moment, so that they might well have spoken with one voice. "We probably would have done what we did" was the gist of their remarks.

I ventured one further question: "Why?"

"I don't know," the General answered, "but it seemed the right thing to do at the time. And I suppose I felt that it was my duty toward my people."

"Yes," the Prince said, looking in an absent-minded fashion at the dwindling fire in the hearth, "it was our duty. The people had put their faith in us. We could not very well disappoint them. We just could not let them down!"

The meal had come to an end. I remembered, from one of Thomas Jefferson's letters, that in Virginia it had been the custom to remove everything from the table as soon as dinner was over. When that had been done, I suggested a glass of punch.

"I wonder," the General replied, "whether you have anything a little less strong. I had to give up punch toward the end of my life. Perhaps I had too much of it when I was young."

The lights flickered and went out, and our guests had disappeared.

"Would you prefer a glass of Beaujolais—a very light French wine?"

"That would be very pleasant, and, as a favor, would you do me the honor of presenting me to your cook? I have rarely tasted such a turkey, though I am more accustomed to the wild variety, and as for the dressing, it was of such excellence I would like to pay her my compliments."

So we asked Jo to come out of her kitchen, and she was much pleased by the pleasant things the General told her. Then she noticed the Prince, who had once more fallen into a quiet reverie. She went to his chair, knelt down before him, took his hand and kissed it. William looked up in happy surprise.

"This," he whispered, "and now, after all these many centuries!"

"Now more than ever," said Frits, who had tears in his eyes.

"Then it was not all in vain?" the Prince asked, speaking more or less to himself.

"*Mon prince,*" the General answered, "such things as you have done are never in vain."

The Prince bowed to him. "Will you share the compliment with me?" he asked.

"Gladly," the General replied, "but on condition that I may also share the other compliment," and, going rapidly over to Jo, he gave her a right hearty kiss.

After that touching little incident, the talk took a lighter turn. We had our bottle of Beaujolais, and once more, when the clock began to strike the hour of midnight, the candles slowly went out. When we lighted the lamp, our guests were gone. But we had not noticed the manner of their departure. That was part of the mystery.

CHAPTER III

Sir Thomas More Is the Guest of His Old Friend
Desiderius Erasmus

"Frits," I said when he came to our house for an American Sunday-morning breakfast—waffles and sausages and lots of coffee. "Listen, my good Frits, I have had an idea. You remember that Erasmus had a very dear friend, old Sir Thomas More?"

"Of course I remember him. If only from that sketch by Holbein, the pencil drawing showing the whole More tribe, one of the most delightful family portraits that were ever made. Didn't he lose his head? Didn't he get into some kind of scrape with Henry VIII? On account of the wives? Yes, I remember him very well."

"This is just an idea," I answered, "but our beloved Erasmus has been very kind to us. Now, suppose we arrange a little surprise party for him. Don't tell him who is coming, and then suddenly let him see who it is!"

"People don't like surprises," said Jimmie, giving Frits his third cup of coffee. Being a very methodical sort of person, she does not like surprises herself and feels convinced that all other people must share her prejudice.

"That goes for bookkeepers and public accountants, people who are not allowed to have any imagination," I hastened to reply, remembering Jimmie's pride in the fact that in all the many years of our marriage she had never been out one cent on her monthly bank statement, a talent for which I greatly envy her, "but men and women of a broad, humanistic culture love surprises."

"Is that so?" came from the good James. "Well, have it your own way, but I think you had better warn him just the same."

"That would spoil the fun."

"O.K.! Try it and let me know."

We both promised that we would let her know, and then, while Frits' waffles were being done, I went to my workshop and hastily jotted down a few notes about Sir Thomas.

Spring was coming to our island.

Sir Thomas was born in 1478. He was decapitated in 1535. He studied at Oxford, where he became interested in literary studies—nothing very profound, just that enthusiasm for the New Learning which was then as fashionable as an interest in the New Economics is today. After college he went in for the law (you should have let the law alone, Thomas!) and showed such talent for that kind of work that he attracted the attention of good King Hal, who all through his life had a considerable need of clever lawyers.

In this way More was drawn into the life of the court (watch out, Thomas! No good can come of it!) and was appointed Lord Chancellor. (What became of your predecessor, my good Thomas? You know perfectly well—he died a prisoner just in time to cheat the axman. Watch out, Thomas!)

Shortly afterward, Henry started upon his Reno career. His Lord Chancellor informed him that he could not send Catherine of Aragon a-packing without a better excuse than he was able to offer. Just because he had never liked this spouse, who could not give him a male heir (sufferers from your particular ailment, Your Majesty, often have difficulties in such matters, and, as a matter of fact, they should not be allowed to marry at all), just because he was crazy to get the handsome young Anne Boleyn (who was no fanatic but not too easy, either)—that, in the eyes of his more serious-minded subjects, was not really a good ground for a divorce. (Be careful again, Sir Thomas! You have interfered with the matrimonial plans of a very determined young woman, who has now sworn to get you!)

Came the trial of poor Catherine, who never had a chance. Came the secret marriage of Anne and Henry, and next Anne was with child. (Watch out, Anne, lest it be a girl! Henry wants a boy, and you know, once he has set his heart on anything, he is going to get it.)

Then (in order to prevent still more scandal) it became absolutely necessary to get this divorce and to get it right away. And so out went Catherine, and in came Anne. But not for long, Three years later, she was caught in a trap. Was she guilty or innocent? Nobody quite knew, but when you are sixteen years younger than a husband who is a lecherous, prurient, and lascivious old satyr, small wonder you occasionally look out of the window, though the story that she had been too friendly with her own brother was, of course, nonsense. Such a filthy accusation could only arise in the atmosphere of that Tudor cesspool in which an uncle was willing to condemn his own niece to death so as to catch a few further crumbs from the royal table.

But ere that ill-fated lady had walked to the block (no matter what else you may be able to say about these flighty young Englishwomen, they surely knew how to die!), Sir Thomas himself had lost his head.

Does anyone today still remember the case of Elizabeth Barton? It was not unlike that of the Mother of God, who was indirectly responsible for the fall and the death of Robespierre during the end of the French Revolution.

Yes, her name was Elizabeth Barton, and you should not get her mixed up with Clara Barton, who started our American Red Cross and who was a very different kind of lady. Elizabeth Barton was a native of Kent. That is why, in the heyday of her fame, she became known as the Nun of Kent, or the Maid of Kent, which reminded the people (and how they loved all those goings-on at the court!) of the Maid of Orléans.

Like her French counterpart, Elizabeth was of exceedingly humble origins, a woman-of-all-work, an illiterate household slavey, to be exact. While working for the business manager of the Archbishop of Canterbury, she was taken ill. When she recovered she had gone completely crazy. She heard voices and saw spooks. Whenever she was in a trance, she predicted the future—mostly blatant nonsense like the high-sounding quatrains of Nostradamus, the famous Franco-Judean soothsayer. But among the simple countryfolk it was soon being whispered about that she was a true prophetess and spoke with the voice of God. (Why, by the way, do all those voices of God invariably talk like ignorant peasants, and why are they so rarely able to write their own names?) But the humble and the meek, bless their loving hearts, flocked to Canterbury and worshiped their Cassandra, and in this way they caused great scandal among the good folk of the town.

"Whatever is done, let there be no scandal," has ever been the wise slogan of Mother Church. Nothing easier than that, when the guilty party is a humble maidservant and her employer happens to be the Archbishop of Canterbury.

Next item on the program: Elizabeth Barton has entered a convent and is now a nun. Does she therefore disappear from the scene? By no means! She has found a kind of manager and publicity agent—one of the monks told off to investigate her case has come to believe in her. His name is Bocking, and he is convinced of her "mission." (Why do people with missions always have such strange and futile missions? Why don't they ever have "missions" to stamp out cancer or abolish war?) Soon pilgrims from all over England are hastening to Canterbury to worship this new saint. Even the Lord Chancellor has become mildly interested in the case, as might any intelligent man who wishes to learn something at first hand about manifestations of abnormal psychology. (Again, watch your step, Sir Thomas. There is nothing extraordinary about the hallucinations of poor Elizabeth Barton. She probably suffered from some kind of religious mania, but from the slight available data it is difficult to make a very precise diagnosis. Watch out just the same, Sir Thomas! Such cases are apt to be very messy!)

Even in her nunnery Elizabeth knew what was happening in the big world outside. A wicked king was pitting his will against that of the Pope. The Pope was defending the holy sacrament of matrimony. The King was defying him. The Maid of Kent had made up her mind. For a humble and devout daughter of the Church, there was only one course to follow. She must warn against the dreadful things that would befall the country at large if evil were allowed to triumph over righteousness, and if the King persisted, he could no longer be the ruler of the realm but must die a villain's death. The moment had arrived for the King to take this matter seriously. Off to Canterbury trotted the royal stallion (I mean the horse that carried the King), and His Majesty in person went to interview this poor crazy female.

She recognized him without being told who he was and fore-told his death if he were to insist upon this divorce.

That happened in 1532. Shortly afterward, Henry was obliged to marry his Anne. The nun now became positively wild in her rantings, and the King shed his air of superior indifference. Enough was enough, but too much was too much. Would Thomas Cranmer kindly look into the matter?

Cranmer, lately raised to be Archbishop of Canterbury, would be delighted to oblige. More than that, he would, as long as he was at it, make a thorough job of it. For here was a chance to rid the country of as many of His Majesty's enemies as could possibly be connected with this dastardly plot. What plot? Who knew or who cared? Just mention a plot against the life of a popular ruler, and the people will howl for somebody's blood— a lot of blood, if possible. For the common people deeply loved their bluff King Hal, whom they considered one of their own and who would just as soon sleep with a fishmonger's daughter as with an imperial princess (much rather). Therefore, let his executioners torture the wicked witch until she is ready to con-fess that she has stolen the towers of Westminster Abbey, and then let there be a fine party on Tyburn Hill, and let the crowd watch all these enemies of the royal authority being hanged and cut down before they are quite dead and then have their breasts cut off and their hearts pulled out of their bodies, and let the bodies themselves be hacked into four pieces and hung in iron crates above the city gates, until they shall have rotted away. Whoopee! And did the crowd enjoy itself that blustery day in April of the year 1534, when its happy dream came true!

Now, let us check up for a moment on the hangman's score during this period.

A.D. 1534—exeunt Elizabeth Barton *et al.*

Then suddenly, from unsavory comedy to sublime tragedy: A.D. 1535—Sir Thomas More, accused of having been a part of the great Bartonian plot against the King's life (read: for hav-ing refused to approve of the most scandalous of His Majesty's several divorce suits), is sent to the Tower and is beheaded on a charge of treason.

Comes A.D. 1536, and the King takes his revenge upon his young wife. On the seventeenth of May of that year, Anne Boleyn's alleged lovers are executed, and on the nineteenth of that same month, Anne herself loses her lovely head. Her uncle, the Duke of Norfolk, the presiding official of the court, weeping copious tears of the well-known crocodile variety, has offered His Majesty the choice between having the faithless wife decapitated or burned at the stake. The King has graciously declared in favor of the ax, but with great delicacy he has sent for the executioner of Calais, just across the Channel, to do the job, for once a gentleman, always a gentleman, and no British hands must be allowed to touch the blood of one who had shared the royal couch and who had given the King one living daughter and two dead children.

But why, you will ask, this rage and fury against Anne? Because she has failed to give her husband a son, and because (if the court has been right in its findings) she has planted a few too many horns upon the royal brow, and (most important of all) because His Majesty has already fixed his bloodshot eyes upon still another candidate for the royal favor. The name of the lady is Jane Seymour. Age, twenty-seven. Antecedents, lady in waiting to Catherine of Aragon. Her long residence at court has taught her one thing. In order to play it safe, it is absolutely imperative for anyone who has attracted the King's attention to remind him at every moment of the day and night (but especially of the night) that the road to her bedroom leads past the altar.

Henry takes the hint, and eleven days after her predecessor has lost her head, the wedding bells are ringing, and Jane Seymour becomes the third Mrs. Henry VIII and holds that position until the next year, when she gives birth to a son, Edward VI, who is to reach the age of sixteen. Poor Jane dies of a cold twelve days after triumphantly giving Henry an heir. She is incidentally the only one of his wives for whom the King will wear mourning. I could have omitted this part, for of all these things, poor Sir Thomas was to know nothing. His own legal assassination had taken place on July 7, 1535. His head had been taken to London Bridge that it might serve as a warning to all those who might dare to interfere with the all-highest will. According to popular rumor, his daughter Margaret, a woman of great talent and character, rescued it. When she died, the head was buried with her. But she had lost all of her father's property. It was (oh, Anne Boleyn, with all your charm you were a prize bitch!) bestowed upon Anne's daughter Elizabeth (the "bastard daughter," as Parliament was to call her), and this same Elizabeth was to enjoy it until the end of her days.

So much for the happy days in "merrie olde England"!

Yet, with all this vileness and against this background of murder, rape, incest, and foul deeds of every sort, here was as pure a soul as ever breathed. In an age when politics had descended to such a low depth of corruption that no honest man would have anything to do with them, he played an important role in the affairs of state and gained a reputation for the absolute purity of his public and private life.

For years More's hospitable home in Chelsea had been the meeting place for all the men of wit and learning in London. Ably supported by both his first and his second wives and his eldest daughter, Margaret (who married that William Roper who was to give us Sir Thomas' first biography), the More mansion was the most civilized spot in England. From far and near, people traveled to catch a glimpse of the man who had given the world one of the best satires on both society and government in that semiserious little opus for which he had invented the title of *Utopia*—the place that was "nowhere."

In this story about a mythical island situated somewhere in the New World (first printed in Louvain in 1516), More had described the adventures of Raphael Hythlodaye who had accompanied Amerigo Vespucci on one of his five voyages to the country which was to bear his name. The honest Hythlodaye had entertained his host (Sir Thomas) with a painstaking description of the happiness that was to be found among the inhabitants of this blessed isle of Utopia, drawing some very unfavorable comparisons between their fate and that of the people in England, where the poor were by far too poor and the rich were by far too rich. And he had told Sir Thomas how the Utopians had accomplished their purpose by deciding that everybody must work for his living, and by providing everybody with an equal chance at a good education and by ordering that all the pleasant things of this earth must be equally shared by those deserving them. (Attention, Congressman Dies! I am merely quoting, and if you are interested I will send you a copy of Sir Thomas' book, and someone will perhaps read it to you.)

Contemporary critics pointed out that all this had already been threshed out by one Plato. Yes, in a manner, but whereas Plato had been remote, Sir Thomas More had been very much of this world. And that was probably the quality which had first attracted Erasmus. After they had met, the authors of *The Praise of Folly* and of *Utopia* had remained fast friends until the broadsword of the King's executioner had separated them.

And now they were to meet once more.

The problem of their dinner was really no problem at all. Even so hospitable a house as that of Sir Thomas must have been very British in the food it served, and so we decided upon a *potage aux queues de boeuf* (ox-tail soup, in the vernacular of the day) and then a *gigot d'agneau quimperlaise*, lamb cooked in onions and string beans and stuffed with little bits of pork fat. For the old cookbook I used insisted that this must be a very lean piece of lamb, and the pork had to take the place of the natural fat. Almost any kind of cabbage would have to take the place of a more civilized vegetable, and as for a sweet, we decided to repeat that *omelette flambée* which had been such a success with the Prince of Orange and General Washington.

Then came the matter of beverages, and I was reaching out

for our wine list when Frits said, "Why give him wine? He was an Englishman. Give him ale, he'll like that much better."

I had never thought of it, but of course Frits was right. We could probably import some excellent ale from near-by Flushing (with its constant stream of British visitors), and so everything was ready except for the musical part of the entertainment. We realized that the old gentlemen would much rather talk than listen to music, but Sir Thomas had been very fond of a pleasant melody, and we meant to leave it up to him how much or how little he wanted. We made it, however, a little more serious than on the previous occasion and chose Guillaume Dufay's *Alma Redemptoris Mater* and his *Gloria in excelsis* and Josquin des Prés' *Et incarnatus est*. Then we found a lute solo entitled *Villanelle Alberti Dlugoraj*, composed in honor of the famous Polish lute virtuoso, Adalbert Dlugoraj, by Jean Baptiste Besard, and Clément Jannequin's *Petite nymphe folastre,* together with something from Orlando di Lasso's setting of the seven penitential psalms. Those, we thought, would be enough and even too much, but we intended to be on the safe side.

And now we were faced with the problem of how we could keep all this a secret from Erasmus. We visited him every day for an hour or so and found him entirely engrossed in his collection of Greek and Roman classics. We were very careful not to interfere with his comings and goings and never inquired as to the method by which he reached his room every morning and left it again in the evening without ever being noticed by anyone except the village treasurer, who had to be in our secret but who kept mum toward the neighbors. But just before Frits went back to Amsterdam he suddenly exclaimed, "I have it! We'll tell the old Doctor that for the sake of fairness we have felt obliged to invite Dr. Martin Luther."

"But suppose," I argued, "that he will then refuse to come at all? He detests that German. He may claim that he is not sufficiently strong physically to listen to a Teuton monk drinking beer."

"Yes," Frits agreed, "he won't like it a bit. But he has a great sense of duty. He promised to help us out and will agree with us that Luther, in spite of what he may think of him, was a man who played a very definite role in history. He'll come, all right!"

And Frits had been right. We gently broke it to Erasmus that our next guest was to be his old enemy, the rebel from Wittenberg. He indulged in a slight gesture of mild despair and then said, "But I realize that it cannot be helped. I disliked the fellow thoroughly, but I must confess he was not without a certain talent as an orator and demagogue. I would not have cared to do what he did, but it takes all sorts of people to make a world. So go ahead. Let's not speak of it any more. I will be there, and I will try to be very polite and very pleasant."

That Saturday evening, Frits and I stayed at my house until it was well past eight o'clock. Then we walked to the market place—a matter of five or six minutes. Very quietly we opened the front door. Two old gentlemen were sitting side by side in front of the open fire. They were completely lost in each other and did not even notice that we had come in. And so we signaled to Jo Verlinde, who was watching us from the kitchen, to serve them their dinner and not to worry about us. Thereupon we went back to join Jimmie, who was waiting for us at Lucie's studio, leaving the friends to their own devices.

When, late that night, Frits returned home, he found the house in order and on the table a note, hastily scribbled by Jo, saying, "I never saw two people have such a good time. I will tell you the rest tomorrow." The slip of paper was weighted down by a tiny silver statue of the Madonna of exquisite workmanship. On the bottom, in Gothic script, we found the initials, 𝕿. 𝔐.

Sir Thomas More and Erasmus were most happily sitting in front of the fire.

CHAPTER IV

This Time Erasmus Had a Surprise for Us, and We Make the Acquaintance of the Bachs and the Breughels

On Sunday Erasmus' room remained unoccupied, but when I visited him the next morning he was there working as usual. Frits had taken the mail train for Amsterdam. It was during the days of the Great Insanity, and everybody was making millions. Frits, being a prudent sort of person, left the speculative end of his business carefully alone. He smiled his pleasantest smile at all his customers and pocketed his commissions, whether they won or lost. That was a very useful arrangement, for the queer foods and drinks we needed for our guests cost us a pretty penny, and I was working on my *Rembrandt,* which took more than three years for the actual writing, and of course during that time I could not disturb my mind by trying to please the editors of our magazines, who were forever telling me that I did not know what the public wanted.

On that particular Monday morning I found Erasmus in a very happy mood. "That was a lovely thing you did for us last Saturday," he told me. "I am deeply grateful and now I would like to give you a little surprise."

"What is it?" I asked.

"I told you it was to be a surprise. You will meet my Martin Luther."

I tried to find the correct answer in Latin. *"Gratias ornatissime tibi ago."*

The old man smiled. "Cicero himself could have done no better."

He flattered me, for I knew that there must be many and much more elegant ways of giving thanks in his adopted tongue, and once more I tried to get some hint about his plans. But just as unsuccessfully as the first time, though I got the impression that this might be a somewhat elaborate party when he added, "It is an unfortunate thing, but money does not exist in the world in which I now have my being. Therefore, would it be asking too much if I request that you undertake to pay the bills for a rather liberal supply of sauerkraut and Guelders sausages and a few hundred bottles of beer?"

I told him that I thought it could be done.

"Very well, then," he replied, considering the matter settled. "And I shall also have to ask you to change the hour of the entertainment. Suppose we say Saturday at noon and that for this once you and your friend will be our guests."

"Our guests? Will there be many others?"

"I was under the impression that this was to be a surprise party, like the one you arranged for Sir Thomas and myself—but look—I have found quite a lot of mistakes in this modern edition of Terence. Has the race of proofreaders died out? In my time, it was an honor to be a proofreader for a famous publisher."

I was sorry to inform him that proofreading, as a profession, no longer enjoyed the esteem it had done when printing was considered an art rather than a trade. Then I left him, and all week long I was busy with my *Rembrandt* and with a visit of my dear friend, Louis Schrijver, from Amsterdam. But on Thursday, being badly in need of a haircut, I went to the tonsorial establishment of our town treasurer.

"What is the old gentleman up to now?" he inquired.

"I don't know," I answered. "Why do you ask? Anything wrong?"

"No, nothing wrong. I'm just curious. He dropped into my office yesterday and inquired whether there would be any objection to him and a few of his friends meeting in a social sort of way on the market place next Saturday. Of course, I had no authority to grant him that request, but I said I would ask the burgomaster. His Honor told me it would be perfectly all right. Of course, there must be no disorder and no drunkenness."

"I hardly think there will be among the friends of our distinguished guest."

"Then, how about those three barrels of beer you ordered from the inn?"

"You seem to know everything that happens in this village!"

"That's our business. We are entrusted with the care of public order, and three barrels of beer are an awful lot of beer for a little town like Veere."

"Well," I consoled him, "they'll be absorbed by the sauerkraut and the Guelders sausages we have ordered. I suppose you know about that little item, too?"

"I do."

"Then suppose we forget about it, and you come as my special guest and see that nothing happens to disturb the peace of the realm."

"Thank you, but the old gentleman has already invited me and the wife and the children."

That seemed to settle everything, and, my hair by then being more on the floor than on the top of my head, I decided to call it a day. I paid for the operation and went home.

Jimmie and I were sitting on Lucie's stoop at about eleven o'clock on Saturday morning, entertaining Lucie's cat. Lucie's cat had had her third litter of kittens since the beginning of the year and seemed profoundly bored by this everlasting application of Genesis 1:22. And so, although being by nature a mean and unfriendly feline, she now looked for human companionship, and when Jimmie went into the kitchen and got her a dish of cream, she so far forgot her superior attitude toward members of the human race as to accept it. This was so unusual a proceeding on the part of this aggressively independent animal that both Jimmie and I watched her while she neatly consumed our generous gift and never noticed that we had a visitor. Leaning on the arm of his famulus, Erasmus had arrived to conduct us personally to his surprise party.

I begged him, before he did anything else, to sit down, for he looked unusually frail at such an early hour, and not until he was safely accommodated on our wide blue peasant bench did I present him to Jimmie, who at once broke the ice by asking him whether he liked cats, whether he ever had had a cat of his own, and whether he had ever heard of her famous cat, Cocaine, who used to protect the Mad Hatter tearoom from invading rodents and once killed a rat almost as large as a Saint Bernard dog.

Erasmus said that he knew a lot about cats. He had never had any of his own. "You see," he remarked, "they are a little undependable and for a man of my restless habits of life they may prove a great burden. I had trouble enough packing my books every time I moved. Suppose that at the last moment I should have been obliged to find room for another half-dozen fellow travelers! But my publishers always had cats. They seem to belong to dusty printshops and are forever getting printer's ink in their hair."

Then he changed the subject rather abruptly to compliment Jimmie on her Dutch. This caused my good wife to make a face at me and to remark, "There are those who do not think it quite so good!" but he would not hear of this.

"Our tongue must be very difficult to a foreigner," he said, "but then your English comes rather hard to us—very hard. Some day we shall have a universal language. We have one now, or would have one, if every nation did not insist upon pronouncing Latin in its own way, so that an Englishman and an Italian, while speaking to each other in the vernacular of Cicero, are still completely incomprehensible to each other. I did my best while in Oxford to show them that their way of speaking Latin would have caused Caesar to put them all to the sword, but they would have none of that. Indeed, they rather

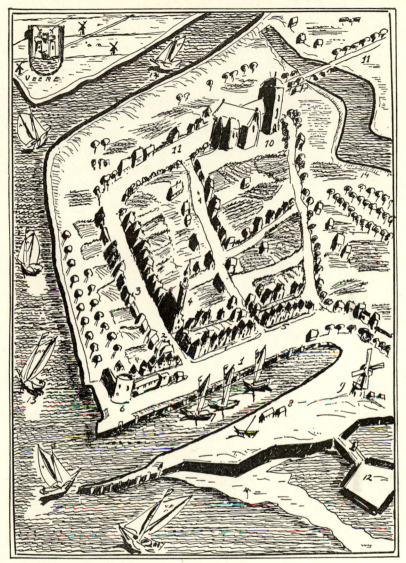

The village of Veere.

1. The harbor. 2. Frits' house. 3. The Market Place. 4. The town hall. 5. Our own house. 6. The old watch tower. 7. The old churchyard hidden behind the church. 8. The old wharf. 9. Our village mill. 10. The old church. 11. The road to Middelburg. 12. A Napoleonic rampart. 13. The Scheldt. 14. The Middelburg Canal.

hinted that it was Caesar who should have changed his way of speaking his mother tongue if he had wanted to deal with them. They are a charming people, those English, but perhaps a bit— let me call it insular. However, I should not complain, for they are the most delightful of friends, and that meeting of last Saturday, which your husband helped arrange, brought it all so vividly back to me. Ah, my dear madam, we live but once, and, in spite of all the discomforts and all the suffering connected with our stay on earth, it is a wonderful experience, but now I am afraid we had better go, for it is almost noon."

"Won't you let me take you in the car?" Jimmie suggested.

"I appreciate your offer, madam, but I think that at my age I had better entrust myself to the old and trusted method of peregrination. And perhaps you will allow me to take your arm. It is a long time since I have enjoyed feminine companionship. Meg More used to pretend that I was a very old man, and in her father's garden she used to play that she had just come upon Methuselah and was bringing him back to the house to tell the little Mores about the deluge and how Noah had built his ark. Yes, indeed, my dear madam, those were happy days, and now all of us are dead, but you are young still and alive, and I must not talk to you that way."

"Not so damn young either," Jimmie replied. Then remembering that she was speaking to one in holy orders, she quickly corrected herself. "Not so very young, I meant."

Erasmus gave her an amused smile. "You forget that I am a Dutchman," he remarked, "and that we are accustomed to rather spicy words."

This gave Jimmie an idea. "Tell me," she asked, "can you swear in Latin, too? I took a lot of Latin at Bryn Mawr, but I never found any out-and-out cuss words. Didn't they have any?"

"Not exactly, in our sense of the word, for they were much too familiar with their gods to feel a great deal of respect for their names. But they could curse most beautifully. Cursing, of course, is something different from swearing. Also, it is much more difficult, and real first-class cursing is very rare."

"I would like to see some of it in Latin."

"Then try some of the papal bulls of the fifty years just before and after the Reformation."

"You mean to tell me that the Popes knew how to curse?"

"My dear lady, they had a genius for it."

"But why don't we know about it? Those papal bulls always seem so dignified to me, the way they start out—like church bells beginning to ring on Sunday morning—boom-boom-boom-clankety-clunk."

"You should read beyond the boom-boom-boom and pay attention to the clankety-clunk. Then you would learn something."

Jimmie was now full of excitement. "Tell me," she said, "what would I learn?"

But the diplomatic old humanist did not fall into the trap. "I must remember my cloth," he pleaded, giving her, at the same time, a look that clearly implied what he thought of his holy garments, "but some day your husband will undoubtedly invite the learned Dr. Luther. He should be able to tell you. He caused several Popes to do some of their most eloquent cursing."

At that moment, we turned from the quay into the street that led to the market place. And there we saw a sight I shall never forget. Fortunately, I was able to make a sketch of it, and what is the use of wasting a lot of words when a few lines and a few daubs of color can tell the story so much more effectively?

Frits was waiting for us on the stoop of his house. "I have just been down there and I have come back to order five more barrels of beer and to telephone for all the sauerkraut and sausages I could lay my hands on in Middelburg. Apparently all of them have appetites like starved oxen—every single member of both tribes."

"Of both tribes of whom?" Jimmie asked, and Frits answered, "All of the Bachs and all of the Breughels are here, and there must be at least a hundred of them."

That, then, was the surprise Erasmus had prepared for us. We could not have thought of a nicer one. Both Frits and I loved the Bachs and the Breughels, and we had mentioned them several times during our dinner conversations, for we knew that during the latter part of his life Erasmus had been a contemporary of Pieter Breughel and could easily have met him in either Antwerp or Brussels. We also remembered that in his own youth he had dabbled a little in painting, and it was quite natural for us to have asked him what he thought of this great Flemish master and his family.

We then discovered that Erasmus shared our opinion that the Breughels had been among the very greatest artists that had ever lived, and we had spent several happy hours looking at some of their sketches I had gradually collected and at those magnificent colored reproductions the Viennese publishers had just brought out and which made most of our own color work look like Cuban cigar bands.

It was, of course, quite natural that, having mentioned the elder Breughel, we should have drifted to Hans Bach, who had been the father of that Veit Bach whom the later Bachs considered to have been the real founder of their clan, probably because he was the first one to go in for music in a big way. Hans Bach must have lived at about the same time as Erasmus, but he told us that he had never heard of him. However, during the six years he had spent in Freiburg in Germany he had heard of another Bach, who was an organist in one of the local churches, and of one who was *Stadt-Musikant* in a near-by village and who sometimes brought his band to play at the fairs in Freiburg, and once in Italy he remembered having listened to a lute player in Venice—or was it Siena or Bologna?—and the Italians, who were rarely good at instrumental music, had explained that it was a *Bacco,* which he had then taken to be a colloquial term for any wandering musician.

That had been the only reference to these strange dynasties of painters and musicians whose genius, like the waters of the Nile, had fertilized the whole of northern Europe and who had prepared the soil for what was to come during the next hundred years. Erasmus had remembered how greatly we loved them and all their works, and this had been his surprise for us.

About the afternoon that followed I could easily write a whole book, for it was a "rare occasion"—to use a well-known bromide. What made it so interesting to us was to observe with our own eyes how all the arts are truly born out of some deep and irresistible emotion.

Those Bachs and Breughels practiced entirely different forms of expression. The Bachs appealed to the ears, whereas the Breughels appealed to the eyes. But how completely they understood each other, even if they failed to use a common language! And since they were enjoying a holiday, they could let themselves go without the thought of possible patrons who might feel inclined to buy their sonatas and fugues or their Madonnas and flowers and landscapes and the merry devils and witches of "Hell" Breughel, the son of old Pieter. They could just be themselves.

Of course, they had done what all good artists do whenever they are not obliged to perform—they had turned the occasion into a large and glorious jam session. Indeed, they were so deeply engrossed in their respective pursuits that they never noticed our arrival but went right on doing what they had been doing from the moment of their arrival. The faithful town treasurer had tried his best to prepare everything for the feast of beer and sauerkraut to follow, and which most of the villagers apparently expected to attend. For ours in many ways was still a good deal of a feudal community, and we never failed to share what we ourselves had with our neighbors. The story of those ten barrels of beer (before the feast was over we had lost count) had spread far and wide, and the large plates of sausages being placed upon the tables made the children stand around with a strange gleam in their eyes. Not that they were hungry —they were merely greedy, and a free meal was a free meal!

But I was going to tell you about our guests of honor. They were sitting in two separate groups—the Bachs on the left and the Breughels on the right. And the Bachs were playing old German square dances for the delectation of the Breughels, while the Breughels were drawing pictures of the Bachs. The versatile Bachs seemed to have brought every kind of instrument known to man. In the middle, old Johann Sebastian, in his best black broadcloth coat (as befitted his rank as a royal Prussian *Kapellmeister*—that title he had so valiantly fought for during the last years of his life), was conducting from a small parchment booklet which looked very much like the volume of the tunes he had collected and arranged for his beloved second wife, Anna Magdalena. On his right, old Veit, the miller and lute player, and his remote ancestor, was tinkling away at his old self-made zither. Behind him, and all around him, were a number of his sons, grandsons, nephews, cousins, and all other sorts and varieties of relatives.

As for the Breughels, the three most famous ones, easily recognizable from their portraits (usually tucked away somewhere in one of their hilarious paintings, but known to all the lovers of their art), and a couple of their less popular brothers and cousins were drawing away for dear life at what I supposed to be "counterfeits" (as they were then called) of the Bachian band. When I discreetly stepped behind them (for I know how much an artist resents having someone peek at work that is still half finished), I saw that I had been right.

But how right Erasmus had been, when, during our first meeting, he had told us that people change but very little even after they have ceased to be counted among the living. For Pieter the Elder had got the whole of the Veere market place into his sketch and had given the scene that timelessness combined with a sense of actuality which might have turned it into a replica of the angels come to Bethlehem to serenade the infant Jesus. I then realized more than ever why he had been called "Peasant" Breughel: every one of the little boys and girls looking hungrily at the food-laden tables had been caught with an accuracy of expression·that might have made their individual portraits stand forever as a symbol of peasant greed. Whereas his son,

Pieter the Younger, had changed those same urchins into imps
—into little demons, ready to stuff themselves with indecent
quantities of greasy sausages the moment no one was looking.
Jan Breughel (the younger son of old Pieter), finally, had concentrated his attention on the physical background of the
market place. All the trees and all the flowers had been treated
with the utmost love and care. Even the insects disporting
themselves on the near-by shrubs had been included and with
such detail that an entomologist a hundred years hence would
be able to decide with absolute scientific accuracy just what
kinds of pests had afflicted the Low Countries in the year 1930.

The other Breughels, each one in his own way, were doing
their best to get the atmosphere of the occasion. I got so enthusiastic that I fished my own sketch pad out of my pocket,
and the moment they noticed that a brother painter had arrived on the scene, they moved over on their bench and begged
me to make myself at home, for that is part of the code of all
good artists, who believe in absolute equality—but it must be
the equality between equals.

At exactly one o'clock Erasmus got up from the chair Frits
had told Hein Verlinde to get him from his house and asked for
a moment's silence. "I hope," he said, speaking slowly in Flemish so that both the Bachs and the Breughels would be able to
understand him, "that you have enjoyed meeting each other
and that you will approve of the slight entertainment we have
provided for you. I wanted our friends here in the beautiful old
city of Veere to realize what we mean when we people of a bygone age speak of our ideals of craftsmanship. It was a craftsmanship that grew out of our comradeship, and that comradeship was born out of the feeling that all of us were citizens of
the sovereign and independent commonwealth of the arts and
letters. I hope that you will rejoice as I do that we had this
chance to meet each other, and now let me bid you to our very
simple repast."

The Bachs and the Breughels

Apparently, Erasmus had known what was to the taste of the people of his day, and in this way he taught us a most valuable lesson. Frits and I would have ransacked our old cookbooks for special dishes with which to please our guests, but now we discovered (what I had always somewhat suspected) that the average man or woman of three hundred (or three thousand) years ago was accustomed to a kind of fare that to us would seem almost unbearably monotonous. And I also began to understand that most of those fantastic festive meals of the Middle Ages and of Roman times, about which we had read so much in our schoolbooks, referred to the same kinds of outrageous feasts that used to be given in New York fifty years ago, when people with more money than either brains or good taste tried to impress the community at large with the vast sums of money they could spend in the form of "conspicuous waste."

At those famous medieval orgies, which often cost small fortunes and not infrequently obliged the hosts to take out an extra mortgage on their heavily burdened estates, it was not really the purpose to delight the palates of the guests with new and harmonious combinations of ingredients that complemented or offset each other. This true secret of all good cooking was not discovered until much later, during the latter half of the eighteenth century. Up to that time, the culinary artist had depended upon the principle that whatever was expensive must also be good. But the complete satisfaction with which these good people, members of the solid middle class of their own times, dug into the heaping plates of sausages and sauerkraut and poured the steins of beer down their gullets showed me that plain food had been the rule for the average man. The occasional gorging on roast peacocks and roast swan, all of them stuffed with every possible kind of spice, and those fabulous desserts in which molasses was used to sweeten sugar, had been a practice of the court and of the castle. And those honest artisans, now turned trenchermen and asking for nothing better than what Erasmus had provided for them, made me suspect that until then we had perhaps slightly overfed our guests, and I made a mental note of it, so that the next time we should not repeat the same mistake.

Did we ourselves get very much out of that day? Yes and no. Yes, because it was marvelous to be so near to the one man I revered as the greatest musician of all times and to be face to face with a painter who some day, when we shall have begun to appreciate him at his true value, will be placed in the same category as Rembrandt, Velásquez, Goya, or Vermeer. On the other hand, the Bachs and Breughels were having such a marvelous time that, just as on the previous Saturday evening, when Erasmus and Sir Thomas More had come together, we felt that we would be intruding if we made ourselves too conspicuous among our guests. However, toward the end of the afternoon I had a chance to see something more of old Sebastian, as all the others called him.

The incident which provided me with this opportunity was not entirely a happy one. Among the members of the Bach family who had come to the party was his eldest son, Wilhelm Friedemann, who, as all the contemporaries agreed, had inherited most of his father's genius. Unfortunately, he had at quite an early age left the narrow path of respectability that had been deeply hollowed out by the footsteps of all the previous Bachs. To state the case bluntly, Wilhelm Friedemann had turned a drunkard and had spent the greater part of his long life (he reached the age of seventy-four) wandering from one pothouse to the next. Having inherited his family's soundness of body, he could stand an awful lot of alcohol, and it never interfered with his ability to write solemn church cantatas and organ concertos and fugues as complicated as some of his father's. Nor did he ever cease to be a thoroughly good clavichord player when he was sufficiently sober to have command of his fingers. And sometimes, while deeply in his cups, he was also at his most brilliant, but in a way which was far removed from the musical standards bestowed upon the world by his eminently honorable father.

The Bachs were having a lovely jam session.

Meanwhile the Breughels were busy drawing.

For, if on such occasions he got hold of some instrument with a keyboard, he would then so curiously inspire the other players that soon all of them would be engaged in a very delightful kind of eighteenth-century swing.

But Lord help the tavern in which he came upon a bass fiddle, for the patrons would then be treated to a regular boogie-woogie performance in which some of his father's and Herr Georg Friedrich Händel's finest oratorio arias would be tortured into absolute caricatures of themselves.

Shortly after the beer had been passed around, Johann Christoph and Philipp Emanuel Bach came to me and whispered that they were afraid that somewhere or other their poor brother had got hold of something a little stronger than beer and they foresaw that we were in for a kind of entertainment that would hardly be to the liking of *"der alte Herr."* As nothing could stop Friedemann, once he was in that mood (as they called it), could we perhaps persuade the old gentleman to take a little walk and entice him away from a scene which would be most painful to him?

Frits (who always took the initiative in a crisis) said, "Sure, just wait a moment," and he suggested to Johann Sebastian that he might like to hear some of his own music as it was now preserved on round, black disks and played by a machine: "If you will do us the honor to visit our house, you can see and hear some of these disks for yourself." In that way we had escaped from the market place just when Friedemann, who indeed had had much more than was good for him, was beginning to play *Jesus, Joy of Man's Desiring* on an oboe. I didn't think that the "Old Wig," as the sons called their father behind his back (but loud enough for me to overhear them), noticed the beginning of this little commotion. We knew that he was slightly deaf and were grateful for his affliction, for by the time we had reached Frits' house, Friedemann was in full action, having switched over from his oboe to a very powerful bassoon, and had changed from *Jesus, Joy* to *O Head So Full of Blood and Wounds,* which was hardly more appropriate as a theme for the *Ländler* into which it was being converted than the *My Jesus in Gethsemane* which followed it.

Inside of Frits' house it was pleasant and cool, and as soon as we had made Johann Sebastian thoroughly comfortable in the chair we had recently acquired for Erasmus (since he was to be our steady house guest he deserved a chair of his own), we started the phonograph. The first thing we played was number one of *The Well-Tempered Clavichord*. Johann Sebastian listened in silence. The gramophone as such did not seem to impress him very greatly, and as time went on and we met more and more people of a bygone age, we were surprised to observe how little interest they felt for most of our proud modern inventions. As soon as they had given them one look, they took them for granted. They were there. They made life a little simpler and that was very nice, but did it really make much difference? Was it really so tremendously important whether a traveler got from one town to another a little faster or a little slower or whether a letter reached its destination within a day or a week—or even a month? Suppose the person who wanted to go from Paris to Rome was just nobody at all—then would it really be of any great importance to the universe at large whether he reached his destination in twenty hours or in twenty days!

Here I would like to make a little digression, for we were to come across this attitude on the part of almost all our guests who belonged to the past. They rarely showed the slightest interest when we did our best to make them see how greatly and profoundly these inventions had changed the lives of a large number of people, who now had a chance to visit all the famous cities about which in olden times they had only read in a travel book by some more fortunate contemporary. They answered "yes" and "indubitably," but made it quite clear to us that they failed to notice any real advantage in this new ideal of making the whole world available to all the people, regardless of their ability to understand it or appreciate it or even admire it.

"Don't you spread everything rather thin that way?" Molière asked, but, of course, he was very fond of irony, so that was about the only reaction one could have expected of him. Pieter Breughel became downright rude when we pointed out that, had he lived in our own time, he could have gone and studied in Paris and London and Madrid and could have visited all those cities in a couple of months.

"Would you mind telling me," he asked, "what I could have learned there that I could not have learned just as easily and much more comfortably right here at home?" and he added, "Rubens painted all over Europe, didn't he? Would you have wanted me to become something like Pieter Paul?" To which we could only answer, God forbid! and that that was about the last thing we would have liked to see happen.

That same feeling of indifference was noticed when we drew our guests' attention (as we used to do in the beginning) to the airplanes which at regular hours of the night flew over Veere on their way from Amsterdam to London. They were somewhat surprised by the noise, which they could not quite place, but few of them even cared enough to go out into the street to look at them in the moonlit sky.

Descartes used these planes to launch one of his embarrassing inquiries into the truth behind the truth, of which he was so fond. "You tell me," he said, "that a hundred years ago when Erasmus went from Rotterdam to London, the trip took five days if he was very lucky, whereas now it takes only a couple of hours!"

"Yes," we answered hopefully, for he at last seemed to have understood what "modern improvements" meant to us.

"And why do these people want to get there in two hours instead of five days?"

"To save time."

"And what do they do with the time they have saved when they get there?"

To which we could not find a fitting reply, knowing that the time thus saved was as a rule wasted on an unsuccessful effort to have some more time to kill at the other end of the voyage. And so, after a while, we avoided the subject of progress altogether because we ourselves were beginning to doubt the value of many of those marvelous inventions which until then we had been taught to accept as the one redeeming feature of an age which was sadly lacking in many of those qualities of charm and leisure and contentment which we used to associate with the era of our grandparents.

Of course, as we went down to the bottom of this superior attitude of our visitors toward all our "improvements"—as we did one rainy Sunday afternoon—we discovered that much of it was merely a pose, for they greatly liked such inventions and innovations as fitted in with their own scheme of living. Erasmus, for example, could never find sufficient words of praise for our open fires and our chimneys. "In my day," so he told us, "chimneys had not yet been invented. I mean this sort of chimney, which really gets rid of the smoke. In our halls in Oxford and Cambridge we had a fire in the middle of the room and the smoke went up through a hole in the roof. It was terrible. The smoke used to make our eyes ache on cold days, and the fires were never able to keep us warm, and we had to go to bed in order not to freeze. The Swiss and the Germans did much better with their tile stoves, but in our own country, with its little peat fires, the winter was a nightmare."

Then there was the Empress Theodora. She took the greatest delight in our windowpanes. Nothing else interested her quite as much. She thought a bullock cart quite as good a mode of conveyance from Constantinople to Adrianople as those trains of which we showed her the pictures. But windowpanes fascinated her.

"In my day," she explained, "we only had a little glass in our chapels and churches, and all of my palaces were terribly drafty. Even when at night we closed the windows with wooden blinds, the wine froze in our tankards."

Voltaire was most of all impressed with Frits' typewriter. "If

I had had one of those contraptions," he said, playing with the keys, "I might really have done a little writing."

"Pardon me," Frits observed, "but the other day an antiquary in The Hague offered me your collected works. I think there were eighty volumes."

"Monsieur a raison," Voltaire answered with a bow, "but with one of these machines I could have written three times as many." And then, as an afterthought, "But Lope de Vega had only a goose quill too, yet he was able to give us two thousand plays. If he had had one of these writing engines, I hate to think what would have happened! All libraries would be so full of Lope de Vega's plays that there would not have been any room for the books of the rest of us."

"I wonder," Frits continued, "how you people were able to do it?"

Voltaire smiled. "Perhaps, Monsieur Frédéric," he said, "there was one thing we had which you have lost."

"And that is what?" Frits asked.

"Time, my dear friend. And perhaps time is more valuable than all the many things you have invented to conquer it."

I shall always be sorry that we did not find out what Johann Sebastian Bach thought of our method of preserving music as if it had been pickles or strawberries. But just when we were on the point of showing him the mechanical end of our concert, one of those things happened which none of us could possibly have foreseen and against which we could not in any way have protected ourselves without being a great deal ruder than either Frits or I happened to be.

Veere had always been quite popular with painters, but during the last two or three years it has also gained a certain renown among musicians who wanted to spend a summer amidst entirely congenial surroundings. And nowadays, wherever there are musicians, there are also bound to be people who make a living by talking or writing about their art—an art which should be heard but not explained. For it is quite as absurd to try and explain what plum pudding or scrapple tastes like or what Rembrandt's *Night Watch* looks like as to re-evaluate a Mozart Mass by means of the spoken word.

That particular summer a dear old lady had descended upon us who was famous or notorious (depending upon your point of view) for her popular lectures on "musical interpretation." Needless to say, she hailed from our beloved republic, and (equally needless to explain) we had avoided her like the plague. That had made her all the more eager to meet us, and now at last she had her chance. Frits' house that afternoon was so full of people that it was quite easy for her to slip past our front door, and, unobserved by anyone, she had gone directly into the kitchen, where the gramophone had been installed for that afternoon. Jo Verlinde, who had volunteered to keep the instrument going (Veere did not boast of electricity), was under the impression that this stranger was one of the regular guests and, polite and obliging as always, she had offered no objections when the creature had put a record of her own choosing on the disk. As for us, we knew nothing about her presence until suddenly we heard Bach's Fugue in G minor, originally written for the organ but now arranged for full orchestra by one of our most popular American conductors. Once this fugue had been started, we had no other choice but to listen to it in silence until it should have come to an end, which it did with a terrific crash of brass and with a dozen bombardons going full blast.

Bach, we noticed, had listened with grave interest. When it was finished, he said, "That really was most interesting. But what was it? Perhaps something by Vivaldi? In that case, he must have written it when he was quite young and still had a great deal to learn."

Fortunately, we were spared further explanations by the fact that it was almost seven o'clock. And so we hastily got out our guest book and asked the old master to honor us with his autograph. Just as he put a dot behind his name and made ready to add his *Kapellmeister* titles, the clock struck the hour for departure. This time there was no candle flicker. It was still full daylight, and no darkness was to descend upon us. But when we had become accustomed to the unexpected silence, our guests were gone. Dozens of half-empty glasses of beer and half-finished plates of sauerkraut bore witness to the fact that there had been a party. And in one corner of the room we found the shoes of poor Friedemann, who had made himself comfortable before he had started to sleep off his jag.

CHAPTER V

We Entertain Three Great Masters of the Spoken and Written Word and Are Honored by the Presence of CERVANTES, SHAKESPEARE, and MOLIÈRE

FRITS AND I were delighted with our last party and expressed our gratitude to Erasmus.

"But who next?" we asked him.

"If you don't mind a suggestion—but I do not want to influence your choice—how would it be if you now varied your diet by inviting a few of the world's great writers? You have had statesmen and musicians and painters. Why not invite two or three of the men who have influenced the world by their pens, either in writing books or plays?"

We told him that such a varied diet would be most welcome and thanked him for the suggestion. Thereupon Frits and I spent the rest of the Sunday going through a list of available candidates. In the end, we agreed upon one writer and two playwrights, for all three of them had exercised a profound influence upon the history of their day. Besides, they would be amusing guests. I copied their names on a slip of paper, and on his way home Frits put this unusual kind of invitation underneath the old lion who guarded the entrance to the town hall.

The dinner we meant to serve that evening was an easy one, for our guests had lived at approximately the same time. But as one of them was a Frenchman, we decided to have more vegetables than usual and leave out the lamb, as lamb is rather an acquired taste with most Frenchmen. The Spaniard was rather a problem, but as he had spent many years of his life in a Barbary prison, we felt that he would be willing to eat anything we gave him—and glad of the chance. I remembered how, in one of his last letters commenting upon the sad state of his finances (in spite of all the hard work he had done) and the even more painful condition of his body, Cervantes had mentioned the fact that, as he had only two teeth left (and they failed to meet!), he was hardly able to eat anything at all. Soft and easily chewed food would therefore be most acceptable to the poor old Don, and the immortal William, too, would probably have a pretty bad set of teeth and would also welcome a purée or a ragout.

This was the menu we meant to place before our guests. We would begin with a fish soup *à la marseillaise*. We thought that they would like this because there was a good deal of onion in it, and we felt sure that we could get enough oysters and shrimps and small lobsters from the local fishermen to turn the whole thing into just that sort of aquatic mishmash which seems to have been so popular with our ancestors. And the orange peels we could put into it would be an amusing novelty for the Englishman and the Frenchman, whereas the bouillon we would use as stock would be good for the half-starved Spaniard.

Our main dish had to be something neutral, and what is more neutral than some kind of chicken? We had had turkey for General Washington two weeks before, and besides, turkeys are hard to get in Europe, for the climate is too wet. But how about a *poularde truffée à la Périgueux*? We thought that Monsieur Molière would appreciate a lot of truffles, and we told Jo to count on half a pound of truffles for each chicken and to use a lot of pork fat. A little more onion would do no harm, and we suggested that she use two hours to get the dish ready instead of the usual hour and a half.

As for vegetables, a salad was out of the question, for although salads had come in with Henry VIII's ill-fated wife, Catherine of Aragon, they would, we were sure, not yet have penetrated far into the lower layers of English society, where the people have been so hopelessly conservative in their way of eating that, even today, a change in the food of the sailors or soldiers is apt to lead to mutiny.

So for the benefit of William Shakespeare it had to be cabbage, but in fairness to Molière we ordered *choux farcis,* small individual cabbages, each one hiding a roll of Dutch *gehakt,* which, according to my wife, is merely a variant upon our domestic hamburger steak, but which is one of the delicacies dear to the palate of every good Hollander. Indeed, when mixed with bread and truffles, *gehakt* is something as far removed from hamburger as Dutch *rolpens* is from Philadelphia scrapple.

Also for the benefit of Molière, there was to be an extra dish of our usual string beans with burned butter, and Cervantes would find a large bowl of ripe olives by the side of his plate. As we could not very well have an *omelette flambée* at every one of our dinners, we ordered a large *gâteau à la parisienne aux pommes et pistaches.*

The taste of pistachio added to a rather fanciful apple tart would strike them as something new, and if Shakespeare decided that it was too "new" to suit him, he could have all the cheese he wanted. As I myself detested cheese, I had completely forgotten to order it for our previous guests. Frits kindly reminded me that very few people shared my absurd prejudices, and he told Jo to see to it that there was a generous collection of different kinds of cheeses, which were to be held in reserve until they should be needed.

As for coffee—yes, why not? We had discovered that even those of our visitors who had been born before coffee had been introduced into Europe took to it as ducks are supposed to take to water. Of course, there was always the danger that it would keep them awake, but we reasoned that they had slept long enough and would not mind.

We knew that the old bard would prefer ale to any other

beverage, but for the other two, we decided upon something more elaborate. Cervantes was to have a bottle of very dry manzanilla from the Sanlúcar district—old, but not too old, as sherry does not exactly improve with age but turns sour. And for Molière, what could be more appropriate than a most excellent Chambertin, a few bottles of which I had come upon in my uncle's cellar and which he—my uncle—had been more than willing to exchange for half a dozen bottles of white Barsac, which he preferred to any of the other wines of France.

For our after-dinner wine, we meant to serve port, and we had been lucky enough to get hold of a genuine bottle of the vintage of 1851, which, according to Professor Saintsbury's *Notes on a Cellar Book,* was one of the best years in the entire history of the wine of Oporto.

And now for the music. Shakespeare would probably prefer William Byrd and John Dowland. We already had a great many Byrd records, and we ordered Dowland's madrigals and his lute songs. Molière, too, was easy, for he would probably like to be reminded of his happiest days at court by hearing the music of his namesake, Jean Baptiste Lully, the Italian who had written so many of the scores for his own ballets and who had also been responsible for the incidental music of his *Bourgeois Gentilhomme.* For the rest, we selected a few records from each of the following operas: *Amadis de Gaule, Persée, Roland,* and *Armide.* We found that we had chosen wisely and also learned (what often had seemed rather doubtful) that the ex-upholsterer to Louis XIII and the former scullery boy of Madame de Montpensier had been great personal friends and that the stories about their animosity belonged to the same category as those whispered about Molière's wife. They may have been true, but just as likely they were pure inventions on the part of the theatrical gossip writers of the middle of the seventeenth century, who, in this respect, were on par with our own Broadway columnists.

Finally there was Cervantes, who had to have a little music of his own, but nowhere could we come upon even a vague clue to his tastes. So on a chance we sent for a few of the records of Antonio de Cabezón and Alonso de Mudarra, whom we chose on the strength of their names. But Cervantes seemed to like Lully much better than his own fellow countrymen, and I must confess that they were pretty dull.

This was our fourth party, and we were beginning to have some doubts about the wisdom of giving our guests music all during their meals. As a rule, they found so much delight in each other's company that they were quite satisfied to sit and eat and talk. But during the first half-hour or so, music seemed quite helpful. It broke the ice and started the conversation going.

As the three men who were to come the next Saturday were well-known public figures, it was not necessary to go into too many details about their lives. The reports I sent to Amsterdam on Tuesday were therefore quite brief.

Shakespeare, William. Born in Stratford-on-Avon in Warwickshire in the year 1564. Exact date unknown, but baptized on April 26. His father, John, seems to have been a glovemaker, but he is also referred to as a butcher and a wool dealer. Whatever he did to make a living, it seems that he was a man of some standing in his own small community, for he was one of the first burgesses of the recently incorporated town of Stratford and was held in sufficient esteem to be elected to a municipal office. The most important authentic document we have about him is the receipt for a fine which he was condemned to pay for maintaining a dung heap in the street in which he lived. This bears out the suggestion—often made—that he had started life as a farmer and had only moved to the city after he had become sufficiently opulent to aspire to a rank in society slightly superior to that of a mere Warwickshire yeoman—a promotion which made him hope that some day he might even be allowed to display a coat of arms of his own.

That seems a rather foolish ambition to us of the present day, but in the early sixteenth century it was the equivalent of every immigrant's dream of driving a Packard as soon as he shall be able to pay a little something on the first installment.

We are ignorant about Master William's earlier years, except that he was apparently his parents' third child, that he probably went to the local grammar school (a survival of an earlier age, when the monasteries had looked after the schooling of all children), and that he might have gone even further in life than he did, but for the unfortunate circumstance that his father fared none too well among his new and unfamiliar surroundings, gradually lost all his property, and became disqualified from holding any further official positions.

Young William was therefore obliged to shift for himself, which he did by acting as an assistant to his father after the latter had gone back to his earlier trade of a butcher. According to highly doubtful popular rumor, he did not succeed very well, being in the habit of delighting the neighborhood boys by declaiming poetry and indulging in highfalutin speeches while cutting the throats of his father's hogs, rather than paying attention to the business at hand.

We do know, however, that at this inopportune moment, and just when he could least afford it, William was rash enough to get himself a wife. Whether this was a shotgun marriage, as many of his contemporaries asserted, or a true love match, that is another problem which never has been settled. The fact that the groom was eighteen at the time of the wedding and the wife well within her twenties—twenty-five or twenty-six—seems to point to a somewhat enforced union. And the further circumstance that Anne Hathaway was fairly far gone when she took her Will in holy matrimony in the fall of 1582 (exact date still unverified) seems to prove that there was some cause for a bit of small-town gossip. Therefore, when in May, 1583, their first child was born, the good people of Stratford had a nice little scandal on their hands, and William thought it wise to move to some other city where he was not quite so familiar a figure and where such an unfortunate incident would draw much less attention.

The widely spread reputation of W. Shakespeare as a lively young man, educated somewhat above his own class and considerable of a "rebel," with but small outward respect for the established authorities, may also have contributed toward his decision to try his luck far from the narrow limitations of his original home. But so little has come down to us about the next eight years of his career that legend has him spending this period as an apothecary, a dyer, a soldier, a public scribe, and a printer. Take your choice. After that, however, his name begins to bob up with increasing regularity as one of those who were then working for the stage. By this I do not mean that he became a success overnight. Far from it. But Shakespeare lived long before an author was considered to be a person of outstanding importance, whose comings and goings were worthy of constant observation on the part of the public at large, and therefore, in spite of years of minute studies on the part of our Shakespearean scholars, we are still very much in the dark about most of the data connected with his professional career. His contemporaries were aware of his existence, but they did not regard him with the respect they bestowed upon his latter-day rival, Ben Jonson. In their eyes he was just another actor-manager-playwright (of whom there were already by far too many in London), a fellow therefore but little removed from the rank and file of those strolling mummers who toured the provinces and whom the authorities treated like ordinary, common vagabonds.

Indeed, were we to invite all the great ladies and gentlemen of the London of the year 1599 (the year Shakespeare acquired a partnership in the Globe Theater) and were we to ask them who among all their contemporaries would have had the best chance of survival during the next three centuries, the name of William Shakespeare would have been among the last to suggest itself. For although toward the end of his London residence, William was deemed worthy of joining the "King's men"—the company of actors enjoying the direct and immediate patronage of His Majesty—at no time were the Londoners thoroughly aware of the true merits of this myriad-minded little man from the provinces, who in his thirty-seven plays did what no one else before or since has been able to do. For he dumped the whole of humanity at our feet and said, "There, my friends! Look at it. I know it is a pretty terrible mess, but don't get angry or annoyed at me because you don't like it. Mankind was not created according to my own specifications. All I can do is to show you what it really looks like. Beyond that, my responsibility comes to an end."

The immortal William, having been the subject of several hundred years of the most minute form of scholarship and criticism, has of course been compared to everything underneath the sun, the moon, and the far-flung stars. I happen to take the members of my own craft a little less seriously (we artists understand each other in those respects), and to me, my dear Frits, he is very much like one of those incredible fellows who handle a steam shovel. They look like nothing in particular. Socially they rate with—well, with other people who handle dredges or steam shovels. As a rule they are extremely careless about their personal appearance. They are addicted to everlasting and very cheap cigarettes, but they handle their unwieldy monsters with the easy elegance of a cowboy nonchalantly riding an unwilling and bucking broncho. Indeed, they succeed so well in hiding the difficulties connected with the steam-shovel technique that they make the spectator feel, "Aw, shucks! Anyone can do that." Let him try, and in the hospital he will have ample time to repent of his foolish action.

The comparison, however, does not stop there. If you will only watch the steam-shovel virtuoso for a little while, you will agree with me that there exists a close analogy between him and the immortal William. Observe him just after he has made a haul. He pulls his levers and, behold! the strange cargo he has just dug out of the soil or fished out of the muddy waters is unceremoniously dumped upon street or quay or wherever the master happens to be practicing his trade at that moment, and there it lies, for whatever it is worth.

William Shakespeare was such a steam-shovel operator, only he dealt with human beings instead of geological deposits. He was just as little concerned about the moral values of the material he dug up as the steam-shovel man who is at this moment digging that new canal near Flushing. Maybe his iron bucket has broken into the grave of a long-forgotten divine, buried in the seclusion of his little cloister garden six or seven hundred years before you and I first set foot upon our beloved island. Or the skulls that came rolling out of his iron scoop were merely those of a couple of notorious jailbirds, hanged for triple murder and thrown afterward into the nearest ditch to be left there to the mercies of the fish and the slippery eels. What is it to him what he brings to the surface? Nothing at all. Maybe some of the rocks he has brought to the light of day contain a tiny amount of gold. Then again, they may be nothing more than petrified mud. He should worry! It is his job to work that steam shovel and dig up whatever happens to be at hand. No one will ever be able to accuse him of not having attended to business. So why not light another cigarette, spit right heartily out of the window of his little caboose which offers him shelter during the daytime, and have a look at his watch to see how much longer he has got to keep on digging before he can call it a day and go home for supper, a glass of beer, and a look at the evening paper?

If you will pay a few moments' serious attention to the material Shakespeare dug up during his career as a playwright, you will know what I mean. Lord have mercy upon us all! What a strange assortment of human beings came a-rolling out of his literary ladle! Saints and sinners, noble heroes and the most contemptible of scoundrels, devoted wives and heartless wantons, people capable of acts of profound self-renunciation and others delighted to commit every sort of crime, wise men and fools, pedantic pundits and easygoing scribes, hopeless vagabonds and priggish courtiers, God and the Devil fighting for the soul of a Hamlet or a King Richard.

Shakespeare, the human dredge.

Other playwrights have done their best to do as he did, but none of them can be ranked with this strange butcher's boy from Stratford-on-Avon. For sooner or later they would get stuck in their own doubts and meditations. Then they began to moralize and were lost. Shakespeare, on the other hand, never preached, nor did he ever draw any definite lessons from the deeds of his characters. But not even the least intelligent of his spectators is ever left in doubt as to which way lies virtue and which way lies vice—what course will lead to death and what course will lead to life everlasting.

All truly great men, ever since the beginning of time, have been condemned to go their way in a state of profound loneliness. That was the price they had to pay for having been "set apart" from the mass of their fellow men. Most of them—as far as I have been able to find out—thought this a fair enough arrangement and accepted it without either complaint or regret. Shakespeare was no exception. He happened to live at a time when the center of the stage of politics was so fully occupied by men and women of extraordinary vigor and violence that even the most extraordinary acts of mere creatures of the imagination were apt to pale by comparison.

A country that had just lived through the panic of the Armada and the fear of invasion and annihilation could not be expected to shed too many tears upon Hamlet's sad plight when doomed to listen to the mournful wailings of his luckless father. And what meant the strange adventures shown in *The Tempest,* at a moment when in every London pub there were a dozen old tars who, for a pint of ale, would tell you twoscore yarns infinitely more exciting (and true too, by God!) than those in circulation about Prospero, Miranda, and the King of Naples? And what were the sufferings of even a King Lear compared to the horrors that had befallen so many of the innocent victims of King Henry's displeasure?

Shakespeare therefore wrote for a generation much too much occupied by the actual business of living—of living madly and wickedly but glamorously—to have any extra time to waste upon contemplating the mere reflection of reality. Even so, he was not entirely without fame in his own day. His ability as an uncannily clever playwright and versifier was willingly acknowledged, but it was left to another generation—dwelling contentedly upon the revenues accumulated by its roving, plundering ancestors—to appreciate his true merits. But so strong is his appeal to our modern interests that, in spite of all the efforts of nine generations of industrious but uninspired commentators to turn him into a sort of annotated textbook of Elizabethan literature, he has triumphantly survived as the most brilliant and the most versatile of all those who ever held up the mirror of their imagination to reveal unto us the wonderful reality of their dreams.

After some eighteen years "on Broadway"—as we would say today—William Shakespeare once more felt a desire to return to a life of greater respectability. He was not exactly a rich man, but he and his Anne had carefully saved their pennies and now hoped to spend the rest of their days associating with ladies and gentlemen rather than be in the constant companionship of tipsy harlequins and bailiff-ridden mountebanks. And so they returned to their native city of Stratford. Anne tended her garden and her beloved mulberry tree (was she indulging in the new hobby of trying to raise silkworms for home consumption?), and Will wrote an occasional play for his London friends, until the year 1613, when the old Globe burned down during a performance of *Henry VIII*—an occurrence in which many pious people hastened to observe an act of divine retribution. Shortly afterward, probably in the spring or the early summer of the year 1616, Will Shakespeare spoke his final lines and quietly bowed himself off the stage of life.

But about this final period of his life we again know very little. And why should we? Isn't it enough for us to have fallen heir to everything his genius bestowed upon us? Must we also know the maiden name of the grandmother of the notary public who drafted the famous will of March 25, 1616?

And now a word about our second guest, Monsieur Jean Baptiste Poquelin, more generally known as Molière. He was born six years after Shakespeare died, and he was the son of a Parisian tradesman who eventually acquired the title of a royal upholsterer. That was a wonderful thing! What greater honor could mere mortal man hope to achieve? If one lived in the France of the seventeenth century and happened to have been born an upholsterer, one either had to become a royal upholsterer or hide one's head in shame and perhaps kill oneself, as poor Vatel did when the fish for the royal luncheon had failed to arrive on time and he would have been obliged to serve his master a meal without a fish course.

Young Jean Baptiste was brought up in a house called *la maison des singes,* or "the monkey house." As the monkey was the symbol for the comic actor, he therefore came by his love for the theater in an entirely normal fashion. His father, however, did not at all share his son's enthusiasm for a career on the boards. Having only recently succeeded his uncle as *valet tapissier de chambre du roi,* the good upholsterer had made up his mind that his son should succeed him. Three generations of Poquelins, repairing the royal footstools and fighting the moths in the royal garderobe—*mon dieu!* what a past and what a future: security combined with honor! Could any Frenchman ask for more?

Yes, one of them did. That was our little Jean Baptiste, who had inherited the quick brain and the cultural ambitions of his mother, Marie Cressé, also the daughter of a member of the upholsterers' guild. He had no desire to spend all his days with a thimble on his finger and a pair of shears dangling from his side. And from his earliest childhood he had only one ambition. He must become an actor.

Here we find ourselves face to face with the question: where and how had Jean Baptiste ever learned anything about the stage?

He had done so, of all things, through another upholsterer, a friend of his father, who belonged to a religious society which had a private box in one of the local theaters. The rest you can guess for yourself. Through influential friends of the King's own upholsterer, the boy was sent to a school patronized by boys considerably above his own rank. It was, however, a first-rate educational establishment and, like all French schools dominated by the Church, it laid great stress upon the educational advantages of amateur theatricals.

At the Collège de Clermont, young Poquelin therefore not only got a thorough training in the classics but also learned to act. His knowledge of his father's character made him clearly realize the impossibility of talking the old gentleman into letting the son of a royal upholsterer choose such a low career. He would have to approach his problem from a somewhat different angle and, after talking it over with his friends, he made the harmless suggestion that he be allowed to study for the bar. The profession of the law might lead one almost anywhere in that highly contentious age, and Papa Poquelin readily gave his assent. In 1641 Jean Baptiste passed his examinations and at the same moment he met his fate. Her name was Madeleine Béjard —age twenty-four—profession, actress—general status, somewhat doubtful. For she had been the mistress of a certain Comte de Modène and was said to have had a child by him. The lady therefore did not at all fit into the solemn life of a respectable *tapissier du roi,* and Papa Poquelin hastened to pack his son off to Narbonne. He could do this all the more easily, as in the year 1642 Louis XIII had gone south for his health, and surely one of his royal upholsterers must accompany His Majesty in case there should be need of his humble services. With the usual and unavoidable result. No sooner had Jean Baptiste reached Narbonne than he hastened back to Paris, renounced all his rights to the succession of the *tapisserie* business, and used the money thus obtained to rush to his beloved Madeleine, with whom he thereupon founded a new theatrical company known as the Théâtre Illustre. Eventually this illustrious theater was to gain undying renown as the Comédie Française, that band of devoted players who were to do so much for the maintenance of that high standard of the spoken French word, which in turn was to make the language of France a vehicle of conversation for the whole of the civilized world.

At first this new venture was not a success, and soon the company had to be dissolved amid an avalanche of debts. The fact that most of those were paid by Poquelin *père* shows that the father must somehow have become reconciled to his son's choice of a career. But the question that faced Jean Baptiste and Madeleine after their initial failure was what to do next.

It was then that Molière took the momentous decision to bring the theater of Paris unto the people of France. The "road" had never before been tried by a group of first-class actors, and they suspected that there might be a living among the dull little provincial towns which were given so few opportunities to amuse themselves. Not much of a living perhaps, but enough to satisfy their modest demands. And so he and Madeleine and their fellow mummers set forth to conquer the Gallic hinterland. It took them almost twelve years to do this, but in the end they were successful beyond anything they had dared to hope.

This could never have happened today, but it was still possible in the middle of the seventeenth century, for, in spite of much evidence to the contrary, Paris had not yet entirely absorbed the whole of France. There were still provincial capitals which had remained important centers of local culture. Paris might scoff at them, but they took themselves very seriously. They had their own aristocracy, which still lived in the same houses their great-grandfathers had built, after the destruction of their castles, during the Fronde, and the long religious warfare had driven them to town. They were conscious that their lives lacked some of the elegance of existence at court, but they consoled themselves for this lack of gaiety by pointing to the seriousness with which they observed the Ten Commandments and all the official holidays and fast days of the Christian church and to the thoroughness with which they educated their children to become pillars of strength for Pope, for country, and for king. (Of course, the king should come second, but it scans better that way.)

These good people were very careful with their pennies, but they would unloosen their purse strings when it came to their own provincial academies of literature, their own religious organizations, their own academies of art. At least once a year they would make arrangements to have the local theater occupied by a troupe of strolling actors. They realized that the Church disapproved with increasing severity of everything connected with the stage, as a possible agent of unorthodox and revolutionary ideas, but since the local bishops depended to a great extent upon the good will of the local marquises and counts and barons, it was to the interest of these religious dignitaries to close an occasional eye. In short, they rarely interfered openly with that annual week of serious theatergoing.

When these honest small-town people discovered that, instead of the usual third- and fourth-rate actors (hardly one of whom could read a line correctly), they were now able to engage a most delightful, courteous, and accomplished gentleman with a leading lady who not only knew how to "lead" but who also was a "lady," and a retinue of fellow actors who were far superior to the common run of Thespians, they were delighted, and there was a steady demand for the troupe of the distinguished Monsieur Molière.

At first Molière contented himself with merely being an actor. He still had to learn his trade. But as time went on, he tried his hand at a little writing and, behold! the world looked and listened and said, "Here is a new sound—a new approach. Here at last is something alive and living. We like it. Let us have more of it."

That, of course, is what every artist hopes for—a public that wants a second and a third and a fourth helping. And Molière, being no different from his fellow craftsmen, wondered how long it would last and when the fickle public would turn its back upon him and say, "Aw, we've heard all that before! He's lost his grasp. Let's go across the street and see what that new fellow has to offer." But in his case the miracle happened. His public remained faithful to him and it has loved him ever since.

With one exception. The pedants, the bigots, the Dr. Panglosses (to whom Voltaire was to pay his compliments a hundred years later), they were all of them greatly upset when it became more and more apparent that this obscure scribbler was going to unmask them and their tribe in a series of plays which attacked no persons and mentioned no names, but which exposed their nefarious activities so clearly and in so amusing a fashion that everybody knew immediately who was meant. And, as a clever poet once wrote, "Hell holds no fury like a little man who has been hurt in his pride."

But what was the anger of the small fry compared to the fury of the clergy when Monsieur Tartuffe appeared upon the scene, that contemptible religious fanatic who first swindled his benefactor, Orgon, and next tried to seduce Orgon's wife, Elvira.

By this time—the year 1664—Molière had returned to Paris for good, was immensely successful, enjoyed the protection of Louis XIV (who actually took a part in his ballet *Le Mariage forcé*, with music by Lully), and therefore thought it safe to go as far as the sky. But there is where he made his mistake, for the sky took offense, and *Tartuffe* was forbidden.

Molière appealed to the King. The King invited the papal legate to Versailles and bade Molière read his play to him. The papal legate told His Majesty that he saw nothing offensive in the treatment of the subject, but the Paris clergy, more papist than the Pope, disagreed, and even the King, who was supposed to be the State (with a capital letter *S*), dared not openly incur their displeasure. Molière then offered to take out the most offensive passages. *Tartuffe* was given. The King, unfortunately, could not be present, as he was with his army in Flanders. The next day the Parisian magistrates, acting under pressure of the Archbishop of Paris, ordered the piece to be withdrawn. Molière sent two of the members of his company to the King in his camp, and the King promised that as soon as he was back in his capital he would see to it that everything got straightened out.

The Archbishop of Paris thereupon attacked the problem from another angle. He could no longer prevent *Tartuffe* from being given, but he had it in his power to embarrass those who intended to go and see it. This he accomplished by making a public declaration that anyone who presented, read, or attended a performance of the play would be excommunicated. Although excommunication no longer meant what it had in the Middle Ages (when it had been synonymous with a living death), the people of Paris—especially the women—were still too much under the thumb of their spiritual shepherds to be willing to run such a risk for a single evening at the theater.

The King confessed that he was powerless if that was the way the clergy felt about it and he suggested that Monsieur Molière had better write something else and forget about this unfortunate experience. Monsieur Molière, as always, professed himself His Majesty's most obedient servant, withdrew the piece, wrote many other comedies, and eighteen months later played *Tartuffe* and found that nobody was any longer sufficiently interested to start a new campaign of denunciation.

Such everlasting quarrels, however, with stupid opponents were bad for Molière's health. The modern diagnosis of his ailment would probably indicate a case of gastric ulcers, which very often are caused by too much worry. Then, as now, a milk diet was prescribed. Molière drank his milk like a good patient, but he continued to write the plays that suited his own fancy and he did so until the last day of his life. But it was a difficult struggle, and in the end he grew very, very tired.

Now, of course, if this were fiction instead of fact, Molière would have had a happy home with a loving wife, where he could have found peace and quiet after his continuous struggles with what Voltaire, three generations later, was to call *l'infâme,* leaving it to his readers to decide what institution he meant by "the infamous one." Unfortunately, in the case of Molière, there was a home, but not the right kind of wife. The woman he had married was very beautiful and the best actress in his troupe, but she had been a source of great annoyance to her husband, not by anything she had done but by the fact that she had been born without a satisfactory birth certificate.

It is only within comparatively recent times that we have got hold of the facts in the case, and now the learned world seems to have pretty well agreed that Armande Béjard was a younger sister of Madeleine Béjard and that therefore the actor-playwright had not been guilty of marrying his former mistress' daughter, but her sister. Why old Madame Béjard had felt it necessary to be quite so mysterious about the birth of her last daughter we do not know. But when Molière—then well advanced in middle age—took this very young girl to be his wedded wife, all his many enemies, led by revengeful Monsieur Tartuffe, hastened out of their hiding places, and the amount of mud they slung would have delighted the hearts of our least scrupulous social columnists.

Since another century and a half had to go by before a lucky find in one of the French archives (O, admirably orderly sons of Gaul!) established the fact that Armande Béjard was really and truly old Madame Béjard's offspring and not her granddaughter, the scandalmongers had it all their own way. Fortunately, King Louis had not yet fallen under the influence of that pious bore, the former Françoise d'Aubigné, that lady born in a prison in northern France, who, in spite of her extraordinary piety, was clever enough to persuade the Sun King to marry her after the death of his first wife. Still being more or less human, at least in his attitude toward his personal friends, His Majesty quickly settled these attacks upon his favorite actor by standing godfather to the first child born to Monsieur and Madame Molière. After such an overt act of royal approval, the people might continue to whisper to their hearts' content, but they were very careful not to talk too loudly when one of the King's secret agents happened to be within earshot. Which proves once more that though kings are an expensive luxury, they also have their advantages, for Molière after that was severely let alone as far as his matrimonial affairs were concerned.

The marriage, I regret to report, did not turn out to be a

happy one, mostly due, it seems, to the difference in age between husband and wife. The two, however, "remained good friends," as we express it nowadays, and after Molière died, it was Armande who had the courage to go to the King and complain that by order of the Archbishop her illustrious husband had been buried like a dog. And she would never have taken this risk unless she had in some way been deeply attached to her Jean Baptiste.

The trouble with me, my dear Frits, is that when I really like the people about whom I am writing, I could forget everything else and could go on for days without food or sleep (or only very little), so as to be able to go on discussing their problems. It is hardly fair of me to ask you to read all this in the little spare time you have. But I love this old Frenchman. I am not by nature much of a theatergoing person, and I would rather read the "begats" in Genesis than sit through the usual comedy or tragedy. Molière, however, appeals so much to me as a human being that I have adopted him as one of my own heroes. I have often wondered why, for the role he played, outside of his activities as a theatrical writer and manager, was not in the least conspicuous. But all his contemporaries (except those with a private ax to grind) seem to have agreed that he was not only one of the most outspoken yea sayers unto life but also that he knew how to express his affirmative attitude toward existence in terms of such charming elegance that he did infinitely more good than the bludgeon wielders who usually take the matter of reform in hand. And it was this fine sense of the feasible which allowed him to do for the theater what Franz Liszt was able to accomplish for music two centuries later.

Before Molière began to write, to act, and to manage, the comedians and tragedians of western Europe had enjoyed the same status as they had done in ancient Rome, where the official world had regarded them as belonging to the ranks of the common vagabonds who were entitled to no better treatment than that which was meted out to bands of ordinary strolling gypsies.

Once an actor had actually sat down at table to dine with the King (a privilege rarely enjoyed by even the highest of court officials), all this was radically changed.

When Franz Liszt comes for dinner (I very much hope we can have him if we can find a congenial fellow guest), we will ask him to tell us how he succeeded in training his princely employers and teaching them decent manners whenever they attended a concert. He did it, of course, by that inner cultivation which made him the social equal of those established in the seats of the mighty. Molière, too, seems to have had that rare gift of impressing his personality upon his environment to a very high degree. Like all sufferers from gastric troubles (my own diagnosis, as I told you, but based upon sound practical experience), he was given to fits of melancholia and of doubt and to deep questioning of the soul. But he was much too well bred to let physical discomforts interfere with his good humor. He remained courteous and considerate. Even when he was suffering intense pain his wit continued to flow as merrily as a mountain stream hastening to the near-by valley. With his happy balance of stoicism and epicureanism (high thinking and intelligent living), he was at home in every kind of society. Conscious of his own weaknesses, he was tolerant in his attitude toward the foibles of his neighbors. He was an obedient son of the Church and carefully performed all his religious duties, but at the same time he, like most intelligent Frenchmen of the age of Louis XIV (the King included), was also somewhat of a disciple of the great Descartes and preferred to erect his spiritual convictions upon a basis of mathematical certainty. (Make a note of it: let us have Descartes to dinner as soon as it can be arranged.)

This attitude toward the universe and its Creator, which during the next two hundred years was to make France the undisputed leader within the realm of thought, was not looked upon with great favor on the other side of the Alps, where now for exactly a century and a half, in an atmosphere of an absolutely unyielding and unbending clericalism, one Italian Pope had succeeded the next and where the whole world was held to be out of step except the battalions of the Castle of San Angelo.

The secret agents of the Vicar of Christ on earth were working with unflagging zeal to detect and expose every sign, however mild, of incipient heresy. Frontal attacks were not, of course, to be feared. Those princes who still acknowledged the supremacy of the Holy See could easily be made to fall in line and rid His Holiness of any direct menace. But the poison of doubt might lie hidden in the most unexpected places—in a picture or a tune or an amusing piece of theatrical falderal—in a funny ballet or an otherwise harmless farce. Wherefore the *sbirri* of an ever-watchful Inquisition must report even the most innocent deviations from the road of rightful thinking.

This chance became very apparent when it began to look as if even the King had fallen under the spell of a doctrine which proclaimed that "doubt was the beginning of all wisdom." But the effort to repress this dangerous upholsterer's son, who had now become one of the unconscious leaders of the movement to set man's mind free from fear of the supernatural, and the attempt to silence him for good—they were both of them continued not only to the moment of Molière's demise, but they were extended even beyond the grave.

Molière, as I told you, went to his eternal reward in the month of February, 1673, and the mode of his dying was as typical of him as the way in which he had always lived. He was only fifty-one, but he had been exhausted by years on the road, by absurd quarrels with dull-minded prelates, and by the death of his two sons and that of Madeleine Béjard, who had started him on his career and who had meant so much more to him than her sister, who was now his wife.

Molière had just finished his comedy about the man who imagined himself to be sick, and now the poor author, who knew that he was in a most literal sense "walking on his last legs," must act that role, although the pain in his innards made it practically impossible for him either to stand or sit down.

"But what else can I do?" he told his friends, who urged him to go to bed. "If I don't act, there'll be no show, and if there is no show, half a hundred people, who depend for their maintenance upon tonight's receipts, will have to let their families go hungry. I could never do such a thing to these good, faithful fellows. I must not betray their trust in me."

At the end of the second act Molière suffered such an attack of cramps that it caused convulsions. He tried to cover up his agony by a few forced laughs and somehow managed to go on till the end. Then his friends carried him home, and there he died, but so suddenly that even his wife was unable to reach his bedside before he had given up the ghost.

The next morning there arose the problem of burial. As soon as Molière had realized that this might mean the end, he had dispatched someone to get a priest. Like a good son of the Church, he wanted to ask forgiveness for his sins and depart, prepared to meet his Maker. The priests of his parish refused to perform this sublime act of mercy for a member of the theatrical profession. Madeleine Béjard, who had preceded him by just a year, had escaped a similar fate by solemnly renouncing her former profession just before she went to her death. But Molière had been stricken before he had been able to write that part into his own role, and, in all fairness to him, it is to be doubted whether he could ever have been guilty of such an act of moral cowardice. There is no secret, however, about the way in which his mortal remains were treated. The Archbishop of Paris (a man notorious for his own loose morals) refused to let this strolling player be buried in consecrated ground and denied a request for such funeral services as were usually accorded to the remains of good Christians. The horrified widow then appealed to the King, and Louis, who seems to have felt a very genuine personal affection for this humble subject who had contributed so greatly to the fame of his reign, did what he would hardly have dared to do for the mightiest of his nobles. He sent word to the Archbishop that he would not tolerate such an insult to the memory of an old friend. Whereupon the Archbishop suggested one of those compromises which sounded very reasonable but settled nothing. As a special favor, two priests would be allowed to attend the funeral, which must, however, be held after sunset and without any special ceremonies. Otherwise the late Monsieur Molière must be buried with the condemned criminals and the people who had committed suicide.

The question of consecrated ground or unconsecrated ground was not specifically mentioned. There is reason, however, to suspect that Molière's grave was dug in that part of the cemetery of St. Joseph which had not been consecrated. But again, we have no certainty. We can only guess, and as a result no one today knows exactly where the greatest of all French playwrights lies buried.

One more interesting fact that throws a most revealing light upon the slender esteem in which the official world of the seventeenth century still held its actors. Molière was never elected a member of the French Academy. And when next you read one of those hopelessly dull French novels which you were induced to buy because you had noticed on the outside that it was the work of a *membre de l'Académie Française*—then remember, my dear Frits, that these honored fossils had refused to associate themselves with the son of a royal upholsterer, although he happened to be the only one of their contemporaries who today is as much alive as he was when he made the whole civilized world roar with derisive laughter at his exposure of those presumptuous pedants who are mankind's most dangerous enemies.

The French Academy refused to open its doors to Monsieur Molière, but—come to think of it—a hundred years later the Swedish Academy deliberately overlooked the existence of Carl Michael Bellman because he liked to associate with cheerful but talented drunkards, who, it is true, were a pretty shabby and dissolute lot but who helped him to create those immortal songs which since then have become incorporated into the folk music of all the Scandinavian lands. And Schubert was never considered a good enough musician by the imperial Austrian authorities to assure him that much-coveted, though humble, "steady employment" which might have made him live twice as long as he did. And Rembrandt died an undischarged bankrupt. And Mozart was obliged to overwork himself into a state of tuberculosis, and the Berlin critics agreed unanimously that Paderewski could not play the piano. And when van Gogh dared to exhibit his pictures in his native land, respectable Dutch burghers deliberately spat upon his paintings, and when Giuseppe Verdi asked to be admitted to the Milan Conservatory of Music, the professors rejected him as being without any talent. There are countless other examples of that kind of stupidity and short-sightedness on the part of those who should have known better, but all this is rather far removed from the subject I was going to mention just now—the case of one Miguel de Cervantes Saavedra vs. the World at Large. And I shall tell you the rest some other time.

It is not going to be easy to be entirely fair, for I might as well confess that I never have been able to understand the Spanish people, do not understand them now, and probably will never quite know what to make of them. I have done considerable traveling. I have lived in many strange lands. I know a great assortment of languages which allow me to get some sort of idea about the mental processes of many distant tribes whom thus far I have only met in the form of postage stamps. But there are two nations entirely beyond my powers of comprehension—the Spaniards and the Irish.

I used to suspect that, in spite of all my protestations of tolerance and liberalism, I might still be a good deal more of a Calvinist than appeared on the surface and that it was the spirit of old Dr. John Calvin which made it impossible for me to do justice to those countries dominated by the Church of Rome. But that could not be true, because I had spent five of the happiest years of my life in the old Bavaria of before the war of 1914, when no woman could get a job of looking after the girls' room in any official building without an attestation from her spiritual adviser that she was regular in her attendance at Mass.

Then I said to myself, "It is the Arabic blood in these proud hidalgos which makes me regard them as something foreign to the rest of Europe." But there is no Arabic blood in the Irish, so that could not be the reason either. Finally, I began to wonder how much the Church might have had to do with making the Spanish and Irish people what they are today. Undoubtedly, it had greatly influenced the spiritual and intellectual and moral development of the Iberians and Hibernians. But why did it fail to maintain its power among the peoples of northern and western Europe, who lived under exactly the same conditions as the Spaniards and Irish? I was never able to find a satisfactory solution, and so I finally deposited the problem in my well-stocked folder marked "Unsolved and Unsolvable Puzzles" and ceased to worry about it.

I suppose we are all of us born with certain blind spots, and the best thing to do is to acknowledge them and then try and let them do as little damage as possible. For why bother about such personal idiosyncrasies when there are so many other things which need our immediate attention and which are capable of being changed for the better by our own individual efforts?

The name Don Miguel de Cervantes Saavedra sounds very elegant, and I suppose it means something to a Spaniard. I have, however, given up inquiring into the meaning of names, as it is a practice apt to lead to serious disappointments. Take, for example, that interesting Russian, Count Leo Tolstoy, the author of *War and Peace*, the best historical novel thus far written. Count Leo Tolstoy! How very typically Russian! And how romantic!

The heavy-browed Muscovite nobleman with his bare toes sticking out of the mud and with his well-worn peasant blouse! Only a true aristocrat could afford to be quite so demonstratively democratic. Then I learned Russian, and the first adjective I was asked to decline was *tolstoi,* or "fat," and so the author of *Anna Karenina* and the *Kreutzer Sonata* was, after all, nothing more impressive than Mr. Leo Fat.

A few years later I fell under the spell of the Provence language and took such a liking to that land whither culture and learning had fled after the fall of Rome that I decided to learn the vernacular of the picturesque Monsieur Frédéric Mistral. Until, one day, Jimmie asked, "Still busy with Fred Northwind?" The spell was broken. Fred Northwind would have fitted into a drugstore in Dorset, Vermont, or he might be running a gas station in Old Greenwich, Connecticut, but as the leader of a glorious literary movement, God forbid! As such a leader he was out.

And so I gave up, and although I have had ample opportunity to find out from those of my Spanish friends not yet shot by the noble General Franco, I have most carefully refrained from inquiring into the meaning of both *Cervantes* and *Saavedra*. But I knew the man himself fairly well from the novel written about him by the excellent Hermann Kesten. What a curious life he had lived! Surely not since the late lamented Job has any innocent creature suffered quite so many undeserved blows from a relentless and unreasoning fate as poor Don Miguel.

As quite a young man Cervantes took service with the famous Don John of Austria, who set forth to destroy the power of the heathen Turks in the eastern half of the Mediterranean in the ever-memorable year, 1571. The infidels were annihilated according to schedule, but during the proceedings Cervantes was badly wounded in no less than three spots and was permanently deprived of the use of his left hand. Being an optimist, he merely remarked that he had lost his left hand for the greater glory of the right one and continued to fight as a soldier of King Philip. At the same time, being also a rather practical soul, he felt that the sacrifice he had made for his God and his sovereign entitled him to some slight acknowledgment of his services and that a promotion to a higher rank with more pay might not be entirely out of order.

Duly provided with a letter of recommendation from his commander in chief, the noble Don John, Cervantes bade farewell to the fleet and sailed for Spain. Not far from Marseille, his ship was captured by the navy of the Dey of Algiers (the great-great-grandfather of the creature who gave our young American navy its chance to distinguish itself two hundred and fifty years later), and both the crew and the passengers were sold into slavery.

Alas for that magnificent letter of introduction signed by the Christian commander in chief! The wily heathen figured that a man carrying such credentials must be a person of great importance and therefore, when the moment came to discuss his ransom, they doubled the ante. And in order not to lose this fat prize, they were very careful not to let their prisoner escape and deprived him of all personal liberty. Cervantes found this not at all to his liking and, being endowed with a glib tongue, easily persuaded one of the blackamoors standing guard over him to join him in an effort at escape and show him the road to the sea. At the last moment the poor infidel remembered what had happened to others who had indulged in similar activities (they had been skinned alive) and deserted his companion while they were only halfway to the coast.

Don Miguel was easily recaptured and this time was thrown into a dark dungeon and told to stay there until his ransom should have been paid. When at last it arrived, it was found that his parents, by selling all their belongings, had been able to scrape together only a measly three hundred crowns. The Algerian financial experts were outraged. "What! three hundred crowns for a distinguished Spanish nobleman traveling with a letter of introduction from Don John himself! It's an insult!"

They were willing to let Cervantes' brother go free for this trifling amount, but Don Miguel himself had to remain where he was until several thousand more ducats should have been raised and paid over the counter.

Cervantes, knowing only too well that his parents could do nothing further for him, decided to help himself. Once more he ran away. Once more he was caught, but this time he was condemned to two thousand strokes with the cat-o'-nine-tails. As a rule, twenty blows were enough to kill a man, but the sentence was never carried out. For this Spaniard was a most likable fellow, and Hassan Pasha, the Algerian viceroy, so greatly admired his wit and steadfast courage that he had taken him under his special protection. Business, however, was business, and three thousand ducats would not be a penny too many for this strange Spaniard who, in rags and loaded down with chains, could still stalk around with a dignity few Turks possessed.

Once more Papa and Mamma Cervantes—poor folk at best— began the hopeless task of raising what to them must have seemed like several million, and once again the monks who specialized in these labors of mercy began to travel between Algiers and Valencia to make offers and listen to counteroffers.

These endless years of waiting grew unbearable to Cervantes, and so, for a change, he induced several of his fellow prisoners to join him in an effort to steal a frigate and make a bold run for liberty. The plan might have succeeded if it had not been betrayed by one of the very monks—a Dominican—who had been entrusted with the task of buying his freedom from his captors in Algeria. A third attempt at escape under Moorish law meant a sentence of death, but Hassan Pasha still loved his proud don. Once more Cervantes was forgiven.

Finally, after an interminable period of horse trading, the parties of the first part (the relatives in Spain) and the parties of the second part (the Algerian dealers in human flesh) came to an agreement, and, just before he was packed off to Constantinople to be sold in open market, Cervantes was set free. He landed in his native land in November, 1580. It was nine years since he had last set foot on Spanish soil. Anyone less optimistic would have said, "Enough is enough! I probably was not born under a lucky star. I'll take a little job somewhere far removed from all human traffic and live there ever after." But not Don Miguel de Cervantes Saavedra! Not he. For now he ventured forth upon an even more perilous voyage than that of a sailor bound for the north African ports. He became a hack writer in the Spain of the latter half of the sixteenth century.

By this step Cervantes merely changed from one kind of slavery to another. In Algiers the weather at least had been pleasant. But Madrid, then as now, was a dreary, wind-swept jumping-off place. Only, once you left it, there was nothing to jump to. His first efforts at his new profession were harmless enough. He wrote a pastoral novel called *Galatea*. It had a moderate success, and he even got a few hundred ducats for it, which was very unfortunate, for he now did what so many of our own young men in Greenwich Village do when they sell their first article to a magazine that is solvent. He got married and quickly discovered that there is very little truth in that old saying that two can live as cheaply as one. When, as usually happens, in such cases, the two became three, and then four and five, it meant ceaseless toil for the father, endless drudgery for the mother, and misery and hunger all around.

At first, there was his wife's dowry to help him out. But one small orchard, five vines, four beehives, forty-five chickens, one rooster, and one tankard for kitchen use do not go far toward supporting a family. At best they will keep them alive for forty-five days, but even so, roast chicken gets a little tiresome after six weeks, and a rooster can only be turned into soup. Cervantes, at his wit's end, now began to make those desperate efforts to provide for his family which were to occupy all his days and nights until the end of his life.

Like practically all people brought up in a bureaucratic state, Cervantes felt that his worries would come to an end the moment he should be appointed to some public office—any public office at all. In order to accomplish this, he must first reach the ear of the King. Perhaps—so he reasoned—if he were able to remind His Majesty of the services he had rendered the country at Lepanto and of the loss of his left hand while defending God and country, the good monarch would listen to his appeal. He wisely felt that, since his chances were extraordinarily slim, he might as well ask for a whole stable instead of a single horse.

And so he began by modestly suggesting himself for one of the four vacancies that just then had to be filled in the New World. These consisted of a governorship in Guatemala, a treasury job in New Granada, an auditor's position in Cartagena, and something else of similar importance in La Paz.

The answer Cervantes received was a suggestion that he content himself with something a little less ambitious and not quite so far away. That something "a little nearer home" consisted of collecting the wheat needed to provision the fleet which was then being equipped for the conquest of England and the Low Countries.

At last, here was something definite, and Cervantes acquitted himself so thoroughly that the Church excommunicated him for plundering the peasants, while the public accountants looked into his books, found them in a hopeless state of confusion, and suggested his immediate dismissal.

Reduced by these unfortunate adventures to such a state of abject poverty that he was obliged to borrow money to buy himself a new pair of pants, Cervantes once more turned his thoughts toward literature as a possible means of support. He sold himself to a publisher who promised to pay him fifty ducats each for six new plays, provided he—the publisher—liked them as well as any ever written in Spain—no small order in a country where during the sixteenth century every one of the inhabitants seems to have written at least a dozen plays.

All Cervantes gained from his new venture was a first prize at a literary contest in Saragossa. This first prize consisted of three silver spoons. As spoons are of little use unless you have something you can stir with them, he was no better off than before. Meanwhile, having made his peace with the clerical authorities, he was once more allowed to help equip the royal navy. But he was born a schlemihl and never was able to escape from the ill luck that dogged his footsteps. For when he entrusted several thousand reals he owed the government to a merchant who happened to be going to Madrid anyway and who promised to deliver this sum to the royal treasury as soon as he should have arrived, the messenger disappeared together with the money, and Cervantes was forced to borrow the sum from his friends or spend the rest of his days in jail.

From all this it somehow looks as if Cervantes did not have the makings of a good bookkeeper in him. But undaunted by this sad experience, he once again tried his hand at business, once again lost his last centavo, and once more went to the debtors' prison. After this last experience we lose sight of him altogether, until his name is being mentioned as the author of a manuscript volume which was being passed from hand to hand and which was said to deal with the strange adventures of an imaginary Spanish knight known as Don Quixote de la Mancha.

The first notices that have come down to us about this famous opus are not exactly flattering to its author. Lope de Vega, the human play factory who turned out more than two thousand comedies and tragedies in a single lifetime, informed a friend that he had read part of this *Don Quixote* and that it was about the worst piece of writing that had ever come to his notice. This may have been due to malice and spite, for it seems that Lope de Vega had heard of certain rather satirical references to himself said to be contained within the pages of a new and as yet unfinished manuscript also dealing with the doleful don. And in all fairness to the Spanish public, I must hasten to inform you that when Cervantes' book finally appeared in print, it was so successful that within two weeks after its appearance no less than three publishers in Lisbon had stolen it and were keeping the presses busy with their pirated editions.

This was very flattering to the author but not exactly profitable from a financial point of view. Cervantes therefore went to the law, got an injunction against the Lisbon publishers, and devoted himself to his hero from the district of La Mancha with renewed zeal. At last he seemed on the road toward fame, for after the book had finally appeared in full, it was hailed with delight by that part of the Spanish nation which could read and which thereupon told the rest, which was equally pleased.

This may well surprise us of the nineteenth century, who derive our pleasure from the ingenuous hidalgo because he is such a wonderful caricature of the Spaniard of the sixteenth century, but Cervantes' contemporaries do not seem to have looked at the noble don in that light. They accepted him as the true representative of all the virtues they considered most truly Spanish and they were full of admiration for his unselfish devotion to the highest ideals of a kind of chivalry which by then had disappeared from every other part of the world and which continued to exist only in this remote part of the old continent because nothing new had as yet come to take its place. And so they eagerly awaited its final conclusion, taking a sincere personal delight in all the absurd situations in which the poor don found himself, and not in the least aware of the impression the book was making on their neighbors north of the Pyrenees, who saw in this paean of praise to the immortal aspirations of Spain nothing more or less than its obituary. Here lies the soul of Spain. R.I.P.

Cervantes should now have become a man rich in money as well as in fame, but his success only brought him further misfortunes. No sooner had this labor of his pen started upon its world-wide conquest than he was obliged to defend himself against a new and most dangerous enemy—a plagiarist of unusual skill who undertook to compose a rival series of Quixotic adventures following so carefully in the footsteps of the original hero that it was very difficult to determine which was the real Don Quixote and which was the false one.

Even the most painstaking scholarship of the last three centuries has not yet been able to find out who was responsible for this fraud. The thief wrote under the pseudonym of Fernández de Avellaneda, but that does not help us very much. At one time or another, almost every Spanish writer of note, from Lope de Vega (who once more had become reconciled with Cervantes) down to Blanco de Paz (an old and most persisting enemy), has been suspected of having had a hand in this plot to deprive the real author of his just rewards and to rob him of his well-deserved fame.

Avellaneda's book made its appearance in Tarragona in 1614 and it had an unexpected result. Cervantes, annoyed beyond words at this unfair competition, and afraid that it might interfere with the success of Part II of his work, now set out to prove that he was the undoubted author of the original *Don Quixote* by paying much closer attention to his style than he had done before. In modern parlance, he took his book out of the "pulps" and now wrote as if he hoped to qualify for the "slicks."

But it was too late. A lifetime of toil and the years of his Algerian captivity, together with his endless struggle against poverty, were beginning to tell. He was sixty-nine years old. Everything he had ever tried to do had ended in failure. Early in April of the year 1616 he took to his bed. He did not have a cent to his name and lived in one of the poorest quarters of the town, but until the very end he remained a soldier and, above all things, a Spanish gentleman. And just like Molière, who was to die practicing his craft, Cervantes continued to write until the moment of his death. He was buried with the simple ceremonies of a member of the Tertiary order of the Franciscans, and his bones were laid to rest in one of Madrid's many churches—one attached to the convent of the Trinitarian nuns. His grave has never been found, and after his only surviving child, an illegitimate daughter, had died in the year 1652, nothing remained on our planet to remind us of Don Miguel de Cervantes Saavedra except half a dozen immortal characters in a book, but what a book, my dear Frits, and what characters!

The clock struck seven. When, according to custom, we opened the door, Shakespeare and Cervantes were standing outside, waiting to enter. That, however, took considerable time, as these two punctilious gentlemen were most particular as to who should precede whom. In the end, the Spaniard won out, and we invited our guests to warm themselves before the fire and to partake of a glass of sherry and a biscuit.

We were sorry to discover that even our combined store of Spanish was not quite up to the task of conversing with Don Miguel in his native tongue. Fortunately, he had acquired a smattering of Italian during his long residence in Algiers (where that tongue seems to have been more generally spoken than Spanish), and so we got along quite nicely, and whenever we got stuck, I could always draw a picture, which not only settled the difficulty but also caused great merriment to the good don, who was as simple-minded in all his reactions as a boy of ten.

At first Cervantes was almost entirely eclipsed by Master Will Shakespeare, who was very much the man of the world in his fine velvet coat and somewhat given to patronizing his humbler Spanish confrere. But he did not overdo it, and besides, Cervantes was much too civil to show that he noticed this superior attitude on the part of his English friend. And so everything went along quite harmoniously, with Erasmus inquiring into the kind of work Mr. Shakespeare might have done while alive and asking Cervantes whether, during the years he had spent in Valladolid, he had ever come across the tracks of the famous Cardinal Ximenes, who had spent much of his time in the Franciscan monastery of that city.

The fire was very pleasant that evening. The sherry was just right. But where was our third guest, Monsieur Molière, and should we wait for him or should we go ahead and have our dinner and take it for granted that something had happened to prevent this most polite Frenchman from being on time? It was then that Erasmus suggested a compromise.

"In my days at college," he said, "we used to give our professors fifteen minutes' leeway. If, fifteen minutes after the glass had struck the hour, the professor was not present, we would leave. We called it the 'academic quarter of an hour,' and both the students and the professors observed it most carefully."

I assured him that that pleasant habit had prevailed until my own university days some twenty years before, but the last time I had been in Germany I had heard that it had been abolished as a "barbaric remnant of medieval superstition." I had not been able to understand why such an amusing but entirely harmless custom should have been honored by the name of a superstition. It had been a cheerful little game between the students and their professors which neither side had ever taken very seriously, but now that life in Germany has become so hopelessly self-conscious, everything that contributed to the lighter sides of existence is sure to incur the displeasure of the new masters. At that moment Shakespeare joined in and remarked:

"Ah, you are speaking of the Germans! If I remember correctly—but my memory is not what it used to be—I said something about the way I felt about them in *The Merchant of Venice*. I think it was in the first act, right at the beginning. In my day, London was full of Germans. I am afraid they were not very popular, but then, as a people, we were never much given to liking foreigners. That went for Scotsmen, too. Indeed, after my gracious mistress, the great and glorious Queen, died, I found it very difficult . . ."

But we never discovered what Shakespeare had found so difficult, for at that moment the door opened, and in came Monsieur Molière. He bowed low, the feathers on his hat almost sweeping the floor. The top of his head was enveloped in a red handkerchief which looked as if he had borrowed it from one of the local fishermen.

"Gentlemen," he said before we had a chance to offer him our welcome, "gentlemen, I am desolate! I offer you my excuses, but a terrible thing has happened, as you will notice for yourselves. I have lost my wig!"

We assured him that this made very little difference to us— that wigs were so rare nowadays that we expected nobody to wear one—but this would not satisfy him.

"You were so generous as to invite me here for dinner tonight. It was the first invitation I had received in almost three hundred years, and I, who have sat down at meat with His Majesty himself, I must confess that sometimes I miss a little social excitement. And now, to find myself in the presence of this distinguished scholar—I recognize him from his pictures and how much, as a young boy, I enjoyed his *Éloge de la folie*—your humble servant, Monsieur Érasme! But to return to the cause of my unfortunate delay—I lost my wig and in a curious way, too, through sheer curiosity.

"You see, I was a little too early and I decided to take a walk. This is a charming village and such nice people! Well, I lost my way but I met a lady who spoke perfect French and, if I am not mistaken, she recognized me, for, in describing your house to me, she quoted something I once wrote so that I would be sure to find it. And when I looked at her (rather quizzically, I am afraid), she added that while very young she had been devoted to a certain Monsieur Racine. Her mentioning the name of Racine cannot have been mere accident either. Indeed, I suspect that she must have known how I felt about Racine—a marvelous talent—a genius when it came to writing verse—but a hopeless bore the moment he put aside his goose quill and tried to behave like a human being.

"I assure you, however, it was a joy to come to a little village like this, so far away from civilization—oh, I beg your pardon! I mean, of course, so far away from Paris!—and to find that my beloved France lives here too, and so I bade the good lady farewell and walked down to your harbor and, as I am alive and talking to you, there—right before my eyes—I saw a sight I shall never forget. Of course, I must have been deceived in what I thought I noticed, for such things simply could not be. This country is far away from Spain, and it must have been a mirage. And so I went down to the water front to make sure, and it was then that a gust of wind came and blew off my wig, which fell into the harbor, and no one was there to fish it out for me, and anyway, I was too fascinated to think of anything else.

"For there—though I am sure you won't believe me—right there on your dike—dike, I think you call it—and staring at a near-by windmill—I saw—so help me all the saints in heaven!—

I saw the noble Don Quixote wildly waving his lance and making ready to charge the windmill that stood on the other side of the canal—and the next moment . . ."

But here he was interrupted by a cry of despair from Cervantes. *"Dios mio! Dios mio!"* he shouted. "Is that crazy fool at it again? Can't he ever leave me alone—even for a single moment? What will he do next?"

This may have been meant as a purely academic question, but we had our answer right away. From the market place there arose a loud hue and cry. Our guests, of course, had no idea what was being said, but Frits and I did, and Erasmus, too, was familiar enough with the Zeeland dialect to know that someone was loudly hollering for the police and that others were crying out, "Hang the dirty thief."

Frits and I rushed to the door. We beheld a queer sight. The whole street leading from the market to the harbor was filled with small children shrieking loud imprecations at a man on horseback. That man on horseback—as we did not have to be told, for there was no other like him in this world—was the noble Don Quixote himself, and right behind him we noticed his faithful servant, Sancho Panza.

One glimpse at the situation made it clear that we had arrived just in time to prevent a scandal. When a mob of children in the Low Countries begins to take off its wooden shoes and prepares for battle—then something has to be done, and right away, or heads are sure to be broken. And so we pitched in, and Frits, who is much better at handling crowds than I—probably because he is much less self-conscious—pushed two of the most belligerent youngsters away, banged their heads together (just for good measure), and shouted, "Here, you rascals! This won't do. Behave yourselves. What's the matter with you? Have all of you gone crazy?"

"No, Mynheer Philips," and the voice was that of a woman in Arnemuiden costume, "I know it won't do, but please look at that big crazy galoot on his old nag and dressed up in a kitchen stove! I had come to Veere to try and sell a few chick-

The moat had baffled the noble Don ready to charge our windmill.

ens, and now will you please look at what that fellow has got on the end of his stick?"

We looked and burst out laughing, for at the end of the don's lance there was a chicken, neatly speared and floating in the air way above the heads of the crowd. Apparently the don, having been unable to charge his windmill because of the intervening canal, had found some other outlet for his playful activities. He seemed quite satisfied with himself and showed no sign of any desire to placate the outraged chicken woman.

God only knows how the incident would have ended if it had not been for Cervantes coming to our assistance with all possible haste of his gouty feet. He walked straight up to the don and spoke to him sharply in what must have been an Andalusian dialect, for neither Frits nor I understood a word of what he said. There was no doubt, however, about the efficacy of his words. Immediately, the don was all smiles. He bowed low to his creator, climbed off his horse, took the chicken off his lance, returned it to the Arnemuiden *vrouw,* and then, with a noble flourish, tried to kiss her hand, a courtesy she avoided by smacking him firmly across the cheek.

"Hold on, that's enough," Cervantes commanded. "Get back on your horse and try to behave yourself. I want to eat my dinner in peace. You may ride around the village all you like, but there must be no more scandal, or I shall give the whole of my next chapter to Sancho, and I won't even mention you."

Don Quixote turned pale. "Oh no," he begged. "Please, my good master, don't! Please don't! I will be very good. On my word as a nobleman, I shall cause you no further trouble."

Thereupon he stiffly and (it seemed to me) somewhat painfully swung himself back into the saddle, turned to his equerry, commanded, "Right face, march!" and disappeared in the direction of the harbor.

"What was it?" Erasmus asked as we returned, while I told Jo Verlinde to serve the first course.

"Nothing of any great importance," Cervantes answered. "My poor don thought that those were Saracen heads. After I had shown him that they were merely ordinary chickens, he was terribly ashamed of himself and begged me to apologize to the noble lady with the basket and to make the necessary amends."

"I have already done that," Frits reassured him. "I told her to leave her two fattest chickens at our house and to present two others to Lucie with my compliments. That means that we shall have to eat chicken for the rest of the week, but that is better than to have a riot on our hands."

By this time the soup had been finished, and the second course was ready to be served. From upstairs came the soft strains of Lully's *J'ay perdu la beauté,* and, as I had expected, Molière was delighted.

"That lovely music," he exclaimed. "It brings everything back to me. Yes, indeed. Those were very happy days, and His Majesty was most gracious. But how long ago it all happened!"

Then he devoted himself to his food and indulged in a description of some of the dishes he had enjoyed at Versailles, until something Shakespeare said caught his attention.

Ever since he had come back from calling Don Quixote to task, Cervantes had been complaining of the trouble the irrepressible don was apt to cause him and how, almost every week, he was called upon to settle some "misunderstanding," as he called it, between the impetuous Knight of the Mancha and some harmless bystanders. This provoked Frits into asking both the Frenchman and the Englishman whether they, too, had never been able to rid themselves of the creatures of their imagination. Erasmus answered for them.

"I'm afraid not," he said. "It's always been that way. I am considerably older than these gentlemen, and they won't mind if I answer for them. Every author, every playwright, every musician—in short, every artist—must be prepared to spend the rest of eternity accompanied by the creatures of his imagination. It is their curse, but it is also their reward, and I am sure they would not want it otherwise."

Frits looked rather surprised at this statement. "Wasn't that rather the exception than the rule—what happened here to-

The noble Don had stolen a chicken.

night?" he inquired, filling the glass of the immortal William, who seemed to have a first-rate thirst and who, after a single glass of wine, and having expressed his preference for ale, was now drinking it at such a rate of speed that I had already or-

Molière without his wig. The handkerchief he borrowed from us.

dered Hein to go to the village inn and get some more. "Don Quixote is, of course, one of the most restless of all literary characters. But I am sure that most of the others are not quite like him."

"If you are under that impression, my good friend," Erasmus, who was sitting nearest to the window, told Frits, "then please look at the house opposite—that old empty house near the corner."

All of us leaned forward in our chairs to catch a glimpse of the house he indicated. According to the people of Veere it had once upon a time belonged to a retired sea captain who had hanged himself in the attic out of sheer boredom. Since then, it had stood unoccupied, for the villagers believed it to be haunted. As far as any of us knew, the front door had not been opened for more than fifty years. With its broken windows and its cracked stoop, it looked eerie enough to satisfy any lover of the supernatural. The two figures, however, who were leaning against the iron railing that led up to the front door did not in the least seem to mind, for they were engaged in a most animated conversation. One of them was tall and lean, the other short and dumpy.

"There he is," Shakespeare said, "and I might have known it! My melancholy Dane."

"So might I," Molière added. "He never stays far behind when I happen to go anywhere. My poor imaginary invalid."

"They seem to enjoy each other's company well enough," Erasmus observed.

"They are having a marvelous time," Shakespeare told us. "Hamlet is forever telling his companion what is wrong with his soul."

"Yes," Molière interrupted him, "and my poor dear *malade,* who never listens to a word Hamlet is saying (for he is much too interested in his own miseries), then regales the Dane with a long recital of his sufferings, how he has just tried a new remedy for constipation and how he has heard of still another physician who can cure the stone by making his patients drink gallons of warm horse urine and so on and so forth, year after year and century after century."

"Now, isn't that curious!" came from the kitchen. It was the good Jo Verlinde, who was bringing in some more bottles of ale. "Pardon me," she said, "but I could not help overhearing what the gentleman with the kerchief just said. Well, I used to hear my grandmother say that that was really the best possible remedy for anything that ever ailed you."

"And right she was, too, my good woman," Erasmus observed, smiling at her from behind his glass of wine. "My own great-grandmother—at least, I called her my great-grandmother, and she was born in 1398—well, she too always claimed that a glass of that beverage taken every morning before breakfast would let you live to be a hundred. She should have known. She died at the age of a hundred and two, long after I had taken orders." As our other guests also seemed to have some private information upon this curious subject, the conversation might have

Hamlet was soliloquizing to the Malade Imaginaire and was apparently failing to amuse him.

continued for quite a long time, but just then we noticed that Perrels, our village constable, was approaching the two pale figures sitting on the stoop of the deserted house and was asking them most politely to move on.

"Shall we invite them to come in and give them something to eat and drink?" Frits suggested. But neither Shakespeare nor Molière would hear of this.

"It's been hard enough on me to have had that morose Scandinavian hanging around my neck all these centuries," Shakespeare said. "Please let me have at least one evening I can call my own and can be myself and need not play the role of the man who wrote *Hamlet*."

"As for me," Molière added, "I could live most happily without ever being reminded of my relationship to that old fraud whom I bestowed upon the world. For all I care, he can go and sit down on one of your dikes. Perhaps he will even catch a cold and die of pneumonia!"

Then Erasmus spoke, addressing himself to all three of our guests at the same time. "I am very much afraid, my illustrious friends," he observed with a great deal of dignity, "I am afraid that that can never happen."

"Why not?" they asked.

"Because, most unfortunately, you gave them life everlasting."

This was so pretty a speech that Molière got up, begged to be allowed to say a few words, and, in a charming flow of language (hexameters as eloquent as those of Racine), proposed a toast to the learned Dr. Erasmus, "the first and greatest of us all." Whereupon Shakespeare, not to be outdone in this exchange of urbanities, paid a most eloquent tribute to the merits of his esteemed colleague from Spain. Whereupon Cervantes compared both his fellow playwrights to that noblest figure of all time (we thought he was going to say Homer!), to the immortal Don John under whom he had fought at Lepanto, and, in a sort of singsongy voice, improvised a hymn of praise to all the famous writers of both the English and French nations. At the end, completely overcome by his emotions, he broke down and wept bitter tears into his second helping of the dessert. I was on the point of asking Jo to bring him a clean plate when he begged me not to bother.

"There have been too many days when I went without any food at all," he said. "What are a few tears mixed with such a delightful meal? And that slight touch of garlic in the chicken! It was perfect!"

After that we settled down to the serious business of talking, and the conversation was magnificent, for, cleverly encouraged and guided by Erasmus, all three men were now completely at their ease and felt that they could say whatever was on their minds.

Indeed, that night we learned more about the world in which they had spent their days than we could have done from a library full of books. But if we had expected (and why not?) that we might hear some intimate and exciting secrets about the reign of Queen Elizabeth and that of the great King Louis of France and those of the second and third Philips of Spain, we were to be sadly disappointed. As far as our guests were concerned, those mighty potentates had existed only in so far as they had favored the arts or had failed to do so. Politics, so they hinted rather broadly, had never interested them. They had considered it a game for adolescents and, though they were conscious of their own shortcomings, they at least claimed to having behaved as grownups.

Then what did they talk about? What do artists do when they meet? They do what engineers do and polar explorers and lion tamers or any other group of men or women sincerely and deeply interested in their own kind of work. They talk shop! These three writers discussed different kinds of plots. They quarreled how long a play or a book should be (Erasmus was in the thick of the fray when that point was reached and was enjoying himself right heartily). They compared the honesty of their respective publishers, the generosity of their erstwhile patrons, and the fickleness of the public. They paid their respects to their audiences in the theater, and what they had to say

Master Shakespeare spoke a few pleasant words about his distinguished colleague, Señor Cervantes.

upon these subjects sounded exactly as if a group of modern composers and playwrights had been drinking tea in one of the Russian *trakteers* along West Fifty-seventh Street, indulging in the same pastime.

In the end, they even went into details about type and paper and bindings. In short, they thoroughly enjoyed themselves, and we—Frits and I, mere innocent bystanders—were so fascinated by their conversation that neither of us took the precaution to watch the clock. Midnight therefore took all of us by surprise. Among ordinary mortals, this might have caused a panic. But our guests were not of this world. They silently slipped back into that twilight in which they now had their being, and Frits and I were left alone with our memories.

Just before I went home, Hein came in with a slip of paper. "Two bottles of wine," he said, "and nine bottles of ale."

"Save that piece of paper," Frits told him. "Some young man can now get his Ph.D. writing a dissertation upon the subject of Shakespeare's attitude toward alcohol."

"Sorry," Hein answered, "but I need it to check up on the fellow in the inn."

I had to agree that on the whole that seemed a better and surely a more practical plan.

CHAPTER VI

The ARCHBISHOP OF BITHYNIA and the ARCHBISHOP
OF CYRENAICA Carry Us Back to Another
World Which We Would Just As Soon Forget

FRITS AND I had something on our minds, something we felt
that we must talk over with Erasmus, for he was the only person
who could tell us what to do. Wherefore we asked him whether
he could see us for a few moments early on Monday morning.
Frits had driven down from Amsterdam in his car, saying there
was no use being in town on Mondays, as business was apt to be
slack. People were making so much money that they were taking long week ends. His second in command could easily take
care of whatever had to be done.

This is what worried us. Everything so far had gone much
better than we had dared to expect. But we realized that we
were engaged in a very delicate experiment. One false move on
our part might spoil everything, and, if possible, we meant to
avoid such a disaster. As Frits was much more of a diplomat
than I, I let him explain the situation and sat quietly by, not
saying a word.

"This is our trouble, dear Doctor," Frits commenced. "Both
Hendrik and I have been so happy at the way our little dinner
parties have gone so far, we want to be sure we don't make any
mistakes. Therefore, we want to ask you what will be the best
policy. Should we always invite people who are like each other
at heart—who speak each other's language—people who have the
same point of view and who will take no offense at each other's

opinions, even when they don't agree—or should we ask men and women of completely different characters and with entirely different views, so that there will really be a clash of opinions?"

"For example," Erasmus interrupted him, "should you ask a Crusader to break bread with a Turk, and a Pope to share a bowl of soup with a heretic?"

"Yes," Frits answered a little hesitatingly. "Yes, that was more or less the idea."

Erasmus made himself a little more comfortable in his high-backed chair and took time with his answer.

"I don't believe," he finally replied, "that I can answer that question with a direct yes or no. Like everything else, it depends. As a general rule, I would suggest that, in order to make any kind of meeting as pleasant and successful as it can be, you should try to bring together people who more or less share the same general point of view, at least as regards the essentials of life and thought. Otherwise, both sides will be too much on their guard to speak freely. They will spar for conversational advantages. They will do their best to trip each other up on insignificant details.

"I don't think, however, that I can lay down any hard and fast rules. It will depend so completely upon the temperament of your guests. If they happen to have been brought up in the old school of what in my day we used to call 'gentlemen,' they will be like well-trained fencers who are engaged in mortal combat but who, even then, will carefully observe all the rules of the game. If, on the other hand, they have never been taught to respect anybody else's opinions but have been told to think only of themselves and feel convinced that they must always be right and that everybody else therefore must invariably be wrong—in that case, I would most strongly urge you to avoid bringing together whom God in His wisdom has put asunder. But, if you will pardon my preaching a little, all of us can learn only from our own experience. So why don't you try both systems? Why don't you sometimes invite only congenial souls who will agree on the main points and then again, once in a while, just to see how it works, risk a meeting between the other kind?"

"That is rather what we ourselves had thought, too," Frits answered, "but we wanted to know how you felt about it."

"I have now told you, but may I remind you of one thing?"

"Of course, sir," Frits said, dropping the rather official "Doctor" for the more familiar "Mynheer." "What is it that you want to remind us of?"

"That the initiative for these somewhat extraordinary dinner parties lies with you and must always remain in your hands. As I remember, there were no restrictions placed upon your choice. You were given complete freedom of action, and I am afraid that you will have to observe that rule to the end. I shall, of course, always be delighted to be present. You have no idea how starved I was for a little good conversation, and our daily fare (though, of course, I should not complain) was apt to grow a bit monotonous, whereas your cook—a most estimable woman, too—is a true artist. The things she can do to a chicken" (I made a hasty mental note of this little aside) "are both wondrous and marvelous. But I can only come to you in the quality of a guest. I must have no voice in telling you whom you should ask."

We stayed a while longer, then excused ourselves, returned to Frits' house for our eleven-o'clock cup of coffee (an ancient and most agreeable Dutch institution), and then sat down to the difficult task of arranging our next Saturday's dinner.

"For this once," Frits suggested, "we might do what Erasmus hinted at. We might invite two people who we are sure will most cordially detest each other."

This gave me an idea. "My dear Frits," I said, "do you remember—you must, even if vaguely—that once upon a time there was a terrific religious row that lasted for centuries—a quarrel that had something to do with the two words *homoiousia* and *homoousia,* or something like that?"

"How do you spell them?" Frits asked.

I spelled them—correctly, I hope, but I was by no means certain.

"I don't get them," Frits answered. "They sound exactly alike. Write them down, will you?"

I wrote them down, but with some difficulty, for although I had been talking about them in my books for some thirty years, I never could quite remember how they were spelled. Frits examined the piece of paper I pushed over to him.

"They are the same!" he told me. "I can see no difference."

"Don't you notice that extra *i*—that extra iota in the first word?"

"Now I do, but what difference does that make?"

"It makes the difference of hundreds of years of fighting and squabbling and brawling and wrangling and of people hating and killing each other and throwing each other out of jobs and exiling each other and appealing to Pope and emperor to tell them who was right."

"And who was right?"

"I don't think they ever were able to decide. And so they went on squabbling and fighting and hating and killing each other."

"All for that one *i*?"

"Yes."

"It sounds silly."

"It was damned silly."

"Then why did they go on doing it?"

"Why do people always go on doing silly things?"

"I don't know. I don't even know what these fool words mean."

"Careful!" I warned him. "If one of these Homoiousians or Homoousians were to overhear you, he would heave an ax at you."

"Don't be absurd."

"I've never been more serious in my life."

"But what do these words mean? What do they mean?"

I told him once more that I had forgotten. Whenever I had been obliged to mention the Council of Nicaea in any of my books, I had found it necessary to look the words up. As soon as I had carefully spelled them out I had forgotten them again.

"Is that old encyclopedia of yours still in your bedroom?" I asked. He told me it was, so I went upstairs and came down with the volume N–M. "Here it is," I told him, but I was mistaken. I should have brought the volume A–B, for the famous controversy was mentioned in connection with the name of Arius, the African theologian of the early half of the fourth century, who became a priest in Alexandria and there developed that strange and obscure heresy which, in one disguise or another, has survived until today.

What were the principles involved?

I had often tried to understand them, but I had always failed, and so I decided to read Frits the whole part of the article that had to do with the famous controversy.

"Finally," so it said, "the controversy about Arius' heresy assumed such proportions that it reached the ears of the emperor in Constantinople. Now to be emperor of the whole empire, Constantine saw in one undivided Catholic Church the best means of counteracting the vast movement within his widespread realm toward disintegration, and he at once recognized how dangerous strife might prove to its unity. Constantine had no understanding of the questions at issue, and so no course was left him but to summon a general or oecumenical council, which was convened at Nicaea in the year 325, and it was there that the problem of homoiousia and homoousia was thoroughly discussed and was decided against Arius (the champion of homoiousia), who was thereupon anathematized by the council and banished to Illyria."

Here Frits interrupted me. "Wait a moment, please," he begged, "and never mind Arius, but what did the two words mean? That is what I want to know."

"Have you *Webster's Dictionary* here?" I asked.

"No."

"Then come home with me—it's about time for luncheon, anyway—and I'll read the definitions to you out of Webster."

We went home, and this is what old Noah told us:

"**Homoousian:** Holding, in accordance with the Nicene Creed, that the Son of God is consubstantial—that is, of the same essence or substance with the Father."

As for **Homoiousian,** it got the following definition. "One of the large body of 4th-century conservatives who shrank from affirming that the Son is identical in essence with God the Father, but were willing to say that the Son is 'essentially like' the Father, or 'like the Father in all respects.' "

I closed Webster's mighty tome and said, "Now, is it clear to you?"

"No," Frits answered. "I heard you mumble a few sounds. But I have not the slightest idea what they meant."

"Neither did that old cutthroat Constantine, but he made a good thing out of it just the same."

"I know he did. He made a good thing out of everything he touched, but I still feel a little doubtful about the whole business. Why should we waste a whole evening on a couple of slogans that have been dead and gone these last sixteen hundred years."

"My child," I answered, "let old Professor Doctor H. W. v. L. give you a little lecture. Ever heard of Bolshevism and Fascism and Nazism these last few years?"

"I think I have."

"Know what they mean?"

"Not exactly. In a vague way yes, but the more I read about them the more they strike me as being like Caesar."

"All things to all men?"

"Yes, exactly. Last year I was in Italy, and almost every month I have to go to Germany. Of course I talk to everybody I meet, because I have always done it. I am often told that I should be a little more careful. Perhaps I should, but, anyway, so far nothing has happened to me, and I will say in self-defense that I listen just as willingly as I talk. In that way, I hear a lot."

. "And because you heard a lot you know what they are all about—these Fascists and Bolshies and Nazi boys?"

"No! As I just told you, every time I come back from one of those trips I seem to be more mixed up than before."

"All the same, one of these days our modern Homoiousians and Homoousians may get us into a war from which the world will never recover."

"That is perfectly possible."

"Then, don't you see what I am driving at? Such magnificent-sounding phrases which nobody quite understands have done more harm and have raised more hell in this world than all the clear, hard thinking of all the best philosophers of the last three thousand years. I sound as if I were preaching, but all of history is there to prove it. And an evening with two of the holy men who were actually at Nicaea might be very interesting, especially if they were on different sides of the fence. They have now had almost sixteen hundred years in which to quiet down, therefore they should be able to take a broad view of the question. Not too broad, I am afraid. Fourth-century Christians were not built along that line. But sixteen hundred years in which to think things over should have given them at least a little—well, let us call it perspective."

"Fine! Go ahead and ask them. I will be there. But what, for goodness' sake, are we going to feed them? What did they eat in Asia Minor in the year three hundred and so much?"

"I've already thought of that. They were simple country folk. We will probably have to invite a couple of bishops, but that means nothing. They, too, must have come from some small mountain village in Asia Minor or Armenia or from the Egyptian desert. I figured it all out, and here is the menu."

Frits took the piece of paper on which I had jotted down an outline of our meal.

He read it and shuddered. "A plate of barley water without salt—roast mutton done in garlic. No vegetables, but a lot of olives on the side and some sort of corn bread. We might try that recipe for Thomas Jefferson's spoon bread which Rita Bonsal gave me. And a light Greek wine mixed with rosin."

"Terrible!" Frits said, giving me back my slip of paper. "Do you mind if I have something else before we sit down to the formal meal?"

"Not in the least. I'd already made up my own mind to do the same thing."

"Well, in that case, here is luck to your little experiment, but how about Erasmus? He's so fussy about what he can eat and what he can't. Hadn't we better warn him, too?"

"Of course, the poor old dear, but that too has been arranged. Lucie has promised to fry us one of her Dutch steaks and prepare some fresh asparagus. She told me to invite you and Jimmie, too. Dinner in her studio at six sharp."

"Will Erasmus come when he knows that two ladies will be present?"

"Why not? He is forever telling me about the lovely young girls he used to meet at Thomas More's house."

"That was four hundred years ago. Since then a great many things have happened."

"Anyway, we can try."

"Of course we can."

At that moment Kaatje came in to say that luncheon was ready, and we went to the dining room at the back of the house where Jimmie had been busy making a cream sauce for a dish of fresh shrimps. Lucie had dropped in too. She told me that that morning her cat had presented her with its fourteenth litter of kittens since she had taken the creature in and that she had saved one for us—almost white but with a brown nose and a little shock of brown hair on the top of its head. "Looking," as she explained, "exactly like the youngest of the Fratellinis."

"When can we have it?" Jimmie asked.

"In about six weeks."

"I'm glad," Jimmie answered. "My dachshund is getting awfully lonely without some kitten to play with."

And then we had our luncheon.

On Monday I had been obliged to go to Middelburg to try and get hold of at least one bottle of tolerable Greek wine, and

so it was not until Tuesday that I was able to sit down to work
and dig up the names of two authentic delegates to the Council
of Nicaea. I was rather aimlessly turning the pages of Hefele's
History of Councils when the girl from the post office brought
me a special delivery. It was from Frits in Amsterdam.

My dear Hendrik:

I was so excited about that last dinner of ours
with the immortal William and Jean Baptiste and Don Miguel
(what fun to have met them at last in the flesh or whatever they
were, instead of merely knowing them from my schoolbooks!)
that I forgot to tell you what I had wanted to ask you ever since
that first evening with Erasmus. So I will put it down in writing—I hope that you can read it.

I am afraid that you are doing more than your share. I loved
to read those Plutarchian essays on our guests you sent me, but
they were more than I needed. The actual facts about these
worthies I can easily enough find out for myself. I bought that
little ten-guilder encyclopedia—the Dutch one—and I will say
that it gives me my money's worth, at least in the matter of
dates and facts. But that is as far as it goes, and it does not help
me much in understanding the queer fish that swim into our
net. That is where your letters have helped me out no end, and
I now·want to ask you to do me a favor.

I love it when you let yourself go and write as if you were
talking to me. For then I get a pretty true picture of what to
expect.

On the way up north I happened to travel from Roosendaal
to Haarlem with a man I used to know in Utrecht and who has
just been appointed professor in history at the university here
in Amsterdam. I didn't, of course, tell him what we had been
doing, but I let him read your Shakespeare and Molière letters.
I thought he would be interested, for he had written a very
learned treatise in two volumes on the influence of French literature on the foreign policies of France during the seventeenth
century. He behaved true to type. He read your stuff and said

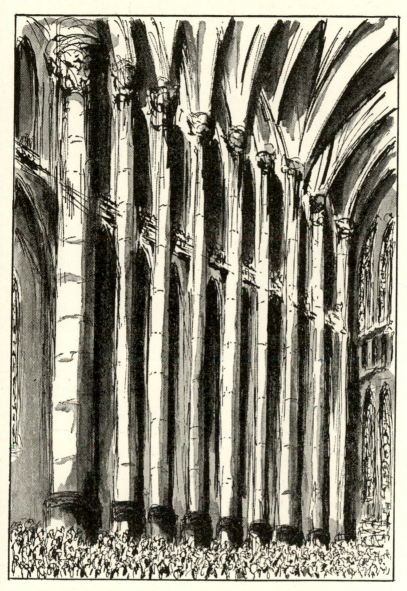

Veere's church as it had been in the happier days of its youth.

with somewhat of a sneer, "Very amusing! Very amusing indeed, but that is journalism. That is not history." I agreed, but I asked him, "Isn't that the reason people read it instead of reading history?"

"I suppose so," he was kind enough to agree, "but we historians do not write for the masses. It is sufficient for us to get the approval of our own colleagues."

It was hopeless to try to make him see things from my angle, and so I dropped the subject, but please go on giving me "journalism," if that is what you write. For then I shall be able to see the subject from all sides. Then I shall be able to walk clear around it and not merely admire the façade, as I usually do when I read the work of professional historians.

Perhaps I am wrong. Lots of people tell me so. They insist that you write "subjective history" and that a true historian should try to be completely "objective." I answer that it is too bad, but that just cannot be done—that it is possible to write "objective mathematics" and that you can be objective when dealing with chemical reactions or logarithms, because then you handle immaterial objects, if you know what I mean, though sometimes it strikes me that mathematics is a borderline case. But the moment you touch the human race, you have got hold of something very slippery—something that will never react twice the same way to any given stimulus and that absolutely refuses to obey any set of definite laws.

I know the old argument that two and two will always make four, whether you are adding elephants or mice, but two great generals or statesmen or ordinary common citizens will never add up like any other given pair of generals, statesmen, or ordinary common citizens. That is what makes history so fascinating. An Alexander the Great and a Napoleon may each conquer the world, but that is all they have in common. Even at this job they will go from entirely different angles, and I rather think that if they were to meet, they would hate each other like poison.

I don't know the reason. I listen to my doctor friends who tell me that it is all a matter of the endocrine system—that the pituitary gland rules the world, or the thyroid gland, or something of the sort. The psychoanalyst fellows come to my house, look at my beautiful wife, drink my whisky, and waste my evenings trying to explain something that makes no sense. They juggle with complexes and repressed desires until I am ready to fall off my chair from sheer exhaustion, and in the end they leave me as wise as I had been before, if you don't mind my quoting a little *Faust*.

Once in a long while I come across an old-fashioned theologian. Somebody brings him to the house as a sort of historical curiosity. His type has sort of disappeared from the modern scene, and I am sure that he knows what we think of him and therefore is always more or less on the defensive. But when he loosens up a bit (he likes my whisky as well as the psychoanalysts do), he gives clear proof of the fact that he is just as set in his opinions as he used to be four hundred or a thousand years ago. And sooner or later he will seriously inform me that I am all wrong in expecting science and reason to solve this world's manifold problems, and he hints—and in no very discreet terms, either—that our only salvation lies in accepting his own sliderule solution about a personal God and His only begotten Son and a lot of other things I completely fail to understand.

I listen to all of them as patiently as I can, but I prefer to stick to the philosophy of life I have distilled for myself out of my own experiences and out of what I have read these last twenty years. I don't doubt that in another twenty thousand years we shall have gathered enough facts to let us catch a glimpse of a few of the laws of history. But until then we may as well confess that we shall have to "guess," and, in order to guess rightly (or as rightly as possible), I want to be able to walk around my historical figures—to get at them in as personal a way as possible, as we have been doing these last few weeks with those people who were our guests.

So please just give me your own opinion rather than the mere facts. You save yourself a lot of time and I will get much more out of it.

Tell Jimmie I have looked all over Amsterdam to get her some catnip for her kitten, but I can't find the stuff. Perhaps Dutch cats drink gin when they want to go on a spree. But of course in America, where you have prohibition, they must find some other way to get a jag. That's not bad for a foreigner who has never been in America, is it?

Stay in Veere another year, and I will speak your language as well as if I had been born in the States.

My love to Jimmie and Lucie, and tell Hein Verlinde that I found a kind of rope that is twice as tough as steel wire. The next time I come down in the car I will bring him about twenty meters so that he can try it out.

Yours as ever,
F. P.

To which right away I made the following reply:

My dear Frits:

Thank you and thank you a lot for your letter. I have relayed your message to Hein Verlinde. He gets a little bored playing those records upstairs, and as a reward he deserves something that is of some practical use to him in his own job.

As for the contents, etc., etc., I feel very much flattered that you see things so completely the way I do. I am quite conscious of the rather low esteem in which the professional historians hold the work of those who, like myself, try to bring the story of the past to the masses of our fellow countrymen in such a way that they will not only read what we write but also may derive a few lessons from the past that will prevent them from repeating at least a few of those mistakes which caused such terrific suffering among their ancestors.

Whether this can be done or not, I am sorry but I cannot possibly tell you. Often I despair of the human race ever learning anything at all from experience. It is very eager to do so within the realm of the sciences, but history has not yet reached the rank of a science and may never do so. However, I should leave that sort of moralizing to the good Lord. It is up to us to work, to labor unceasingly toward that most desirable goal when statecraft shall be based upon history, and when a statesman will be obliged to study the lessons of the past, just as a doctor must familiarize himself with all the branches of the medical profession—anatomy, physiology, and the materia medica—before he is allowed to practice.

Today nobody gives the matter a thought, and look at what we have got! We were just beginning to recover from the effects of one terrible war and we are already on the point of starting another one. For almost twenty years I have been shrieking from the housetops, "For God's sake, learn your history, or we shall soon be in another mess infinitely worse than the last one." But the cultural level of our present-day statesmen is steadily growing lower and lower, and the final result will be a catastrophe from which our civilization may never be able to recover.

The other day I got hold of a book by a German professor. His name was Lessing, like that great German liberal of the eighteenth century. I have heard that the Nazis are after him and that he is now hiding in Czechoslovakia. [FOOTNOTE: Professor Lessing was shot to death while working in his hotel room in Marienbad. A band of young Nazi gangsters was responsible for his murder.] I found the book in the library of a friend and was not able to read all of it, but while turning the leaves I came upon this passage: "The purpose of history," he wrote, "is to give meaning to that which in and by itself is without sense."

There, in one single sentence, you have the kernel of the problem that faces us. We must use history to give sense and meaning to events which, if left to themselves, would only make nonsense.

Ever since Darwin coined the word "evolution" most people in America seem to have taken it for granted that evolution was something automatic—a constant and irrepressible upward process, carrying us from the single cell to the complicated mammal and from the era of the cave man to the perfections of a future race of supermen. Those well-intentioned citizens must have overlooked certain other chapters in Darwin in which he pointed out that evolution, which merely indicates "motion," may mean a motion downward just as well as one upward and that for every species which has moved upward there have been a hundred others which have moved so deep downward that in the end they were annihilated and ceased to exist altogether.

Old Sir Thomas Gresham, that shrewd man of business of Queen Elizabeth, coined a neat phrase: "Bad money will invariably drive out good money." I suggest that we go a little farther and lay down the law that bad politics will drive out good politics, just as bad music will drive out good music, and bad manners will drive out good manners, unless the good politics and the good music and the good manners and the good everything else are forever watched over and protected by those who intend that the good shall prevail over the bad.

But it is terribly difficult, as I have found out, to convince most of my neighbors on the other side of the ocean of the necessity of modifying their optimism about evolution by a dash of that much less palatable tincture brewed by old Sir Thomas Gresham. They are busy making a living and claim that they have no extra time to waste upon such difficult problems. In which they resemble a certain type of our businessmen who never can go to a doctor for a checkup, and then drop dead some fine day from an affliction which, if detected in time, could have been relieved with no trouble at all.

I shall, however, go right on doing what I have done these last thirty years. And perhaps a hundred years from now someone will begin to suspect what I have been driving at all this time.

Take these two men we have invited for next Saturday. They represent two rather abstruse ideas which, as far as I can discover, no one as yet has been quite able to understand or even to define. If you study the proceedings of the Council of Nicaea itself (it lasted from May 20 to July 25 of the year 325), you begin to suspect that the vast majority of the delegates had sense enough to realize that, as they were dealing with words and not with concrete facts, they would never be able to reach a definite conclusion. They suggested all kinds of middle-of-the-road compromises. But such middle-of-the-road compromises were the last thing the fanatics from the extreme right and from the extreme left wished to see adopted. They had grown drunk on the sound of their own eloquence and insisted that the council call black, black, and white, white, and cease to bother about those intermediary colors which are the common colors of our universe, in which very few things are either entirely black or entirely white. And, unfortunately, on such occasions it is always the most uncompromising fanatic who will win out, because the matter under discussion means infinitely more to him than it does to the middle-of-the-road liberal.

In Nicaea, the Homoousians were just a little more violent than those who favored homoiousia (wait a moment, I must look it up again, for I never can remember), and so that extra letter *i* was rejected. All those who remained faithful to their little *iota* lost their jobs. They were denounced as heretics and were proscribed by the official Church and they either died in exile or wandered about in the deserts of Africa and eastern Asia, and there they and their followers continued to exist for another couple of centuries, fighting hopelessly but bravely for a cause which no one had ever quite understood and which no one could ever hope to understand.

Had this been the only instance of such a useless and futile quarrel, we could easily have overlooked it. We could have told ourselves that the sort of people who then dominated the Church were men of little learning. A few, of course, were well prepared for their tasks, but most of them were crude natives from the hinterland of Asia Minor and the desert regions of Africa, poor peasants who knew no better and whose power of reasoning was on a par with that of the religious zealots who disgraced the early history of our great American experiment. Indeed, we would have found it very difficult to differentiate between Cotton and Increase Mather and the leaders of the conflicting factions at Nicaea.

But alas! In later ages, in the fourteenth and fifteenth centuries, when the best brains of the civilized world had been incorporated into the Church, the same sorts of quarrels about mere words were just as common as they had been in the fourth century. And today we are in the midst of another outbreak of that kind of idiotic violence.

I therefore thought we ought to meet two of the most outspoken representatives of the absurd Homoiousian and Homoousian dispute. As I said to you last Sunday, they now have had sixteen hundred years in which to quiet down and get hold of their tempers and behave like civilized human beings. Let us give them a chance and see what we can learn from them. I have been able to find but few men of any particular kind of ability among the members of this famous congress, which, whether we like it or not, decided the fate of western civilization for a thousand years afterward. And so I have gone through the list of those who were present and more or less at random I have selected two of them. One was the Archbishop of Bithynia, the province in which the town of Nicaea was situated, and the other was the Archbishop of Cyrenaica, in Africa. I tried to get a European, but it seems that on account of the vast distances, only a few men represented the West—the best known of them being a certain Hosius or some such name who was Bishop of Cordova in Spain. The Archbishop of Bithynia will represent homoousia, and his colleague from Cyrenaica will speak for the other side. We ought to have a very interesting and highly illuminating evening.

As for the dinner, it should, I repeat, be very simple. The Church of the fourth century had not yet gone in for any of those luxuries which were so typical of the papacy a thousand years afterward. But I think that we ought to have our table set with all the pomp and circumstance we can find here in Veere.

We might even borrow some of Lucie's nice china, and I shall bring out all our silver. Such small-town officials are always very jealous of their dignity and painfully suspicious of being slighted. So let us do a little splurging and show them that we are highly flattered by their willingness to honor our humble home with their presence.

Jimmie sends you her love, and if you want to come by train, she will pick you up at Middelburg on the 3:07 next Saturday, catnip and all.

As every yours,
H. W.

And now, I am sorry to say, I have to report one of the most absurd and grotesque and also most unpleasant incidents that ever happened to me. Saturday came, and Frits arrived at the appointed hour. Lucie had given us a fine meal, and at half-past six we were ready to receive our guests.

Erasmus arrived at a quarter of seven and gratefully warmed himself before the open fire. We had, in the end, refrained from asking him to join us at Lucie's, as he had always insisted upon being kept in ignorance about the preliminaries of our dinner parties. Then the clock struck seven, and there was the usual knock at the door. But instead of both our visitors' showing up at the same time as we had expected, there was only one of them. He told us that he was the Archbishop of Bithynia. He spoke very little Latin, but Erasmus knew enough Greek to put him at his ease, though our guest at once informed him that his accent was abominable and that he had probably learned his Greek from one of those heretics who, after the Council of Nicaea, had fled to western Europe to eke out an existence as a teacher of the Hellenic tongue.

I noticed that he insisted upon using the word "Hellenic" instead of "Greek," and I asked Erasmus to find out why he preferred that name to the older one. The Archbishop, as soon as my question had been translated, gave me a scornful look. "He does not in any way want to be associated with the ancient

Greeks," Erasmus repeated with a happy twinkle in his eyes. He says that the ancient Greeks were immoral and ignorant heathens and that nothing should be allowed to remind the world of their existence."

"A happy beginning," Frits remarked to me under his breath.

"A lovely beginning," I agreed, and then there was another knock at the door, and I got up to open it to one of the hairiest creatures I had ever seen. In very bad Latin he announced that it was his duty to be where he was that evening—he had not wanted to come at all—but since he had been formally ordered to put in an appearance, he was where he was and hoped that he would not be obliged to stay too long.

I asked Erasmus to explain to His Grace how happy we were to see him and introduced Frits to him and then remarked courteously that he undoubtedly remembered his old colleague from Nicaea.

"I remember him only too well," he answered and, picking up a handful of olives from the table and stuffing them into his mouth, he asked, "Why am I here, and what is the meaning of all this?"

Erasmus explained as best he could that we had craved the pleasure and honor of this meeting because we hoped that we might learn something from him that evening.

"If these people want to learn something tonight," His Grace snapped back, "then why did they invite that ignoramus over there?"

Most of this remark was fortunately lost in the noise of a stack of plates being dropped in the kitchen. "I'm awfully sorry that I was so clumsy," Jo explained to us afterward, "but just when I had those plates in my hands to put them into the stove and warm them, I saw the bald-headed fellow scratch himself with one of your forks, and the face he made was too much for me."

Well, to make a pretty long story as short as possible, that is the way it went during the rest of the evening, only there was not much of a rest of an evening, for our dinner was over almost as soon as it had begun. In order to avoid further complications, Frits had suggested that we sit down right away and eat. Then there was a new and quite unexpected difficulty. As always, Erasmus pronounced a simple Latin benediction. No sooner had he reached the amen than he of Bithynia protested. "This will never do," he announced and, folding his hands, went into a Greek invocation that lasted a full ten minutes. When he had finished, he of Cyrenaica gruffly announced, "Now it is my turn," and favored us with a fifteen-minute sermon, except that he folded his hands and closed his eyes, wherefore we realized that he was not really preaching but was also pronouncing some kind of blessing.

While all this was going on, I caught a glimpse of Jo in her kitchen. She was lifting up her hands in despair, and the gesture plainly indicated: "How can you expect a cook to do her best when you make her wait half an hour before she can serve the soup?"

I answered by a shrug of the shoulders that as far as I was concerned, the situation was also beyond me, and then he of Cyrenaica boomed a very loud amen and crossed himself three times in a way I had never seen before, and Frits passed him our bottle of Greek wine.

About what happened the next moment, neither Frits nor I was afterward able to give a very coherent account, and when we asked Erasmus what he remembered, he politely declined to be involved. "They were your guests," was all he would say, stressing the word "your." "And please remember that I had nothing to do with inviting those two dignitaries." But as we reconstructed the scene an hour later for the benefit of Jimmie and Lucie, this is how the events had followed each other.

Immediately after finishing his plate of soup, he of Bithynia made a remark which neither Frits nor I understood, and Erasmus refused to tell us what he had said. "It would place the Church in a bad light," he pleaded, "and you should not ask this of one of her most faithful and obedient children."

We noticed, however, that he of Cyrenaica greatly resented

The holy men of Nicaea at once got into a slight argument.

some words his colleague from Bithynia had just spoken. The next moment he had grabbed a bottle of French wine, which stood in front of Erasmus, and had hurled it at the head of his enemy. After that, everything had become exceedingly vague. For he of Bithynia had reciprocated by picking up Frits' carving knife (Frits loved to do his own carving) and throwing it at the bearded man. Fortunately he had missed him, but the knife had hit one of our pictures and had broken the glass, and that had been the beginning of one of the finest pitched battles I ever witnessed. Here is the blow-by-blow account.

Bithynia got both his hands into Cyrenaica's whiskers, and Cyrenaica tried to strangle Bithynia. In doing so, they upset the table. The candles fell on the floor and went out, but by the light of the open fire we could observe the two holy men rolling all over the floor. They would undoubtedly have murdered each other if the tablecloth, acting as a sort of swaddling cloth, had not decided to take part in the fun and had so cleverly draped itself around the two struggling figures that neither of them was able to use his arms.

It was Jo Verlinde who saved the situation. As soon as she noticed what was happening, she had rushed out of doors and intercepted the village constable, honest old Perrels, who, as luck would have it, was just passing by our house, bound for a final trip of inspection before withdrawing for the night. Meanwhile Hein, the cook's husband, who was assisting her in the kitchen, had quickly rolled up both his sleeves and, having shed his slippers to get a better foothold, had grabbed one of the two contenders by the leg and was pulling him away from underneath the table. Next, authority in the person of the village constable had appeared, and all of us had set to work to put an end to this unseemly fight. This had been no easy matter.

The holy men had continued to wrestle with each other like drunken women, and it was not until both of them had been slightly sobered up by a few blows with the flat of Perrels' saber that they ceased, at least for a moment, to belabor each other with whatever came to their hands.

Then we were faced with the problem of what we should do

with them, for it was not yet nine o'clock, and we would have them with us in Veere until midnight. But Frits, with his uncanny gift of making everybody do what he wanted, took Perrels aside and, while Hein and I held the two clerics down by the simple expedient of sitting on them, held a council of war with the constable. At the end of it, Perrels rearranged his uniform, which had gone slightly awry during the struggle, and, addressing himself to the two persons, announced in his best professional manner: "In the name of the Queen, you are both of you my prisoners. You had better come along peacefully, or it won't go well with you."

It may have been that our two distinguished visitors recognized the voice of authority or they may have been too exhausted by their pugilistic efforts, but they showed no further desire to resist. Their fury, however, in regard to each other was in no way abated, and the last glimpse we caught of the archbishops as they approached our Veere prison showed them frantically gesticulating and once more trying to pull each other's hair and whiskers.

Perrels, however, had handled tougher customers than these unfortunate zealots. He held both of them firmly by what would have been their collars if they had not worn a sort of loose tunic, and I suspect that when they woke up the next morning their shoulders must have felt rather painful.

But we never found out. Our local jail boasted of two compartments. When in the morning Perrels went back to release his charges, he found them gone. Good old Perrels! He was a discreet and obliging person, for the case never appeared upon the police blotter of the good city of Veere.

It took us almost an hour to repair the damage. Then Jo invited us to come to her own kitchen (a rare honor and one which the ever-tactful Erasmus was kind enough to notice in a few flattering sentences), and the three of us sat down around her stove, opened a bottle of Vouvray, and had one of the merriest laughs of our lives. The incident had been ludicrous be-

The strong arm of the law was obliged to conduct the two holy men to the town jail.

yond words, and I am sure that neither Frits nor I would have missed it for anything in the world.

Afterward Frits and I smoked, and Erasmus ate some of Jo's cookies, which he always told us reminded him of the days of his childhood. Then he looked at us and said, "And now, my children, I hope you have learned at least one lesson."

"What lesson?" I asked.

"Never, if you can possibly help it, have anything to do with theologians."

"Yes, sir!" Frits answered. "I think we have learned that lesson. And one thing we promise you—from now on we shall be a little more careful about whom we invite."

"Amen," Erasmus added. Then noticing that the clock would soon strike midnight, he whispered, as was his custom, "*Tempus abeundi.*"

This time we responded with a grateful amen of our own. Darkness descended upon the room, and we knew that Erasmus had left us.

CHAPTER VII

We Invite Two Guests of a Very Different Sort, and DESCARTES and EMERSON Come to Make Us Forget Our Visitors of the Week Before

QUITE AS WE had expected, Lucie and Jimmie were delighted when, the next day at luncheon, we gave a circumstantial account of what had happened the previous evening. But their hilarity did not decide the problem that faced us: whom should we invite next?

It was Lucie who gave us the hint that led to one of the most delightful evenings of that interesting year. "Why," she asked us, "don't you, by way of contrast, invite one of the most logical brains of all times?"

"Whom do you mean?" Frits asked her.

"A Frenchman, a certain Monsieur Descartes."

"A wonderful idea!" we both agreed, and that same evening the name of René Descartes, carefully spelled out on the usual slip of paper, was placed underneath the stone lion of the town hall, and I was refreshing my memory upon the subject of Cartesianism.

But while looking for a French life of Descartes, which I knew must be somewhere in my library, I happened upon a collection of Emerson's *Essays,* and that gave me a thought. Both Frits and I were a little wary of inviting a single guest. It had worked in the case of Erasmus, but would we ever find another Erasmus? So why not ask Emerson, in addition to Descartes? He knew enough French to be able to converse with Descartes, and both of them were gentlemen. Even if they disagreed, they would hardly behave the way the two holy men from Nicaea had done. I therefore wrote the name of Ralph Waldo Emerson on another slip of paper, took my bicycle, went back to the town hall, and left it in the usual hiding place. I noticed, by the way, that the slip of paper bearing the name of René Descartes was already gone.

After I had got back home I decided that I had better attend to our menu immediately, for though Descartes had spent twenty-one years in Holland, he had always remained most aggressively French, and I knew that he would be a connoisseur of both wines and food. As for Emerson, he was easy when it came to satisfy his tastes. He was a New Englander and had undoubtedly been brought up in the appalling doctrine that you must never notice what you eat.

Our soup would be *consommé de volaille aux laitues farcies* —a stock of bouillon with braised lettuce, cut in halves, cooked some ten minutes in the bouillon and then removed so as to leave a clear soup. With this we would serve *petits pâtés à la Mazarin*—small meat patties served warm. There was to be no regular first course. Instead we would have *crevettes à la chinoise*—shrimps done in the Chinese manner with champignons and bacon. These were to be served in the small Quimper dishes we had bought in Paris a few years before and had found to be more useful than the shells out of which most Dutch people eat their shrimps, for the shells are very wobbly and are apt to slide off the plate while being passed around.

As for the main course, I discovered a delightful new way of serving chicken in *La Cuisinière bourgeoise* of 1746, a so-called *poularde masquée*—a chicken rolled up in slices of bacon and broiled on the spit. With this we were to have a fricassee of artichokes, done after a recipe of the year 1651, for it seems that during the seventeenth century artichokes were never eaten as we eat them today, when most of the juices of that pleasant vegetable run down our sleeves rather than down our throats.

For our dessert, Jo promised that she would undertake the

difficult task of providing us with *beignets à l'espagnole,* a delicacy first mentioned in a cookbook entitled *Les Soupers de la court*—and if these orange fritters had found favor in the eyes of Louis XV, they were sure to please Monsieur Descartes, who, in spite of his reputation of being a dangerous mental revolutionist, had never ceased to be a stanch supporter of both Church and state.

The wine was a simple problem. A white Bordeaux, a Château La Tour Blanche, would do for the shrimps, and a Musigny —a red Burgundy—would go well with the chicken. I also decided on coffee, for Erasmus was sure to drink it, and Descartes might like it, especially if we could induce him to mix it with a few spoonfuls of cognac. As for Emerson—he used snuff. Why shouldn't he drink coffee?

The musical program was not so easy. A man like Descartes, who had so far committed himself as to write a regular treatise upon the subject of music, was bound to know the difference between one tune and another. We already had the records of an Orlando di Lasso *Benedictus* and of part of his setting of the penitential psalms, and to these I added Nicolas Gombert's *In festis beatae Mariae Virginis,* and then I took a chance (for Descartes lived a century before Bach) and sent to Amsterdam for Johann Sebastian's B-minor Mass and for several of his chorales.

This, too, was to prove a fortunate choice. Descartes was so delighted with the music of Bach that after dinner he asked for some more, and we were fortunate enough to have most of the *St. Matthew Passion* and several excerpts from the *St. John Passion,* of which our guest liked the aria *Es ist vollbracht* so much that he implored us to repeat it. As for Emerson, he was polite, but his praise of Johann Sebastian reminded me of General Grant, who, after having heard Jenny Lind sing, remarked that she undoubtedly must be "a very good woman."

I will confess that Emerson's apparent lack of any kind of musical understanding did not in the least surprise me. The atmosphere in which he had grown up had hardly encouraged him to take a serious interest in anything as exciting as the

works of Johann Sebastian Bach. He was, however, very patient
with us, and we from our side were very careful not to expose
him to anything that might have caused acute suffering to one
brought up on hymns and whatever went by the name of music
in the Boston of the first half of the last century.

Here is the outline of the life of René Descartes I wrote for
Frits to refresh his memory.

Little René was born in the year 1596 in a small village in
Touraine. His grandfather had been a physician and had married the daughter of a physician. Young René therefore came
quite naturally by his love of science. But his father, Joachim
Descartes, had preferred a legal career and had (according to
age-old French tradition) married the daughter of another high
law officer. After the death of his first wife, Descartes *père* had
married again and had moved to Brittany, and it was in Brittany that René had spent most of his youth.

Meanwhile his father had obtained an office which automatically made him a member of the lower nobility. That was a
matter of routine in the France of the monarchy but it meant a
lot to young René. He never forgot what he owed to his rank.
No one ever lived who so diligently and so honestly tried to bestow a knowledge of the truth upon his fellow men, but there
was nothing personal in all this. Descartes was like certain doctors I have known who spent all their lives in research and who
not infrequently made discoveries which proved to be of the
greatest benefit to their fellow men. But nothing would enrage
them quite as much as being reminded of the role they played
as the good Samaritans of the human race. It was not the human
race which interested them. It was the behavior of a certain
kind of microbe which exasperated them, and they were out to
get that microbe and destroy it, and that the human race was
the gainer by their labors was a matter of complete indifference
to them.

Nor was this in any way a pose on their part. They were entirely sincere in their attitude of aloofness from all human emo-

tions, and that was perhaps what made them such excellent research men. They would not have been tolerated more than five minutes in a hospital ward, but in a laboratory they were magnificent. René Descartes rather belonged to that type, except that he was much more religious than scientists are apt to be. For the rest he was just as casual in his attitude toward his fellow men. He preferred to pursue his own lonely way. He was a bad mixer, or perhaps it would be better to say that he was no mixer at all. During his more than twenty years in the Low Countries he most carefully avoided learning any Dutch, so that he could not possibly be tempted to waste his valuable time talking about this and that with a neighbor who might invite him in for a friendly pipe of tobacco. This unwillingness to learn the language of his adopted country may strike one as curious, but it allowed Descartes to maintain that social seclusion which he needed to accomplish the task he had set himself after he had finished his *Wanderjahre* as a student and a soldier and was ready to tackle the problem of the riddle of existence.

These *Wanderjahre* had first of all carried him from his native France to the Netherlands. There the struggle for liberty had gradually been converted into a game of military chess. During one half of the year, both parties remained in their winter quarters, but as soon as it became warm enough to enjoy life in the big out-of-doors, they went forth to lay siege to each other's cities. During the seventeenth century such an assault was rarely an affair of violence. Why kill your enemy and run the risk of being killed yourself when you could force your will upon him (the ultimate aim of all sound strategy) by much less dangerous methods? For when, by dint of a most elaborately conceived "plan of attack," you had finally brought him to the point where you could say, "Tomorrow, my honorable opponent, if I blow up my mines, you will lose three counterscarps, five banquettes, four lunettes, nine redoubts, and two bastions, whereas at best you can demolish only two miles of my trenches," your honorable opponent, if he is a man of sense, would take a pencil and a piece of paper and would carefully figure it out for himself and, if thereupon he came to the conclusion that you were right, he would present you with his sword and would answer, "Monsieur, you win and I lose, and now let us go and have a drink and arrange for honorable terms." It goes without saying that in order to fight your campaigns that way, you must be both a first-rate engineer and a first-rate mathematician. By an act of great good luck the two sons of William the Silent who succeeded him as leaders of the newly founded Dutch Republic were unexcelled at solving such puzzles, and this fact was soon known all over Europe. From far and wide, ambitious young men who wanted to become professional military men began to hasten to the Netherlands that they might take a postgraduate course with these famous teachers of the art of strategy.

In the year 1618, René Descartes arrived at Breda and enrolled as one of the pupils of Maurice of Nassau, who was then in Brabant, preparing for further campaigns in the southern Netherlands. What curious times those were! In spite of all its bitter religious wars, Europe still enjoyed that "unity of civilization" which had been born of the medieval conceptions about a political and a religious superempire. Another century and a half were to go by before an exaggerated notion of nationalism was to divide the countries of the Continent into those hostile little nations, each one of which tried to develop a civilization and culture of its own as opposed to the civilization and culture of its neighbors. But when Descartes was born, it made little difference whether one's cradle stood in Stockholm or Naples, in Vienna or Madrid, in London or Amsterdam. You not only were a Swede or an Italian or a Spaniard or an Austrian or a Dutchman, but you also *ipso facto* were the member of a sort of supernational club, for which you qualified by having been born of fairly honorable parents, by having enjoyed a reasonably sound education, by speaking a sufficient amount of Latin to make yourself understood by your fellow members, by having enough respect for your own habits, customs, and prejudices to be willing to let others enjoy the same privileges without trying to reform them.

This, of course, was a thoroughly undemocratic arrangement, but it had existed for so long and it was so completely a part of the accepted order of things that nobody took offense or felt the need of another system, which would have opened the doors of their club to anyone, regardless of the fact that he might be highly unwelcome to those who already occupied the premises.

Let me give you René Descartes as exhibit A-1. He is born a French Catholic but is serving under a German Protestant prince who is the head of an army of Dutchmen. As soon as he has reached headquarters, he finds himself a member of a happy international company of military students, gathered together from every corner of Europe that they may study their strategy at first hand and with the best of all teachers. In order to while away the tedious hours of garrison duty, these young men engage in mathematical contests and offer prizes for the best solution of a given problem.

One day young Descartes, trying to figure out a problem which had been posted on a church door but which happened to have been written in Dutch, asks a stranger to translate it for him in either French or Latin. The stranger obliges, for he himself is a mathematician and doubts very much whether this young man can make head or tail of the puzzle that has proved too much for the best brains of the army. Early the next day, Descartes brings him the solution. Naturally, the two become fast friends, and the French cadet goes to the city of Dordrecht to spend some time with his newly made Dutch acquaintance, who proves to be the head of the Latin school in that city and a mathematician of more than local repute.

Compared to the methods of making war as practiced in our own day and age, we surely might learn a thing or two from these fighting men of the seventeenth century.

From the Low Countries Descartes proceeds to Germany to be present at the military operations which were the prelude of the great Thirty Years' War. After paying his respects to Austria and Bohemia, he crosses the Alps and goes to Italy. For he has had a strange and mysterious experience—a sort of vision— and he feels in duty bound to make a pilgrimage to the village of Loreto and there to give thanks to the Virgin Mary for that divine revelation which has come to him in the twenty-third year of his life and while studying mathematics in the city of Ulm, in southern Germany.

What had occurred to him in the ancient town on the Danube throws a most interesting light upon that strange mixture of intellectualism and religious devotion which was so typical of the people of the age of the baroque. Their heads were filled with mathematical formulas worthy of the twentieth century, but their feet were still firmly rooted in the soil of an almost medieval faith. In most ways they were of this earth earthy, and this to an extent and degree which nowadays makes us shudder, yet they could, at the same time, lose themselves in divine meditations which are equally ununderstandable to modern man.

Remember that Descartes, who wanted to be known as the exponent of reason—the protagonist of the ideal of a *clara et distincta perceptio rerum* (a clear and distinct perception of all things)—the man who wished to reduce the whole secret of creation to a few mathematical formulas—remember that this same courageous and irrepressible champion of intellectual freedom was capable of swallowing the story of Loreto, hook, line, and sinker, and saw nothing incongruous in mixing his theory of coordinates and curves with a firm belief in a miracle which had completely defied the law of gravity. For it was to Loreto, a small village on the Adriatic a few miles east of Ancona, that the house of the Virgin Mary, originally located in Nazareth, had been transported at the end of the thirteenth century, when it was being feared that the Saracens might conquer Nazareth and destroy this most holy relic, which had been the Virgin's home at the time of the Annunciation. A few angels had bodily lifted it up and had carried it safely from Palestine to Italy—there could be no mistake about it. In order to make sure that it was the original edifice and none other that had been brought to Loreto, the governor of Dalmatia had sent messengers to Nazareth to observe whether the house was still where it used to be. They came back and reported that it was gone. After that, who dared doubt the authenticity of this miracle? Certainly not René Descartes, the famous mathematician, although in the practice of his trade he must have known that it would have taken uncommonly strong angels to carry so much masonry (the house was built of solid stone, 28 feet by 12½ feet wide and 13½ feet high) all the way from Palestine to Italy, and that in only a couple of hours.

A moment ago I mentioned Ulm. Descartes studied there together with a mathematical friend who was also a devout Rosicrucian. It may have been his close association with one who was deeply lost in the occult contemplations of the Rosicrucian faith which caused him to fall victim to a very serious attack of melancholia. Or it may have been the gloom of this ancient fortress on the Danube. Or again, he may have been upset by the consciousness that he was on the point of making a discovery which would ultimately change the very basis of all science. For he suspected that the methods he had laid down for the study of analytical geometry might also be applied to every other department of mathematics, and mathematics to him meant the beginning and end of all creation. A little more light upon the subject, and he would stand forth as the founder of a new world of the intellect. But the light he prayed for came in the form of three dreams which had nothing to do with science.

In the first one he saw himself walking down a lonely country lane and he had grown lame when a storm broke loose and he was obliged to find shelter in a church. In dream No. 2, which was more or less of a continuation of the first one, he heard terrific claps of thunder while his own body was giving off sparks of fire. In dream No. 3 he happened to open a volume of Decimus Magnus Ausonius, the author of a charming and idyllic voyage down the Moselle River, a little book which does for that river what Smetana's tone poem does for the Moldau. The first line that struck his eye read as follows: "What way of life shall I now follow?"

When Ausonius wrote down these words, they may have meant almost anything at all, but it most certainly had no reference to his immortal soul, for this fourth-century Roman poet was so little of a Christian that he insulted his converted neighbors by presenting them with an ode bearing the outrageous title of *Cupid Crucified*. Of course, Descartes probably did not know this, but had he done so, it would have made very little difference, in view of the mood in which he happened to be when attracted by that line. He was well within his twenties. Thus far, although he had been a faithful student of many branches of learning, he had not really accomplished anything of lasting value. The question that faced him was—what way of life should he now follow?

Descartes hoped to find an answer to this question in Loreto, and he did. The well-bred young French aristocrat, who had frittered away his time vaguely thinking of a military career or of succeeding his father as a practitioner in the law, now became the great crusader for a new philosophy of life—a system of thought—in which nothing should be left to chance and in which creation should be reduced to a few mathematical formulas.

In order to do this, as he realized very clearly, he would have to withdraw from his fellow men. Epoch-making ideas are rarely born of the noise surrounding a cocktail party or any other social event. They need silence and loneliness to come to full fruition. Descartes studied the map. Where could one hope to find the environment best suited to a life of quiet study and contemplation, during the first half of the seventeenth century? He thought of Italy, but he was essentially a man of the north. He hated hot afternoons and stifling nights. He felt sure that such a climate would kill him. There was only one alternative —the Low Countries by the North Sea. And so, after a farewell visit to his native land, where he put his affairs in order, that he might be certain of a small but absolutely dependable monthly income (even philosophers must eat), he proceeded toward Holland. He arrived there in the spring of 1629 and was not to leave it again for any length of time until a few months before his death in the year 1650.

With the possible exception of Beethoven, few people have so often changed their actual residence as René Descartes. In the Frenchman's case, this constant moving was not caused by quarrels with dishonest landladies and objectionable neighbors. He was not of a suspicious nature and, as a rule, got along very pleasantly with his fellow men. Indeed, as he was soon to discover even in this land where he did not understand a word of the language, he got along much too well with them for his own good. His kindhearted neighbors would insist upon visiting this lonely stranger and would then invite him to drop in for a social glass of beer. That was, of course, very nice and hospitable, but it interfered with his work, and during the latter half of his life Descartes was so "drunken with the desire for knowledge" that he had no time to waste upon the ordinary amenities of his daily existence.

First of all, Descartes went to Franeker, a small town in the province of Friesland. There the hardheaded Frisian Calvinists had founded a university of their own that they might safeguard their young men from those liberal heresies which were then being openly taught in the universities of Leiden, Oxford, and Utrecht and keep them within the bounds of those sound Calvinistic doctrines as understood among their own fellow Frisians. If those excellent dominies had so much as suspected that they were harboring the inventor of Cartesianism in their midst, they would have been as greatly perturbed as the trustees of the University of Tennessee would have been had they discovered that a certain young man by the name of Darwin was teaching the natural sciences in their undergraduate department. Descartes, however, kept his ideas so carefully to himself and was so noncommittal upon the subject of his studies that he was never molested, although he spent his time in Franeker

The old Dutch cities had that quiet dignity which the philosophers craved.

finishing his very unorthodox *Rules for the Direction of the Mind.*

Having finished this small volume, Descartes crossed the Zuider Zee and went to Amsterdam. Not, as we would surmise, to find a publisher, for the book was not printed until half a century after his death, but to lose himself in the only kind of environment that really allows one to enjoy complete loneliness —a big city.

There exists a letter Descartes wrote about his new home. I will show it to you some time. He is much more flattering than another Frenchman who, a century or so later, complained to a Dutchman: "Your city reminds me of ancient Egypt—marble palaces built for cows." There are no traces of that sort of French wit (often hardly distinguishable from plain rudeness) in any of Descartes' letters. He is even grateful toward those whose hospitality he enjoyed (also a virtue rarely found in foreigners), for he recognized that the Dutch had to work hard in order to provide him with the peace and quiet he needed for his books. They maintained an army on land and a navy on the seas to protect him while he fished and meditated—a combination of the active and the passive life that suited him to perfection.

After five years in Amsterdam, Descartes suddenly left the capital and went to live in Deventer, the town where Erasmus had gone to school. There he seems to have mixed "applied physiology" with his mathematical studies, for it was in Deventer that he became the father of a child whom he duly recognized but who died at the age of five. But even without this little unfortunate incident, Descartes would have found something to keep him busy and interested, for 1633 was a year all scientists had reason to remember. It was the year of Galileo's famous encounter with the Inquisition.

Already sixteen years before, the Inquisition had deemed it necessary to warn the learned world against becoming too deeply interested in the works of that highly suspicious Pole, Nicolas Copernicus, who some three quarters of a century before had written a treatise suggesting that the sun, rather than the earth, might be the center of our universe, which of course was in flat contradiction of the Book of Genesis. Since then (Copernicus had not dared to publish his theory until he knew that he was dying) the whole of the civilized world had accepted this new theory, just as no sensible person in the days of Columbus any longer believed that the world was flat. It was, however, one thing to be firmly convinced of the truth of a fact but something quite different again to say so in public. And now Signor Galileo was in trouble for a new and even more dangerous scientific heresy. Would his fellow mathematicians and astronomers come forward and boldly defy the established clerical authorities by taking his side?

Only a few of them did so, and I am sorry to say that Descartes was not among those few, although he was in an almost ideal position to act as the champion of a new idea. He was financially independent and as long as he remained in the Low Countries, no one could touch him. The Estates-General were very jealous of their authority, and it is a matter of record that not a single refugee who had invoked the hospitality of their country was ever surrendered to the Pope, the emperor, or the Inquisition. These foreign guests were supposed to refrain from getting themselves mixed up with local politics. As long as they observed that very simple rule, they were safe and they knew it.

But when Descartes was obliged to make his choice and was forced to make up his mind whether he would declare himself on the side of Galileo, who was now in the "protective custody" (as we would call it today) of the Inquisition, or against him, he refrained from taking a definite stand and he was even more careful than before to cast his ideas in such a form that nothing he wrote could possibly be construed as being in direct contradiction of the first chapter of Genesis.

This strikes us as unworthy of so great a man, but perhaps he had his reasons. He had a purpose in life, a purpose greater than himself, greater than everything else. He intended to reduce all he knew to a single volume which was to bear the

Among those flat meadows, Descartes could both fish and meditate.

modest title of *The World* and which, as he had planned it originally, was to accept the Copernican theory as an established fact and as the basis of all his further astronomical theories. The volume, in its original conception, was never finished. It is therefore impossible for us to know whether he would actually have had the courage to defy the Church or would again have looked for some kind of compromise. But this much is certain —he meant to write such a book and in it he intended to give the world his final opinion upon all the burning questions of the day. And we had better let it go at that.

Meanwhile, he was beginning to suffer from his old complaint. There were too many people around him to let him work in peace. Once more he packed his few belongings and this time he moved to Utrecht, where one of his pupils held a professorate at the university.

There, however, he was to discover that when it came to "heresy snooping," the Protestants were just as much on the job as the Catholics. Not that he suffered from any direct interference with his personal freedom. No matter how bitterly the Calvinistic dominies might rage against this foreigner and ask what he might mean by this and by that, the magistrates were there to defend him and protect his rights. Descartes, however, hated all strife and he quietly moved to Leiden (the Harvard of the seventeenth century), where the atmosphere was notoriously liberal or "libertine," as the people then used to say, and where he was certain that he would be left alone.

It was during this Leiden period, which ran intermittently from 1636 to 1641, that he published the first part of that *Discourse of Method* which was to be the basis for all his future explorations within the realm of metaphysics.

Have you ever been in Rynsburg or Endegeest? I have. They are small villages near Leiden. They look like most other villages in the province of South Holland, and few people know their names, although they played a very important role in Dutch history. During the Middle Ages they had been part of the richest monastery in the northern half of the Low Countries. That monastery had been suppressed by the Reformation, and the villages and territories formerly belonging to this clerical establishment had been taken over by the Estates of the province of Holland. These administered their newly acquired territories through a commission, very much the way the city of Washington today is being administered by a commission appointed by Congress. These two villages therefore stood under the direct supervision of the central government at The Hague. The arrangement was hard on the local politicians, but it was a godsend to a philosopher in search of a place where he could live and think as he pleased without being obliged to give an account of himself to a board of aldermen who did not have the slightest idea of what the learned man was talking about and who had never read beyond the third chapter in Deuteronomy.

Rynsburg and Endegeest were and are small villages. But their names will be forever remembered in connection with those of Descartes and Spinoza. Our ancestors, my dear Frits, did not believe very much in democracy and equality and fraternity, but when it came to liberty they accepted no compromises. Spinoza and Descartes had a right to speak and think and write the way they pleased, and if the dominies would kindly remember this, it would greatly please Their Lordships of the Estates and it would save the clerical gentlemen a great deal of trouble.

According to Descartes' letters, the years he spent there in the heart of the province of Holland, with its endlessly changing patterns of sky and cloud, its tranquil meadows which invited quiet contemplation, and its canals where one could go fishing and meditate upon the riddle of existence, were the happiest period of his life. Whenever the spirit came upon him to see something of his fellow men, he could take the early canal boat for Amsterdam or Leiden or Haarlem or The Hague, spend a few hours with his friends, and sleep again in his own bed that selfsame night. In case of danger from some suspicious divine in a near-by city, he could withdraw within his own bailiwick, knowing that Rynsburg was his castle and that Their High and Mightinesses in The Hague would never surrender him to his enemies, for by this time such enemies not only had come into existence but they had become very active and finally they even went so far as to proceed openly against this dangerous papist who, while protesting himself a faithful servant of his own Church, might (if certain rumors about his writings had been reported correctly) cause much greater harm to the established order of things of every church than a full dozen heretics after the pattern of that abominable Michael Servetus, who had also attacked religion under the disguise of science, although, of course, in his case, the truth had triumphed, and the learned doctor had been burned alive by order of no one less than John Calvin himself.

When I was a great deal younger than I am now, I used to wonder how in heaven's name these heresy hunters were ever able to track down such spiritual irregularities, when the person in question had never committed himself publicly, had never published any of his ideas in book form, and had lived the life of a hermit. Since then, I have had occasion to find out. Do you mind if I make a slight detour of an autobiographical nature?

During the Red-baiting period that followed in the wake of the Great War in our own United States, I had a great deal of trouble. I was investigated—I had my rooms broken into—I had my mail stolen—I had my trunks opened by the F.B.I.—and suffered all sorts of annoyances and inconveniences, because I was suspected of what was explained to me later as "radical leanings." Being a completely nonpolitical sort of person and with no interest whatsoever in economics (either applied or theoretical), I never really had the slightest idea why all this should have happened to me, until one day I got my answer and was able to solve the riddle.

Twenty years before in Harvard, inspired by a youthful ambition to become a famous linguist. I had among other things (such as Arabic and Japanese) taken a course in Russian. That course in Russian now came home to roost, for to the average patriot of the year 1918, the word "Russian" was absolutely identical with "Bolshevism." Furthermore, as the secret agents of the government discovered, I still had a copy of Makarov's Russian dictionary on one of my bookshelves. That looked highly suspicious, didn't it? Besides, hadn't I openly bragged of my familiarity with a great many other foreign tongues? Why had I bothered to learn these if I had not planned to avail myself of them when the time had come to study the dangerous revolutionary isms that were then being evolved in half a dozen European nations?

"Preposterous!" you will say. Of course it was, but no more absurd than the idiot who wrote to the Department of Justice, explaining that he had heard me click my heels while bowing to a lady. Question: Why did I click my heels when bowing to a lady? Answer: It was an entirely unconscious act, the result of having spent five years in Germany and Austria.

"Ah, you see! He confesses that he has spent five years in Germany and Austria? And why did you spend five years in Germany and Austria?"

"Because I wanted to teach in an American university, and thirty-five years ago you could not get a job unless you had a German Ph.D."

"Perhaps so, but it still sounds highly irregular. He owns a Russian dictionary and has spent five years at a German university. We had better keep him under close supervision."

And as a result of my heel clicking and my juvenile ambitions to be taken for a great linguist, I was for quite a long while hunted like a dangerous criminal, though few people surely had been so consistent in their dislike of the unholy Teuton as I. The only difference between me and my inquisitors, as far as I could see, was this—that whereas I was able to fight the Germans rather intelligently because I had taken the trouble to learn their language and to understand their queer psychological make-up, these other self-appointed saviors of the Republic were obliged to get their information from the spy stories in our popular magazines and the works of "Treat 'Em Rough" Guy Empey.

I am afraid that in this respect very little has changed since the days of Descartes. This Frenchman, going his own way, politely but adamantly refusing to associate with any of his neighbors, keeping his opinions strictly to himself, receiving no callers yet forever getting letters from all sorts of people with famous names—no, he could not possibly be what he pretended to be. He must be up to some sinister, deeply laid plot. It was dangerous to attack him openly, for apparently he enjoyed the protection of some very influential personages. He had been seen at the court of the Prince of Orange at The Hague and for a while, so it was said, he had even tutored the children of King Frederick V of Bohemia, who, after the loss of his German and Bohemian possessions, had found an asylum in the Low Countries.

Descartes therefore was too well entrenched to be disposed of by the usual methods of innuendo and insinuation. The assault against him must be carefully planned, and it must be made by someone who could not be dismissed as merely another small-town divine with a personal grievance. Such a person was found in 1639. His name was Voetius (born Gysbert Voet), and he was the rector of the University of Utrecht. He used the indirect method to make his attack. The death of one of his fellow professors gave him his opportunity. In his funeral oration the speaker mentioned that during his lifetime the departed had been honored with the friendship of the great Monsieur René Descartes. Of course, the man in question was dead and beyond the reach of criticism, but perhaps there were others among his colleagues, still very much alive, who were also in correspondence with this foreign Catholic in whose *Discourse on the Method of Rightly Conducting Our Reason* the author was said to have stated that all the learning he had so far acquired, instead of showing him the road to the truth, had merely filled his mind with doubt, wherefore he felt compelled to suggest an entirely new approach to wisdom—an approach which would teach the pupil not to trust anything found in the books of others but to depend entirely upon what he himself could observe with his own senses. There (so he hinted) you had the nigger of heresy in the woodpile of the revealed faith. The *clara perceptio,* which was Monsieur Descartes' strong point and which, translated into plain language, meant nothing more or less than that "seeing is believing" and which insisted that all knowledge must be founded upon personal investigation and experimentation, was really nothing but an appeal to doubt.

Such a point of view was in flat contradiction to the accepted philosophy of the times, which still stuck to the good old nursery discipline represented by the two famous lines:

"Papa, why is two times two four?"

"Because Papa says so."

Those who had ears to hear knew what the learned Professor Voetius meant. Monsieur Descartes had been publicly denounced as an enemy of the Christian faith.

I am glad to report that once again the heresy snoopers failed in their attempt to dispose of their enemy. After they had summoned Descartes to appear before a council of professors to try him on his doctrines and after he had refused to do so and had thereupon been condemned by default, pressure was brought to bear upon the Utrecht faculty by the authorities in The Hague. They let it be known that Monsieur Descartes was a very great friend of theirs and must not be exposed to any further annoyance.

After that, the Frenchman was allowed to think and write as he pleased and could give himself wholeheartedly to his self-appointed task of trying to discover whether all the problems of heaven and earth and of life and death could actually be reduced to a few definite laws based upon reason and revealed by personal investigation rather than upon the authority of a few ancient prophets and half a dozen old books.

Descartes and Emerson

Three times during the twenty years he spent in Holland Descartes paid short visits to his native land. The first time he went there in connection with that small property which provided him with the leisure every good philosopher needs, for, as Emerson was to observe a little later, "The man of thought should not dig ditches." On the last occasion he had gone to Paris to inquire into the possibility of being appointed to a post in the local university. But he reached the French capital at the very moment the French nobles, exasperated at being a little too drastically "centralized" by Cardinal Richelieu and by his successor, Cardinal Mazarin, were on the point of getting involved in a civil war of their own.

Being above all things a man of peace (in spite of his career as a soldier), Descartes had not waited for the fighting to begin but had hastened back to Holland. After this last adventure, however, he began to show signs of increasing restlessness. In spite of the failure of all the attacks that had been launched on his doctrines of the desirability of doubt *(De omnibus dubitandis)*, he no longer felt entirely at ease among his Dutch neighbors. And though nothing was done to disturb him in mind or body, he realized that this particular chapter in his life was drawing near its close. When in the year 1649 he received a most flattering offer from the Queen of Sweden, requesting the distinguished Monsieur Descartes to move to her own country and initiate Her Majesty into the principles of higher mathematics, he decided to accept.

This was not the first time he had been urged to leave the Low Countries and betake himself to Stockholm, but until then he had always refused. What was generally known about the daughter of the great Gustavus Adolphus did not paint that lady in very rosy colors. She was said to be possessed of a decidedly masculine brain and to be very bright, but in a great many other respects she was reported to be decidedly queer. (Report correct. H. v. L.) She was, however, a bona fide queen, and in the middle of the seventeenth century the protection of a royal majesty was nothing to be dismissed airily by a professional philosopher who was said to hold some very extraordinary opinions within the realm of religion.

In September of the year 1649, René Descartes caught his last glimpse of the coast of Holland. After a tempestuous voyage on board one of Her Majesty's ships of the line (sent specially to call for the famous philosopher), he safely reached Sweden and proceeded to the royal residence. He soon became aware that everything was not entirely as he had been made to anticipate. Queen Christina did not intend to hide her famous catch under a bushel, and Descartes greatly resented being paraded around as if he had been an intellectual freak, instead of a most serious man of science.

In addition to this unwelcome publicity there were Her Majesty's dreadful habits in regard to the hours she kept. Descartes, like Berlioz a few centuries later, belonged to that type of Frenchmen who used their bed as their office, study, dining room, and parlor combined and who therefore spent as much time as possible among the pillows. Far different Her Majesty, who had inherited her father's matutinal habits and was apt to send for her private philosopher at the ungodly hour of five in the morning that she might happily engage him in a few hours of mathematical discourse before her frugal breakfast at seven o'clock.

Then there was another and even more disastrous peculiarity of the great Christina. She was a fresh-air fiend with a love for subzero temperatures. Imagine a Frenchman who had already complained of the damp rooms of the Low Countries, where at least he was provided with a peat stove from early October until late March. Try and conceive of this poor creature being obliged to talk Cartesian philosophy to a most unattractive Swedish lady at five o'clock in the morning in an unheated room in some gloomy palace at Stockholm or Uppsala—and that in the month of January!

I need not tell you how it ended. A cold accompanied by a fever—then double pneumonia—then death. After an illness of only ten days, on February 11 of the year 1650, René Descartes died. He was just fifty-four years old.

And now, since you prefer general impressions to facts, I suppose I should tell you something about Descartes' influence upon the world at large, including you and me. But here I hesitate, for my own philosophy of life is about the same thing to me as my watch. I have not the slightest idea what makes either of them go, but I know very well what they tell me. I am definitely conscious of the influence which such men as Immanuel Kant and Baruch de Spinoza have exercised upon my own way of thinking. But I am completely lost whenever I undertake to read more than a few sentences at a time of—let us say—*The Critique of Pure Reason,* or more than one postulate of Spinoza's *Ethics.* This of course is not entirely my fault. The authors of those books had every reason to make their literary products sufficiently obscure not to let them be understood too easily by their enemies who might be lurking behind almost any pile of printed rags in one of the local bookstores. And I will say that they succeeded beyond their fondest expectations.

During the Middle Ages the hardy scribe who dared to investigate nature by the Cartesian method of direct and personal observation used to surround himself with stuffed crocodiles (gruesomely suspended from the ceiling) and stuffed turtles hanging from the walls, and on cold winter evenings, when he knew that his house was being watched by his neighbors, he would drop an occasional handful of copper filings on the fire. This would then cause strange lights to arise from the chimney, and the frightened crowd of onlookers would hastily take to its heels. The learned man inside, so they shouted to each other as they ran, was in cahoots with the Devil. Better leave him alone! And the learned man could thereupon return to his anatomical dissections or to his mathematical studies, safe for another year or so, when the Inquisition might hear about the spooky manifestations that had taken place near his home.

After that, the thumbscrew could easily make him confess any thing his judges wanted to hear—and that was the end.

During the seventeenth century, the world had advanced a little. The crude old methods of concealment were no longer necessary, but a diffuse style, hiding all the more dangerous parts of the text from the ordinary reader, was still a useful asset if one wanted to end one's life peacefully in one's own bed. Wherefore, as far as I am concerned, a Chinese grammar makes easier reading than the average treatise on philosophy of the seventeenth and eighteenth centuries.

I can, however, get a fairly clear concept (we are back at the *clara perceptio* of Descartes) of what those pioneers of the intellect tried to prove, and as a result I understand why Descartes should have been so successful and why, at the same time, his doctrines should have caused such a panic among those who held that the world had reached a point at which there was nothing more to be discussed and nothing further either to be doubted or to be proved.

This demand for a static universe is as old as the human race, and I am sure that the cave dwellers were already in the habit of killing those of their neighbors who doubted the desirability of living in wet and drafty caverns and who insisted that a hut made out of clay and reeds would not only offer better resistance to rain and sun but would also be a much more healthful place of abode for the children and the old folks.

You may have noticed that I am stalling a bit, for the moment will soon come when I shall have to jump right in and tell you what Cartesianism (as the whole system of Descartes' philosophy came to be known) has done for me.

For one thing, it has taught me to respect man's intellect as the beginning and the end of all progress, and that progress is something that can be achieved by our own deliberate efforts as soon as we shall have the courage to rid ourselves of most of the accumulated rubbish of the past, to clean our cranial attics, and to begin all over again, letting ourselves be guided only by that which we ourselves can see and observe. This does not mean that I am unaware of the existence of certain forces or powers which, for lack of a better word, we call "supernatural." But we should cease to depend upon them for guidance in matters pertaining merely to our health, our physical and emotional well-being, and the conduct of our daily lives while spending our brief span of life on this planet.

Descartes was as drunk with mathematics as Hokusai, the great Japanese painter, two hundred years later, was to be drunk with art. In the case of Hokusai, it was the delight he took in a mere line, a passion I can fully understand and appreciate. It is not so easy for me to follow Descartes in his love for mathematics, of which subject I am shamefully ignorant. But the reason he gave for his worship of figures and formulas makes sense as far as I am concerned, for during the first half of the seventeenth century mathematics was the only branch of science that could be depended upon for the "certainty of its demonstrations and the evidence of its reasoning."

Descartes therefore decided to apply the "mathematical method," or the "reasonable method" (or whatever you want to call it), to every department of learning, and in that way it became the starting point for all his further achievements as well as the cause of the failures which in the end were to destroy Cartesianism as a workable philosophy of life. When Descartes started out, there was an urgent need for a system that would place the mind before the heart and should let intelligence play the role it ought to play in shaping our daily existence. But in the end, his system led to the unrelenting one-sidedness of so many modern experiments in which there is no longer any room for the ordinary human emotions. And when that happens, man ceases to be a human being and becomes a cog in a machine.

Do you know what I dislike most in Descartes—what I consider his greatest weakness? The fact that he never had a dog or a cat—not to mention a child (for he never took much interest in his short-lived illegitimate daughter)—or even a bird in a cage to call his own and to share his loneliness. Suppose he had

picked up some amiable pooch during one of his solitary wanderings and had installed him in his house and had made him
his daily companion! He would then never have been able to
write the nonsense he did about the "soulless" lower animals.
He then would have understood that every living being has
some kind of soul and a direct claim to our love and compassion.

Often this precious substance—which we call the soul—is present only in an infinitesimally small quantity, and I do not pretend that the memoirs of a sea urchin or a poison-ivy plant
would make very interesting reading. Nevertheless, wherever
there is a living spark, there is also a soul—a certain consciousness of existence with needs and desires and aspirations of its
own. And as everything created by God bears the breath of life
in it, no dog or cat or fish is a mere automatic something which
ticks like a watch and strikes the hour like a clock, without
knowing what it is doing.

This Descartes never even seems to have suspected. Had he
done so, he would not have hit upon that, to me, slightly absurd maxim of *cogito, ergo sum* or "I think; therefore I am."
For while there is no serious argument against this statement,
it is really no more satisfactory in explaining the riddle of
existence than Schopenhauer's equally cryptic *volo, ergo sum:*
"I will; therefore I am." For granted that thinking or willing
are the proof of existing, then why not go just one step farther
and say that thinking is merely the proof of my ability to think
and has nothing to do with my existing?

But enough of all this, for I am not very clever when it comes
to solving that kind of philosophical crossword puzzle. The only
thing I ask while burning the midnight oil with Spinoza or Descartes or Kant or Nietzsche is this: what can this man give me
to help me go through life with a maximum of usefulness to
myself and my neighbors and a minimum of friction with my
own conscience?

I will humbly give Descartes thanks for the tremendous service he rendered unto mankind by insisting that—in the affairs

of the physical world at least—only seeing is believing. I omit reference to the spiritual world, for that lies beyond my sphere of interest and observation.

I realize, of course, that there are many people who made Descartes their only guide (as there are others who accepted Spinoza as their sole guide) and who have followed him patiently to those sublime heights to which all great philosophies must eventually lead. I fear, however, that there are only a few among us mortals who can hope to travel so far and return to tell the tale, for it is very lonely among those snow-covered peaks. The air is hard to breathe. The silence is frightening, and a single false step on that icy plateau, and one is lost forever. Being people of the plains, you and I, my dear Frits, we can only indulge in an occasional visit to the Cartesian Alps, just as once in a while we may decide to go to the Swiss mountains for a bit of exercise and a change of air and then will hasten back to our own mud flats, refreshed and invigorated and ready to pick up our humdrum daily existence where we had left off, but happy that we are back among our own familiar surroundings.

Far different is the story I shall now tell you about that kindly, simple, and lovable soul, Ralph Waldo Emerson, who, as far as I am concerned, had only one flaw—his addiction to snuff. Voltaire, too, was an eternal snuffbox toter. But he partook of his Copenhagen rappee with neatness and elegance, whereas the sage of Concord was forever dribbling the disgusting brown stuff down the lapels of his suits, so that his family found it very difficult to make him look neat when he went forth upon those annual lecture trips which were his chief source of revenue during most of his life.

This noble citizen, as completely without guile as any newborn babe, saw the light of day on May 25, 1803. The place of his birth was Boston, a town in Massachusetts which obtained its city rights two hundred and six years after they had been bestowed upon Nieuw Amsterdam.

Emerson's father was a minister. Seven of his immediate ancestors had been ministers. Not to become a minister in the Emerson family was almost as incongruous as to be devoid of political aspirations should you happen to have been born into the Roosevelt family. And so young Ralph Waldo went to Harvard (class of 1821), and after a few years during which he tried his hand at schoolteaching (which he hated) he returned to Cambridge, studied theology, and qualified for the ministry by getting his preaching certificate in 1826.

Meanwhile, many of the followers of the old Yahweh, as He had been demonstrated unto the faithful by Increase and Cotton Mather, had fallen under the spell of the liberalizing ideas of the eighteenth-century philosophers and had incorporated themselves into still another sect which became known as the Unitarians, so called because they accepted only God the Father, but dispensed with the rest of the Trinity.

No other group of men ever tried so hard and so sincerely to follow in the footsteps of the Master. The only trouble with them, according to their enemies, was that they overdid the thing and became so much like Christ that they were no longer fit to be members of an ordinary Christian church.

The Unitarians based their beliefs upon the Bible and upon the Bible only. They insisted that they should have the right to read and interpret Holy Script as they pleased, but they cheerfully and conscientiously accorded this same privilege to everyone else, and ever since the beginning of their existence as a corporate unit they have been among the most courageous and intrepid champions of human freedom.

It is extremely difficult to trace them down to their original lair. I tried to do this in my book *Tolerance* and did not get very far. There are vague traces of the Unitarian philosophy (that term suits them much better than the word "religion") among some of the more obscure heresies of the Middle Ages. There were Unitarian movements among the Protestants of Hungary and, of all places, Poland, but these were duly suppressed during the seventeenth century. Holland had its share of Unitarianism during this same period. In England, the Act of Uniformity of the year 1662 caused two thousand clergymen with Unitarian leanings to lose their offices. But this outrageous and unfair treatment became the very reason for their existence as a definitely recognized new denomination. For the victims of this purge were now forced to combine that they might let the world know where they stood in regard to the Trinitarian idea which still dominated the minds of most people.

The Unitarians wholly rejected the old Calvinistic and Lutheran doctrines of salvation, inherent guilt, and eternal punishment, and together with these they denied the possibility of miracles. Finally, at least to a certain extent, they even began to lose faith in the Bible as the only book that could show mankind how to live noble and decent lives. They began to suggest that other works, or parts of other works (say the last chapter of *A Tale of Two Cities*), might reveal the inherent divinity of the human soul quite as correctly as many of the stories in the Old Testament.

Let me, as a matter of personal pride, say that our much-abused old Harvard became, very early during its career, a veritable stronghold of Unitarianism, translating the *Veritas* of its college seal into "Prove all things and hold fast to that which has proved true." And—what is much more to the point—it has steadfastly tried to live up to this idea, for which it deserves the gratitude of the whole of the Republic.

The backwoods divines of New England had, of course, greatly disapproved of this new heresy. They denounced the Unitarians as libertines, and when Joseph Priestley came over from England in 1794, to found the first Unitarian congregation in the New World, he was received with all that lack of warmth and cordiality for which New England has gained such a sad renown. The good dominies need not have worried. Unitarianism will never be a mass religion. From a purely numerical point of view, the Unitarian Church has been an out-and-out failure, for even today there are fewer than 150,000 Unitarians in the whole of the United States.

Religion, fortunately, is not like pig iron or peanuts. It can be definitely expressed in mathematical terms, but such terms mean nothing in matters of the spirit. If, however, you want to know what influence Unitarianism has exercised upon the civilization of which it is a part, look at the number of Unitarians you will find in such books as *Who's Who in America*. You will then discover that an amazing proportion of the staff work of our army of progress is being done by people who in some direct or indirect way are proud to associate themselves with the Unitarian movement.

And now, back to Ralph Waldo Emerson, about whom I can be very brief, for his life was as placid as that river along the banks of which he spent most of his life, and his career was devoid of anything even remotely bordering upon the spectacular.

At the age of twenty-six Emerson married, and at the age of twenty-nine became a widower. Then he got into a very polite but also very definite disagreement with his flock. He was willing to celebrate Holy Communion in his church but only as "an act of spiritual remembrance." This, so his congregation complained, was going a little too far. Their pastor could not see it that way. They insisted, and Emerson resigned. This meant that he ceased to be a regular minister and could only lay claim to the rank of a lay preacher. But from that moment on, the whole world became his parish.

Emerson was a man with a very distinct feeling for form. The curtain had now descended upon the first act of his life. There had to be a short interval before the beginning of Act II, so he took ship and sailed to England, where he became fast friends with, of all people, that old grouch and grumbler, Thomas Carlyle. This must have been a curious relationship: the acrimonious Scot, suffering from the effects of bad food on a weak stomach, and the perfectly normal Emerson, who, after he had overcome a threatened attack of tuberculosis during his early youth, went so serenely through life that it often seems as if nothing could touch him to upset his perfect equilibrium of body and soul.

The two men, however, complemented each other to perfection, and they remained faithful correspondents till the end of their days. They had one bond in common which must have given them great satisfaction. They both believed that the progress of the human race depended upon the kind of leadership it was given and was willing to accept. On account of all the Nazi and Fascist nonsense about their famous Führer and Duce, we of today have become highly skeptical about any kind of leadership. We have even begun to deny (what the world has known ever since the beginning of time) that an army (or a ship or a factory or a hospital or even an ordinary, everyday family) without a recognized "head" will soon degenerate into a mob. But Emerson and Carlyle—neither of them fools—knew their history and had the courage of their convictions.

I often meet people who, when they hear me talk like this, tell me that I too have been touched with the Nazi blight. Lord help us! I loathe everything connected with the absurd and preposterous theory of a *Herrenvolk*. As if these delivery boys and barbershop assistants, now strutting around in big brown boots and turned into "gentlemen" (by act of their Führer), could ever hope to re-create a world after their own unpleasant image! They will, however, be able to do a vast amount of harm unless we, who still believe in freedom, stop quarreling as to who shall be our leader and whether we should pay as much attention to the opinions of Albert Einstein as to those of the charwoman who keeps his classroom clean.

I therefore like Emerson for having said what he did upon the subject of the Representative Man (good old New England understatement!), and I hope he will tell us something more about his ideas upon the subject when we see him. In one of his books (I am quoting from memory) he defines the great man as the man who does not remind us of anyone else. I must ask him whether he still sticks to that opinion, for that would let in Adolf Hitler, which God forbid!

After his return to America, Emerson went to live with his mother in the old family manse in Concord. In order to provide for his very simple needs, he lectured. Two years later, in 1835, he married for the second time, built himself a house near that of the old family homestead, and became Concord's most distinguished citizen. He no longer shared his friend Thoreau's opinion that the philosopher should earn his living by the sweat of his brow. He had tried that sort of thing in a very mild way on his own farm and had come to the conclusion that hands covered with blisters from digging ditches were not very well suited to holding a goose quill in the evening when their owner had withdrawn to his study to confide his ideas to his notebooks.

The lecture business, when Emerson took the road, was still a very uncomplicated affair. Lecturers were not yet billed like so many bales of oratory and shuttled about from Chicago to Miami, and from Miami to Seattle, with slender regard for their well-being but with both eyes firmly fixed on the box-office returns. During half a century (Emerson lived to be almost eighty) this lay preacher traveled leisurely up and down the land, spreading his gospel of physical and spiritual independence and urging his listeners to try all things and hold fast to that which, after due experience, had proved to be best.

Once in a while, when Emerson spoke a little more plainly than usual, the rather aggressive disciples of John Calvin would try to stir the community up against him. For example, in 1838, when in a famous lecture he pointed out several of the defects of historical Christianity and begged his listeners to cast conformity behind them and get in direct touch with the Deity, his words caused a terrific stir among the deacons and supervisors and trustees in charge of New England's churches and theological seminaries. There even was a little witch hunting, lest some of the younger men studying for the pulpit might become contaminated by this dangerous doctrine which made man an actual partner of God during his peregrinations on earth.

Emerson was asked to explain himself further upon the subject, but this he wisely declined to do. He felt that he was entitled to judgment by a jury of his peers and maintained that his detractors hardly qualified as such. Whereupon the parsons, finding him beyond their reach in the lofty citadel of his own pride, did what small dogs do when they can't provoke a bigger one into a fight. They yelped at him, and all through life the Concord sage was followed by accusations of intellectual snobbism and a request to come down from his high perch and move among the crowd and show whether he was really made of a different clay.

There it was again—the well-known old argument about the fact that all of us are made out of the same common clay! Of course we are, but we should not forget that, in the hands of a Michelangelo or a Rodin, that bit of common clay may be transformed into something very different from the mud pies made by little children at the seashore.

As for the other charge, that Emerson preferred his own company to that of his fellow men in the mass, I think it was perfectly true. He undoubtedly preferred his own company and that of a few friends to a roomful of people with whom he had nothing in common. But if he did not exactly love all his fellow men, he certainly had a deep respect for the integrity of their individual opinions. And while he was constitutionally incapable of slapping them on the back, he was forever trying to show them a better and happier and more reasonable way of living and thinking. If that tendency to "wander alone" is all that can be held up against Ralph Waldo Emerson, I take it as convincing proof that he was indeed one of the noblest citizens our republic has thus far produced and one of the most truly "representative" Americans who ever lived.

Emerson, as I told you a moment ago, lived to be almost eighty. He was a steady and regular worker, not at all like Carlyle, who would gorge himself with literary labors until he almost died of the effort and who would then spend years basking in the gloom of his own melancholy meditations. And while his output was fairly large, it was as nothing compared to that of such men as Voltaire or certain other writers engaged in the difficult business of making people think for themselves.

Did he derive complete satisfaction from his labors? It is difficult to tell, but I am rather under the impression that he was never quite contented with what he had accomplished, either in prose or in poetry. He primarily thought of himself as a poet, but he understood very clearly that in his case the main qualification for the poet's calling was not present. He lacked an ear. Poetry is primarily a verbal kind of music, and music was not exactly an art which had enjoyed great popularity among the earlier settlers of New England. Emerson wrote poetry like some conscientious Boston citizen who has learned to play the piano because he has liked the playing of others, and who therefore knows that the thing can be done well, but who has overlooked the fact that other pianists, being imports from Russia or Poland, have started out with certain natural advantages which he himself can never hope to acquire.

Emerson was conscious of his handicap. He knew where Mount Parnassus was situated. Occasionally, he could even admire it from afar. But the Muses would never invite him in for a social cup of ambrosia and afterward, perhaps, a little dance on the green. Being the sort of person he happened to be, he never expressed any regret at having missed out on so many good times. He was a New England gentleman, and his wife probably would not have approved of such goings-on. Nor, for that matter, would his neighbors. The arts were a dangerous pastime, for they might make one feel what a marvelous thing life could really be if one approached it from the angle of the senses. Concord Common, after all, was not exactly the place for a *Kleine Nachtmusik,* nor would it have fitted into the New England scheme of things if Louisa May Alcott, garbed in cheesecloth, should have volunteered to lead the Russian ballet through some of its more intricate steps.

But Concord was a very nice place in which to spend one's days, and it offered certain advantages one could never have

hoped to find in Salzburg or Vienna. For example, when your house burned down (as happened in the case of Emerson), your neighbors would rebuild it for you; when you grew very old and became a little vague and began to wander without exactly remembering who you were or where you lived, some stranger would kindly take you by the hand and guide you safely home. And those little amenities of life and those quiet and unassuming civilities made up for a great many other things. And so a blessing upon the good people of this modern Athens. They may not always have understood very clearly what their sage was trying to convey to them, but at least they did not crucify him.

Concord is still there, and it has retained more of its ancient charm and atmosphere than many a famous European shrine. And there by the banks of the Concord River one can, provided one finds a place to sit down, meditate quietly upon the strange fate of America.

There was that earlier period of which Emerson wrote—the America of the Currier and Ives prints—the endless fields and prairies and forests, which seemed to contain enough food to feed all the hungry multitudes of this earth. There were the small villages inhabited by self-reliant citizens, each one of them inspired by the ambition to give his children every possible educational advantage that they might go through life as useful Americans, functioning to the best of their abilities and taking an interest in all the truly worth-while things of life. And those unhurrying people were still animated by an unconscious desire to be friendly, for was not every man a potential friend? And they still strove with all their might and main to make the best of their opportunities, for that was their duty as the members of a nation which had been so richly blessed by God and by nature that it was the envy of all the other people on this planet.

Then came the Civil War, and the Currier and Ives prints ceased to be our symbol. The pictures in the catalogues of the mail-order houses took their place, and the old ideal of manifest destiny slowly gave way to a new one which made the accumula-

tion of material wealth the beginning and end of all human aspirations—with destiny unknown.

This accusation (and I am surely not very original when I make it) has always been extremely popular among the intellectuals of Europe who (unless they had contracts to go to Hollywood or to sing at the Metropolitan) were very apt to weep into their brandies while deploring the "money madness" of America. Being an immigrant myself, I have perhaps a somewhat better perspective upon this endlessly repeated slur upon our national ambitions than one of our native writers. I realize that our present civilization is motivated by a desire for riches, easy or otherwise, but riches at any cost. But I like to substitute the word "European" for "American" whenever this topic of conversation comes up, as it is very apt to do, now that a new wave of refugees is descending upon our shores.

The worst and most indecent scramble for what are sometimes (God knows why!) called "the good things of life" is to be found among the recent immigrants rather than among the older settlers. Not that the early New Englanders and Virginians were averse to the idea of acquiring an honest or dishonest penny. They had lived too long in poverty not to agree with Abe Martin that while poverty was not actually a disgrace, it might just as well be. But the majority of them had come to America to develop a new way of spiritual living more to their tastes than that which the Old World had provided. They were succeeded by hordes of hungry peasants and slum dwellers who were only very little interested in a more inspiring and satisfactory mode of living and who came to the New World for the sole purpose of making a better living. They were like hungry cattle which at last have found their way into a richer pasture and, in their understandable but not very attractive desire to get their share (and perhaps a little more), they trampled under foot anything that happened to come in their way.

One of the first victims of this onslaught was our poor national bird. The old American eagle had at times done a lot of rather unseemly screaming. But it had been a courageous ani-

mal, and those who understood its language knew that it meant business when it wildly flapped its wings and proudly proclaimed itself the protector and champion of all the oppressed of this world.

The newcomers, without any roots in our soil and too restlessly active to become an integral part of the landscape (as the New Englanders had done), were not interested in the message of America. As long as their polyglot boardinghouse served them better meals than they had enjoyed in the Old World, they asked few questions and rarely bothered to wait for an answer. They may have heard vaguely that in the beginning of its independent career this nation, which, outwardly at least, they had now made their own, had been very conscious of its glorious destiny. But destiny, not being convertible into immediate and tangible profits, seemed of much smaller importance to them than the matter in hand, which was the business of plundering a continent (not to be confounded with real pioneering)—and to hell with everything else.

Whether Emerson noticed the change that had come over his beloved republic, it would be hard to decide from his books. His letters show that he was by no means blind to the fact that the United States of America had sold its birthright for a great many barrels of pottage. But either he was too old or too tired to join that small band of brave souls who marched forth to battle the real enemies of their common land—those who despoil the country for their personal profit. Then again, we may have to look for the reason of his apparent blindness or indifference in that quality (so strongly developed in him) which one of our great modern philosophers has called his "fatalistic optimism."

In the feeling that everything in the end would be for the best in the best of all possible worlds, Emerson did not stand alone. Most of his contemporaries shared this view. It was part of their heritage. It had come down to them from the days when the name of America had still been synonymous with the words "hope" and "abundance."

I told you that Emerson died the same year I was born, and

so I enjoyed the privilege of sharing our planet with him for only three months. It is pleasant to remember that for a short time at least I was the fellow passenger of a man who wrote with his heart rather than with his brain.

For we need both kinds of philosophers to maintain a rational balance, and so, my dear friend, until Saturday, when we shall have both the prophet of the heart and the champion of the intellect underneath the same roof. I hope they enjoy their dinner. Good night.

The next Saturday was one of those rare days in October when the Low Countries enjoy their few days of Indian summer. I was very busy at that moment with my slightly idiotic efforts to get Rembrandt discharged from the bankruptcy court. I had discovered that this had never been done and felt that we owed him some kind of redress. From a purely legal point of view, the thing was feasible. My lawyer in Middelburg had so cleverly worked up his case that it was absolutely foolproof. But the Dutch courts were invoking some obscure statute of limitations and were trying their best to make us drop the matter. And so I had spent most of that week with my good and learned friend, Dr. Heyse, who had dropped practically all other business to help me get Rembrandt out of his sad predicament. As usual, I was pretty well tired out when Saturday came around, and in order to get a little fresh air before our guests arrived, I had followed the Vrouwenpolder road and had just reached the lovely old grain mill, which was to burn down the next summer, when I was attracted by a rather unusual sight.

On Saturday our shrimp fleet never left the harbor, for all the sailors had gone home to spend Sunday with their families in Arnemuiden. Knowing this, I was very much surprised to see a small craft making for the mouth of the Scheldt, and what made the case even more interesting was the fact that the sails did not bear the letters *VE* or *ARM,* which would have indicated that the craft hailed from our own harbor.

After a while I was able to make out the letters *ZA*. The ship

therefore must have come all the way from the village of Zant-voort, on the coast of the province of North Holland. As we did not see a North Holland fishing smack from one end of the year to the next, this was a very unusual occurrence, and I wondered what could possibly have carried this vessel so far out of its course. A few moments later the Zantvoort boat made for the shore. It was high tide, and the skipper, who apparently knew his business, had no difficulty in landing his solitary passenger.

The passenger, attired in somewhat outlandish clothes, shook hands with the captain, who had accompanied him on shore, and then began to plow through the sand, evidently bound for our village.

By now I had become familiar with the unusual ways in which some of our guests proceeded to their rendezvous with us, and I therefore was not at all surprised when the stranger appeared to be no one else than Monsieur René Descartes. To make sure, I addressed him in my best Parisian French and asked him whether I had the honor of speaking to the distinguished Sieur de Descartes.

The recent arrival to our shores, holding on to his cape with his left hand, removed his hat with the other, gave me a low bow, and said yes indeed, he was René Descartes, very much at my service and deeply appreciative of the trouble I had taken to come all that way to welcome him.

I assured him that it had been no trouble at all and that I intended to take him home right away and let him recover from the discomforts he must have experienced in the little cabin of his boat. And then I told him how greatly I had been surprised to see a Zantvoort fishing smack in our part of the Low Countries.

"Ah," he answered, "and so you noticed! Well, it happened this way. We so rarely have an opportunity to revisit the scenes of our former happiness—not that I am not completely happy where I am now" (how often had I heard this before by now!) "—but I thought it would be pleasant to catch one more glimpse

of those charming villages where I spent so many happy years of my life and did some of my best work."

I answered that I was afraid that he had found things rather changed.

Descartes stopped in his tracks. *"Pour l'amour de Dieu!"* he begged, *"ne parlons pas de ça!* Physically, these villages have lost all of their former beauty and attractiveness."

"Yes," I said, "there have been a great many improvements."

"If those sights I had to endure are supposed to be improvements, monsieur," he replied, "then René Descartes is almost grateful to Her Majesty of Sweden for having been too parsimonious to provide him with a decently heated study. *C'était vraiment exécrable! Pis que ça, c'était laid."*

We had meanwhile crossed the bridge over the old moat and were walking between the fortifications that Napoleon, almost a hundred and fifty years before, had ordered to be constructed when Veere had been one of the ports from which he hoped to invade England. Descartes was delighted with what he saw. "These ramparts are very cleverly constructed," he told me, "much better than we used to do in my day. You may remember, monsieur, that I used to dabble in that sort of thing at one time of my career." I told him that I was familiar with the years he had spent in the field and that I had often visited the city of Breda.

"Ah yes, Breda," he answered. "It was there that I so greatly surprised one of your fellow countrymen by showing him that a Frenchman too could know something about mathematics."

Soon afterward we walked past my house. Jimmie was sitting in front of the stove, holding Noodle on her lap and reading the latest batch of American magazines. I pointed to the cheerfully lighted room. "In there, Monsieur Descartes," I told him, "you will find a great many of your first editions."

"Tiens! I would like to see them. Your printers were very good to me."

I remembered that it was impossible to take him in. Our tacit understanding had been that our guests would enter only the

The figure looked like Monsieur René Descartes.

house in which they were to be entertained, but I promised him that as soon as we reached our place of destination I would send someone to get those volumes for him. And since it was still too early to go to Frits' (it was only a quarter to seven), I suggested that we walk to the end of the harbor, for there I would be able to show him the kind of architecture to which he must have become accustomed during his long residence in Amsterdam and Leiden and Rynsburg.

The so-called "sea gate" stood wide open. We passed through it and for a while leaned across the old stone parapet, while I explained that on the other side of our harbor there used to be a tower exactly like the one behind us. But it had been used as a storehouse for gunpowder and during a thunderstorm had been struck by lightning, and the whole structure, together with parts of the city wall, had been blown into the sea.

"Yes," Descartes remarked, "the German monk who invented that terrible chemical compound did, I am afraid, more harm than good." He said this as casually as one of our contemporary scientists might observe that, while Alfred Nobel had undoubtedly meant well when he invented his dynamite to help the farmers of Sweden remove stones and tree stumps from their fields, he might perhaps have done less harm if he had stuck to engineering instead of switching over to chemistry.

I very much wanted to continue our conversation along this line for a little longer, but just then our attention was attracted by the sight of a small boat that was being rowed toward Veere and seemed to be coming from the island of Noord Beveland.

"Another visitor," Descartes asked, "and so late in the evening?"

"That is not what strikes me as so curious," I answered, "but a native from either of these two islands would have waited for the seven-o'clock ferry, which would have brought him here in five minutes and at much less expense. It will take this man at least half an hour and it will cost him a guilder or even more."

"Perhaps he is in a hurry," Descartes remarked.

"Even so, he is taking a risk, for the tide runs very strong

here. With only one man to row him, he may be carried out to
sea."

The tide, however, was considerate, for the rowboat made
straight for our dock, and I could observe the person who was
sitting in the stern. I was familiar with that long, falconlike
nose and those eyebrows. It was Ralph Waldo Emerson.

"Do you know this person?" Descartes asked.

"I do, but of course only from his pictures, as he died when
I was only a few months old. He will be your fellow guest this
evening. He is an American. His name is Emerson."

"Connais pas," Descartes answered with that sense of finality
a true Frenchman can put into these two words when he wishes
to indicate that not only does he not know someone but, furthermore, that he has not the slightest interest in ever meeting
him.

This hurt me a little, and I was on the point of answering
rather sharply that other people besides the French have occasionally written good books or have had brilliant ideas, when
I remembered that Descartes had died more than a century and
a half before Emerson was born and therefore could never
have heard of him.

A moment later, Emerson's boatman called out to me. "Hey,
Mynheer, help this old codger get on land. He seems to be pretty
stiff—rheumatism or something. And how am I going to be
paid? He said he had no money, but he was so pleasant about
it that I decided to take a risk."

I told him that if he would come around next morning to
Frits Philips' house we would give him a rijksdaalder, which
was more than twice as much as he had expected. He therefore
changed his attitude and became quite cheerful. "Oh," he said,
"a friend of Mynheer Philips? Then everything is all right,"
and between us we helped the Concord sage set foot on Veere
soil.

"An uncommonly kind citizen," he observed. "I am sorry I
couldn't reward him. But I got lost while coming here. I am

afraid I was always rather vague about such things as finding my way, but invariably there was always someone to help me out, for that seems to be the way our world is run."

Here was an example of that "fatalistic optimism" of which I spoke a moment ago and which was so characteristic of many of Emerson's contemporaries. I would have loved to go a little deeper into the subject, but for the moment I was chiefly interested in finding out how, in the name of a merciful heaven, he had ever found his way to Noord Beveland, which is such a lonely place and so completely cut off from the mainland that it is much easier to travel from Amsterdam to Paris or London than from Amsterdam to this island.

Several times during the rest of the evening I did my best to return to this mystery and get at least some vague idea of where he had been before he got to Noord Beveland, but his answers were always so hopelessly vague that to this day the problem remains as much of a puzzle to me as it was that night. He tried very hard to remember the names of a few places he thought he had visited during the afternoon, but he must have been thinking of something else when he passed through them and, being hopelessly unmusical, he had a bad ear for unfamiliar sounds. We thought we caught the name of Bergen-op-Zoom, but as that town was about thirty-five miles away from us and was situated way inland, that did not help us very much. So in the end we dropped our inquiries. Our guest had reached his destination, and that was all that mattered.

It was now well past seven o'clock, and I hastened with our two guests to Frits' door. The meal seemed to have been well chosen, except that Emerson mistook our Bordeaux for a cheap Italian wine which he said he remembered from his last visit to the Continent, a remark that made Descartes shudder and ask for another glass.

As for the conversation, that too was not quite what we had expected. Here we had two of the rarest brains of all times brought together underneath one single roof, but somehow or

other the talk refused to get started, and even Erasmus seemed at a loss how to bring a little life into the somewhat dreary intercourse.

The music, too, failed to unloosen our guests. Descartes made bread pills and drew imaginary lines on the tablecloth with his butter knife, while Emerson told us that something in Gombert's *In festis beatae Mariae Virginis* reminded him of a hymn he had sung as a child in Boston. We therefore sent word to Hein Verlinde to turn off the phonograph, and at the same time I asked Hein to go to my home and ask Jimmie to give him the original editions of the *Principia philosophiae,* the *Discourse on Method,* and the *Passions de l'homme,* all of which I happened to have.

Hein returned in less than ten minutes, and then a miracle happened. Descartes, placing his hands tenderly on those old parchment bindings, became a man transformed. *"Mes enfants!"* he exclaimed, "my own dearly beloved children!" and I expected that he would kiss his paper offspring. But ere he could do this, Emerson too arose from the lethargy that had held him in its clutches all during the evening.

"Of course! Now I understand," he said with more emotion than I had thought him capable of. "Now at last I understand! I knew Dr. Erasmus the moment I set eyes upon him, but I had not quite caught the other gentleman's name. I am rather deaf and I am very bad at catching names, but now I understand. It is the famous philosopher, René Descartes!"

Blessed be the great of heart, for they are like children in their vanities. Descartes had spent all his days trying to avoid coming in contact with his fellow men, but he had felt deeply hurt that a fellow guest had been ignorant of his identity. Now the ice was broken, and, after that, everything was easy, and during the rest of the evening the two men behaved like old friends.

Emerson confessed that mathematics had always been a closed book to him, and Descartes replied that an intelligent man should be ashamed of such a remark. "There is nothing quite as

simple in all the world," he toid Emerson. "Just let me show you," and he went (just as an example of how really simple they were) into a discussion of co-ordinates, using our beautiful table-cloth as his blackboard, to the great horror of the good Jo, who whispered to me that his pencil marks would never wash out and that it would be a complete loss. To which Erasmus, who overheard her, made reply that she would be able to sell that tablecloth to a museum for almost any price. Whereupon she felt better and went back to her kitchen to prepare the dessert.

And then—I have no idea how—the subject came up of the law of probability, and this in turn led up to a discussion of the game of chess.

"Chess?" Descartes said. "I used to play it, but that was a long time ago."

"So did I," Emerson answered. "I learned it as a child. My aunt taught me. But I never was very good at it. I played it as badly at seventy as I did at seventeen."

"Monsieur is too modest," Descartes answered in his best French style. "But I will tell him what we will do. As soon as this excellent repast shall have come to an end—and the chef of His Majesty's household could not have done better than your honored *cuisinière*—we must have a game of chess just for old times' sake."

This was agreed upon. We happened to have two boards, and while Descartes played Emerson, Frits played me. Erasmus begged to be excused. Chess had not been played in the monastery where he had spent his youth, and afterward, so he had always felt, he had been too old to take it up seriously.

May the blessed souls of Morphy and Steinitz never learn what happened that evening after the dishes had been removed in Frits' little house in Veere. Never, I think, since the old Persian shah bestowed his incomparable game upon the world at large, has there been a tournament betraying so little natural ability on the part of all the participants. Neither Frits nor I was much better than a third-rate player. We had always played chess for the fun of it, and one might as well try to become a

violin virtuoso for the fun of it as a chess champion. We were, however, so much better than our famous guests that, when the time came to change partners (Emerson had been forced into an ignominious mate by Descartes), we were almost ashamed of ourselves when we had to take them on as our opponents. It was just like playing with a couple of not overbright children. Indeed, I was only prevented from giving Descartes fool's mate by a sense of humility. After all, I could not very well go through life remembering that I had beaten the greatest of all mathematicians in three moves, and so, just before the fatal move of my queen, I hastily changed my tactics. In this way I managed to prolong the game for another thirty moves before Descartes exclaimed, "Monsieur is much too good for me. I had better take on Monsieur Emerson once more. I may then have another chance of winning."

However, as both our guests seemed to enjoy themselves thoroughly, we did not think that it was up to us to interfere with their innocent pleasure, and so almost a whole hour went by before Frits, remembering that we still had a bottle of Tokay left in the cellar, suggested that we come up for air and spend the rest of the evening talking.

The short space of time that then followed made up for the disappointments we had experienced during the first part of our meal. For now, at last, both Descartes and Emerson were able to let themselves go. They not merely talked. They seemed to be striking sparks.

And what did they talk about?

Erasmus had given them their lead: what would our world be like if we allowed free rein to human intelligence in our warfare upon the unknown forces of nature?

Both our guests were in their true element, and I did not wonder that the University of Paris and the learned divines of Yale (the great stronghold of orthodoxy in the America of the first half of the last century) had been so profoundly upset by the teachings of these two men. For if the broad and tolerant ideas of these faithful searchers after the truth, arrived at by

294

personal observation, should ever be allowed to prevail, the whole fabric of our present society, which alone makes the continued existence of a class of official guardians of the "revealed truth" possible, would come to an end. It would collapse like an old and outworn edifice struck by a storm of enlightenment.

Shortly before midnight, the now familiar sputtering of the candles began. It was the well-known sign of departure. At the last stroke of the hour, the light went out, and our guests had disappeared.

When Jo brought us a lamp from her kitchen, we found an old-fashioned golden ducat on the table. By its side was a slip of paper on which a hasty hand had scrawled, "This is for the wonderful *cuisinière,* who this evening contributed so greatly to the happiness of her very obedient servant, R. D."

The greatest mathematician and the worst game of chess.

CHAPTER VIII

In Order Not to Be Too One-Sided, We Plan to Invite Two Members of the Feminine Sex, and the EMPRESS THEODORA OF BYZANTIUM and QUEEN ELIZABETH OF ENGLAND Make Their Appearance

SO FAR we had invited only men, and Jimmie and Lucie were becoming more and more insistent that we pay some attention to their own sex. "When are the ladies going to appear?" Jimmie used to ask us every Sunday. Not because she was much of a feminist. On the contrary, from the very beginning she had insisted that there were not enough women in history who came sufficiently up to our specifications to provide entertainment for even one single evening. This we had always stoutly denied (more out of politeness than out of conviction), but as Lucie had invariably taken Jimmie's side, we had never got very far.

That Lucie and Jimmie—both of whom were such strong personalities that the average male looked pathetic compared to either of them—that they should be so hard on their own sex had always surprised us, or at least we had pretended that it had done so. Way down deep in our hearts, we knew that they were right. Lucie—as great an artist in her own right as anybody in the land—maintained that women hated going in for public life, that a woman in an office was an anomaly, something like the proverbial trained seal (wonderful that a seal could play a trombone at all, but why should it?), and therefore out of her ele-

ment and necessarily unhappy. Jimmie, whose precise mathematical brain would have let her run (and successfully, too) any public accountant's office, was even harder on her sisters. "I used to work for a living," she often said, "and I hated it, except that it gave me the independence I loved. But men have made enough of a mess of this world without us women making it still worse."

"Then," we inquired, "what should the dear creatures do?"

"What they have always done and what they can do best."

"And that is?"

"Have children, manage their households, and run their families. That is enough of a job to keep any woman busy all the time."

"But how about our American women who live in flats and have no households to run because their households run themselves?" I realized that I was being hopelessly commonplace, but any port in a storm.

Lucie was not in the least baffled. "Those are mere superficial details," she said. "I don't want them to go back to the Middle Ages and be household slaveys. I was talking about the important things in life. I am no longer so young. I have not had an easy life, but a terribly interesting one. I have tried it from all angles and have come to the conclusion that your average woman in public life is a nuisance to herself and to all the others with whom she has to work. I know that many of them are much brighter than the men who are holding the same kinds of jobs, but that is not the point. We were talking about their efforts to achieve happiness by trying to run the world at large instead of their own families. Maybe they can do it in America. Maybe you've got a different breed of female over there, but I doubt it. Now look at . . ."

"Lunch is ready," Kaatje said just then, poking her nose into the door with the air of a frightened little mouse.

"Go ahead," I called after the others. "Just a moment, and I will be there. I think I've got something."

And I did have something, as the others agreed after I had

read them the names of my candidates—the Empress Theodora of Byzantium and Queen Bess of England.

"That should make for a very interesting evening," Lucie said. "One of the two ladies, if I am not mistaken, started life in a rather humble position, and the other was the daughter of that dear King Henry of England—the one with all the wives. They must have a lot in common."

"Yes," Jimmie added. "Any girl with that kind of father must have known a thing or two."

"And both of the dear ladies were in politics," Frits said. "We can now find out whether Lucie is right when she says that women are no good in public life."

"That depends upon what you mean by public," I suggested.

"Keep it clean, pleeese!" Jimmie asked me. "You know perfectly well what I meant, and no need referring to the Empress' earliest profession."

"Noodle has run away," said Francine, the cook, coming in from the garden.

And so we never found out what Lucie meant, for when Noodle ran away, the universe ceased to function until he had been found again. However, he was soon found and at the usual place—the village butcher's garbage can.

After lunch I spent a few minutes on our next meal. Our two prospective guests had lived ten centuries apart. It would therefore be rather difficult to give them something that would appeal equally to both their tastes. But if we served them lamb (about the hardest thing to get in Holland, where the people won't eat it), we could prepare it in two different ways. I suggested this the next morning to Jo Verlinde, but she said, "Don't give it another thought. I'll fix something they both will like."

"Remember, they're ladies from the days before forks."

"From what I've seen of some of your other friends, they managed just about as well," said the excellent Jo, who, as the keeper of a boardinghouse, had her own ideas about the table manners of most foreigners.

Our village arising from the morning mists.

"I know, but no fancy gravies, if you please," Frits begged of her. "Their fingers get sticky, and they wipe them on the table-cloth and on the curtains and chairs, and after they get through dribbling the sauce all over themselves they spill it on the floor."

"Their palaces must have looked like pigsties," Jo observed. "We had a couple of Greeks once at our boardinghouse. The man was Greek and the woman was Italian. They stayed three days. I had to have their room repapered after they left."

"Yes, and now we'll have a Greek of our own here next week, and what do you mean to give them that you think they will both like?"

"Stew," said Jo. "They can eat that with a spoon if I make it pretty thin. Otherwise, they might use their fingers for the larger pieces. I even noticed that famous English writer—the one with the big forehead and the skinny legs—he was pretty good too when it came to eating with his . . ."

"That will do, Mrs. Verlinde," I said. "He was a great man and—please remember that even in the case of William Shake-speare fingers were made before forks."

"But I'm the one who's got to clean up the mess afterward."

"All right then, have your stew, and what will you put into it? Plain lamb stew is not very interesting."

"Garlic for the Greek."

I shuddered. "Don't worry," said Jo. "Your nose will warn you which is the dish with the garlic. And in the other, I will put some mint. I hear that they like mint over in England. We were there once for three days, in a little town on the coast. Then we got so hungry we came right back."

And that is the way it was decided. It did not promise to be very much of a meal, but what we knew about Byzantine cook-ing in the sixth century indicated a purely Levantine kind of kitchen, and that kitchen has not changed very much during the last fourteen hundred years. We could give the ladies some corn bread to dip into their goulash and then eat it in the good old medieval fashion, when the bread had also served as a plate.

301

"Will you want anything else?" Jo asked.

"Yes," I said, "lots of cabbage."

"The stuff smells the house up something terrible!"

"I know it, but they had so few other vegetables. They will be accustomed to their daily cabbage. What would you suggest?"

"A salad."

"Neither of them ever saw a leaf of salad as long as she lived."

"We can't always have beans."

"No, we can't. They are getting pretty tiresome. Think of something else."

"Potatoes?"

"Were not invented until years later, and when they did come to Europe, the people would not touch them. They used to eat the leaves (which made them sick) and threw the rest away."

"How about peas?"

"No, but that gives me an idea. We will feed them the pods. They will like those better, anyway, than the peas, and you can mix them up in your stew."

"And then afterward," Frits said, "let us do something funny. Let us give them ice cream."

"A lovely idea—and not warn them what it is!"

"They probably would eat that too with their fingers," Jo once more put in.

"They will drop it soon enough," Frits consoled her, and so we left it at that. A nice, garlicky stew with something civilized on the side for Erasmus, Frits, and me, and ice cream as a surprise and novelty for our guests. As for beverages, Elizabeth would probably prefer beer (the sourest beer we could get) and any kind of Greek wine the ship chandler in Flushing could get us, mixed with rosin, for the benefit of the Empress.

The musical part of the evening, too, was going to be very complicated, for Theodora's music would be Greek to Elizabeth, and Elizabeth's music would mean absolutely nothing to Theodora, because she would have been accustomed to an en-

tirely different scale. If we could only find some early Greek music! But we tried very hard, and nothing turned up that was any good. There were records which called themselves "Delphic hymns" and which claimed to be the real thing, but they had been reconstructed from very doubtful originals (after all, what do we know about Greek musical notation? Nothing!), and I refused to buy them but ordered quite a number of Gregorian chants. I asked for the oldest ones they had, some of which, curiously enough, were on records sung by the seminary choirs of Montreal. For good measure, I also bought a pilgrims' song called *Congaudeant catholici,* which was said to go back all the way to the twelfth century, and a so-called "double organum" on the Georgian chant *Haec dies.*

The musical program for Her Majesty of England was much easier. We needed only to repeat the madrigals and motets of William Byrd and Thomas Morley and John Dowland, and she would be quite happy. She had always loved the theater. She had even acted in some of the masques given at her own court, and she would undoubtedly recognize several of the tunes.

As a special compliment to the lady, who was said not to be lacking in vanity, I sent for John Wilbye's *Lady, When I Behold* and his *Adieu, Sweet Amaryllis.* And so the stage was set for our first ladies' evening. Frits went back to Amsterdam on the late train on Sunday, and I tried to refresh my memory on the subject of that most mysterious of all early medieval rulers, the Empress Theodora, wife of the Emperor Justinian I.

And now I shall have to try something that is far from easy—I shall do my best to paint you a picture of that world of the first half of the sixth century—the world into which Theodora was born.

The Roman Empire of the Caesars no longer existed. The city of Rome, conquered and plundered half a dozen times, lay in ruins. Somewhere among those ruins lived the local bishop, who was gradually beginning to lay claim to the headship of the whole of Christendom. His arguments were plausible. Accord-

ing to tradition, he was a successor of that well-beloved apostle who had been pointed out by Jesus as the stone on which he intended to build his Church on earth.

According to that same tradition (a tradition probably based upon fact) Peter had actually gone to Rome and had there been executed, and his body had been deposited there in stately loneliness in a small wooden structure consecrated to his memory—the old church of St. Peter. And furthermore, although Rome was no longer but a shadow of its former self, it was still surrounded by a nimbus of glory. The name was synonymous with dignity and power, and such a reputation, once established, can never be entirely extinguished.

Quite natural, therefore, that the Bishop of Rome did not feel that he was like the other bishops. If the Church meant to survive, there must be one head, one man whose word counted for more than that of all the others. And the Bishop of Rome was indeed the logical candidate for that high office.

It was only human that the Bishop of Byzantium did not share this view. It was true that Constantinople, in the minds of many people, was a new and upstart city, compared to Rome, but it now happened to be the residence of the only person who represented authority in the old Roman sense of the word—and that point was greatly in its favor.

As a result of these conflicting ambitions, there arose a long period of strife between these two mighty bishops. Occasionally the Bishop of Jerusalem also put in a claim to supremacy, for he lived in the city in which the Lord had lived and died and he felt, therefore, that he was a little closer to those events out of which the Church itself had been born. And then there were dozens of other bishops, in France and in Spain and Syria, who resented the claims of supremacy of their Roman colleague, but this was the era of the great migrations, and their territories had been so thoroughly plundered by successive hordes of barbarians that their part of the world hardly counted.

As for Britain, nothing much remained of it but a name and a vague recollection of a pleasant and prosperous island which

for almost four hundred years had been an ideal place for Roman officials and officers in which to settle down after they had retired from active service and were ready to enjoy their pensions. And finally there was Africa, but the desert which now stretched for a thousand miles along the southern coast of the Mediterranean was something very different from what it had been in the days of Augustus and Tiberius. Then it had supported millions of people for whom there was no longer any room on the continent of Europe. Now the jackal howled his doleful song amid the ruins of old country houses, and pillar saints were scratching themselves on the roofs of temples long since fallen into decay. Indeed, wherever one looked it was a sad picture of downfall and neglect, but there is one thing we ought to keep well in mind. To the people of the fifth and sixth centuries of our era, the tragedy was not half as real as it is to us who look at all these events from a great distance.

When your Aunt Emily is run over by a truck and killed on the spot, it is a matter of profound grief to all concerned. When, on the other hand, the dear lady takes thirty years in which to die and when during these thirty years you have asked her nurse at least once a week, "And how is dear Tante doing today? Not so well, I suppose," and when for thirty years the nurse, who has waxed comfortably stout on the job, has assured you, "The dear soul! No, she is far from well but she is holding up bravely," you will in the end have grown so familiar with the old lady's unfortunate state of health that you no longer care about the outcome either one way or the other.

Should she ever really die (which you have begun to doubt), then it will be necessary to bury her and put a slab of something on her grave, for that is the decent thing to do, after which you can conveniently forget about her because she has long ceased to be a true object of pity to anyone. And the same holds good for any human being or human institution that has outlived its own usefulness. It has degenerated into an expense and has become a bore.

The Roman Empire, like Aunt Emily, had taken an outrage-

ously long time a-dying. That is why so few people realized what was happening. When one fine day news reached them that the Emperor intended to leave his palace on the Palatine and move across Italy to Ravenna, where he would be much safer because the surrounding marshes were guaranteed to kill anyone who undertook to lay siege to the city, the Romans shrugged their shoulders and said yes, and so what? For by then they had heard that story too often to believe it, and even after they had been forced to take it seriously and realized that their emperor was actually gone, it still failed to impress them, for they knew perfectly well that there was nothing they could do about it.

And here I touch upon a very interesting chapter in history. Has there ever been an empire, large or small, white or colored, on the decline, running downhill, slowly but steadily and century after century, but downhill all the time, that could possibly have saved itself by its own efforts? The answer, I grieve to say, is no. Empires are like families—I almost feel inclined to say they are like individuals. Once they are on the downward grade, there is apparently nothing that can avert their final doom.

This is not a popular view of the situation. Ever since printing became as cheap as it has been these last five decades, amateur and professional historians have tried to prove that the Roman Empire might still be in existence if only the poor, misguided Romans had had sense enough to fill up the marshes of the Campagna (the malaria theory of Rome's decay), or if her professors of economics had been able to convince the people of the fallacy of the prevailing theory about wastelands (the old story of the neglected farm and the boys and girls rushing toward the fleshpots of the near-by city), or if only the magistrates had been a little more severe with the early Christians (read Bolsheviks), with their absurd ideas about share and share alike and their refusal to carry arms, and if only Rome had followed a different immigration policy. And so on and so forth through the entire list of plausible postfactual ifs.

I disagree. Even if the Roman emperors had been wise enough to foresee everything that was going to happen and had had the power to bring about the necessary reforms, even then Rome would have gone to perdition. Its very inability to change from what it was into something else was in a way proof of its strength and grandeur. Rome meant to be as it was, or it intended not to be at all.

And what did the contemporaries of this glorious tragedy make of it? As I already told you, the average man, busy with his daily chores, went on living as placidly as before, unless some definite catastrophe, like the sack of Rome by the Vandals or the conquest of Constantinople by the Turks, brought it to his immediate attention. For the rest of the time he was as unconscious of it as we ourselves are of the fact that right under our own noses our own civilization is rapidly coming to an end.

Suppose, my dear Frits, that you had taken the lovely Byzantine Theodora out for dinner (which at one time of her career you could have done for the price of a meal and a little present: "Oh, darling, you will give me a little present, won't you?") and had asked her whether she did not think the world was in a dreadful mess—what with Rome gone and revolution rampant in every part of the empire and no respect any longer from anybody for anything—I am quite sure that she would not have had a very distinct idea of what you were talking about. The world around her was the only one she had ever known or expected to know, and there could be nothing wrong with a society in which the daughter of a man who had fed the bears in the circus and had kept their cages clean—a girl who had started with nothing but her good looks and her hard common sense— could work her way up from the streets of Constantinople to a bedroom in the imperial palace. Surely a world in which all that was possible could not be called a bad one. A crazy sort of place, perhaps, but had it ever been otherwise and had not all the great philosophers of antiquity taught that life was as meaningless as a cork bobbing up and down on the waves of

the sea, as aimless as a kite that has lost its string, as senseless as the death of a child struck by a bolt of lightning?

Of course, you must not tell anyone else that she had mentioned the old philosophers, for they were no longer allowed to teach their doctrines, and people were no longer allowed to read their books, and it had now become clear why there was so much wickedness and unhappiness in this vale of tears. She had learned this from the so-called "new men"—those wandering preachers who told the story of a Jewish Messiah Who had been the Son of the true God, Who like a common slave had suffered death on the cross but Who had arisen from the grave and had ascended toward heaven, where He now sat in full splendor on a throne next to that of His Father. Their new prophets disapproved of everything the old philosophers had taught, and their sermons had convinced her and all other good subjects of the Emperor that theirs was the right approach to salvation and that the Greek sages had been all wrong when they maintained that this life was the beginning and end of all things.

Not at all! Our present existence did not really count. It was like one of those dark anterooms in the imperial palace where poor petitioners were obliged to spend days and sometimes years before they were finally allowed to enter into the presence of the All-Highest. But when that glorious moment came, they would be richly compensated for their long wait in that gloomy place. For then they would behold the great King himself, seated upon a golden throne, a throne which had been so cleverly constructed that it seemed to make the basileus ten times bigger than he really was.

On both sides, in magnificent garments of purple brocade, richly embroidered with pearls and other precious stones, stood His Majesty's counselors, his ministers, his spiritual and military advisers, and his ordinary men-at-arms. They did not move, having for years trained themselves in the difficult art of maintaining a complete rigidity for hours at a time. And there they stood to bear witness to the power and the strength and the glory of their imperial master, world without end, amen.

And the poor supplicants would thereupon kneel down that they might hear their sentence or receive their reward according to circumstances, and after that dreadful moment of suspense, their eyes aching from having beheld so great a majesty, they would slowly slink out of that terrifying presence to surrender themselves meekly unto the palace guards who had been waiting for them outside and who would either clothe them in the splendid raiment of high office or would cast them into dark dungeons where they must contemplate their sins until the end of time.

And your beautiful Byzantine companion would have assured you that this was a much better arrangement than the old one, which, it is true, offered far-greater opportunities for enjoyment during a few short years on earth but which took it for granted that thereupon your life would be snuffed out like a candle. For now a new something had been added to the tragedy of existence. Hope had come into the lives of all people. No matter how terrible your fate had been on this earth, whether you had spent all your days in a dark mine without a glimpse of the sun, whether you had been chained for thirty years to the oar of an imperial galley, whether with blinded eyes you had been made to pull a stone in a grain mill, you now had been given assurance that the hour would come when an all-wise and all-merciful God would call for the documents in the case, would study them carefully, and would then do justice, regardless of the high-priced lawyers who had been hired to present the arguments brought forward by your persecutors and tormentors.

The former dancing girl was entirely right. Shortly before she had been born, a great change had come over the world of the Mediterranean. Remember that during the last centuries of imperial Roman rule, half the people had been slaves. Of the other half, ninety per cent had been paupers, while the remaining ten per cent had been much too rich. Under such circumstances, there had been little chance of justice for the average man. At all times he had been at the mercy of those who had command of the sword or whose gold could find its way

into the pockets of the magistrates. He could be sent to the gallows or the rack on the perjured testimony of a corrupt witness, for he had no way to defend himself. He could be deprived of his home, of his wife and children, to pay for a debt he had never contracted. But before this new tribunal, situated in the heart of the kingdom of heaven, all people were equal. Neither rank nor caste was there accepted as sufficient grounds for "preferential treatment." There the soul stood, naked before its Creator. There, with anxious eyes, the poor sinner watched while the golden scales were made ready to weigh his fate.

Into one of those scales the recording angel, who acted as general secretary, would pour the sum total of one's sins. Into the other would go the accumulation of such good deeds and tender thoughts as one had bestowed upon one's fellow men. Then the room would grow very silent, for not even the breath of a small child must disturb the pendulum in its search after the right balance. It was then, just before their fate was to be announced, that the most ruthless of conquerors, the mightiest of princes, the craftiest of women, were known to have blenched with fear, for at last they were forced to realize that this was a universe based upon moral law, in which nothing was left to either chance or accident and which was ruled by but a single question, asked of both master and slave: "Hast thou been truly faithful to My commands?"

All this was not just a pretty fable to the people of Byzantium of the sixth century of our era. To them it was truth, and heaven and hell were actual facts, as visible and tangible as the mountains on the other side of the Bosporus. And it was against such a background of stark realities, both in this world and the other, that Theodora, the daughter of Acasius, keeper of the bear pits in the municipal circus, rose from the streets of Constantinople until she had reached the golden steps that led directly—so she hoped—to the throne of God.

But please do not try to re-evaluate this strange personage in terms of her modern equivalent of the woman with a mission. She was nothing of the sort. This tiny creature with the big

black eyes was as hard as rock. She did not know the meaning of the word "scruple." She may have had a conscience, but she never allowed it to interfere with anything she really wanted to do. Her strength lay in the fact that she was possessed of a body that men wanted and wanted more than anything else in this world. She used her physical attractions, as saints have used their spiritual holiness, to achieve the apparently impossible, and, fortunately for the people of Byzantium, that lovely body had been equipped with a brain as sharp and as relentless as a surgeon's scalpel. A little Byzantine girl, thus equipped, could go very far. Theodora did.

We do not know when the future Empress was born, and most of our information about her life and adventures comes from highly doubtful sources. It goes without saying that she had many enemies. There were, in the first place, the ladies of the court, who had been obliged to watch her rapidly increasing influence upon the Emperor Justinian and who probably never tired of asking each other, "What has she got that we haven't got?"

And then there were the palace eunuchs, for Constantinople has always been much more of an Asiatic city than a European one, and the official world was heavily dominated by the *castrati.* Such unfortunate folk are apt to be rather malicious (and who can blame them?) and especially in matters of sex are not to be trusted as impartial witnesses. Once she had married the Emperor, Theodora was forever surrounded by eunuchs (servants, soldiers, even an occasional general), and her reputation suffered accordingly. And finally there was one man (though not a eunuch) who, for reasons unknown to us, bore a deep hatred toward his imperial mistress, and it is, of course, his words that have survived instead of those of his less bitterly prejudiced colleagues.

His name was Procopius, and, as a high Byzantine official under Justinian, he had direct access to all the local scandals of his day. What actual grievance he had against the lady and why he should have been quite so vindictive whenever he mentioned

her name, we have never been able to find out, and nowadays there are those who have rather taken him under their protection and who insist that he was better than his reputation and worthy of our close attention. I have never been convinced by their arguments. I still see in Procopius a past master at innuendo and insinuation, who must have had some private ax to grind and who ground it with such enthusiasm that very little he tells us about the Empress is to be accepted at its face value, but has to be weighed and considered and reconsidered with the utmost care and even then should not be believed too wholeheartedly. Unfortunately, his work is the most complete and detailed account of the lady's life, and we have to consult him whether we like it or not.

Here are a few of the incidents with which I think you should be familiar before you offer your hospitality to the Byzantine Empress next Saturday. The real truth you will probably learn from her eyes.

According to rumor, Theodora was about twenty years younger than her husband. She therefore must have been born some time early in the sixth century. The place of her birth is not known. It may have been Constantinople and it may have been the island of Cyprus, but the Byzantine Empire was as cosmopolitan as the United States of America today, and people rarely inquired into the geographical and racial antecedents of their neighbors. Had they done so, they would have discovered that their Emperor did not have a drop of Roman or Greek blood in his veins, having been born in what is now Yugoslavia and having at a tender age been brought to Constantinople by his uncle, Justin I, an illiterate peasant from somewhere in Asia Minor.

This noble sovereign had, like most of his predecessors, reached the throne as commander of the palace guards of the Emperor Anastasius, who in turn had reached the throne because he had married Ariadne, the widow of the Emperor Zeno, who in turn had reached the throne because he had married

the above-mentioned Princess Ariadne when she was still the maiden daughter of the Emperor Leo I, who, although a Thracian peasant, had come to the throne by the will of his soldiers, thereby succeeding the Emperor Marcian, who had come to the throne by marrying the sister and successor of the Emperor Theodosius II, and so on and so forth.

If from the above you come to the conclusion that the home life of the Byzantine rulers was not quite as peaceful or as beautiful as that of dear Queen Victoria and her amiable and accomplished husband at a somewhat later date in history, you will have guessed right and you will probably agree with me that any young woman who undertook to associate herself with what we might call "the palace set" did so at her own risk. Theodora must have realized this very clearly but, having been brought up amidst her father's bears, she felt that she could face any situation that would present itself. With her beautiful black eyes wide open, she was willing to incur the risk of some small possible mishap (such as being sewed up in a basket and thrown into the Bosporus) as long as there was a chance—no matter how small—that she might some day occupy the imperial throne.

She was too much of a daughter of the people not to know that luck is ninety per cent of everything you ever get in this world, but what of it? She had done pretty well for herself thus far and saw no reason why good fortune should cease to smile on her. The days were long since gone when, in order to keep body and soul together, she had been obliged to take a job as a chorus girl in the ballets at the hippodrome. There a rich Byzantine official had noticed her and, as he was about to be sent as governor to a very dull province somewhere in northern Africa, he had decided that this lovely child would be the best way of keeping himself amused during the years of his lonely exile.

The improper arrangements were promptly made, and Theodora sailed across the Mediterranean and settled down as the governor's lady in Pentapolis.

Then as now, a town in the Libyan desert was not exactly the

sort of place that would appeal to a young lady of fashion, and Theodora, tiring very soon of both her lover and her new place of residence, escaped to Alexandria. There she hoped to find more and livelier entertainment, but her expectations came true in a way that cannot have been entirely agreeable, for she gave birth to a son while still in a state of unmarried felicity.

We know about the existence of this child by indirect evidence. Shortly after Theodora had come to the throne, a young man suddenly appeared from somewhere in "Arabia"—then almost as vague a term as "Africa" is today, for it might mean any place south of the Mediterranean and east of the Indian Ocean. This bright lad was rash enough to call the Empress "mamma" and to insist upon some kind of recognition, either in affection or cash or political preferment. After which he disappeared from the scene as suddenly as he had arrived and as thoroughly as if he had never existed.

This story has been dismissed as another spiteful bit of scandal heaved at Her Majesty by the notorious Procopius. It fits, however, most admirably into the more authentic facts connected with Theodora's career, both before and after she had become a respectable woman. She was as vengeful as any heroine out of the Norse sagas and was possessed of an elephantine memory when it came to any slight she had suffered at any time of her career. She did not live long enough to catch up with all her enemies, but those she could reach paid a terrible price for their carelessness in allowing themselves to be caught within the jurisdiction of the imperial household's detectives.

Her husband, a greatly superior type to her in this respect (though in few others), rarely could bring himself to the point where he destroyed those who had tried to do him harm. His lovely wife rather despised him for this, which she regarded as the sign of a weak character. But realizing that after all he was the boss, she did her murdering on the quiet and was then very much surprised that dear so-and-so had been found in his own garden with his throat sliced from ear to ear or that the body of one of her dearest ladies in waiting had just been fished out

of the Golden Horn. And the Emperor seems to have been so completely lost in his infatuation that he asked no embarrassing questions. For she possessed him as entirely as any female has ever possessed her male, and after her death he never married again, nor, as far as we know, did he ever look at another woman. And this was the same Justinian who will ever be remembered as the great lawgiver of the Eastern Roman Empire and in some ways as one of the most outstanding figures of the first ten centuries of the Middle Ages. In the common language of today, the little lady must have had what it takes!

As for the match between the Emperor and his chorus-girl bride, it had been accompanied by a number of difficulties. The family of his uncle, to whom Justinian owed his claim to the throne, had not exactly shouted with joy when they heard the news. His aunt, the Empress Euphemia, a sort of Byzantine version of Queen Victoria, had been horrified at the idea of getting this sort of person in the family and, mustering the help of the high ecclesiastics at court, had hastened to revive an almost forgotten law which forbade a Byzantine ruler from marrying anyone who had ever in any way been connected with the stage. Fortunately for the loving couple, the old lady died soon after her nephew had announced his engagement. That left only Uncle Justin to deal with, and Uncle Justin was by no means as particular as his wife had been. Besides, his future niece was an uncommonly handsome girl, and when she looked at the old gentleman with those great big black eyes of hers, he probably would have given her his capital city had she asked him for it.

After that, things took their normal course. The high ecclesiastical dignitaries did what high ecclesiastical dignitaries usually do if sufficient pressure is brought to bear upon them from the right quarters. The senators (for outwardly Byzantium continued the original form of government of the Roman Empire) were also able to take a hint. So did the imperial advisers. The law forbidding the marriage between Byzantine emperors

and ladies of the stage was duly repealed, and Justinian and Theodora were married and lived happily together for almost a quarter of a century.

This was an extraordinary record when we remember that those two imperial lovers were completely different in character and invariably disagreed upon questions of foreign or domestic policy. History, however, has been very lenient in dealing with the lady from a political point of view, and most modern writers seem to agree that, without her, Justinian never could have hoped to accomplish what he did.

Perhaps the Emperor's most outstanding characteristic was his strict devotion to duty and his ability to do lots of hard work. Finding that the laws of the Roman Empire had multiplied and increased at such a rate that not even the most learned of judges could find their way among these thousands and thousands of statutes and ordinances, Justinian set out to codify and classify them. In this he had the wholehearted support of his wife, but she did not at all approve of her husband's religious policies and, least of all, of his desire to extend the limits of his empire farther westward.

Theodora's own particular interest lay in the East. Her love of luxury, her gift for squandering large sums on jewelry, her insistence upon the pomp and circumstance of an Oriental court —all this indicates a Cypriote background rather than a Greek or Slavic one. So did the relentless cruelties with which she punished every act of rebellion against her, and so did the private spy system she organized and by means of which she was aware of everything that was being said about her, not only in the capital, but also in the provinces. Did such a report indicate the slightest possibility of danger to the imperial safety, then silent messengers would promptly sally forth from the white palace overlooking the Sea of Marmora. They would rapidly row to an unknown destination and, a few hours later, they would return as mysteriously as they had left, for that was the way Her Majesty liked to have things done.

Yet, with all that said and held against her, it must be stated

on Theodora's behalf that she never became the sort of monster into which women of her tastes and antecedents are so apt to develop. In matters of real importance she never allowed her feelings to run away with her common sense and gradually she became so valuable to Justinian that after he had made her his wife he also elevated her to the rank of coregent of the empire and made all officials take an oath of loyalty not merely to himself, but also to his Empress. And finally, in the case of unexpected difficulties, such as revolutions or mutinies, the Emperor's wife, though the most feminine of women, stood bravely by his side and fought as valiantly as any mere man.

For example, if it had not been for her, Justinian would hardly have survived the rebellion of the year 532. This was the so-called Nika insurrection which grew out of an athletic contest (the Byzantines took their games almost as seriously as we do) that had degenerated into a political free-for-all. Before it had been squelched, it had cost the lives of more than thirty thousand citizens. On this occasion the mob had tried to break into the imperial palace, and it was the Empress who had so quickly and energetically organized the few soldiers and guards who happened to be available that the attack on the imperial quarters was repulsed, and the dynasty was saved.

After that incident, Theodora seems to have become even more indispensable to her husband than before, and he let her do as she pleased. He had at last come to appreciate—what most of his subjects had understood long before—that this doll-like creature who happened to be his wife was of greater value for the defense of the realm than those supposedly impregnable walls that Theodosius II had erected during the middle of the fifth century so that the new capital of the Roman Empire should never suffer the same fate as the old one and be overrun by the barbarians.

I have sometimes felt that this extraordinary woman would be a most valuable asset to the congress of matriarchs who, these last few years, have played such a role in shaping the destinies of our fair republic. I am afraid, however, that we shall never

see the like of her on our side of the ocean. She would never get past the immigration authorities. Moral turpitude would keep her out.

From Florence a car will carry you, in a little over three hours and right across the Apennine Mountains, to the city of Ravenna. It is a dreary little city, and I advise you to make sure of your exit before you bid farewell to the indifferent spaghetti of the Grand Hotel Byron and set out for the most magnificent collection of mosaics to be found anywhere in this world.

Today Ravenna lies six miles away from the Adriatic, but two thousand years ago it was a lagoon city like Venice and, like Venice, it developed into a flourishing center of trade at a time when most of the rest of Italy was still a land of farms.

Under Augustus, Ravenna was elevated to the rank of a naval base, the headquarters of the Adriatic squadron, with a harbor large enough for two hundred and fifty ships. But the city did not really come into its own until the year 404, when the Roman Emperor Honorius, feeling that his old residence could no longer offer him sufficient safety, betook himself and his court to this strongly fortified Adriatic harbor, where the sea offered a means of escape when every other road should have been cut off.

Then occurred one of the most far-reaching events of the fifth century. In the year 476 the last of the Roman emperors of purely Roman blood, who bore the absurd name of Romulus Augustulus (both of them diminutives), was pushed off the throne by the commander of his foreign bodyguard, a Teutonic chieftain by the name of Odoacer. The new ruler felt so sorry for the poor, handsome, but incompetent young man that he spared his life and allowed him to spend the rest of his days at the villa that Lucullus, the well-known war profiteer and the most spectacular and the earliest of all gourmets, had built several hundred years before on the shore of the Bay of Naples. A few years later. Odoacer was in turn murdered by still another foreigner, by the name of Theodoric, head of the tribe of the

Ostrogoths but a baptized Christian and a barbarian with the advantages of an education in Constantinople.

Theodoric made Ravenna the capital of his own Ostrogoth empire and started a building boom which ended with the construction of his own grave, a most extraordinary piece of work, especially considering the time it was built, as the roof consists of a single slab of stone almost thirty-six feet in diameter. How did they ever get it up there, with their primitive tackles and pulleys? I am sorry but we don't know.

In the year 539, this Ostrogoth state was overthrown by the Byzantine general Belisarius. Ravenna then became the capital of all the western European possessions of the Eastern Roman Empire, and one of the most interesting cities of the early medieval world. For by this time there existed a definite Byzantine style in architecture as well as in most of the other arts. And just as we know more about Roman circuses and Roman public buildings from the remnants that are to be found in the provinces than in Rome itself, so we can learn more about Byzantine art in Ravenna and some of the other little cities along both sides of the Adriatic than in Constantinople, where the Crusaders and the Turks had so willingly co-operated in destroying everything that was beautiful.

Ravenna, therefore, is well worth a visit. Provided that one knows what to look for. In the evening, if one feels so inclined, one can listen to the grass growing in the streets. But few spots are so full of memories. Not the sort of memories that are so typical of our beloved Veere, where they are mixed with the healthy sound of mooing cows and grunting pigs and little boys and girls carrying pans of dough to the baker to be converted into bread. No, in Ravenna one is on every side surrounded by the recollection of beautiful things that are gone forever and never will come back. One can there watch Dante, a broken and desperate man, wearily spending his last years in this dull little provincial city, wandering in solitary meditation through the near-by pine groves, paying an occasional visit to his only surviving child, a daughter who had buried herself in a nunnery,

and carefully choosing the spot in the church of San Francesco where he wanted his grave to be dug.

Or one may come across the shade of Lord Byron, forever in search of some cause that will make him forget the hurt of his childhood days and this time listening to his last great love, the Countess Teresa Guiccioli, who has inspired him to devote his life and fortune to help her Italian fellow countrymen gain their freedom from the deeply hated Austrians. Nor should we forget the faithful Anita Garibaldi, who has accompanied her husband here on his campaign for the liberation of their fatherland and who is to die here of one of those marsh fevers which have been the curse of this region ever since the days when the Etruscans and Romans were fighting each other for the mastery of the Adriatic.

But the wise visitor, having had his fill of tobacco, Chianti, and romantic daydreams, will wait until toward dusk before he pays his visit to the church of San Vitale. For the mosaics inside are very, very old, and the colors have grown tired and need the light of the dying sun to come back to life.

San Vitale was begun by Theodoric and completed by Justinian. At the time of its construction it was considered such a magnificent and daring experiment within the realm of architecture that Charlemagne used it as the model for his own cathedral at Aix-la-Chapelle. From the outside it now strikes the modern spectator as being very much like just another small-town church, such as one might find in any of our better suburbs in the Middle West. But no one visits this structure to look at the bricks. The mosaics are the thing. They were put there while Ravenna was a metropolis and the capital of one of the Emperor Justinian's western provinces. That makes them almost fourteen hundred years old.

The art of mosaic making has almost completely died out, until today it takes its place with falconry and archery. A great many people even experience considerable difficulty in knowing what all these bits of colored glass may mean and complain that these portraits affect their eyes in the same way as Gregorian

music affects their ears—as something too stiff and too lacking in animation to appeal to their modern taste. Should you find yourself in the company of barbarians of that kind, bribe the sexton to take them away by a promise of showing them something really worth while—"dirty pictures of the old Roman days." Then sit yourself down in a quiet corner and pay your respects to Their Majesties.

On one side of the altar you will see the Emperor Justinian, surrounded by Saint Maximian, the Archbishop of Ravenna who consecrated this church in 547, and a few of his servants and bodyguards. The Emperor, as you will notice, has been provided with a halo, which was his good right as a successor to those rulers who during the beginning of their career had been closely identified with the sun-god and his shining orb. And on the left side of the choir niche you will see the woman he made his wife and with whom he shared his life and his throne.

The dancing girl of Constantinople's hippodrome, the courtesan of half a dozen cities in Africa and western Asia, also wears the attribute of power and sainthood. She stands in front of a small drinking fountain, probably placed there by the artist for the sake of balance, for on the left side of the picture there are no human figures. There is merely an indication of a dark gallery, apparently leading to the interior of the palace. It is screened off from the rest of the building by a curtain that one of the servants is in the act of pushing aside, indicating that Her Majesty is about to withdraw into her own apartments. A retinue of ladies in waiting fills the right side of the panel. A severe-looking duenna stands immediately behind the Empress, who carries a chalice in her delicate hands. Her sandaled feet protrude just the tiniest little bit from beneath her heavy ceremonial robe. She wears a crown and enough jewelry to ransom a dozen kings. But soon you will begin to be aware of only one impression. The picture will dissolve itself into a pair of eyes, the eyes of the Empress Theodora, and in them you may read that mysterious chapter of history which is called Woman.

She, to whom posterity affectionately refers as "good Queen Bess," was the unwanted offspring of Henry VIII and Anne Boleyn—unwanted because she should have been a boy and happened to be a girl. Indeed, the desire for a male heir to the throne was so great and so universal among the English people then that even today there are novelists who stoutly maintain that all of us are mistaken when we continue to prattle about a woman having laid the foundations of the British Empire. According to these learned and not-so-learned scholars, the midwife who saw the royal baby safely into the world had been paid handsomely for her part in one of the most colossal frauds of all times, and no one ever revealed the secret that Elizabeth had been really a boy.

No one at the time of Elizabeth's birth knew exactly when Henry had married his greatly desired Anne. This probably had happened in the latter part of January, 1533. But the marriage was not declared valid until May of the same year, and the child made its appearance the following September. Those who wished Anne Boleyn no good (which included the greater part of the English nation as well as most of her own relatives) had undoubtedly used this somewhat premature arrival of a child as a most welcome excuse to spread a little more scandal. But that does not explain why a girl should have been substituted for a boy, when it was known that both parents had ardently prayed for a son. It only makes the problem a little more difficult and, heaven knows, the life of bluff King Hal was complicated enough without this additional touch of mystery and mystification.

And now we come to a chapter in history in which I always lose my way. I refer to the matrimonial affairs of Henry VIII. I shall therefore open the good Dr. Ploetz at the right page of his trustworthy compendium and do my best to keep the record straight until I have our next week's guest safely on her throne, but I do not guarantee perfection even with this safeguard.

When Elizabeth was born there already existed a half sister, sixteen years older, issue of the marriage of Henry and Cather-

ine of Aragon, his first wife. While Elizabeth was in her cradle, her mother was beheaded for incest, as infidelity alone was not enough of a charge in the eyes of her outraged husband. At the same time, Anne's child was declared a bastard, which she may or may not have been. We don't know. It is very difficult after these many centuries to make sense of the subtle legal decisions that Henry was able to cajole out of his bishops and legal advisers while outside the judicial chamber Jack Ketch was idly handling his collection of swords and axes.

At the age of four, Elizabeth must have heard of the arrival of a baby half brother, Edward, Henry's son by his third wife, Jane Seymour, who, being luckier than her predecessors, died a natural death (of puerperal fever) when her child was twelve days old. After that there were no more little half brothers and sisters in Elizabeth's life, as was to have been expected with her kind of father. There were, however, three more stepmothers.

First of all (now let me carefully follow the record), there was Anne of Cleves, a plump, red-faced German princess who was supposed to bring the Defender of the Faith, now in open conflict with the Pope, the support of the Protestant rulers of Germany. She was so completely unlike the miniatures which the advocates of this match on the Continent had sent to Henry that he immediately sent her back whence she had come, for princesses, unlike department-store merchandise, can be returned after more than three days.

Next came Catherine Howard (No. 5). That was in 1540, when Elizabeth was seven years old, and two years later this new stepmother suffered the same fate as Anne Boleyn. She was decapitated for "immorality"—both before and after marrying the King. In her case the evidence seems to have been true enough. Catherine Howard apparently had had several lovers, one a cousin, another a musician, a third one—I am sorry, but I have forgotten what he did for a living. Why Henry had not looked into this matter a little more carefully before he married the lady we do not know, unless he had so greatly desired to

gain the support of the influential House of Howard that he had decided to leave bad enough alone. But shortly after the wedding had been celebrated, his faithful friend, Archbishop Cranmer, began to do a little investigating of his own. He started asking questions among the former servants of the new Queen and soon had got all the details he needed for his purpose by bribing a former parlormaid. With his news he hastened to the King, and His Majesty lost no time but acted with his usual energy, at least in matters affecting his matrimonial happiness.

One of his wife's former lovers was imprisoned and, having been very thoroughly tortured, confessed everything. The Queen, threatened with a similar fate, agreed that all this young man had revealed was true enough but swore that since she had been married to the King she had been a model of virtue.

It did not do her any good, for on February 13, 1542, she lost her head. Elizabeth was then nine years old.

A year later Henry married Catherine Parr (Ploetz listing No. 6), and in her the King at last met his match. The lady, who had already been married twice before, stood for no nonsense and, as a result, was one of the two of the six wives to survive her royal Bluebeard.

I like Catherine Parr. She was a woman who knew what she wanted and got it. Without waiting for Henry's funeral flowers to fade, she married her fourth husband, an adventurous gentleman by the name of Thomas Seymour, brother of the late and lamented Jane Seymour (Ploetz listing No. 3), the mother of Edward VI. Her married bliss (not so blissful if she had known that her handsome husband was making far from proper advances to her charming young stepdaughter, Elizabeth) lasted only a short while. But it gave Catherine an opportunity to finish her one and only literary achievement, a book entitled *The Lamentation, or Complaint of a Sinner.* I do not recommend it as bedside reading or any other kind of reading. It is very dull. However, it shows us Catherine Parr as a Christian lady who took her religious duties very seriously.

In other ways, too, this good woman gave evidence of her respect for the teachings of the Master. As soon as she had become the mistress of the royal household she made it a point to be kind and affectionate to the royal stepchildren, who, for almost the first time in their young lives, were treated like human beings. Mary was already too old and too set in her ways to be a favorable subject for further pedagogical experiments, but Elizabeth and Edward, the little King, were no longer treated like prisoners, were sent to Hatfield House, and were there educated by private tutors and given the freedom of the park and gardens.

True enough, Elizabeth was still officially a bastard, and if Mary, not in the best of health, and Edward, a weak and delicate boy, should not live very long, then Elizabeth, legitimate or not, was the only logical candidate for that vacancy.

Elizabeth was now fifteen years old. She was bright. She was not overly handsome but had a good figure and a quick wit. In addition to these virtues, she was as vain as a peacock and as haughty and overbearing as any Tudor. She therefore should have been quite contented with her new status, except perhaps for the slight inconvenience of having to be somewhat on her guard against the advances of the latest husband of her stepmother and benefactress, Catherine Parr.

This young gentleman was not thinking solely of amorous adventures when he paid court to his wife's deceased husband's young daughter. Amorous adventures would undoubtedly be very nice, but they came second. No, there was something else. Thomas Seymour had done a little figuring about the future, and this had given him an idea. Suppose his wife should die, suppose that Edward should die, suppose that Mary should die —then he only need marry Elizabeth to become King of England! It was as simple as that!

Had Thomas Seymour been a little more discreet, this nice little plan might have worked, but shortly after his wife's death, he got himself into very serious trouble. While at the head of England's navy, he had indulged in a bit of private privateer-

ing. Private plundering was no serious offense on the part of a commander in chief of a fleet in the latter half of the sixteenth century. But private privateering was in direct competition with the official privateering of the government. Then, as now, the English courts took a very serious view of such an act, and Thomas Seymour lost his head.

After his departure, Elizabeth was to enjoy a period of almost four years during which none of her friends or relatives came to a violent end and during which she was able to enjoy herself without that everlasting and uncomfortable question: "Who is going to be next?" Her amiable half brother, Edward, was on his throne. Her not-so-amiable half sister, Mary, was in her closet saying her prayers, and all seemed serene and quiet along the banks of the Thames. But underneath this outward appearance of "ye olde merrinesse," certain things were happening that were far from merry.

Sir Thomas Seymour, whom I dispatched a few sentences ago, had had a ward, an honest-to-goodness ward, not the kind you are so apt to see in the movies. Her name was Jane Grey. She had been a mere child, only nine, when she had been allowed to go and live with Catherine Parr. When Catherine died, she should have returned to her own parents, but she refused to go back to her happy home, and nothing could make her budge, an act for which we can hardly blame the poor child. From her earliest days on, her parents (her mother belonged to the royal family) had been brutally severe with her. Noticing their daughter's precocity, they had intended to turn her into the prodigy of the age and they had filled her innocent head with so much Latin, Greek, Arabic, Hebrew, and Chaldean that it was ready to burst. Going to the Parr home, where she had been allowed to be her own age, had been like going to paradise, and to make the visit to dear Aunt Catherine's even more wonderful, there was Aunt Catherine's husband, who had promised her that some day she would marry young King Edward and would be a real queen with a crown on her head. As both children were exactly eleven years old when this pleasant plan was made, little Lady

Jane would, of course, have to practice a little patience, but she could use that interval to learn a few more languages.

It was Edward who put an end to her dreams. He refused to improve in health, and it was beginning to look highly doubtful whether he would ever grow into manhood. And so Lady Jane, with the approval of Edward (who, when it came to the other sex, did not at all take after his royal father), was quietly married to the fourth son of the Duke of Northumberland, the man who was then the power behind the throne.

But now Jane discovered that she had only jumped from the frying pan into the fire. The Northumberlands were a bad lot. Jane soon came to hold them in a profound, if slightly adolescent, detestation. No. 1 of her hates against the tribe was her husband. She tried to find consolation in a renewed pursuit of the classics and of those Oriental languages in which she was then being coached by the stern but learned Dr. Aylmer, the famous antagonist of John Knox.

Alas, books of grammar proved to be but a bad substitute for a happy home life, and Lady Jane was taken sick with a serious illness from which (most unfortunately for herself) she recovered. For in the meantime, the Northumberland faction had been very busy. Sure of the support of the Protestants, who feared that if Mary, the daughter of Henry and Catherine of Aragon (Ploetz listing No. 1), should succeed Edward, the son of Jane Seymour (Ploetz listing No. 3), there would be a violent reaction in favor of Catholicism, the Duke of Northumberland had decided to make young Edward sign a document by which he declared that, in case of his own demise, Lady Jane Grey would succeed him to the throne.

On July 6, 1553, Edward died, aged not quite sixteen, and Lady Jane Grey, of exactly the same age, was proclaimed Queen. When told of her elevation, she was so badly frightened by the news that she fainted. Then she accepted her new dignity, out of respect or fear of her parents and guardians, but without any mad desire for the high office that was being forced upon her.

Nine days later the troops of Mary, the daughter of Henry

and Catherine of Aragon (wife No. 1), entered London. Little Lady Jane Grey was taken prisoner and was sent to the Tower, and there in the Tower, seven months later, little Lady Jane Grey's head was brutally chopped off her lovely shoulders, and that was the story of Jane Grey as it must have been known in all its gruesome details to her contemporary, the Princess Elizabeth, who was twenty years old when all this happened.

This tragedy must have filled her with serious forebodings for her own fate. Mary, her dear half sister, was now Queen, but Mary was an old woman and a most fanatical Catholic, while Elizabeth was at best a halfhearted Protestant. So far Mary had been obliging enough toward her illegitimate half sister, who, as she realized, would become her successor in case she herself should die without issue. To prevent this, she married the son of no one less than the Emperor Charles V, the obnoxious Prince Philip, who, as King of Spain, had sworn that no heretics would be found alive within his domains if he were only given six years in which to purge his realm of the enemies of the true faith.

Stout British hearts trembled at the prospect of the Spanish Inquisition establishing itself in their midst, and stout British fists were clenched in silent menace. Soon there were rumors of plans to proclaim the Princess Elizabeth ruler of the realm in place of her sister, and every time these rumors were whispered a little louder, the executioners in the Tower hopefully anticipated a speedy increase in their revenues.

It was during this period that Elizabeth got thoroughly versed in that art of dissimulation which was to be of such great value to her when she was obliged to play the role of loving sovereign to many of her subjects whom she intended to send to the gallows at the first possible opportunity. And, in addition, she now learned to play Br'er Possum and to make herself practically invisible whenever her spies informed her that the Spanish councilors of King Philip were once again trying to persuade His Majesty that, for the sake of his own safety and that of his wife,

he had better rid himself of the continued presence of this obstinate and headstrong English princess.

Philip realized that he could do this if he wished to. Mary, his wife, had fallen desperately in love with him and would grant him whatever he desired. In March of the year 1554 things reached such a pass that Elizabeth was actually sent to the Tower in some sort of "protective custody." But the English people, none too squeamish about spilling the blood of their great noble families, drew the line at beheading a Tudor, even if legally this particular offspring was considered to be a bastard.

Parliament, now the center of the Protestant opposition, hastily and eagerly rushed to the defense of their princess in distress. It would not even listen when, as a compromise, it was suggested that Elizabeth be excluded from ever succeeding to the throne. It grew even more deaf to the agitation against the Princess Elizabeth when it was rumored about that Mary was on the point of presenting her Spanish husband with an English heir. This anticipated happy event soon proved to be a false alarm, but there was always the chance that some day it might prove true, and then the cause of Protestantism in England would be lost forever. The future looked very dark indeed, for the Queen had not only been busy with that bassinet that was never to see service, but she had also spent her leisure hours (except when she was writing letters to her dear Philip, begging him to return to her from Spain) rallying all her Catholic supporters around her and by the severity of her anti-Protestant measures was rapidly gaining for herself that name which will be hers until the end of history—"Bloody Mary."

Two months after Elizabeth had been confined in the Tower, Mary discreetly let it be known that she was once more "expecting." That was an excellent excuse for Elizabeth's friends to insist upon some act of clemency to celebrate the event, and Mary graciously permitted her beloved sister to proceed to Hatfield House, where she was to perfect herself further in the knowl-

edge of the Latin and Greek tongues and other branches of learning that had very little to do with statecraft.

Elizabeth, however, feared that, in her case at least, out of sight might not be out of mind and, having a natural bent for publicity, she started building up a fascinating myth about a poor English princess, without one single drop of foreign blood in her veins, a strict Protestant who abhorred popery, who spoke the English language as colorfully as the ladies of Brighton's fish market, who loved all English sports (had not Dr. Ascham, her private tutor, written the best textbook on archery?), who could drink honest English ale with the stoutest bumper lifters in her navy, and who, because of all these virtues, was in constant danger of death at the hands of those foreign adventurers who had descended upon her hapless native land and who had vowed that they would once more make England a fief of the Holy See.

In all this, if the public had only known it, their bonny English princess showed that fine Italian hand she had acquired from diligently studying the writings of a well-known Milanese publicist by the name of Baldassare Castiglione, who, in his guidebook to princely deportment called *The Courtier,* had laid down those principles by which both a prince and his advisers might hope to perfect themselves in the difficult art of ruling their subjects according to their own plans, specifications, and ideas—and still keep their heads on their shoulders.

But the people of England were only interested in one thing —how could they rid themselves of Catholic Mary and make the realm safe for the Protestant faith? People forget easily, and the average Englishman was beginning to look back with unmitigated longing upon the reign of good King Hal, who had been a fine, outspoken figure of a man, if perhaps a little too easy-going in the matter of acquiring his wives and disposing of same. And now here was his own daughter (God bless her!), who had to go back two whole centuries to come upon a non-English ancestor. And this lovely young woman, who was so completely one of their own, was living under the shadow of

the scaffold while her sister, blood-smeared Mary, who was only half English (and who, besides, was married to a Spaniard), was sending her Protestant subjects to Tyburn in ever-increasing numbers and was now even threatening the life of her own kin.

Such a state of affairs was intolerable, and conditions were rapidly growing worse. Mass had already been reinstituted, and shortly afterward the Pope's authority had been re-established. Any day now, the lands taken away from the Church during King Henry's blessed reign might be returned to the original owners, the bishops and monks of detested memory. At that moment a merciful heaven answered the prayers of all honest Protestants. On November 17, 1558, Mary died, and Elizabeth succeeded her amidst the general jubilation of the populace.

The new Queen was twenty-five years old and she was going to reign over England during the next forty-five years. At last she was safe, or so she thought, for another Mary—far more dangerous than her namesake of the Tudor tribe—was now to appear upon the horizon to make the first twenty-nine years of Elizabeth's reign as troublesome and dangerous as anything that had gone before.

This other Mary, known to us as Mary, Queen of Scots, was the daughter of James V, King of Scotland, and of his wife, a French duchess belonging to the House of Guise. This lady had been united in holy wedlock with her Stuart in the year 1538 and had given birth to her daughter in 1542, and with the arrival of this child there opened up such a chapter of trouble as the world had rarely seen.

I can only give you the bare outline of this famous case. Mary of Scotland was the exact opposite of her English cousin, Elizabeth. No man ever went crazy about Elizabeth of England, whereas every man lost his head (often in the painful and literal sense of the word) the moment he beheld the steady blue eyes of this beauteous Franco-Scot princess. It may be true that in her case nature had been considerably helped out by art, for it is chronicled that when the axman picked up her head to show it to those who had witnessed her execution, he discovered to

his great dismay that her famous auburn tresses were not the lady's own but merely a wig. I feel inclined, however, to believe that she had been forced to such little beauty aids owing to the illness that had attacked her as the result of her many years of close confinement in a number of unhealthful jails. Before that time, her charms must have been considerable and entirely her own. Otherwise she could hardly have been the subject of so many and such desperate lovers' quarrels. Most of these have been repeatedly dramatized by some of our most gifted playwrights and authors, and I need not repeat them to you in detail. I can start with the year 1565, when Mary, after a career as fantastic as that of any modern Reno heroine, finally married one Henry Stuart, Lord Darnley, in his own right a claimant to the Scotch throne. He was said to be inclined toward the Catholic faith, which may have been a recommendation in the eyes of Mary, but was not likely to make him more popular among the rank and file of his wife's subjects. His weakness, his indecision, his vulgarity, and his tendency toward every known form of dissipation soon made Mary loathe him, for Mary was a lady. She found solace for her disgust in the company of her Italian secretary, David Rizzio.

This young man had come originally to Scotland as a member of an embassy the Duke of Savoy had sent to Scotland. When that mission came to an end, he remained behind as bass singer in the quartet which provided the musical programs for the royal chapel. It was then that he became acquainted with the Darnleys. An intelligent and wide-awake young Italian, he soon knew how matters stood between the royal couple and how much Mary needed someone upon whom she could really rely. He was just the right man for that job, but, curiously enough, according to the best available material, he was very careful to observe the greatest possible delicacy in his personal attitude toward his royal mistress.

Rizzio therefore might have played quite a role as the power behind the royal couch, but he was a Piedmontese, and his inborn desire for a fine and glittering accouterment soon got him

into trouble, for in Scotland, any kind of display of wasteful luxury was like waving a red cloth before a bull. Within a few months the Italian's elegant manners, in such sharp contrast to their own lack of finesse, had made the royal secretary and lute player highly unpopular among the native nobles. Meanwhile, his satins and silks and the fine feathers on his hat were being greatly resented by those at the bottom of the social ladder, and his ability to divert Her Majesty's troubled mind by singing sweet ballads and madrigals was regarded with deep suspicion by everybody.

There is nothing easier in this world than to make a boorish yokel suspect a man of superior manners who happens to be attractive in the eyes of his wife. There were many people in Edinburgh who would benefit if this objectionable jackanapes were removed from the scene. They now sought out Darnley and whispered unpleasant innuendos into his tipsy ears. His boozy brain took fire. The idea of a Stuart being turned into a cuckold by an Eytalian ballad singer, and underneath his own roof too, was more than his Scottish pride could stand. On the evening of March 9, 1566, a group of Darnley's friends broke into the royal palace, rushed into the Queen's dining room, hacked and stabbed Rizzio to pieces, and for good measure threw his body out of the window.

Mary held her peace. She was with child, and so there was little else she could do—for the moment at least. In June her son was born. He was given the name of James and grew up to become James VI of Scotland and James I of England.

There is little doubt about the child's complete legitimacy, for he grew up to be the same kind of inarticulate and clumsy fellow his father had been.

That father, meanwhile (though he did not know it), was enjoying his last days on earth. Early in January of the next year he fell sick. By now he had so thoroughly disgusted everybody (both the Protestants and the Catholics) who came in contact with him that Mary, by way of contrast, was enjoying a short-lived period of popularity. She decided to pack her husband off

to the country that he might recuperate—but out of her sight. A near-by country house, Kirk-o'-Field, was chosen as his place of convalescence.

On February 9, Mary visited the patient, returning to Edinburgh that same evening. A few hours later, the place was blown sky-high by means of barrels of gunpowder concealed in the cellar. The next day the bodies of Darnley and his page were found in the bushes outside the house. They had apparently survived the explosion, had tried to escape, and had been murdered by the conspirators who had anticipated such a possibility and had hidden themselves in the near-by woods.

Scotland sat up and took notice. Two murders in royal circles in less than a year's time were almost too much of a good thing, even in a country where violent death was by no means uncommon and was considered part of the national game of politics.

When shortly afterward the local gossips were able to inform their neighbors that Mary now planned to marry the Earl of Bothwell, who was said to have been responsible for the plot against Darnley's life, the Scotch divines had at last solid reason to denounce their French Jezebel as a scourge of God and to insist that something be done about her before the whole of the nation perish. To appease their wrath, Mary married her Jamie in a Protestant church. But it was too late, for by this time the public had learned that the noble Earl already had had quite a number of wives and that it was highly doubtful whether he had been legally set free from his latest partner.

That was the final.straw which broke the rugged Caledonian back. The whole of Scotland arose against its Queen. Mary was forced to send Bothwell away while she herself was taken to Lochleven, an old castle situated on an island in a lake and therefore thought to be an ideal prison.

But Mary was a lady who knew how to make use of those bewitching eyes. Those lovely orbs persuaded one of her guards to close his own while his charge walked out of the front gate.

Mary was now once more a free woman, but had not yet

quite understood that her Scots would have no more of her. She hastily gathered a few faithful old henchmen around her royal personage and boldly marched against her enemies. She was defeated and, being unable to escape by sea, she fled to England, and from English soil she appealed to her dear Cousin Elizabeth to provide her with an asylum.

Elizabeth answered as graciously as it was within her nature to be (and she could be quite gracious when it suited her purposes) that she was delighted to welcome her dear cousin and would gladly protect her against her former subjects. Then the fat was in the fire (or, to put it more elegantly, Mary was in prison), and she was to stay there for nineteen long years and to become an ever-increasing source of annoyance and irritation to her jailers. For Catholicism was by no means dead in England. It had merely gone underground, there to smolder like a forest fire which seems to have been put out but which returns to life the moment everybody has gone home and there is no one to watch it.

The great Catholic families had withdrawn from public life as soon as Elizabeth had succeeded Bloody Mary. They still had a common ideal but no particular reason to turn it into a fighting cause. For Elizabeth was a reasonable woman who had no objections against an honest Catholic, provided he kept his religious convictions to himself and did not call her a royal bastard in public or try to poison her. But now, with Scotch Mary in their midst, the Catholic minority felt that it had an issue around which it could rally. Mary had a great many friends on the Continent. All the Catholic rulers were on her side. The Emperor was on her side. The Pope and the King of France positively loved her. Here, at last, was their long-awaited opportunity, and eagerly they accepted the game all Europe was to watch for nineteen long years, never quite knowing who was going to win.

On one side of the board sat Elizabeth, with her hennaed curls and her painted cheeks. On the other side, the lovely fingers of her gracious Majesty of Scotland were cleverly moving

the pieces according to the whispered advice of discreet councilors. And all the rulers of Europe stood around in a wide circle, kibitzing to their hearts' content and making secret bets as
to the outcome of the match.

In the beginning it looked as if Mary would be victorious.
But she played a woman's game, while Elizabeth became more
and more masculine in her style as the years advanced. And
Mary—as I told you—was not only a lady but also an incurable
cheat. Elizabeth knew this. Every letter from Mary was duly intercepted, read, studied, sealed up again, and forwarded as if
nothing had happened. Whenever Mary was discovered to be engaged in another plot against her dear cousin's life, her imprisonment was made a little more severe, and unmistakable hints
were given as to what ultimate fate such conduct on her part
must lead to. Mary then humbly thanked her dear cousin for
this renewed manifestation of mercy, but the very next day she
would be devising some still more elaborate plot to rid England
of that accursed virgin who refused to go to Mass and who held
her fate in her hands.

So the years passed in endless intrigues, and today I think
that most people outside of the Society of Jesus and a few ir-
reconcilable Irishmen agree that in the end there was really no
other choice left to Elizabeth but to rid herself of her rival and
to do this by the only method that was guaranteed to be absolutely effective.

In the year 1586 a new plot against the life of Elizabeth was
unearthed. One Anthony Babington, a former page of Mary,
was the intermediary who had arranged everything. Mary was
heavily implicated. She was brought to trial and condemned to
death. Elizabeth had already caused enough heads to roll during the last thirty years not to wish for further unpleasant
memories. She refused to sign the death warrant. She claimed
that it might lead to complications with her presumptive successor, James of Scotland, if she should cut off his mother's head.

Those were panicky days for England. The rumors about a
fleet of hundreds of ships of tremendous size then being con-

structed in Spain to reconquer the British Isles for the Catholic faith had put everybody on edge. The people wanted to be rid of this Scottish trollop who was making friends with their enemies and who—some fine night—might cause all Protestants to be murdered in their beds. Elizabeth still hesitated. Decapitating a cousin was something different again from performing the same operation upon a mere subject like Essex, who had been under the mistaken impression that certain "alleged" familiarities with the person of the anointed Majesty entitled him to strut around as if he had ever been accepted as her official lover.

It was Mary's own son who settled the problem. If James of Scotland had as much as hinted that he wanted his mother's life spared, Elizabeth would have been relieved of the most difficult decision she was ever forced to make. But tongue-tied Jamie Stuart knew what he wanted. He wanted the crown of England and informed Elizabeth that if she would guarantee him the succession in England, he from his side would try to "digest" his grief at his mother's untimely demise and to forget any personal resentment he might feel against the person responsible for her execution.

By this infamous letter about his hope to be able to "digest his grief," James Stuart signed his mother's death warrant. At eight o'clock of the morning of February 8, of the year 1587, a clumsy axman hacked Mary's lovely head from her equally lovely shoulders, and Elizabeth was doomed to spend the rest of her days remembering the hour when the Earl of Shrewsbury had presented himself in her closet to inform Her Majesty that it was all over and that her rival would never again be able to disturb the peace of the realm.

I suppose that I should now tell you about the great conquests that were made during Elizabeth's reign—how the foundations were laid of that great empire which will always be identified with her name. But you learned all that at school, and I am really much more interested in those subtle qualities

of mind and heart which decided the outcome of the struggle between these two extraordinary women than in all the wars that were fought during this most famous of feminine duels.

In practically every respect Mary was superior to Elizabeth. She was better-looking. She had enjoyed a much better education and was full of that charm in which Elizabeth was so conspicuously lacking. Elizabeth realized this, but I don't believe that personal spite or jealousy had much to do with her final decision to send her cousin to the scaffold.

When Elizabeth signed Mary's death warrant, she was fifty-four years old. She had lived a hard life and had learned to master her emotions, which probably had never been very strong. Let Mary have her lovers. Let Mary but turn her eyes toward a jailer to make him a devoted slave forever after. But let Mary remember that this homely, overdressed spinster had something which she herself could never hope to acquire—a passion for her native land so profound and so sincere that it influenced her in all her decisions and governed her in everything she did.

Mary was out to make a career.

Elizabeth was intent upon founding a nation.

In the end, both women got their wish, and the world at large caught its first glimpse of that curious institution known as the British Empire.

All this, poor Frits had to read and digest on the way from Amsterdam to Middelburg when he came to Zeeland the next Saturday. It was a cold and blustery day, with occasional downpours which made the island of Walcheren look as if it had only recently emerged from the Flood.

At half-past six that evening Frits and I took a walk. We were now fairly familiar with the habits of our guests and knew that most of them liked to use their unexpected leave of absence for a short constitutional through the streets of Veere before the hour had come to knock at our door. This time we seemed to be

out of luck. Everything was serene. It was rather cold, and nobody was abroad. Even the dogs had withdrawn to the warm kitchens of their respective homes. We went as far as the tower on the water front and then turned back to go to Frits' place on the market. In the harbor we noticed a small sailing vessel that had just arrived. The men were still busy taking in the sails. The tide was beginning to run out, and we saw that a ladder had been put up to the side of the wharf to allow a passenger to reach the top of the dock.

At the same moment we recognized this passenger as one of our guests. It was impossible to mistake her identity. No other woman had ever worn a peruke of such a brilliant hue, nor would any other mortal have heaped quite so much jewelry upon a pair of such ancient shoulders. Strings of pearls were wound around the lady's neck. Other pearls, as large as small pears, were dripping from her ears. She wore a lace collar at least two feet wide. The wind was blowing it around her head, and the same merciless gust of air brutally exposed a pair of very spindly legs encased in heavy woolen stockings.

When the Queen beheld us, she quickly pulled her skirts down around her knees and addressed us in a way which showed she had been in the habit of expressing herself without mincing her words and expected to have her commands obeyed, no matter to whom she was speaking.

"God's wounds!" she shouted. "And has it come to pass that I shall stand here showing my old buttocks while two miserable wretches grin at my discomfiture?"

"Please Your Highness' grace," Frits answered with more elegance than I had ever seen him demonstrate on any previous occasion, "but we had stationed ourselves here expressly that we might bid Your Majesty a right hearty welcome."

Elizabeth turned on him ferociously. "By ye gullet of God, young whippersnapper, if one of my courtiers had spoken to me thus, I would have had him up at Tyburn and higher than Tom Wyatt himself!"

Frits, fearing that in his ignorance of the older English vernacular he might have used the wrong expressions, was seriously taken aback.

"I am sorry, madam," he answered, "but what can I possibly have done to incur Your Majesty's displeasure and to deserve such a severe condemnation?"

"Ye damned Dutch windmill!" now spoke the royal Majesty, "is that the way to greet a gracious sovereign who sent her men to help you defeat your Spanish enemies in your hour of need and who never yet has been paid back as much as a penny of the money she wasted?"

I knew only too well to what the old harridan was referring. During the beginning of our war of independence, she had actually sent a few thousand soldiers under command of her friend, the Earl of Leicester, to help us beat the Spaniards. But this adventure had ended sadly when two English officers betrayed the Dutch cause and sold out to the enemy. I decided that with a person of Her Majesty's rather positive views, it would do no good to beat around the bush.

"Your Majesty surely is not referring to Stanley and York? I realize that that unfortunate accident happened while My Lord of Leicester was absent on a mission to London, but . . ."

"*Touchée!*" she interrupted. "You may not know your manners, but at least you have not forgotten your history."

I confess that I looked puzzled, and she noticed it. "God's breath!" she fairly shouted at me. "He stands there and is perplexed. Is that the way to greet the Queen?"

"If it please your most glorious Majesty," I said, assuming a humility I by no means felt, "but what have my friend and I done amiss to incur this most unfortunate displeasure on Your Majesty's part?"

"You stand there and ask me!" with the full accent on "stand."

I began to suspect what she was driving at, but the last thing I wanted to do was to kneel down and kiss her hand, as I knew had been the custom at the court. In the first place, the planks

Queen Elizabeth had just set foot on our native soil.

of the dock were soaking wet, and in the second place, how could I have explained such an act of debasement to my Veere neighbors, who, I felt sure, were looking at us from behind the closed curtains of every window along the quay. I would have been the butt of all their jokes, for a Zeelander is a stiff-necked creature who never bows his back to any other human being, least of all to a foreign potentate.

"If it please your gracious Majesty once more," I replied with my most polite bow and clicking my heels in the best Austrian fashion, "but this is the way we would salute Her Royal Highness, our own Majesty, the Queen of the Netherlands."

Elizabeth looked puzzled. "So you are a kingdom now! In my days you called yourself a republic. I never liked republics. They have no respect for authority."

"Indeed, Your Majesty" (I had never in my life been guilty of so many "majesties" in so few minutes, and I wondered how we would feel when a little later in the evening, we would have to deal with an empress), "indeed, Your Highness' Grace, we are now happy to call ourselves a kingdom."

"And you are ruled over by a woman, as England was in my day?"

"Not only that, Your Majesty, but by a woman whose high sense of duty is only matched by that love which the great Elizabeth bestowed upon her own domains."

"That was rather well spoken. Perhaps, after all, you are a gentleman, though at first I took you for some excise fellow, come to collect on my pearls."

"If I were here to collect on the pearls that drop from Your Majesty's lips, I would be my country's benefactor. It would pay our national debt."

Heaven only knows what inspired me to utter this drivel, but it seemed to please the old lady more than anything else we had said. She became almost friendly as she answered: "Then, if that be the way you salute your own Majesty, it is well by me. I shall say no more about it, but for God's sake lead me to a warm place where I can rest mine ancient rump. We had a

dreadful crossing. I am frozen through and through, and I am very, very hungry."

"If it will but please your gracious Majesty," Frits broke in, "it is but a step to my humble home. Indeed, you can see it right from where you are standing."

"From where Your Majesty is standing," Elizabeth corrected him.

"From where your gracious Majesty is pleased to be standing," Frits repeated with a deep bow and going her a couple of degrees better.

"That will do," the Queen replied, and the three of us turned into Market Street, and I went a little ahead so as to make sure that all would be in readiness for this rather exacting guest. A few minutes later we were in the room where the fire was burning brightly and where a table covered with flowers and shining pewter promised that soon Her Majesty's desire for food would be appeased.

Erasmus was already on hand. He was waiting by the side of the fireplace, an open book in his hand. He saluted Her Majesty with an elegant Latin phrase.

"God's odds!" the Queen replied, "have I escaped from one lunatic asylum but to enter another? Now who may that worshipful body be with the long ears and the funny nose?"

"Those are the selfsame words with which Your Majesty's most gracious father deigned to salute me when I had the honor of being presented to him."

"My father! My 'most gracious father'! That ox, that bull! 'Most gracious' indeed! And where may you ever have known my father?"

"In London, Your Majesty."

"So you have been in London?"

"Quite often, Your Majesty, and in many other cities of your fair land. There is no better country anywhere on this earth."

If this remark pleased Elizabeth, she gave no sign of it, for she curtly answered, "I am not aware, sir, that I asked you for your opinion."

Erasmus was not in the least offended. He merely smiled while offering the Queen the chair we had specially ordered for him when we knew that he was to be our regular guest. Then he spoke, and this time in Italian. "As Your Majesty undoubtedly knows, he who gives without being asked gives twice."

"Who said that?"

"My good friend, Sir Thomas More."

"Thomas More! So you knew Sir Thomas? He died before my time, but I read his book—a lot of falderal! The very idea of trying to found an 'ideal state'! It can't be done. Not as long as people are the fools and the knaves and rogues they are now and probably always will be. The people, indeed! You should know the people as I came to know them after four and forty years, or was it five? I have forgotten and I no longer care. It happened so long ago."

Erasmus smiled at this lamentation which sounded far from convincing, but the Queen did not notice it. "Sir Thomas More indeed!" she went on. "The poor old visionary! I heard it said, however, that he was a fine man."

"No finer English gentleman ever lived."

"Yes, and what did he get for his trouble? He tried to be honest when everybody else was a scoundrel and rascal. I have been told he served my father faithfully and well for a great many years. Then he disapproved of my father getting a divorce, and it was off with his head!"

Erasmus whispered, "I am afraid that was true, your most gracious Majesty."

Elizabeth patted the old man on the sleeve. "Yes, it was an old habit with Father—that and having bastard children."

Again I saw Erasmus quiver. "I am afraid that your most gracious Majesty is right once more," he replied.

"Well," said the Queen, looking around her with satisfaction, "this is a pleasant room. The candles remind me of Hatfield House. I am feeling faint. Why don't we eat?"

"In a moment, Your Majesty," I hastened to inform her. "The soup is being served this very minute."

Elizabeth looked at me with suspicion. "You are not by any chance waiting for another guest?" she asked.

"Oh no, Your Majesty," I lied. "That is to say . . ."

"Come on, you scurrilous varlet! Speak up! Since when does the Queen of England have to wait for the arrival of another guest? This is an insult. An infamous insult!"

I offered a rather faint apology. "Maybe Her Majesty has lost her way," I explained. "You see, we did not go forth to meet her," and I stressed the "her."

"Your Majesty this and Her Majesty that! Good God! young man, you have not been rash enough to ask two queens to sit down at the same table and underneath the same roof?"

This time I could honestly reply. "We would never dream of such a thing," I assured her.

"Then why did you call that other person 'Her Majesty'?"

"She happens to be an empress."

The oath that greeted this announcement I cannot repeat in print, but it left very little to the imagination and clearly indicated what the Queen felt about her sisters of the sacred blood. Then, in a quieter voice, she continued, "An empress indeed! In my day there was but one empress—the wife of that German idiot. Is it she?"

"May it please Your Majesty's grace, it is not."

Elizabeth grew impatient. "By God's wounds, are you going to speak in riddles all evening? That will make for a right merry party!"

Frits came to the rescue. "Her Imperial Majesty comes from Constantinople," he told her.

"Constantinople! I knew that I was being imposed upon the moment I set foot in your miserable village. From Constantinople indeed! And you expect Elizabeth of England to break bread with a Turk?"

"She is not a Turk, your most gracious Majesty. She is a Greek."

Elizabeth waved both her arms toward heaven. "A Greek! May all the saints have mercy upon me, as my sister Mary used

The Empress of Byzantium stood in the doorway.

to say, and get spanked for it. I knew a Greek once. He was a doctor. He tried to cure me of the pain in my legs. He told me I must stop drinking and swearing—I had him hanged."

"This is a different kind of Greek, Your Majesty. The Empress is a Byzantine."

"I never heard that word before," Elizabeth announced. "What is a Byzantine?"

"It was the name given in olden times to the eastern half of the Roman Empire," Erasmus volunteered.

"Did Will Shakespeare ever mention it?"

"I am afraid not, Your Majesty."

"Then there was no such country," Elizabeth curtly announced. "My little Will knew his world as well as any man. If he had never heard of it, I surely shall not bother to find out where it was. Besides, all that interests me just now is when I am to be fed. My entrails fairly rumble with hunger. They are as empty as my exchequer used to be most of the time. Only, then I knew what to do."

But we were never to find out by what means her gracious Majesty managed to fill her empty coffers, for at that moment (it was now ten minutes past seven) there was a very soft knock at the door. Frits jumped to his feet and unlocked the door. The Empress Theodora floated into the room. I use the word advisedly. She seemed to be unaware of the law of gravity. She moved neither her hands nor her feet, but like a piece of thistledown she let herself be carried by the air. She wore a long purple mantle. Her feet were clothed in tiny golden sandals. On her head she carried the diadem with which I was familiar from her picture in San Vitale.

"Your Majesty," I began, when I suddenly remembered that I had forgotten to inquire who of our guests ranked whom, but, having started, I could not stop and so I decided that the Empress must rank the Queen, and I turned my head toward Elizabeth. "Your Majesty, may I ask you to greet a fellow guest? This is Her Imperial Majesty, the Empress Theodora of Byzantium."

But the outburst of fury I had expected did not take place, and an entirely different Elizabeth, fairly beaming good will, arose from her chair, took three steps forward on her high-heeled red satin slippers, and, taking Theodora by the hand, said, "I have read and heard so much about you, my child, that I have always wanted to meet you, and now I actually have that pleasure. Do come in and join me by the fire. It is rather cold outside and you must be very tired."

The Empress smiled a faint smile of recognition, but as Elizabeth had spoken to her in English I knew that she had not understood a word that had been spoken. Once more it was our dear Erasmus who saved the situation by addressing the forlorn little figure in classical Greek. He bade her welcome in the name of the Queen of England (Bretannika he called it) and invited her to be seated.

And it was Erasmus who took the lead in the conversation, for we found that the lovely Theodora spoke nothing but Greek, understood only a few words of Latin, and claimed a complete ignorance of the Russian I tried on her. Whether she was actually ignorant of this Slavic tongue which she must have heard almost every day at her court among her servants and the officers of the guard, or whether she thought it the better policy not to betray her familiarity with that barbaric vernacular, I could never decide. For I did what I always do under such circumstances: I took a pad of paper and drew pictures of what I wanted to say, and Theodora was as delighted as a child with these scrawls. In fact, before she left she gathered them all together and murmured something about *mneme* or *mneia*, which I took to mean that she wanted to keep them for memory's sake, whereupon I signed them as best I could with my name written in Greek, a fact which highly pleased her and for which she thanked me with a nod of her little head, done with such grace that it will forever be my *mneme* of that evening.

The seating of our guests was a very delicate matter, and I was sorry that we had not taken the trouble to provide ourselves for this evening with a round table. That always makes it so much easier, for then there is no formal head of the table, and none of the guests can feel slighted. If I remember correctly, we had placed Erasmus at the end of the table that was farthest from the door, on account of his susceptibility to drafts. The Empress sat on his right, the Queen on his left, and Frits and I took the other two seats at the foot of the table.

As for our worries about our guests' ability to handle their forks, there again we had guessed wrong. For although neither of them used that instrument to pick up their food and carry it from their plates to their fingers, they were so clever at maneuvering their spoons that the meal passed off without any accidents. The only mishap occurred when Jo brought in the lamb stew with garlic. Poor Jo was so fascinated by the Queen's red wig that she did something of which I had never before known her to be guilty. She allowed the spoon to fall out of the large Delft dish in which the stew was being served, and this act of clumsiness was answered by a resounding blow on her buttocks by the royal hand. But it was all done in a spirit of good nature, for by this time her gracious Majesty had disposed of her seventh mug of ale and was as merry and drunk as a lord.

At first we had not noticed it, but after the eighth bottle had been consumed (I figured that we had only six more), the Queen suddenly got up and demanded, "What has become of that music we heard a moment ago? Let's have another tune—a pavan or something. I want to dance." And fitting her actions to her words, she took poor Frits by the hand and said, "You lead me, young man, and God have mercy upon your soul if you step on my toes. My corns ache."

Fortunately, Frits was an excellent natural-born dancer, and although he had no more idea of the figures of a pavan than I have about flying, he let the music guide him and so pleased the Queen that she kept him on his feet for almost half an hour, while Jo in her kitchen was growing desperate, wondering what would become of the rest of the meal and how she could keep her stew warm for that second helping for which the Queen had asked before she left the table and turned Frits' respectable home into an improvised night club. This reference to Her Majesty's healthy appetite sounds rather plebeian, for as a rule royalty is supposed to dine only on a couple of green peas and a single grape, but these two august ladies were honest trencherwomen, and we seemed to have ordered exactly the right dish for them, except that Elizabeth almost immediately switched over from mint to garlic and wanted to know why, in the name of all the devils in hell, her thrice-damned French cooks had never served her so delicious a dish—a question to which, of course, we could not supply an answer.

And so, between Erasmus' witticisms in his mellifluous classical Greek and Elizabeth's slightly ribald (which is rather an understatement, I am afraid) and quite tipsy odds and ends of prose and song, the dinner passed to the complete contentment of all the guests, and afterward, full of good food and good cheer, we sat around the fire and plied our guests with coffee and cognac.

The Empress, after a moment's hesitation, expressed her delight at this strange beverage which was new to her but which she seemed to like, whereas Elizabeth took one sip, spat it out into the fire, and announced that she would not have used the stuff to wash her pigs in, but added that she would like to have just a wee bit more of that mild French wine we had just served her, but this time in a glass that was a glass and not a thimble.

And what did we talk about? You may not believe it, but we spent a whole evening discussing the subject of knitting! I don't know how it came up, but after the ladies had withdrawn for a moment, the Empress to rouge her lips and the Queen to paint her face, Elizabeth came back and informed us with a happy grin, "You know, that child wears a pair of woolen panties! I would have given five counties in Ireland for such a pair when I was still living in that drafty old palace of mine."

Erasmus was too tactful to translate this remark, but the Queen could not be stopped. "Don't mind that old bishop, my child," she said, "and show these gentlemen your shift. You have the loveliest legs I have ever seen and you need not be bashful. Remember you are dead."

This time Erasmus was obliged to repeat what had been said, but Theodora absolutely refused, and, remembering something of Her Majesty's past, I could well understand her present delicacy. Elizabeth, however, was peeved. She called her a prude, but seeing that scolding would do no good, she asked the Empress where she had got them.

"They were sent to me from Cyprus," Theodora answered by way of Erasmus. "That is where I was born."

"Cyprus," Elizabeth mused. "That sounds familiar. Master Shakespeare must have written about it in one of his plays."

I told her that that was most likely, for he loved to have his heroes visit strange places. The Queen, however, was not interested in geography. Her mind was still firmly fixed on her rival's underwear and she asked many further questions which none of us could answer. All this greatly perplexed the poor Empress, who had not the vaguest idea what her bibacious rival was talking about. She turned to Erasmus to enlighten her, who, equally baffled, requested that I get him the Greek dictionary he had brought with him the Saturday before, when we had discussed a rather obscure passage in Plato. "I thought that I knew my Greek," he said, "but knitting and purling and drop-stitching are expressions that rarely occur in either the classics or the writings of the Holy Fathers."

When a few minutes later I returned from upstairs, there was no longer any need of this *Thesaurus,* for Elizabeth, having satisfied her first curiosity and having made her companion thoroughly uncomfortable (we never saw those divine legs of Theodora about which the Queen had waxed so enthusiastic), had dropped the subject and had now started to discuss the subject of taxation—direct taxation vs. indirect.

Frits told me afterward how this change had come about. She was especially interested in the wool that had been used for the Empress' panties. Where was it grown? On the near-by islands? Did those islands belong to her empire? If they did not, was the wool taxed on being brought into her own empire? Or did the government tax the finished products and let the consumer pay an indirect tax? And how high was the tax?

Erasmus translated those questions as rapidly as they were fired at him, and to our great surprise the answers came as quickly as they had been asked. Apparently this lovely princess was familiar with all the details of running a government, and Elizabeth was so delighted that she said, "Old Tom Gresham ought to have been here. Those two would have got along marvelously. They both can rattle off figures like gutters full of rain. My God, what a woman! Such a face and such a brain! It's unfair. I had the brain, for no one ever called me a fool. If only I had had the face too!" Then once more changing the subject with that disregard for her hearers' attention which showed that she had always talked to people obliged to agree with her, she asked what time it was.

I told her: "Twenty minutes before twelve."

She sighed. "It has been very pleasant here tonight. Much better than I had expected. And soon it will be all over again. That place" (all our guests referred to their present abode as "that place") "may suit John Knox and his crowd, but it's a bit dull for—but never mind—I'm not expected to talk about it. That was the condition on which they let me go. So suppose we say it is all right—wonderful even—yea, it is marvelous!—the Goddamn hole!—never mind—I did not say that, and you did not hear it. Twenty more minutes of liberty. I suppose by now there are only fifteen. Give me another glass of ale, and then let's dance. 'Let us die dancing, as we have spent our lives dancing.' Did I invent that just now or did I hear it somewhere? Tell your fiddlers upstairs to play us another tune. How about *The Lord of Salisbury*? I think I recognized that and Tom Morley's *It Was a Lover and His Lass,* and tell them to make it merry—merry—merry!—it is a long time since I have used that word—and *Fair Phyllis,* if they can play that. I used to love it."

I went into the kitchen to tell Hein to stop washing the dishes and go upstairs and play those records. "Anything gay," I said. "She probably won't notice whether they are the ones she asked for or not." But I did not bother to enlighten Her Majesty and tell her that what she had taken for a band of minstrels was nothing but a flat disk of rubber that came from the river where her friend, Sir Walter Raleigh, had hoped to find his city of eternal life. For by now I realized how little our modern inventions impressed our guests. Besides, every minute counted.

Hein wiped his hands on a towel and came out of the kitchen. Elizabeth noticed him. "God's wounds!" she said. "And where have you kept this handsome young fellow all night? He even wears a beard. Essex once tried to grow one. To make him look older, I suppose, and a little less like my son. I made him shave it off, though. I wanted no familiarities of that sort at my court. Tell me, my good man, who are you?"

"I am the cook's husband," Hein replied.

"Is she as good in your bed as in her kitchen?" the Queen asked.

"Even better," Hein answered, who had not exactly been brought up as a courtier.

Elizabeth was delighted. "That is what I want to hear," she said, "an honest man! At home, everybody would have made a long face and would have refused to tell me the truth. They thought they could fool me. They thought that they could fool Elizabeth! But Elizabeth fooled them forty-four years—or was it forty-five?—and she died peacefully in her bed." Then to Hein: "Where are you going?"

"I am going to start the music," Hein told her.

"No," said the Queen, "you are not. That other young man" (pointing to Frits) "can do that, and I will dance with you."

The remark Hein made in Dutch shall remain untranslated. It was along the line that whatever had got to be done had got to be done, but the Queen paid no attention, for she had noticed that Hein was in his stocking feet.

"Why don't you wear your shoes?"

This time Hein was up to the occasion. "The better to be able to dance with Your Majesty," he answered. "These marble tiles are very slippery."

"Then I shall do likewise," said the Queen and, sitting down on a chair, held both feet out to Hein and told him, "Take them off for me."

I then understood why this woman, who had been famous for her penny-pinching and had never paid any of her debts if she could possibly help it, had squandered such large sums upon her bootmakers. Her feet were very well shaped, very short and very narrow and so entirely out of keeping with the rest of her that they could have been called positively beautiful.

Upstairs a needle scraped, and then we heard the first bars of *It Was a Lover and His Lass.*

"Come on," said the Queen, giving Hein a resounding smack on his ears.

"I am there," Hein answered, with a mighty blow on the royal buttocks.

"You should have been in my navy. You have the makings of a fine boatswain," the Queen told him.

"I am in the navy anyway," Hein replied, "and I know a much better place than an uncomfortable bunk in Your Majesty's navy."

Then he took his hand in hers, but she said, "No! put it around my waist," and off they went. Erasmus and I had watched this little comedy with sincere enjoyment, but we did not know how it had affected the Empress, who never betrayed her emotions, not even by a change in the light of her eyes.

It was now five minutes of twelve. Frits had switched over to *Fair Phyllis.* The Empress leaned over to Erasmus and whispered something into his ear. Erasmus repeated the remark to me. "Her Majesty wants you to ask her to dance with you."

It was the last thing I had expected, and I was a bit frightened. I could dance about as well or as badly as any other nonprofessional, except the tango, which I had learned in the Argentine and which I loved. I had no idea, however, what "dancing" meant to a Byzantine empress of the sixth century. I decided to make it something slow and rather stately, as different as possible from the rapid twirling of the Queen and Hein who were indulging in a sort of sixteenth-century jitter-bugging

I put my hand around Theodora's waist. I touched her as gently as I would have touched the feather mantle of an Hawaiian princess. There was an instant response. Her body seemed to nestle in the hollow of my arm. Those incredible black eyes looked up at me. She leaned forward, and her gentle little breasts touched me. I suddenly understood a thousand years of history. I knew what no mere scholar had ever found out. But through the noise of the gramophone, now going at full blast (for Elizabeth had been shouting, "Louder, much louder!"), I heard the faint sound of the town-hall clock, making ready to strike the hour of midnight.

I had known only one woman who had ever affected me that way. I used to call her by a Greek name. I wondered what had made me do it. The clinkety-clank of the chimes (half of them blown away by the storm still raging outside) got mixed with the tender notes of the clavichord and the scraping sound of the fiddles.

The candles began to flicker.

The room grew dark.

The candles went out.

Jo, who by now was familiar with this ritual, was already bringing in our kerosene lamp.

Our guests were gone. Underneath the table I noticed the little dancing pumps of the great Queen. I felt something cold and unfamiliar in my hand. I opened it and looked. There lay a beautiful pearl held in a small Byzantine cross.

The Royal Majesty dances.

CHAPTER IX

ROBESPIERRE and TORQUEMADA Provide Us With a Nightmare We Shall Never Forget

NEITHER Frits nor I felt like going to bed. The evening had been much too exciting, and besides, there was the whole room still to be cleaned up. The table was in terrible disorder, for our guests had not exactly been what one would feel inclined to call "neat eaters." So Frits did what all good Dutchmen do when they mean to make a night of it. He called out to Jo, "Teeeeeea, please!" and Jo shouted back, just as cheerfully, "I've already started it."

Then Hein asked, "What shall we do with Her Majesty's shoes?"

"Keep them," Frits answered, "as a souvenir."

"As if I will ever forget this evening!" Hein answered. "No thank you! I've danced with the Queen of England, and that was enough of a job for a little shrimp fisherman from Veere."

"I tell you what," Frits suggested, "suppose we send them to the museum in Amsterdam. Tell them we found them in an old house in Flushing where Leicester had left them when he returned to England."

"Will they believe you?"

"Well, those slippers are genuine enough. They can have the material examined, and then they will find out for themselves."

It seemed a good enough idea, and we put the royal dancing pumps away in the cupboard. Frits was to take them with him the next evening, when he went back to Amsterdam. But when we came to look for them on Sunday afternoon they were gone.

After Jo had brought the tea, we all sat down in front of the fire. "Forget the dishes till tomorrow," Frits suggested. "You worked hard this evening. Come and sit down and have a cup of tea with us."

"I got a pound of *speculaas*," said Jo. "I thought we'd need it."

"That reminds me," Frits said. "The other day Erasmus said that he remembered a sort of cookie one of his aunts used to make for him when he was a child and came home for his holidays. He would love to eat those cookies again. He described them. They sounded like *speculaas*. You must make him some next Saturday. He asked me for the recipe. He wanted to translate it into Latin."

"I'll give it to him in Dutch," said Jo. "I'll write it down tomorrow."

Then we drank tea and ate our *speculaas*, but none of us said anything. We had enough to think of.

Finally I asked Frits, "If you were to sum up those guests of tonight (and God knows! they were as different as they could be, yet in a way they were alike), what would you say they had in common?"

Frits stirred his tea and then, sort of musing to himself, he said: "What did they have in common? Well, let me think. That is a hard question to answer. What did they have in common? I would say just one thing."

"Yes, and what was it?"

"If you pin me down to just one thing, I would say it was the fact that neither of them had any inhibitions. The old story—the streetwalker behaved like a queen, and the queen did her best to behave like a streetwalker. But neither of them had any real inhibitions. They both were exactly as God had made them."

"A refreshing experience."

"A wonderful experience, and now I will tell you what we

should do by way of contrast. Our next guests should be the exact opposite. They should be walking inhibitions."

"Have you any candidates?"

"Yes, I do, for I have been thinking about them all evening."

"Who are they?"

"Two men. Robespierre and Torquemada."

"That will be a cheerful party!"

"Not exactly. But a very interesting one."

"It's O.K. by me. Go ahead and invite them, and please, Jo, get some more hot water. I feel like a lot of tea tonight."

"As long as there's water, there's tea," Jo told him, falling back on a well-known old Dutch expression, and so we sat and talked for several hours, but I do not remember much of what we said, which is just as well, for experience has taught me that after one o'clock at night, even the most brilliant minds in the world are apt to talk nonsense.

The meal? There was a problem. What were we to feed these two fanatics? I knew that Robespierre, like the late Theodore Roosevelt, was passionately fond of oranges. He ate oranges as Voltaire used to drink coffee. He ate them in the morning and he ate them at night. So four dozen oranges were duly noted down on Jo's order slip. But oranges do not make a meal, so what else were we to give them? I knew that both these men would be much too much interested in themselves to think of anything else, which is probably the reason why one eats so badly in the homes of people with a cause.

After consulting my faithful *Cuisinière française,* I decided upon a plain vegetable soup (ordinary Dutch vegetable soup) and then for safety's sake (you never could tell with a person like Torquemada) I thought we had better have fish—boiled cod with mustard sauce (Robespierre, with his everlasting stomach trouble, would eat it too and be uncomfortable), boiled potatoes and carrots—for no Dutch cook would ever dream of serving boiled fish without at the same time serving carrots. It is part of their culinary ritual. I found a most suitable dessert

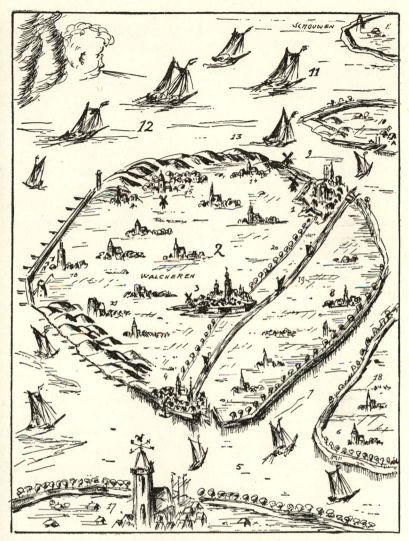

The Island of Middelburg.

1. Veere. 2. The Island of Walcheren. 3. Middelburg. 4. Vlissingen or Flushing as we call it. 5. The western Scheldt. 6. Borselen. 7. The Sloe. 8. Arnemuiden. 9. The eastern Scheldt. 10. Noord Beveland. 11. The Westgat. 12. The North Sea. 13. The Roompot. 14. Vrouwenpolder. 15. Domburg. 16. Westkapelle. 17. Breskens. 18. Zuid Beveland. 19. Canal from Veere to Middelburg. 20. Road from Veere to Middelburg. 21. Zoutelande.

called *jacobines*. Jo would have some trouble making the paper cups in which they would have to be prepared, but Lucie, who was very clever at such things, would no doubt help her out. As for wine, any ordinary Bordeaux would be to the taste of Robespierre, and Torquemada would probably drink nothing.

I ruled music out altogether. My guests were not the sort of men to care for any of the arts.

As for their police records, here they are. I shall go into considerable detail about Robespierre. He happens to interest me greatly, for he is the closest counterpart I can think of to that man now causing so much trouble among our eastern neighbors. I refer, of course, to Adolf Hitler, and by understanding Robespierre we may come to a fairly close approximation of the complicated character of that German rabble-rouser who may at any moment turn our world into a shambles.

A little boy was sitting on his tiny wooden trunk. He was waiting for the stagecoach which was to take him to Paris. His name was Maximilien Robespierre, though he was also known as Maximilien de Robespierre, the way his father preferred to write his name. That father was a very curious person, and if he had done nothing worse in his life than bestow a patent of nobility upon himself to which he had no right (it is still a doubtful case), his small son might not have turned into the self-righteous pedant who thirty years later was to cause such endless misery all over France.

The Robespierres were said to be of Irish origin. I feel inclined to believe it. Their fanaticism was Hibernian rather than Gallic, because it was accompanied by an absolute inability to forget any slight against their dignity, and there was no sense of humor in them. They were hopelessly serious. Life to them was serious. And nobody who did not take life seriously had the right to exist.

Arras is a terrible French nest. It reminds one of Noyon, a little farther to the south. Picardy at best is a dreary region: rolling fields without any charm, and cut into irregular pieces by those hollow roads which no historian thus far has been able to explain. And it always rains in Picardy. Small wonder that both Robespierre and John Calvin hailed from this region. It does not make for happiness.

Maximilien's father was a lawyer, a descendant of a long line of advocates. His mother was the daughter of a local brewer. She had improved her condition in life when she married a member of the bar, but it was the brewer's family which had to take care of some of the Robespierre children after the mother had died and the father had disappeared. He evaporated. One day he was still there. The next day he was gone. Some said that his wife's death had so affected him that he could no longer stand the sight of his children. Others insisted that he could no longer face his creditors. We do not know. Occasionally his name bobs up in letters that arrived in Arras from a number of German towns. Finally one day little Maximilien heard that *cher papa* was dead.

With both father and mother out of the picture, there was nothing the Carrauts (the brewer family of Maximilien's mother) could do but take care of the orphaned children as best they were able to. That meant a great deal of extra expense, and French families in the provinces are not fond of extra expense.

Maximilien had one brother and two sisters. They admired him and remained faithful to him unto death and, as far as one of the sisters was concerned, until long after death. The brother lost his life at the same time as Maximilien. One sister lived on and on—a gaunt reminder of the great revolutionary age—a tall, angular woman with whiskers and a bonnet, never going anywhere, never seeing anyone, spending her days in a room full of relics of the days when her brother had been dictator of France.

There were many such sinister women in the France of the thirties and forties of the last century. They were the former wives, sisters, or girl friends of the men who had died trying to establish the rule of the people. The people had turned against them and had slain them. A few of their womenfolk had been overlooked and had survived, hiding themselves in some obscure jail or in a faithful friend's cellar. When the danger was over, they had returned to live lives that no longer had either purpose or meaning. They became ghosts, and personally I have known a few very old men and women who remembered such cases.

"They were terrible," they told me, "those animated indictments of man's folly. Most of them turned the recollection of their departed brothers and husbands and lovers into a kind of private religion. They talked endlessly about their sainted Maximilien or their blessed Georges Jacques and prayed for the day when they might join them. Whenever they ventured forth to buy a few pennies' worth of bread or chicory (for all their possessions had been confiscated, and pensions were, of course, out of the question), nursemaids would grab their charges firmly by the hand and drag them away before they could be contaminated by a touch of 'the monster's sister.' But sometimes in the evening there would be a knock at the door, and an old man would stand before their carefully locked gates. He would identify himself as a friend or perhaps a collaborator of the former member of the Committee of Public Safety. He had escaped to America or India. He had had all sorts of adventures, few of them pleasant. Now he felt that the end of his days were approaching. He must once more talk to someone who had been related to 'the noblest mind that ever lived' and then he could die in peace. He talked until the early hours of morning and then left after kneeling down before the portrait of his hero. A few hours later, the gendarmerie would find his body hanging from the rafters of a mean room in a shabby hotel. Those were grim days. Those were terrible days. For the gods were on a gambling spree, and human lives were the stakes for which they played."

Maximilien was a very bright child. He was a little prig, and none of the other boys liked to play with him. He was excellent at his lessons and was quite willing to let others know it. He was brought up by his God-fearing aunts to become a good Christian, but their conceptions of the Christian virtues were those of middle-aged French spinsters. Life in that bleak house on that dull street in Godforsaken Arras must have been far from amusing. And, in order to save himself, Maximilien withdrew into a little dream castle of his own construction, a little castle on a little hill, but dominating the entire landscape. There he could feel himself superior to everybody else. He knew what was being said about him in the town—that he was not a legitimate child, that he had been the reason why his lawyer father had been forced to marry his plebeian mother. Within the walls of his little private stronghold, people who whispered such things were at once thrown into a deep dungeon where they perished slowly, while the lord of the manor came down once in a while to look, through a small peephole in the door, at their agonies.

Some day that little castle would become a reality and grow into a very big and real castle, and the owner would become a very great man. So let us keep our secret thoughts to ourselves and prepare for a career.

Examinations meant nothing to Robespierre. He was born to take examinations and to pass them, too. The state needed bright lawyers, for the administration of France had become so complex that there had to be some kind of official for every twenty ordinary citizens. The Church, too, needed stanch, dependable supporters, for heresy was rife. It was a new kind of heresy which did not bother about religion in the stricter sense of the word, and therefore it was all the more difficult to combat.

This new creed had placed man instead of God in the center of the universe. It even went so far as to preach man's divinity. This must inevitably lead to chaos, for with God deposed as the ruler of heaven and earth and all men regarded and treated as equals, what would become of authority—of the authority of the Pope, of the bishop, of the village priest?

Maximilien never bothered his little head about such things. He stuck to his lessons, went to Mass, and partook of Holy Communion. Little Maximilien therefore must be given every opportunity to go as far as he could. A scholarship was found for him at the college of Louis-le-Grand in Paris. His shabby clothes were carefully packed into his little wooden trunk. The aunts gave him their blessing. He was hoisted to the top of the diligence and rattled off to the capital.

Robespierre did not like his new school. He was a pale and unattractive-looking boy. His manners were awkward, provincial, lacking in charm. But when it came to Latin compositions, he easily outdistanced all his classmates. One day Louis and Marie Antoinette were to visit the college. Robespierre, as the brightest boy in school, was chosen to compose the ode of welcome. He was provided with a new and beautiful suit of clothes —real silk for the first time in his life. He was to be the hero of the occasion. The others would have to kneel by his side while he recited his noble-sounding verses, done in the best style of Virgil and Ovid, and attracted the attention of Their Majesties by the elegance of his diction and deportment.

It happened to rain that afternoon. The royal procession was delayed. When it finally arrived, the Queen was out of sorts and in no mood to listen to a small boy spouting ununderstandable hexameters. She told her husband that they had done enough for one day. The King told the coachman to drive on. Little Master Robespierre, in all his finery, was left alone, still kneeling in the mud, still holding on to his drenched manuscript. It had not exactly been a day of triumph. He had been laughed at.

Maximilien Robespierre was not the sort of boy who liked to be laughed at. He never forgot his humiliation. Thirteen years later he was to settle the score when he demanded that Louis and his wife perish on the guillotine, insisting that they must die that France might live.

In due course of time Maximilien was graduated. The aunts went to see their priest. The priest went to see his bishop.

Surely so good a scholar and so faithful a son of the Church was worthy of some recognition. The good bishop appointed Maximilien a judge in the diocese of Arras. The little wooden trunk made its reappearance in the city of its origin. But this time its owner returned as the holder of a degree, a large number of medals and prizes, and a fixed position with a fixed income.

He associated himself with the life of the town, spent more money on good clothes, joined the local literary and musical society called—believe it or not—the "Rosati," and at its annual public meetings recited verses of his own making. These bits of poetry, a few of which have survived, were pretty terrible, but it is said that the Arrageois loved to hear him recite. He had such a lovely voice.

Soon after his appointment, Robespierre resigned. In his capacity as judge of the criminal court it would have been his duty to condemn a man to death. The idea of shedding another person's blood was too much for him. He withdrew. For he loved humanity. He loved humanity so much that he intended to make it happy. In order to make it happy, he must first of all make it perfect. That meant that he must re-create mankind after his own image.

During the first ten years of his public life Robespierre tried to achieve this purpose by peaceful means. Then he began to notice that most people were very obstinate when it came to having their vices replaced by virtues. This he could not tolerate. If his fellow Frenchmen would not bend, then he would break them. And he lived up to his convictions. Before he himself had his jaw shot off, more people had died in consequence of his having scribbled his name at the bottom of a piece of paper than had during the reigns of the fourteenth, fifteenth, and sixteenth Louis.

That was quite an accomplishment for an obscure lawyer from a small provincial town. What interests me is the curious spiritual and emotional development of that kind of man with that kind of background who, in spite of all his natural disadvantages, was to put his imprint not only upon the history of France but also upon that of the whole civilized world.

I think it was Christian Friedrich Hebbel, the German tragedist of the first half of the last century, who favored us with the curious theory that every great artist was a potential great criminal and vice versa. I have not given the matter much thought and, anyway, I am probably not bright enough to give you the answer.

Hebbel, like Spengler, is one of those writers you like to read because most of the time they make you so angry that you are stirred up to do a little independent thinking. Occasionally you say to yourself, "There at last they seem to have got something!" and you leave the beaten track of your own conventional method of reasoning to find out to what new conclusions their line of thought might lead. Sometimes you are left standing in unpleasant loneliness before a high and unscalable wall of pure nonsense. But occasionally you will discover a narrow gully through which you are able to crawl into an unsuspected realm of fresh speculations, and this idea that the creative artist is merely a criminal who has missed his real vocation and that a criminal is an artist in his approach to his unpleasant vocation —well, let me see!

According to the same Hebbel, Shakespeare, if he had not found an outlet in writing about murderers, would himself have turned highwayman and would have ended on the gibbet. But what was the criminal trying to prove when he told us about the world's great lovers?

Poe, Strindberg, Dostoevsky, and Nietzsche were undoubtedly very fond of writing about those of their fellow men who were victims of what we nowadays call an "abnormal psychological development." In the language of the fellow in the street, they were "nuts," and while this is a much less attractive diagnosis than the dignified expression "abnormal psychological development," I am not sure but that it covers the case just about as thoroughly and as well.

At the same time, it must be confessed that many great creative artists have undoubtedly been borderline cases who would have come to an unfortunate end if it had not been for the nimbus of their "artisticity" which saved them from being hanged or put away in some convenient Schlüsselburg or Bastille.

This man Hitler, whom a great many people have denounced as one of the world's most dangerous criminals, started his career as a would-be artist, a painter and architect. He was so completely lacking in ability that every art school rejected him. It is perfectly possible that his repressed artistic sense thereupon took the form of some subtle kind of insanity, for frustration in the case of little minds is apt to do terrible things to their owners. And let us remember that frustration is most dangerous of all when it is based upon considerations of moral perfection on the part of the patient, for such moral considerations make it impossible for the victim to accept life as it is, and he will spend all his energies trying to remake the world as he thinks that it ought to be.

Robespierre, as I see him, was not a borderline case. He was way across the line. Ever since he had been sent to Versailles to represent the people of his native town, who were now going to assist their King in his efforts to save the country from bankruptcy and disorder—ever since that fateful day when the little old wooden trunk had once more been packed (but now with the garments he was expected to wear at the royal session)—he had felt convinced that at last his opportunity had come. He would mold the minds of his fellow men as a sculptor gives shape and form to a dead lump of clay, and France would rise gloriously from her present state of decay, and a simple lawyer from Arras would be her savior—a simple lawyer without title or wealth but strong by reason of his incorruptible virtues and the integrity of his private life.

When I was the last time in Germany, I heard endless tales about the incorruptible virtues and the integrity of the private life of their new prophet, Adolf Hitler. I was told what an extraordinary fellow he was. "He does not drink, he does not eat meat, he does not smoke, he has never kissed a girl. He devotes all his time to a single ideal."

"Himself?" I asked upon one occasion, trying to be facetious.

Alas! revolutions are not exactly the right time to be funny. My friends hastily took me away and advised me to take the next train back to Holland. Otherwise I might fare badly and even be killed.

A century and a half ago, a similar unguarded remark about the Great Incorruptible of the French Revolution would have caused an identical reaction. For the virtuous ones take themselves very seriously.

Mirabeau, the exact opposite of Robespierre, an aristocrat by birth who had lustily plundered life of all its more delectable fruits and who knew his fellow men from *A* to gizzard and then back again, listened to Robespierre just once and then summed him up in one single sentence which said about all there was to be said upon this unpleasant subject. "That nasty-looking, nearsighted lawyer from the little town in Picardy," he announced to his cronies, "will go very far: he actually believes everything he says."

Robespierre *did* go far, and here is a short outline of the last ten years of his life, for, after all, I will need a few background facts so that you will be able to understand why it was possible for a man of such mediocre abilities to get as far as he did.

The future dictator of France began his career as a moderate. Like most Frenchmen of that prerevolutionary epoch (and this cannot be stressed too often), he was a confirmed monarchist. It was not until long after that endless series of blunders and stupidities by which the King and his consort had alienated the affections of their loyal subjects that the word "republic" began at last to be whispered about as the only way out of a situation that had become absolutely intolerable.

Even then, the glamour that surrounded the throne was so enormous that when the famished mobs at last broke into the palace grounds of Versailles and sent a delegation of ordinary citizens—butchers, seamstresses, fishwives, and professional cut-throats—to tell Their Majesties that they must proceed to Paris and come and live "among their own people," three of these emissaries promptly fainted when at last they found themselves in the royal presence.

Robespierre, during these first years, was no exception to the general run of his fellow members of the Constituent Assembly. France must be regenerated. Virtue must be re-established. The rights of the common people must be defined, and henceforth these must be respected. But woe unto him who would dare to lift a finger against the sacred person of the King, the highest embodiment of the law!

That was the first phase during which our hero often spoke, established a reputation more for his eloquence than for the soundness of his ideas, and remained just one among a thousand other legal luminaries who, like himself, had come to Versailles to save the fatherland by giving it a new kind of civil and financial administration that should be a little more in keeping with the spirit of the times.

Then came the second phase. That was the period during which the stout and indolent, though amiable and good-natured, ruler of France gave evidence that he was a true member of the clan of the Bourbons, in that he was quite as unable to learn anything new as to forget anything old. That was the era during which the throne and the great nobles around the throne indulged in their clumsy plots to betray their country and surrender France to the foreign tyrants who had sworn that they would not rest until they had rid the world of the double menace of rebellion and revolution. For by then the dreadful specter of revolution had at last reared its ugly head, and the rest of Europe knew it.

Revolutions, as Egon Friedell has so well pointed out, are only possible when the army is no longer dependable, and the army becomes undependable only when the people (the soldiers' own mothers and fathers and brothers and sisters) are actually starving.

Why such a condition should have been allowed to develop in France, still the richest and the most fertile country of Europe, is another one of history's mysteries. Even now, when we have all the facts at our disposal, it is not easy to make a correct diagnosis. But I can venture a bold guess at the cause of most of the trouble.

A king is merely a symbol, and symbols, being inanimate objects and existing only in the imagination of the people who have created them, are often the cause of great confusion. They will satisfy everybody for four, five, or six hundred years, and nobody will dream of asking for a new form of government. But finally someone, somewhere, thinks that he has found a new symbol, much more in keeping with the needs of the times, and he will speak to his neighbors about it, or he will write a little pamphlet and will ask his fellow countrymen, "What do you think of my suggestion?"

If he is too far ahead of his contemporaries, the gendarmes will call for him, and the courts will give him a very heavy sentence—they may even condemn him to die. But if he is moderate in his recommendations and if what he says is appropriate and makes sense, then he is sure to find a hearing, and if those responsible for the show at the palace know their business, they will hasten to bring about such changes as are deemed necessary. This, however, they can only do if they have absolute control over their actors. I have been told by people who knew about such matters that no really good actor will ever completely identify himself with his part. In order to give the best possible performance, he must remain outside and above his role, for should he, wearing the costume of Hamlet, allow himself to become a real Hamlet, the results would be terrible.

By far the best kings and emperors and Popes and even presidents of the United States were those who were also good actors and who realized that the play is the thing and that there is a vast difference between actual life and life as represented on the stage. And knowing their craft, they were always willing to listen to the advice of their stage managers, and the show would thereupon be a success.

England is perhaps the best example of what can be accomplished if the leading figures can be made to realize that they are but mummers, dressed up to represent certain symbols in the pageant of statecraft, but that they are not supposed to make up lines of their own as they go along or to add little bits of business that are not in the script. That undoubtedly is why the British crown has survived all those upheavals which have destroyed practically every other throne in Europe.

But in the France of the eighteenth century, as in the Russia of the twentieth, the poor hams who went about dressed up in the garments of state made the fatal mistake of thinking themselves called upon to act. They were under the erroneous impression that they themselves, instead of the crown they wore and the scepter they carried and the ermine mantle that rested upon their shoulders, interested the populace and that it was before them personally that their subjects so humbly bowed their shaking knees. When at last some courageous courtier informed them of their error—and in a most tactful manner, too—and told them that they were supposed to content themselves with merely ornamental roles and must leave the heavy acting to their prime ministers and councilors, they said no, they would not dream of doing such a thing. Their names appeared upon the program in big black letters, and they insisted upon continuing as the stars of the performance.

Then catcalls began to resound from the gallery, and overripe vegetables commenced to descend upon the stage, and there were unseemly scenes outside the royal entrance when the performers left to go home.

Did all this remain unnoticed in the ancient kingdom of France? By no means. For more than three generations it had been practically the only topic of conversation. All the brightest minds were thinking overtime, trying to find a solution. Whole libraries were being filled with books and pamphlets suggesting methods by which lamentable conditions could possibly be improved. All the available knowledge of the whole civilized world, presented from the "new" point of view—the point of view, emphatically laid down by Descartes, that only "seeing is believing"—was gathered together in the famous encyclopedia of Diderot and d'Alembert, Voltaire, Rousseau, and the other philosophers and pseudo philosophers of the last half of the eighteenth century.

Even the clergy, who as a rule showed little direct interest in matters of this sort, took a hand in the debate and strongly urged that there be certain changes in the management.

It has become the habit during the last century and a half to blame the royal advisers for the eventual collapse of the monarchy. They are accused of having been too much interested in keeping everything in their own hands to listen to those who advocated a policy of compromise. Undoubtedly a few of His Majesty's ministers were too set in their ways to lend a favorable ear to any kind of recommendation that might interfere with their own privileges. But others had clearly noticed the handwriting on the wall and realized that if the public were exasperated beyond a certain point of endurance, all sorts of unfortunate consequences might follow—that the monarchy itself might be destroyed. Personally, I feel that even at that late date they might have been successful had they only been obliged to deal with the chief male performer. Unfortunately, the star had a wife who also considered herself a great actress but was merely a prima donna in the worst possible sense of the word. And when this Austrian princess, billed under the name of Marie Antoinette, made herself the center of a cabal which deliberately obstructed and prevented every innovation and made itself guilty of serious acts of sabotage, going so far as to call in foreign stage managers and directors to take the place of the domestic ones, then all indeed was lost.

In the upheaval that followed, the old Bourbon Theater was completely ruined, the furniture was thrown out of the windows, thousands of innocent people were trampled to death together with a few of the guilty ones, and the props of royal authority were burned in the market place amidst an orgy of wild rejoicing on the part of the public.

But as soon as this had been accomplished, new props and symbols had to be devised, new actors had to be found to give them life, and new stage managers had to be appointed to tell them how to do it. With the inevitable result that little provincial directors now hastened to Paris and suggested that they and their friends be entrusted with the job for which, in their own opinion, they were much better fitted than any of their metropolitan rivals. Besides, they ought to be given some recognition on account of their long-standing devotion to the cause of the New Theater.

It was during this period that Robespierre played that part for which he will be remembered long after most of his fellow actors shall have been forgotten.

He had begun to lay his plans—and most deliberately, too—while he was only a member of that Constituent Assembly which was to give France a new and more practical form of government. He had proceeded very slowly and carefully. He had figured out (he was a mighty good figurer-outer of those kinds of details) that, in order to achieve his purpose, he must first of all find an instrument with which he could force his will upon his opponents. Such an instrument was not to be found in the sleepy city of Versailles, still dominated by the guards of the royal palace. Neither could he make an appeal to the whole of the French nation. The country was too large and was still too much divided in its opinions to act as a unit. Every province was still the enemy of every other, and there was only one group that could be drilled and disciplined into a concrete army of opposition, ready and able to follow the bidding of its leader.

That group of people were the disinherited ones who dwelled miserably in the Paris slums. Badly housed, badly fed, badly clothed, disregarded and neglected for hundreds of years, but now at last beginning to realize their own strength, those unfortunate men and women were only waiting for someone to place himself at their head and give them a chance to avenge themselves for the centuries of oppression and maltreatment they had endured.

. Long before anyone else was bright enough to understand this, Robespierre recognized the fact that these ill-disciplined hordes, if properly handled, could be made to serve the purposes of revolution or at least his kind of revolution.

As a preliminary step, Robespierre became a member of the Commune of Paris. At first he kept himself discreetly in the background. His hour had not yet come. There still was a lot of preparatory work to be done, but it is characteristic of the men of his type that they are usually able to proceed very slowly and know how to bide their time, where other more impetuous people would rush ahead and spoil their chances and get themselves in trouble.

Also with an eye to the future, he had joined one of the most radical political organizations—a sort of eighteenth-century Tammany Hall, called the Club of the Jacobins, because it held its meetings in a cloister which had formerly belonged to the Jacobins, the name by which the Parisians had always known the order of the Dominicans. Originally, this organization had been a small affair, founded by a few Breton members of the Constituent Assembly. They had feared (and rightly so) that the government intended to let the Assembly meet and talk and talk and meet until the nation should have grown tired of these endless debates, when the government could step in and say, "In this way, nothing will ever be accomplished," could send the orators about their business, and then once more could inaugurate a strong-arm policy which must lead to the re-establishment of the absolute monarchy of former times.

These shrewd Bretons had come to the conclusion that the Constituent Assembly could never amount to anything until the people of France should have been sufficiently aroused to realize the issues at stake. But this could not be done until the French nation, long since deprived of any direct voice in the management of its own affairs, had been so thoroughly re-educated in practical politics that it was able to take a real and direct interest in the work of the Assembly.

The Jacobins therefore intended to give the French a course in elementary politics, and soon every French city and village had a Jacobin club of its own where the leading citizens with left-wing tendencies met two or three times a week (finally, every evening) to talk and discuss and harangue and attend dinners full of wine and rhetoric, at which the evils of the situation and the lamentable conditions of the French kingdom were threshed out amidst an incessant deluge of inspired if rather mediocre eloquence.

It cannot, however, be sufficiently stressed that, in spite of the deep interest they took in the affairs of the day, the Jacobins too were still far removed from any actual desire to get rid of the monarchy and to replace it by a republic. Even such honest moderates as Mirabeau and the Abbé Sieyès were proud to be counted among its members. Then someone hit upon the idea of strengthening the power of their organization by establishing a regular system of correspondence between all the individual clubs. That gave the more radical elements their chance to find out who their friends were.

In the meantime, other political organizations were being formed among other members of the Assembly. There were the Feuillants, former Jacobins who, recognizing that their old club was drifting more and more toward those extreme principles of which they themselves could never approve, had founded a middle-of-the-road association of their own which also had its headquarters in a former monastery, that of the reformed Cistercians.

And then there were the Girondists, originally a small number of members from the Gironde district—the region around Bordeaux, the old home of that most reasonable of all citizens, the Sieur de Montaigne, whom we hope soon to have as one of our Saturday-evening guests. They foresaw the possibility that some day, due to the duplicity of the Queen and the lack of force and insight of the King, they might be under the necessity of establishing a republic. But they wanted it to be a republic of gentlemen—of men of learning—of what the Romans used to call the "good citizens." They did not want to repeat the mistakes of the old Greek democracies, which had invariably degenerated into mere mob rule.

All the best brains of the Assembly gradually drifted toward the Girondists. That meant that they withdrew from the clubs of the Jacobins and the Feuillants. The Feuillants retained, until the end, some semblance of respectability. But the Jacobins fell rapidly under the domination of the extremists. They were the Bolshevists of the great French Revolution, just as the Girondists and the Feuillants were the Mensheviks. Benjamin Franklin might have felt at home among the Girondists, while Sam Adams of Boston would surely have raged among the Jacobins, spurring them on to ever and ever greater efforts to rid the country of its tyrants.

That was the general setup of French political life as long as the King and Queen were still playing bezique in Versailles. And now let us see how Robespierre set to work to make himself master of the situation.

In order to do so he had to play a role—a role so simple that everybody at all times could see him and hear him, applaud him, and follow him. He therefore endeavored to make himself the embodiment of civic virtue. That would give him an opportunity to denounce all those who opposed him as traitors, for all he had to do was to accuse them of being lacking in that most praiseworthy quality.

Perhaps Hebbel was right, after all. Perhaps every great statesman and every great leader is at heart an artist. In the case of Robespierre, his histrionic genius manifested itself within the field of the drama. For the Revolution from then on became a tragedy, with Maximilien taking the role of the star.

Robespierre's first great opportunity came during the debate upon the foreign policy of the kingdom of France. This happened after the Constituent Assembly had been dissolved to make room for the more practical Legislative Assembly, which was to give France its new form of government. The Girondists and the more moderate elements were in favor of a foreign war. A foreign war, so they reasoned, would unite the hopelessly divided French people and turn them into a nation inspired by a common will to conquer or to die. Therefore, let France declare war upon all European tyrannies and let her battalions march forth to carry the blessings of liberty, equality, and fraternity to all the world.

The Jacobins strongly opposed such a plan. They knew that the court also hoped for a war, for then, in case of victory, the Austrian and German armies would make short shift of the rabble which now kept the royal children awake with their unseemly ravings right underneath the windows of the palace. And Marie Antoinette was using every opportunity to encourage her Austrian relations to do just that—to mobilize and rush to her defense and break the power of the Revolution.

Within the Legislative Assembly the radical members—almost all of them Jacobins—had preferred to take the seats high up along the walls. That is why they were called the Mountaineers, or, for short, the Mountain. The Feuillants gradually disappeared from the scene. It then became a struggle between the moderates, or the Plain, because they occupied the seats on the floor, and the radicals, or the Mountain, who sat up high in the galleries.

Now, after all these years of patient waiting, Robespierre was in his true element. His original shyness had left him. At last he was certain of himself. He not only could speak but he knew that when he asked to be allowed to say a few words the people, not only of Paris but of the whole of France, would listen to him. And he had plenty to say.

The royal family had already been moved from Versailles to Paris, where it would be safer among its loyal, loving Parisian subjects, as the Jacobins had proclaimed from the housetops when they forcibly took the King and Queen from Versailles to the drafty and uncomfortable old palace of the Tuileries—a residence which, since it had not been occupied for almost seventy-five years, was by then completely stripped of its furniture. Here Their Majesties camped out rather than lived.

And then the King and Queen committed a dreadful mistake —the mistake that was to cost them their lives.

Marie Antoinette had a friend, the handsome, energetic, but very superior Count Fersen, a young Swede who, as Rochambeau's adjutant, had played an honorable part in the American Revolution and who, after a few years' residence in his native land, had returned to Paris as a special envoy of the King of Sweden.

Fersen—we might as well give him due credit for the honesty of his emotions—felt profoundly sorry for the poor royal family which was now so completely at the mercy of the Paris mob and who were treated no better than common, ordinary criminals. He made all the necessary arrangements for their flight. One night he smuggled them out of the palace, packed them all into an enormous traveling coach, and sped them on their way toward the frontier. When it seemed that they were safe, that nothing more could possibly interfere with their flight, he left them to their own devices. He should have known better. He should not have let them out of his sight until they were under the protection of the Austrian hussars who were waiting for them at the other side of the village of Varennes.

But who shall save those whom the gods have doomed? The Queen, the beautiful Queen, had decided that as soon as she should have reached the city of Strasbourg she must absolutely have her hair done by her own favorite barber. This Figaro therefore had been sent several days ahead of the royal family that he might have everything ready for the great moment.

A little personal recollection. On the morning Queen Victoria of Spain arrived in Paris after having escaped from her turbulent country, I was sitting with Jacques Worth, the famous French couturier, whose grandfather had been responsible for so much of the glory of the Second Empire. He excused himself to answer a telephone call. The moment he put down the receiver he threw both hands toward heaven in a gesture of despair. "They are hopeless," he said. "Will they never learn? That was the Queen of Spain at the Meurice. She asked me to send one of my *vendeuses* to the hotel as fast as I could. Her Majesty wants a few new dresses. Yesterday she lost her kingdom. The first thing she thinks of the moment she is safe in Paris is a few new dresses. Will they never learn?"

I answered, "Probably not," and he replied, "No! They never will."

Marie Antoinette was a sister under the skin of the last of the Spanish queens. She was fleeing for her life and she must have known that it was her last chance. But she must have her hair fixed by her own coiffeur. This loquacious creature had, of course, been unable to keep his mouth shut. Wherever he had stopped, in order to make himself important, he had hinted at certain other personages who would soon follow him—friends of his—and: "Ah, if only you knew who they are, then wouldn't you be surprised!"

His listeners were more curious than surprised. Stories about the possibility of a flight of the royal couple had been circulated for weeks. Now it appeared that, after all, there was something to those rumors! Everywhere all good Jacobins began to look for a mysterious traveling coach carrying the royal couple toward the frontier.

The rest of Fersen's beautiful plan was botched by the King. A terrific gourmand (there was little of the gourmet about him), he must have his meals at the regularly appointed hours. He insisted upon stopping for a little snack, for it was getting late and there was no telling when he would have another opportunity at a juicy leg of chicken. The royal barouche was halted. The village was awakened by the noise of a foreign family loudly clamoring for food. A few clever citizens put two and two together. They thought that this so-called Austrian baron bore a striking resemblance to the King's effigy on the coins in their pockets. They began to ask questions. Someone rang the church bells. The whole neighborhood, fearing that the Austrians had come to murder them, got mobilized. And early the next morning, the King, still eating chicken legs out of his picnic basket, was on his way back to his capital. So was the Queen. So were the royal children.

After that, as every good Frenchman asked his neighbor, how could anyone ever again trust this miserable Austrian woman and her stupid husband? But the realization of how nearly this plot had succeeded set loose such a panic and caused such an outburst of fury at the treason of the Capet family (for everybody now referred to His Majesty as the Citizen Capet, the original name of the dynasty) that the fate of both the King and the Queen was sealed.

France declared war upon Austria, the Tuileries were invaded by the Paris mob, the Swiss guards were massacred almost to the last man, and the King, wearing a red revolutionary beret, was taken to the old fortress of the Knights Templars in the heart of the city, where he was imprisoned with the rest of his family.

The building of the Parisian municipal council was broken into by the mob, which now began to rule the capital by means of its ward assemblies. General Lafayette was proscribed and had to flee for his life, surrendering to the Hapsburgs, who, with proverbial Austrian stupidity, treated him as a criminal and for years held him locked up in that uncomfortable prison from which he addressed his futile appeals to America to do something for him, please.

And as a last straw, the Duke of Brunswick, a martinet of the old school but now in command of all antirevolutionary armies, issued his famous manifesto in which he threatened to hang every Frenchman who did not at once surrender to his troops. That was hardly the way to make himself popular with Their Majesties' jailers. Had they been leaderless, they might have trembled before His Highness' sesquipedalian literary effort, and the fear of the Prussian veterans might have caused them to proceed rapidly in a westerly direction. But that is where the Austrians and the Prussians made their mistake. The Revolu-

tion had at last found its master. The Jacobins had forced the
Girondists out of office. The Jacobins were now running things
and were running them with great skill, considering that most
of them were very young men in their early thirties, with practically no training in applied politics.

I am, after all, giving you a pretty detailed description of this
phase of the Revolution. But we who are living today ought to
know all this. We ought to be thoroughly familiar with these
developments, for they are once more taking place, and this
time right under our own noses, though we pretend not to see
them. I know the answer—why bother? History never repeats
itself—and that, of course, is true, but only to a limited extent.
The sorts of men who in days of stress are apt to come to the
front—or to the surface—and take hold of the situation and
finally dominate it usually bear such a striking resemblance to
one another that we can almost speak of a regular "revolutionary type."

The Nazis are the Jacobins of today, and for every Nazi
leader I can offer you a Jacobin equivalent. Hitler himself is an
exact copy of Robespierre. And if he had been in the Frenchman's shoes he would have done exactly what Robespierre did.
He too would have waited in the background while others did
that "dirty work" which is an inevitable part of every revolutionary outbreak during its preliminary stages.

Robespierre was much too shrewd to identify himself openly
with anything that happened during the first outbreaks of
violence. But from behind the scenes he helped to spread that
panic which swept over France when the attempted flight of the
royal family, the organization of an army of refugees in the
Rhine region, and rumors of fifth-column activities among the
remaining nobles had begun to make people expect to find a
spy underneath every bed and a traitor hidden in every cupboard.

Meanwhile, the organization of a nation-wide counterattack
in the form of terror—of wholesale murder and wholesale executions—was entrusted to another obscure young lawyer, a certain

Georges Jacques Danton. Like Robespierre, Danton had realized that the Revolution could not be won without the support of an armed force and that that armed force lay ready at hand in the slums of Paris. But for the rest there was nothing in common between these two leaders. For Danton loved his women, his food, his wine, and everything else that life offered to a young man whose health was indestructible, whose appetites were insatiable, and who was profoundly conscious of his ability to dominate his fellow citizens by means of his spectacular gifts as a rabble-rouser.

Danton despised the sickly Robespierre, who spent several hours every day swathing his inflamed legs in flannel bandages, who did not appear at the club until his barber had put a last touch on his severely fashionable wig, who never indulged in intoxicating beverages (lovely phrase, so dear to the hearts of all pure souls!), who worked for hours over every page of his interminable speeches, about whom there was not a single story to connect him with a member of the opposite sex, and who, wherever he went, enveloped himself in a cloak of self-righteous virtue. There was not a grain of self-righteousness in Danton, and virtue in his eyes was something that was all right for his aunts in the old home town in Champagne. As for him, life was there to be enjoyed with all the senses—and a curse upon this miserable pharisee who always made you feel conscious of your own shortcomings.

However, for the moment the two needed each other. They carefully hid the knives they hoped some day to stick into each other's backs, and while Robespierre, who was the more careful and cautious of the two, agitated behind the scenes, Danton was allowed to rush out in front and stem the tide of defeat by a series of exploits which will forever associate his name with that of some of the world's most successful assassins, except that he took no personal delight in seeing his victims being sent to their fate. He was much too fond of life to deny others the same rights he claimed for himself.

This is a pretty serious indictment, and I should therefore add that Danton also was a devoted patriot and that like all good Frenchmen he detested a lack of logic. It irritated him when other Frenchmen refused to avail themselves of their God-given power of reason to solve those problems of statecraft which, when all was said and done, were not really very different from simple problems in mathematics. (O René Descartes! How thoroughly you had prepared the way for all this!) He felt no personal hatred toward the King—the poor *bonhomme* who would have made such an excellent locksmith, such an exemplary father of a family, but who was so hopelessly miscast in the role he had been forced to play. However, if that honest Citizen Capet insisted upon letting himself be led by the nose by his beautiful and ambitious wife, it was up to him, Georges Jacques Danton, to show the poor dupe how such women should be treated.

As for the fops and the gilded popinjays who were still dreaming of a Versailles resurrected from its slumbers by the elegant officers of the imperial Austrian armies—they were beyond salvation. Like the dynasty they had served so faithfully and so ineffectively, they would have to go—and the sooner the better!

Early in the morning of September 2, 1792, the tocsins of Paris began to ring. This was a signal to the gangsters and professional cutthroats of the capital that they could go ahead, that the sky was the limit, and that no questions would be asked. Five days later word went around that enough was enough and that these blood-smeared patriots had better return to their hovels. They had done a thorough job. Most of the leaders of the monarchy, and a great many of the advocates of a constitutional form of government, were dead. Their number will never be known, but it was somewhere between twelve and fifteen hundred. After that, the road was clear. The Revolution could march on. The Jacobins, now dressed in workingmen's garb (the long and sloppy pantaloons as opposed to the tight-fitting *culottes,* or short trousers of the old regime), with their unkempt hair (except Robespierre, who went to the scaffold neatly groomed), their red bonnets of freedom, and their gory sabers, were in full command.

France was at their feet, but at whose feet exactly? The Legislative Assembly had been dissolved. The National Convention had taken its place, proclaiming itself the source of all authority. But who would be the source of all authority within this unwieldy body of yes men, more than one half of whom had never been in politics before?

At first, Danton dominated the meetings. He used his power with so much virtuosity that he considered himself safe from attack. The Austrians and Prussians, who only a few months before had still threatened the country, were being pushed back on all fronts. Soon France hoped to re-establish herself within her natural boundaries, which, as all the world knew, were the Rhine on the east and the Meuse on the north.

Two weeks after the September murders, the monarchy was abolished, and France was declared a republic. The Christian chronology was abolished as a useless relic of a bygone age. September 22 of the year 1792 became the first day of the year of the new era. In December began the King's trial. He was found guilty and was duly executed in January of the year 1793. It was the first time in almost a century and a half that such a thing had happened—that an anointed personage had perished on the scaffold. Europe was so horrified that Austria, England, Prussia, Holland, and Spain actually forgot their conflicting interests long enough to start a common campaign against the long-pantalooned monsters who had dared to lay hands on the descendant of Saint Louis and had rudely dispatched him to heaven.

Once again France heard herself denounced as the enemy of mankind, and emissaries of the Church began to find their way to Brittany and the Vendée, where a few simple peasants still believed in God and in the divine right of their masters to plunder them in the name of authority. These poor Vendéans started a rebellion in the north. General Dumouriez, who, if he had had the courage to march on Paris, could have sent all the Jacobins about their business (the majority of the French people still felt horrified at the legal murder of their King), but who lacked the moral strength to take this bold step, had sold out to the Austrians. Panic once more stalked through the streets of Paris. Once more the time had come to unloose terror.

On March 9, 1793, a revolutionary tribunal was established in Paris. This court did not bother about either witnesses or lawyers, and its sense of justice was not tempered by mercy. It either set free or condemned to death, usually the latter. And a month later, France became a dictatorship. A Committee of Public Safety, composed of nine men, soon afterward increased to twelve, took charge of the affairs of state.

Both Danton and Robespierre were among its members. From that moment on, it was the tail that wagged the dog. Paris ruled France, and Paris in turn was ruled by the worst element of its highly cosmopolitan society, the crackpots, the degenerates, the seemingly inspired but hopelessly impractical visionaries, the theorists who knew life only from the pages of their pamphlets, the pimps and their lady loves, the renegade aristocrats and the unfrocked priests. Anyone who was out of tune with the world, anyone who thought himself a great thinker but who had been condemned to years in the sewers by the indifference of his fellow men, anyone who had a grievance against a universe which had not treated him as he knew he had deserved to be treated—all these poor physical and moral and spiritual derelicts now found themselves in a position to exercise authority.

"Allons, enfants de la patrie!" The day of the Great Revenge had come. And in his solitary room, carefully protected against all drafts (for his health once more was not all it should have been), sat the little lawyer from Arras, the virtuous Citizen Maximilien Robespierre, now holding in his clammy hands the fate of France.

There are several pictures drawn by contemporary artists which show us Maximilien as he looked at that time. A face that gives you the creeps. There is a creature just now in Germany who is beginning to play quite a role as one of Hitler's right-hand men, for he is the head of the Nazi secret service. His name is Himmler. He used to be a schoolteacher. He has the most repellent, most repulsive, and most cruel face I have ever seen on any human being. And he is Robespierre's double: the same tight lips, the same sneer of self-righteous superiority, the same holier-than-everybody-else attitude in the shoulders, which seem to be propelling him toward a secret goal.

Yet, there is no mystery about the role he intends to play. He is inspired, as all people of his type have invariably been, by his love of self. He has never known any other God outside his own ego. When such spiritually misshapen creatures appear upon the scene, there is only one thing we can hope for—that another Charlotte Corday will arise and pierce their hearts with a kitchen knife, as that honest girl from the provinces did in the case of the unspeakable Marat. But people of Charlotte's courage and determination are rare. Nor do many of them enjoy the opportunity that was hers. And when they fail (as a poor, demented fellow failed a little while later in his attempt on the life of Robespierre), their intended victims use the opportunity to proclaim themselves among the potential martyrs and saints. In that case, God help us all!

And now to work, my hearties, and let us see how we can rid ourselves of all those who still stand between us and the supreme power. On June 2, 1793, the Commune arranged a disturbance in the Convention (which still existed, though it had lost all influence) and forced the frightened members of that sovereign body to arrest thirty-one Girondists, thereby making an end of whatever influence the moderates had until then been able to exercise over their fellow members. In July of the same year, Charlotte Corday murdered Dr. Marat, the Dr. Goebbels of the Reign of Terror, also a cripple, also animated by the deepest hate and contempt for his fellow men.

Apparently no honest patriot was to be safe any longer from

the intrigues of the foreign enemy. The moment had come for the Committee of Public Safety to roll up its sleeves and show that the Revolution meant business.

In August, the whole of the French nation was mobilized. A mathematical genius by the name of Carnot was given the task of organizing the army, of raising the necessary money in a state that was so hopelessly bankrupt that the francs were no longer worth the paper on which they were printed, of establishing wages and the price of all commodities, of creating order out of chaos, and, as a side line, of constructing a modern centralized nation out of the ruins of a hopelessly outworn feudal state in which every province, every town, and every hamlet had been a semi-independent unit with its own tax system, its own dialect, its own caste system, its own customs and habits, and its own set of laws.

With the indefatigable Carnot looking after the practical sides of life, Robespierre could at last devote himself wholeheartedly to the business of giving the Revolution that ideal twist which was to turn it into the greatest moral experiment of the ages and which was to make Christianity look like the amateur effort of a well-meaning Jewish prophet who had not quite known how to handle the situation.

First of all, a lesson had to be taught to those misguided Vendéan peasants who still fought the battalions of the French Republic and who marched into battle carrying pictures of their saints. Between October and December they were almost completely annihilated. A revolutionary tribunal was established at Nantes. It condemned more than fifteen thousand persons to death. That was too large a number to shoot or to hang, for the bankrupt Republic could ill afford so much gunpowder and rope. So the victims were loaded on barges and then dumped into the rivers and drowned. If their relatives walked far enough downstream, they could fish out the bodies and give them Christian burial. The Republic was too busy to bother about that detail.

In October, Marie Antoinette was brought before her judges

and, after one of the most degrading trials in history, during which a serious effort was made to force her small son to accuse his mother of illicit sexual intercourse with her own child, she was condemned to death. The details of her execution, the unspeakable horror of her last few hours on earth, made no doubt a pleasant subject of conversation at the dinner table of the Duplay family, where the virtuous Maximilien lived when he was in town and where he became almost human enough to ask for the hand, in virtuous matrimony, of the oldest daughter, Éléonore, whose steadfast loyalty to her hero was so great that she might have served as a model for Beethoven's heroine in *Fidelio.*

Anyway, things were happening. The Queen was gone, and less than two years later her small son was to disappear, probably dying as the result of the neglect he had suffered while being boarded out with the family of a drunken shoemaker.

On the last day of October of the year 1793, twenty-one Girondists, the old enemies of the Jacobins, were decapitated. After that, the lists of the condemned began to grow at a hideous pace.

Robespierre was a most methodical person. Nothing in his life was ever left to chance. Everything must be duly card-catalogued. He specialized in little books, and in these little books he noted down, in his small, fussy handwriting, the names of all those who might be suspected of "anticivic tendencies." It was not necessary to have indulged in an act of treason. A suspicion of being suspect was enough to entitle a person to a *carte de permission* to the Elysian Fields. For death had now become a matter of jest. People were no longer decapitated. They were "suppressed" by that marvelous new piece of machinery invented by the ingenious Dr. Guillotin. This God-fearing teacher in the Jesuit college of Bordeaux, wishing to save the victims of revolutionary justice the agonies of those last frightful moments when the axman was placing their heads in just the right position on his block, had taken some of the medieval decapitating machines as his model and had so greatly

improved upon these clumsy contraptions that now the operation could be performed in exactly three manipulations. In less
than a minute and a half from the moment the victim was put
on the plank he stood before his Maker.

This innovation, by the way, had led to one of the most
curious labor troubles of the age. In France the hangman's
profession had always been regarded as an honorable craft. The
office had passed from father to son until several of the oldest
families of executioners could boast that they had been in the
business for more than three centuries with never a mistake or
a complaint. They now found themselves in the same desperate
plight as that of the weavers of England a few years later, when
steam threatened to drive out the old hand looms. No longer
was it necessary to pass through years of faithful apprenticeship
to learn just how the ax should be wielded or the fatal knot
should be tied. Any fool could learn to pull a handle, and
hundreds of years of accumulated skill became useless. And
then there was the loss of those nice old extras—so much for
twenty feet of rope, so much for the sharpening of the ax. All
these welcome little bits of graft so dear to the hearts of honest
Frenchmen had been dispensed with. And as one could easily
move the guillotine from town to town, the local trade was
threatened with a considerable loss of employment, for now
one man could do the work formerly divided among a dozen.

Believe it or not, but in many towns the introduction of this
instrument of mercy led to regular riots. Pickets had not yet
been invented, but it is easy to imagine a group of outraged
members of the Lyons Local 471, Jack Ketch, Chairman, marching up and down in front of the gallows, bearing placards saying, "The government is unfair to organized hangmen."

Yes, those were the days, for now at last the Kingdom of
Virtue was at hand, and Maximilien Robespierre was to be its
prophet and high priest. And so let the revolutionary tribunals,
now established in every part of France, perform their holy
rites. Let all the sentimental dreamers about a constitutional

Liberty, fraternity, equality.

monarchy and the sovereignty of the "intelligent part" of the nation pay with their lives for their absurd notions.

Once the groundwork had been laid for the New Zion and the Lord's anointed had been removed from the scene, it was time to do something about the Lord Himself. So He, too, was abolished, together with His Church, and their place was taken by a curious new faith known as the Cult of Reason.

This Cult of Reason (not exactly in the Cartesian sense of the word!) had for a long time been one of the special hobbies of some of the most outstanding rattlepates of the great Revolution. One of the most energetic prophets of the new creed was that spurious German baron who called himself Anacharsis Cloots (his Christian name was really Jean Baptiste) and whose calling cards informed the world that he was the Official Orator of the Human Race. This singular individual had found his way to Paris early in the Revolution, when all the well-intentioned giddyheads of the whole world were hastening to the French capital that they might be present at the coming of the God of Reason. Even after this new deity had been revealed to them as a goddess of very uncertain antecedents, they did not waver in their enthusiasm. (By the way, the poor girl who played the role of the Goddess of Reason on the occasion of her first public worship had almost paid for this sacrilege with her life. For it was a blustery day when she danced in front of the high altar, and Notre Dame, where the ceremony took place, was as cold as the grave, and the Goddess, dressed only in a thin frock of cheesecloth, had to stand still for such a long time that she caught a *pneumonie* which almost carried her to her grave.)

This silly comedy, however, delighted the hearts of all the idiots who were firmly convinced that now humanity had at last come into its own, and they joyfully set forth to turn the whole world upside down by a series of acts so utterly absurd that we wonder how otherwise not unintelligent people like our own Tom Paine could ever have taken them seriously and why Dr. Schiller, the well-known German dramatist, should have been willing to accept an "honorary citizenship" (made out in the name of Citizen Siller) from a nation which had apparently lost all touch with reality.

But we should remember that all these absurdities fitted into the policy of separating the very conventional French people from their very conventional past, and therefore even such coolheaded and sober leaders as Danton (one of the really strong-minded men of that crazy epoch) were willing to look the other way while the lunatic fringe did its best to discredit everything connected with the rule of the late Citizen Louis Capet.

This feeling of amused indifference was not at all shared by him whom Carlyle called the "sea-green Incorruptible," for Robespierre, who suffered from chronic constipation, had the unhealthy pallor of all such patients, though it never, as far as we know, changed from white to green. This is another interesting point to which I should draw your attention.

Robespierre, in spite of his indifference about human suffering, was at heart a very religious person and, because he was painfully lacking in a sense of the ludicrous, he could not for the life of him understand why all this tomfoolery of the Clootses and their disciples should so greatly amuse Danton and his set of friends. This juggling with the eternal verities disgusted him profoundly, and he decided that the sooner it came to an end, the better it would be for that holy cause of true virtue. And so, while still maintaining an outward semblance of cordiality toward his colleagues in the Convention and Committee of Public Safety, he once more got busy with his little notebooks.

Robespierre had by this time learned the value of the element of surprise. He therefore waited while he set his traps. He sprang them in the spring of the next year, 1794.

Before they knew what had happened, all the more radical elements of the Commune—Cloots and his friends and, worst of all, Danton and his adherents—found themselves in prison. From there they were dispatched to the scaffold with such indecent haste that most of them were dead before they had quite realized how it had all come about. Except Danton, who, being a natural-born actor, had turned his trial and execution into an act of such sublime dramatic quality that even Robespierre must have experienced a few moments of discomfort. But these did not last very long. The conviction that he had acted the only way a virtuous citizen could possibly have acted quickly consoled him for the loss of all his former classmates, friends, and colleagues whom he now had sent so brutally to their doom.

Besides, there was too much to do to waste time upon one's private feelings. First of all, the people of France must be led back to the pathways of Truth. That was easy. A resolution was offered in the Convention whereby that august body declared itself to be in favor of the existence of a Supreme Being. The resolution was passed, and God was once more reinstated on his heavenly throne.

To bring this joyful fact to the attention of all the people, June 8 was dedicated to an official feast in honor of the Supreme Being. That probably was the happiest day in the life of Maximilien Robespierre. Like that other historical figure who resembles him in so many ways (Adolf Hitler), Maximilien loved to devise large-scale public entertainments as evidence of his ability as an artist. Many accounts have come down to us of this noble *fête de l'Être suprême*. We should remember that these reports were not written by men who were Robespierre's friends, but by citizens who wished for nothing as much as for his speedy demise, that they themselves might have a chance to live a little longer.

There is, however, in all these stories about that event an identical strain of honest astonishment that any man not deprived of his senses could so openly have made such an unmitigated fool of himself. Which meant that Robespierre must have been, in his own eyes, at his best. He had most carefully attended to all the details of the show. For it was a "show" in the literal sense of the word—a vast open-air performance, with little maids of honor, in white dresses and with flowers in their hair, singing hymns, and the whole of the Convention forced to attend in formal attire. When everybody was thoroughly exhausted and ready to go home, there came a lengthy harangue by the great Maximilien himself and the unveiling of a gigantic stucco statue representing the triumph of Belief over Unbelief.

This part of the performance, however, was not a success, for something went wrong with the arrangements by which the outer shell representing Evil was to fall to pieces at the touch of Robespierre's torch and reveal the inner shell which was supposed to represent Virtue. But something went wrong. The outer shell did not fall to pieces the way it should have done. The torch failed to set fire at the right moment and caused Virtue to be half blackened by smoke. The whole performance degenerated into a farce of such gigantic proportions that only the fear of those little notebooks the high priest of this occasion was known to carry in his vest pocket prevented the audience from breaking forth into loud guffaws.

Even Robespierre, in his blind self-confidence, could not help but notice that he had not done so well, but it only convinced him that the French people were more depraved than he had believed them to be and that more drastic methods must be used to bring them to reason.

One excellent way of achieving concrete results in the matter of terror was to commit citizens to jail without giving them a chance to defend themselves. It also saved time, and one could use the transmission-belt method in sending them to the scaffold—ten a day—speed it up a bit and make it twenty a day —then thirty, forty, fifty, sixty—with a nice total of four or five hundred a month.

But, as every engineer knows, even a transmission belt will occasionally fail to function properly. On the same day on which the Republic kills a poor, half-witted girl who has been found wandering in Robespierre's street with a kitchen knife in her possession—on that very same day a man with quite a reputation as a practical joker must get up in the Convention and inquire—oh, so politely—to what extent the President of the Committee of Public Safety had been implicated in the affair of the Mother of God.

That question, of course, was absurd, and it should never have been allowed to be asked. The Mother of God to whom reference was made was a crazy old cook who lived in a garret and who had gradually surrounded herself with a small group of devoted worshipers who believed in her sacred mission, called her the Mother of God, and prayed with her for the second coming of the Son. There was nothing very exciting about the revelations made by the police about the existence of such an organization as the Followers of the Mother of God, and under ordinary circumstances nobody would have worried about the identification card which Robespierre had signed for the old lady as head of the ward in which both of them happened to live. Such cards, guaranteeing the bearer to be a good patriot, were part of the daily routine of every citizen of the Reign of Terror. They were about as impersonal as automobile licenses, and what Robespierre wanted to know was how this harmless document had ever got into the hands of the noisy and alcoholic Gascon who was now asking embarrassing questions about the Virtuous Leader and the Mother of God in the Convention. He knew that it was being done to discredit him and make him look ridiculous, but who was behind this move?

In happy anticipation of soon being enlightened upon this point, Robespierre first settled the fate of the Mother of God. She and her disciples—a motley collection of kitchen slaveys, scullery maids, a poor ex-priest who had lost his reason as a result of seeing a batch of his fellow clerics murdered before his own eyes, and several dozen others of the same ilk—were condemned in haste and decapitated in a hurry. A few months before, such a drastic measure would have been sufficient to put an end to all further rumors. But not this time!

For now wherever the Virtuous One goes, he hears half-stifled whispers accompanied by happy giggles: "Look! There goes the friend of the Mother of God!"

Under these circumstances, why not disappear for a couple

of weeks? The people of Paris are short-memoried, and when one comes back, the matter will have been completely forgotten.

Also—another good idea—take daily walks with one's fiancée, the charming Éléonore Duplay, to silence those voices which have been hinting that the great man might perhaps be a bit "queer" in his attitude toward the other sex. Another important item, never to be forgotten. After you have returned from your little holiday, be very much of the gentleman. Even when you refuse a wife's tear-choked pleas for her husband's life, do so with a show of dignified aloofness. All true aristocrats have long since been exterminated, and their elegant manners are supposed to have perished with them. That is why the average run of people are so delighted to come in contact with an official who reminds them of the good old days when the King was still on his throne and bowed low to every serving maid he encountered in the corridors of his palace.

Another item, also very important: and better make a note of it in the little book. Now, more than ever, observe the most scrupulous care in your outward appearance. These last few years, everybody has worn his oldest clothes, has let his hair grow, has avoided cleaning his fingernails because he did not want his neighbors to report him as "suspected of aristocratic leanings as he cleans his teeth and nails twice a day." Go to the other extreme, for people will love it after these years of an affected democratic sloppiness.

To make this new civic arrangement absolutely permanent so that the labor that has been accomplished during so many painful years cannot possibly be undone, the Convention must first of all be discontinued and the Committee of Public Safety must be given even greater powers than it has enjoyed before. This, of course, must be done very adroitly. Above all things, no direct threats. No further invasion of the Convention hall by armed hoodlums, threatening to kill the members in their seats. But a careful juggling of names, coupled with innuendos and whispered hints. "Of course, if it should be proved, as I have been creditably told, that so-and-so feels in such and such a way about my new law on such and such a subject, then I would be regretfully obliged . . ." and here let your voice trail off into a whisper and reach with your right hand meaningly into that coat pocket where, as everybody knows, you keep the little paper-covered booklet containing those "certain names." And when you cannot lay hands on a man who is your enemy, then reach him indirectly through some woman he loves and whom you cause to be placed in custody, just in case . . . but don't finish that menacing sentence. As a matter of fact, never quite finish any sentence. For then your listeners will be kept wondering what more you were going to say, until the tension makes their nerves crack and they are ready to commit any kind of folly and will expose themselves like a blind man defending himself against a pack of wolves and with no other weapons than his bare fists. It is a marvelous plan of action, isn't it, and best of all it is absolutely foolproof. Until the fatal morning when you are caught napping.

One of your colleagues of the Convention, crazed by fear for the fate of his mistress whom you have sent to jail as a hostage for her lover's good behavior, has been driven to the point of despair where he may try to kill you. Get up in meeting and solemnly declare him to be "outside of the law" before he can take any countermeasures. Next let your shortsighted eyes scan the pages of your little paper-covered book and hint in an ominous tone of voice that there are a few others whom in your own good time you will be obliged to bring before the bar of justice. You have done it often. It never failed to work, but this time, something must have slipped up somewhere. There is sudden commotion, the brandishing of knives in the best classical style, shouts of "Down with the tyrant!" references to the Ides of March, all of which you will answer with a renewed gesture in the direction of your telltale little book.

And then—and nobody will ever know exactly how it came about—but suddenly you yourself have been declared "outside the law," the soldiers of the Convention have disarmed the armed rabble in the galleries, and you and your faithful brother, Augustin, and all your most trusted fellow members of the Committee of Public Safety are prisoners and at the mercy of the Convention and of that man whose ladylove from her jail continues to send him little notes bearing but the single word "Coward."

For a few moments at least he has not been a coward, but then the fear of what he has dared to do, that fear which all the people in France feel before the name of the Great Incorruptible, once more lames his efforts. The denizens of the slums have heard what has happened to their hero—their saint. They ring the tocsin. They grab their pikes and axes. They storm the building in which their beloved leader is being detained. They set him free and carry him and his friends in triumph to the Town Hall.

Now at last the conspirators of the Convention realize that everything is at stake. It is either Robespierre's life or their own. Their soldiers are hastily mobilized. The Committee of Public Safety orders the general commanding the troops of the Commune to march to their rescue. The brave general collects his men, draws his sword, and falls off his horse. It is a case of delirium tremens, and the ex-brewer, now known as the King of the Faubourgs, the man who has conducted Louis to the guillotine and has prevented the poor King from making a short speech of farewell by ordering the drums to be rolled, he is out of the picture, sleeping his jag off on the floor of a near-by tavern.

Also it begins to rain—it begins to pour as it has rarely rained and poured in Paris either before or after that terrible night of the ninth of Thermidor (July 27 to the rest of the world). Frenchmen do not like to get wet. The soldiers of the Commune are Frenchmen and so they decide to stay at home and attend to this matter of rescuing their beloved leader in the morning. But when the next day comes, the National Guards of the Convention are there first. They storm the Town Hall and capture it. A few of Robespierre's followers try to jump out of the windows and they break their necks. One of them, a cripple in a little gocart, is pushed down the stairs and lives just long enough to give the axman a most unpleasant problem, how to get this miserable hunchback's neck underneath the knife of the guillotine. A little rough work does the trick, even if the knife also removes part of the shoulders. As for the Virtuous One, who never has condemned anyone to death unless driven by the necessity of re-creating the people of France after his own image, he is lying on a table, his head resting on a wooden ammunition box, his lower jaw shattered by the bullet fired at very short range by one of the soldiers of the Convention.

Choked by blood and spitting out teeth at short intervals, he will lie there on that table until early morning, regretting that he was not able to finish the signature underneath the decree that would have destroyed all his enemies. The document still reposes on the table in the corner. It is an appeal to the people of Paris to be of good courage, "Courage, Patriots! Stand fast for liberty and await further orders." Signed, Ro . . . For at that moment the fatal pistol shot was fired, and the rest of the name was never finished. Gobs of blood at the bottom of the sheet bear silent witness to what happened there on that dreadful night.

The rest of this hideous tragedy is something we would like to forget—a man in extreme physical torture—surrounded by people who hate him so utterly, so bitterly, that they make sport of him and gloat over his agony. "Ah, beautiful one, that is not the way you looked when you sent my father and mother to the guillotine," and "Do you think it hurt my wife as much as it will hurt you when they cut off your head?" And more such cheerful banter on the part of a steady stream of National Guards whose peaceful existence the stricken man on the table had ruined for all time while pursuing his own dream of virtue.

But of all this, Robespierre cannot have remembered very much. Perhaps he vaguely recognized a few familiar faces behind a table in a court of justice.

"Is this the man Robespierre?"

"It is."

"Take him out and kill him."

Then, but still more vaguely, rows upon rows of windows filled with men and women and children wildly shouting and singing, for now they know that they will live and their friends and relatives in a hundred prisons are safe, too, and all of France is saved. And, meanwhile, there he goes, the monster, that little fellow lying on the bottom of the first cart. See him? They say he tried to kill himself. Let us find out whether he can still hear us.

"Robespierre—you monster—you swine—you dirty son of a dog—we hope you roast in hell for all eternity. Look, he can still move his eyes—he must be alive—once more and now all together! Robespieeeeerre! you piece of . . ." for the most cultivated nation of our planet can descend to pretty low depths of vulgarity once it gets aroused.

Then darkness again. Until strong hands lift you brutally from the bottom of that familiar cart (the same cart that has taken most of your old friends to their death) in which you had taken your last ride on earth. An ocean of faces gaping at you, shouting words which you can no longer make out, but there is no doubt about their meaning. Two other hands on your shoulders, pushing you down on a plank dripping with the blood of those who preceded you. And then, a howl of inhuman pain, which comes out of your own mouth or what is left of it. The executioner has torn away the bandage which held the upper and lower parts of your jaw together. You can no longer see the faces. You only hear a hurricane of bestial joy as the axman reaches for the lever that will set the engine of justice into motion.

The crowd roars, "There he goes!" And there you went. Your head with the now uncontrollable eyes rolling wildly drops into the basket.

"Next."

Your head now is no longer alone. It has company.

"Next."

It has still more company.

"Next."

When the nineteenth head has rolled into it, the basket is getting a little crowded. "Take it away," says Monsieur Sanson, Senior, to the Messieurs Sanson, Junior, "and bring me an empty one. We will have a lot more of them, tomorrow morning early." In which that faithful servant of the Republic was very much right. The next day there were half a hundred more friends of the Incorruptible One. The next day, thirty. And so it went until everybody who had in any way been connected with the Man of Virtue had been disposed of.

Then France sat down, said "Zoof!" or *"Là là!"* according to the social status of the speakers, and went on a picnic. The forests were as lovely as ever. The girls and women once more could smile. The grass was as green as ever. The cold chicken was as delicious as ever. The wine tasted even better than before. God was once more in his heaven, or almost, and the mortal remains of Maximilien Robespierre were lying in a bed of quicklime, his head neatly disposed between his legs, for that was the way it had been decreed by his own Committee of Public Safety: "The head of all persons suppressed by the will of the nation shall be placed between their legs before the quicklime is poured on and the grave is closed."

Farewell, Citizen Robespierre. I have been pretty rough on you. I wonder whether you will bear me any ill will when next Saturday I meet you?

And now a few words about our other guest of next Saturday, Tomás de Torquemada.

There used to be a curious old volume in the archives of Middelburg. Did you ever see it? It was more or less their showpiece, and the officials used to bring it out for the benefit of distinguished visitors. It was a record—a sort of private chronicle—that had been kept by one of the minor clerks of the court of justice of the good city of Middelburg during the first half of the sixteenth century. This person must have been a good deal of a sadist but one with a streak of humor in his otherwise despicable soul, plus a very decided gift for the pictorial arts.

This old codger, probably some cleric or scribe, had kept a diary in which he had noted down everything of any importance in connection with the executions that had taken place in Middelburg during his lifetime. As he had attained a very considerable age, there were some sixty of them, almost all of a different nature, ranging from simple hangings to the complicated routine connected with patricide and high treason.

I remember those pictures vividly for one particular quality— a quality you can also notice in those medieval paintings which show us people as either on their way to the scaffold or actually being decapitated or disemboweled. I refer to the apparent indifference or, shall I say, the matter-of-fact way in which these victims of justice (or injustice) accepted their fate. My friends who have watched the firing squads of the great and good General Franco getting rid of Spain's liberals and intellectuals tell me that such a spirit of "So what!" still survives in modern Spain. The doomed man or woman puffs at his last cigarette, throws it away, says, "All right," and falls down dead without any further comment. I suppose the general philosophy of life in the Middle Ages—and even later—was responsible for this stoical approach to death. Residence in this world was, after all, not the thing that counted. Our planet was merely an anteroom to that heaven or hell where one was supposed to spend eternity, and since one would some day have to die anyway, either slowly or painfully in one's bed or quickly on the scaffold, why bother about the slight inconvenience connected with a violent death under the executioner's ax?

I am furthermore convinced that the belief in some kind of divine retribution, then still part of everybody's mental make-up, may have had something to do with this outward indifference exhibited by almost all the patients. They had their hands hacked off and stood there looking curiously at the blood-spouting wrists (our Middelburg artist was excellent at drawing streams of blood spurting from necks and hands and legs of the poor victims, and he apparently knew a lot about the law of ballistics, for his curves were almost always correct).

These murderers and highwaymen had their bowels cut open and took it as unconcernedly as a patient in a modern hospital who is having some abdominal operation performed with a rectal anesthetic. He sees everything but feels nothing. And this may be the answer to the question I just asked myself.

The people of those bygone days took such incidents as being broken on the rack for granted in the same mood in which we of the twentieth century take our operations for granted. They are inevitably accompanied by a certain amount of temporary discomfort, but they are all in the day's work, and in the end we will be much better off for them.

It was therefore with some astonishment that I studied this diarist's last three entries, which covered the years 1506, 1509, and 1511. They had to do with burnings at the stake. But instead of standing unconcernedly in the midst of the flames and mumbling a final prayer, these heretics were angrily waving their fists at a couple of near-by officials, and in the distance one noticed a certain amount of unrest among the spectators, who in all the other pictures had been as docile as the crowds at a movie and who undoubtedly were enjoying the show in very much the same way in which a modern audience contemplates a scene of celluloid horror imported from one of the countries where civil war is now raging.

The old cleric's script was quite illegible to me, but my good friend, the keeper of the archives, who read those pothooks with the same ease with which Jimmie deciphers my manuscripts, translated the lines for me, and so I learned that the "unseemly behavior of the mob" on those occasions had been due to resentment that the executions were being held at the request of the Spanish Inquisition.

As you may remember, the Church never killed anyone. It merely found people guilty and then left the further painful details to the secular arm. And as long as all this was done by

the local magistrates, the populace had offered no serious objections. But when the word "Inquisition" began to be whispered around—usually in connection with the name of Spain—
then there were unmistakable signs of discontent and even
threats of open rebellion.

We usually forget how recently the last of these executions
took place. In Spain, the Inquisition as an instrument of domination over people's minds was not abolished until the year
1834. Torture in forcing confessions from suspected prisoners
and as a means of refreshing the memories of recalcitrant witnesses continued in its courts until 1816, while in Mexico the
Inquisition flourished until the administration of our own President Madison, and even afterward there were outbreaks of inquisitorial zeal in many of the former Spanish colonies. But in
northern Europe, the people, although in many ways just as
cruel as their southern neighbors, have always resented the use
of physical violence to bring about purely spiritual results.

Yes, I know Calvin did torture and burn a most learned
and respected scientist who disagreed with him concerning the
true nature of the Trinity. And during the first years of the
Dutch rebellion against Spain, the rabble would go in for an
occasional outburst of lynching, and several dozen priests were
sacrificed to their lust for revenge. But by and large, such incidents were severely repressed because the greater part of the
community held them in deep horror.

It is claimed that in Sweden the Reformation took place
without a single life being lost. The record in the other countries of northern Europe is not quite so good, but even so, it is
infinitely better than that of the south. Most people accepted
some sort of watch-and-ward society, as we ourselves accept committees of Congressional and civic snoopers who look into the beliefs of our schoolteachers, lest Karl Marx be suddenly discovered in the inkstand of the principal or the teachers be seen
riding broomsticks (made in Moscow) through the fresh air of
night (made in Pittsburgh). Unless such committees are so lack-

The spirit of John Calvin was ever with us.

ing in intelligence or behave so outrageously that they get into the public eye, nobody bothers very much about them, and neither did the people of the Low Countries feel restive as long as the Inquisition had been composed of members of their own race. But when its administration was handed over to foreigners, mostly Spaniards, then there was trouble, and that is easy to understand. For in Spain, unlike in most other countries, the religious troubles were intermingled with racial troubles, and when that happens, the Devil comes into his own!

During the eighth century, Spain had been overrun by the Mohammedans, and for more than six hundred years the Spaniards had spent practically all their energies upon the task of driving out the foreign invaders. They finally succeeded in doing so, but then they found themselves presented with a new problem that just could not be settled.

It has often happened that when one race has conquered another, it is the superior race (from a cultural point of view) which loses out. Most modern historians seem to agree that the Moors were in practically every aspect of life superior to their Christian masters. They were better scientists, better physicians, better merchants and navigators. They knew a lot more about irrigation and the cultivation of fruits and cereals than the Spaniards ever found out. They built better houses, much better suited to the climate of Iberia, and they believed in personal cleanliness and a great many other virtues which were by no means acceptable to their Christian enemies.

The Moors, however, were no angels. They had their full share of human shortcomings. Like all desert races, they were incurably clannish. Every sheik was every other sheik's enemy, and, as a result of an almost endless series of civil wars, the Spanish caliphate finally went the way of all Moslem empires. Granada fell in the year 1492, and, after that, Spain once more belonged to the Spaniards, who ever since have done their best to reconvert the Moorish flower gardens into the wilderness they had been before the arrival of the dark-skinned Moslems and to turn every prosperous city into those clusters of neglected hovels dominated by overstuffed cathedrals which are so typical of the modern Iberian landscape.

Here was the making of tragedy, and Spain has done its best to make it come true. First of all, there was the economic aspect of the case. The average Spaniard, after five centuries wasted on military operations, felt no inclination whatsoever to return to the more peaceful ways of life. He dearly loved to cut a fine figure, but he despised all methods of accumulating wealth which were in any way connected with personal exertion or working in an office. That was why so many Spaniards turned *conquistadores,* which is a beautiful Spanish word, best translated by "pirate" or "brigand."

It was impossible, however, for all Spaniards to engage in transoceanic schemes of conquest. Most of them were obliged to stay at home, and these unfortunate ones soon cried out that they were being deprived of their chances of making an honest living by the descendants of their former conquerors, who had continued to live among them as converted Christians but who, in spite of their regular attendance at Mass, had retained enough of the old Moorish character to be willing to live by the sweat of their brows.

It is very easy for us in modern America to ask the question: "If these people knew why their neighbors of Moorish descent were able to beat them so badly at the game of making a living, then why didn't they do likewise? Why didn't they too take off their coats and set to work?" But that would have been the logical way of solving their problems, and the average Spaniard (no more than any other human being) was not interested in being logical. Once a Spanish gentleman, always a Spanish gentleman. Even when you had to go about with your toes sticking out of your shoes and had to live on dry bread and an occasional glass of sour wine, it still was beneath your dignity to soil your hands with toil.

And so there remained no other choice but to try and get hold of the wealth of their Moorish fellow citizens, and what was a more profitable and satisfactory way of accomplishing

their downfall than by accusing these poor Moriscos of being
backsliders and heretics?

That is why the Spanish Inquisition enjoyed such widespread
popularity and was regarded by most Spaniards as the one institution which could still save their country (and themselves)
from bankruptcy. For from then on, no man with a drop of
foreign blood in his veins, however rich or powerful, was safe
from an accusation of being lacking in that *limpieza*—that purity
of blood which today is the sword that hangs over the head
of every non-Aryan in Germany. The mere suspicion of having had a Jewish or Moorish grandfather or grandmother was
enough to bring the poor victim in contact with the officers of
the Inquisition. Torture and prolonged imprisonment would
do the rest, and at the next auto-da-fé (those sanguinary "acts
of faith" at which often as many as fifty victims were burned
together to the greater glory of God) still another nest of
Morisco families was wiped out and their property was confiscated for the benefit of the Christian community.

As these bloody persecutions did not stop at subjects of the
Spanish crown but quite frequently sent bona fide foreigners
to their death, the Inquisition soon dragged the country into
serious difficulties with almost every nation of northern Europe.
This led to complications abroad and to the loss of still more
colonies, and in the end this policy became one of the con-
tributory causes of Spain's downfall.

It is always rather difficult for the contemporaries of such
great events to get a very clear conception of what is actually
happening. This time, however, the general detestation in which
the Spanish Inquisition was held by all foreign nations—the
obstinate refusal of the Dutch to tolerate its introduction into
their own country—the panic that swept across England when
it was whispered that Queen Mary, after contracting matrimony
with King Philip, would permit her husband's Inquisition to
establish itself on British soil—this wholesale outbreak of horror
shows us that our great-great-grandfathers were clearly aware

of what Spanish Inquisition implied. It meant an end to all those things for which both the English and the Dutch had so bitterly fought for so many years. It meant a return to those unfortunate aspects of the Middle Ages of which those people were trying to rid themselves. And although they might disagree with each other upon a thousand different subjects, upon one point they were in complete harmony—better to die than to submit to this menace of foreign domination.

After which I shall now introduce you to our second guest of next Saturday.

Tomás de Torquemada was born in Castile, the most Spanish of Spanish provinces, and he saw the light of day in the year 1420.

And now, something very curious. His contemporaries hinted at his having had Jewish blood in his veins, and subsequent researches in the archives seem to have proved that this was true. In itself, that is nothing very astonishing. For more than seven hundred years Moorish Spain had been a harbor of refuge for the Jews, and it was full of their descendants. But that the Grand Inquisitor, whose name has become a byword for bigotry and cruelty and persecution, should have been partly Jewish will come as a surprise to a great many people.

But it is not really as strange as it may seem at first sight. Many of the greatest Jew-baiters of history have been at least one half—or one quarter—Jewish. Which is only natural. These poor fellows had something to live down. Having cast their lot with their Christian neighbors, they now felt themselves to be under the obligation to show their loyalty to their new faith by an excess of zeal which no one would have expected of those born into the Christian faith.

The same thing is happening today in Germany, where several of Hitler's most relentless and notorious henchmen are also suspected of a lack of *limpieza,* or racial purity, and are therefore forced to give evidence of their ardent Nazism by being just a little more exaggerated in their sentiments than the undisputed members of the original *Herrenvolk*—the blond Teutons who are now doing the bidding of that Slavic-German halfbreed whom they have accepted as their master and leader.

Young Tomás de Torquemada was a very gifted person. Of that there can be no doubt. He was a brilliant orator and a very hard worker. As soon as he had finished his studies he was appointed confessor to the Infanta Isabella, who in due course of time was to marry her Ferdinand and to become Queen of a united Spain. The influence he gained over his royal mistress during this period was so great that it lasted until the end of his life and protected him, no matter how bitterly he was attacked by both the clergy and the laity. Especially by the clergy, for Torquemada was so full of holy zeal that he tried to be a better Christian than the Pope himself—and that is something the Church has never tolerated.

Spain at the time of Torquemada's coming to power was not yet the highly centralized state it was to become a little later when the Hapsburgs, with their penny-pinching souls, took hold of the country. The authority of the King over those provinces, which only a short time before had had sovereigns of their own, existed only in name. Almost any nobleman with a castle or a pigsty flying his flag dared defy the King's royal majesty. As for money, there was none. Not even the few thousand dollars necessary to stake the Italian adventurer who swore that by sailing due west he could reach the Indies and Japan in less than three weeks and make everybody rich.

Torquemada, who understood the situation much better than most of the other royal councilors, thought that he knew how the problem could be solved. Let him be appointed Inquisitor General, and unity would soon be established, while ducats would begin to flow into the royal exchequer by the tens of millions.

Has there ever been a royal family which refused an offer to enrich itself at the expense of its subjects? Yes, there have been such historical curiosities, but not during the fifteenth and six-

teenth centuries, when a divine prerogative was usually inter-
preted as a very worldly permit to plunder.

So, after some dickering with the Holy See, permission was
obtained to go ahead. Even then, the Popes had serious misgivings about the plan. Previous experience had shown how much
harm that kind of private enterprise within the realm of heresy
hunting might do to the good name of the Church and how
difficult it was to call the Dominicans—the Dogs of the Lord—
back, once they had been let loose and were out of control. But
Spain was one of the Holy See's most devoted children and entitled to a few favors.

In 1481 the Spanish Inquisition, reorganized after the Torquemada pattern, began to function. First of all, it descended
upon Seville, which had been one of the centers of the old
Moorish culture and was therefore held to be a hotbed of racial
impurities and heresies. In the middle of the thirteenth century it had been definitely captured by the Spaniards, and almost half a million Moslems had fled, though enough of them
had remained behind to make them a "problem," provided you
were looking for one.

Torquemada was doing exactly that. There was gold in those
old Moorish mansions, and he meant to get it. Once more
those who could escape left the city and left in a hurry. The
others were forced to submit to a most careful inquiry into their
orthodoxy. The vital statistics relating to Torquemada's activities during the fifteen years that he was Inquisitor General
are very contradictory. In the year 1792, almost three centuries
after his death, a secretary of the Holy Office (what strange institutions have born the name "holy"!) published some figures
upon the subject which he claimed were based upon the official
records in the archives. He reached a total of ten thousand people burned and seven thousand others burned in effigy, for those
who had made good their escape were burned in effigy and lost
their estates. But that was not all. Another ninety-seven thousand suspects had been persuaded to confess their errors and had
been readmitted into the fold. That gives us an average of

about six thousand convictions per annum or twenty per diem, if we allow for all Sundays and holidays, and though Robespierre sometimes reached a higher daily record, he functioned at this rate for only a few months (the heyday of the real Terror), whereas Torquemada kept it up for fully fifteen years.

The outcry made by the victims of this drastic purge not only rose to heaven, but it also reached Rome. There it caused a great deal of consternation, as it was feared that such an excess of zeal might prove to be a boomerang. It might defeat its own end, and discreet notes were sent to Spain urging the court to use its influence and to keep its Inquisitor General within reasonable bounds.

The court felt inclined to listen. It needed funds for a new war against the last of the Moslem strongholds in the south, but the royal exchequer, which by this time should have been chockfull of Moorish gold, was as empty as before. When polite inquiries were made, it was shown that the expense of maintaining the Holy Office was almost as great as its revenues. That excuse was as old as the hills of Aragon, and the court did not declare itself satisfied. Unfortunately, King Ferdinand found it very difficult to proceed with too much energy against the man who was also the keeper of his soul, and, after a little hemming and hawing, Torquemada was maintained in office.

A few of Torquemada's more rapacious subordinates did not fare so well. They had not merely plundered those who were of "impure blood," but quite frequently they had included a great many genuine "Aryans" among those prisoners who were packed off to Seville, where the castle of Triana offered better and more subtle facilities for persuading them to confess and to divulge the whereabouts of their treasures. These prelates were now forced to make restitution, but for the rest, everything remained as it had been before, except that hereafter the Grand Inquisitor of Spain never ventured out of his palace without a bodyguard of two hundred soldiers on foot and forty on horseback. And he became even more eager in his zeal for the purification of his fellow men.

The disappearance of the last of the independent Moorish states from Spanish soil gave Torquemada his greatest chance. He approached Their Majesties and asked to be allowed to expel the Jews as well as the Moors. Their Majesties hesitated. It is true that they were bankrupt. They owed money to everybody in and out of sight, and now this man threatened to deprive them of their chief source of revenue. They suggested a compromise. Why not let the Jews stay, provided they paid so many millions into the royal treasury each year? That gave Torquemada the opportunity to deliver himself of a couple of noble lines.

"God have mercy upon us all!" he complained with menacing mien. "God have mercy upon us all! Judas betrayed his Master for thirty pieces of silver, and Your Majesties now intend to sell your Saviour for ten thousand times that amount!"

When their Inquisitor General spoke that way, there was only one thing Their Majesties could do. They gave in, and three months after the fall of Granada, all Jews in Spain found themselves faced with the choice of being baptized or of leaving the country with the loss of all their possessions.

A few months later, another edict followed. No Christian must have any dealings with a Jew. No Christian must be seen speaking to a Jew. Any Christian woman caught in the act of offering food to a starving Jewish child would have to expiate her crime on the scaffold. With the fatal result that between a million and a million and a half Jewish families left Spain. They were not allowed to take anything away with them except the clothes on their backs. But if they survived the brutalities of their guards and the deprivations on board the vessels that carried them into exile, then it was discovered that they had quite unconsciously deprived Spain of the one commodity it needed most of all.

I refer to their brains. For those ingenious Hebrew brains were then set to work not merely to regain some basis of financial security for their owners but also to do as much damage as possible to their former torturers. And the countries of north-

ern Europe are there as concrete proof of the inestimable benefits which that kind of immigration bestowed upon the nations
that were wise enough to welcome those unfortunate victims of
racial and religious intolerance.

It often took a little time for the newcomers to fit into their
unfamiliar surroundings. But as soon as that difficult feat had
been accomplished, these refugees became assets of immeas-
urable worth. Their international business relations were of
immense value to their adopted countries. Their genius for
business, their almost instinctive feeling for certain types of
commercial transactions which until then had been virtually
unknown in northern Europe, where the merchant was only
too apt to take the short view of the Middle Ages instead of
risking his capital in long-view speculations—all this helped
make London and Amsterdam the centers of the New Capi-
talism.

Their gift for diagnosis, for clever guessing, placed the Jews
in the front ranks of the great physicians. On the negative side,
there was the narrow-minded and intolerant conservatism of
many of their spiritual leaders and the insistence of many of the
refugees upon carrying at least a few stones from their ancestral
wailing wall with them wherever they went. And finally, their
irrepressible love for argument led to conflicts, within their
own congregations, which often became so violent that the
Christian authorities had to interfere, for otherwise those quarrels might have led to murder beneath the star of David.

But such incidents the goyim regarded as purely "local affairs" of the ghettos in which these unfortunate people continued to live long after they had received permission to settle
down wherever they pleased. And whenever possible, the Christian authorities most carefully refrained from interfering in
those bitter disputes, the causes of which were way beyond their
comprehension, while the noisy disputations in which the
scribes indulged on such occasions only irritated them and gave
them a sense of superiority over this race which never apparently was able to learn to leave well enough alone. They were

chiefly interested in the financial contributions the fugitive
could make to the prosperity of their new homeland, and these
were so great that within an incredibly short space of time those
nations which had been wise enough to open their portals to these
hapless wanderers from racial persecution made such advances
within the realm of international trade that they were able to
destroy the power which until then had held a strict monopoly
upon the treasures of the Indies and the Americas.

When we look at it from this angle, we feel almost inclined
to salute Torquemada as one of the founders of the Republic
of the United Netherlands. He did not live long enough to
watch even the beginning of the great struggle which was to
give the Low Countries their freedom, but more than any other
man he made the name of Spaniard a byword for everything
that was most objectionable and detestable in the eyes of the
free people of the north. What followed was but the logical out
come of that policy of repression he had inaugurated.

If you are interested, Torquemada died in the year 1498, still
Inquisitor General of the Spanish domains. The last time he
appeared in public was in the year 1497. He went to the court
to console Their Majesties on the death of their son, the Infante
Don Juan. He stayed over for the funeral. Their Majesties were
touched and grateful. They did not know it, but they were of
fering their hospitality to the man who was chiefly responsible
for the eventual downfall of their empire.

We had invited those two unattractive guests, but neither
Frits nor I looked forward to their coming with any particular
pleasure. We consoled ourselves by endlessly telling each other
that we were only doing our duty. It was not enough that we
should meet all the nice people of the past. We must also learn
something about the unpleasant ones.

Let me state right here that we were not in the least disap
pointed. Both Robespierre and Torquemada lived up to our
worst expectations. No, they did not behave like our two sad

relics from the Council of Nicaea. On the contrary, they were so absolutely correct in everything they said and did that they lacked all spontaneity.

They both appeared at the same time, at three minutes past seven, so as to make a proper entrance, I suppose. Then they both excused themselves for being "a few minutes late" and told us how happy they were at having been invited. And then they sat down and stared into the fire and said nothing. But not for very long, for soon I noticed that Torquemada was showing signs of restlessness. He looked this way and that and even examined the dark spot behind the staircase as if he feared that some unseen enemy was on the watch for him. Next, he picked up the heavy poker—a very old one—perhaps Gothic—which Frits had found at Bal's store in Middelburg and had bought because it was such a magnificent piece of iron. After that he appeared to be a little more at his ease and a few minutes later he began to poke in the fire.

The moment he did so, both Frits and I became aware of a change that took place in the room. I can't quite describe it, for nothing really happened. The walls did not move down upon us; the ceiling remained in its place. But it looked to both of us as if the fireplace had suddenly become full of little figures, tiny little men and women helplessly lifting their arms toward heaven, twisting their bodies in tortured agony, and silently imploring a mercy they knew would not be granted. The contortion of their faces was something terrible to behold, and their hair, standing on end and sending off fiery sparks, added a final touch of horror.

At the same time, from the beams above our heads the limp bodies of a great number of men and women and even a few children began to sway slowly in the draft caused by the opening of the door that led from the kitchen to the dining room, for Jo was entering with the soup plates. She too stopped in her tracks, said, "God help us all!" and dropped all the crockery on the floor with a bang that made both Frits and me jump up from our chairs as if hit by lightning. Apparently we had not been dreaming. Jo too had seen what we had seen. It was going to be a pleasant evening!

Jo returned with a new set of dishes. We sat down to dinner, and the soup was served. Not a word was spoken. Then, during the main course, Robespierre suddenly reached into the inner pocket of his coat, a garment of good material and fashionable cut, in the style of a hundred and fifty years ago, made of blue and white striped silk and showing signs of elaborate care. "Good Lord!" I said to myself. "He is going to put our names down in one of his damn little notebooks." But instead, he pulled out an envelope which he offered me.

"I am not known to you and your friend," he said, biting off his words with great precision, "but I thought that you might like to know something about me. This envelope contains a few clippings. They set forth, as concretely as possible, my views upon improving the lives of the workers in the textile factories of Lyons."

I thanked him profusely and assured him that both Frits and I would be delighted to study those documents most carefully as soon as we had a moment to spare. He said, "Oh, do not mention it. They must be a little out of date. But every statesman should first of all concern himself with the physical well-being of the people entrusted to his care. A virtuous soul can never live in a body that is not properly nurtured. Could I bother you for another orange? You don't mind, do you, if I eat rather liberally of those oranges you have so generously provided for our entertainment? Their juice is very good for my health, and I am considerable of an invalid and must be very careful in what I eat and drink."

I looked at him and noticed that deadly pallor which had led Carlyle into the error of describing him as the "sea-green" one. I assured him that there was another basketful of oranges stored in the cool cellar, for the last few autumn days, in contrast to the week before, had been exceptionally warm.

Torquemada pokes the fire.

"Yes," he answered, "almost as hot as July."

I thought of the twenty-seventh of July of the year 1794 and once more shuddered. He either did not notice it or was thinking of something else, for he again fell into one of his reveries, eating very sparingly and drinking practically nothing at all, until suddenly he once again dug into his inner coat pocket and actually produced one of those little notebooks, the sight of which had made his contemporaries touch their necks and look for the nearest exit. He smiled at us. "I find these little books extraordinarily useful," he announced with a self-contented smile, as if he were announcing some profound new truth. "I dare not always depend upon my memory. And so I make it a rule to write down everything I want to remember, and to do so right away. Such little details have a disastrous habit of slipping from one's mind, and life, after all, is made up of details, isn't it?"

"Yes, of course it is," Frits and I answered in unison and with considerable relief.

There was a grunt from the other side of the table. "I disagree," and it was Torquemada who was speaking. "I never needed anything to refresh my memory. I never forgot a face or a fact connected with the business in which I was engaged."

We did not bother to inquire what that business might have been. We knew. Some of our own ancestors had been victims of the retentive memory of Inquisitorial officials.

After that, silence once more, while Jo changed the plates. By this time Robespierre had consumed all his oranges. I told Jo to ask Hein to go down into the cellar and bring the other basket.

"Ah, you have a cellar here?" Torquemada asked.

"Several of them," Frits told him.

"Are they old?"

"About five centuries," Frits said.

"Do you mind if I have a look at them?"

"Not at all. But you will find the stairs rather steep, and they are, I am afraid, rather damp and dark."

"I know my way about in dark cellars, and a little dampness never did anybody any harm. On the other hand, it is conducive to useful meditations." He grinned as he said this and showed us a row of teeth worn down with decay. Then he took the candle Hein gave him and disappeared into the dark cavity of the open cellar door.

Ten minutes later the Inquisitor General came back. "I like your cellars," he told us, like a future tenant who has just inspected a house which exactly suits his taste. "With careful management, your cellars would hold about forty people."

"But forty people in that small cellar of ours would choke to death," Frits protested.

"Oh no, they would not. A few of the weaker ones might find it a little hard to breathe and perhaps they would not live very long. But what does that matter? They would have to die sometime anyway, and I am told that it is an easy death."

"Easier than some others," Frits shot back at him.

"What was that you just said?" Torquemada asked, giving Frits a very unpleasant look.

"Nothing at all," Frits answered. "Won't you have a little more dessert?"

"No, thank you. I never eat for the sake of eating. And now, if you will pardon me for a few minutes," and he retired to his chair in front of the fire. There, pulling a small leather-bound book out of his robe, he began to read and paid no further attention to us.

That left the other guest on our hands, but by this time he, too, had found something to engage his attention. For the first time during that endless evening we noticed a faint smile on his lips. We did not immediately see what he was doing, but we asked no questions and offered no comment. Then we knew. With two bottles of wine, both of them still practically full, and our bread knife, Robespierre had constructed himself a little guillotine. Then, one after the other, he picked up the oranges Hein had just brought, placed them underneath his contraption, shook one of the bottles until the knife fell upon the

Robespierre had made himself a little guillotine.

The Buddha sent his regards.

orange, rolled the orange a little farther down the table, and started all over again. Finally he took a wineglass, draped a napkin around it, placed an orange on top of the napkin, and put some four or five matches on top of his orange so that it looked like a crown.

"And now I will go after Louis Capet," he said delightedly. "Poor, fat old Louis! Do you know, he was not really a bad fellow at heart. But he never understood the meaning of the word 'virtue,' and so he had to go. Let me show you."

But before he had cut off Louis' head, the candles had begun to flicker. A moment later, they went out. I counted the strokes of the clock. There were only ten.

As soon as Jo had brought in the lamp, there was a knock at our door. We had not expected any more visitors that night, but we were delighted when we saw that it was Erasmus.

"We missed you this evening," Frits said. "Were you ill?"

"Oh no!" he replied, "but I had rather anticipated what was going to happen, and I felt that I could perhaps render you a small service. You may have noticed it. I arranged to rid you of your guests two hours before it was time for them to go. And now, if the excellent Johanna will fix me up a little bit of supper, I shall be delighted. I'm very hungry, and perhaps you will join me."

"Doctor," said Frits, "greatly honored and beloved Doctor, I feel as if I could never eat another meal."

"I know," Erasmus said, while we heard Jo dropping the steak she always held in reserve in her old iron frying pan (for we fry our steaks in Holland), "it must have been quite horrible."

We both answered that it had been much worse than anything we had had reason to expect.

"Yes," Erasmus answered, helping himself to a slice of bread and reaching over for the butter. "Those two people who have just left you loved themselves so much they could never love . . ."

"Anybody else," Frits interrupted.

"Alas, it was even worse than that."

"How could it be worse?"

"Because they loved themselves so much that they were never able to love God."

CHAPTER X

The Buddha Sends His Regrets

"Wow!" said Frits when next day he came in for luncheon.

"Yes, I hear it was pretty ghastly," Jimmie answered.

"Worse than that! It was the most dreadful experience I ever had."

"Well," Jimmie told him, "it was your own fault, wasn't it?"

"I know, but that does not make it any easier."

"And, of course, you will do it again the next time."

"No-o-o-o-o!" we both shouted. "Not if we can help it."

"But history is full of such people," James protested. "They seem to be the only kind that ever come to the top."

"Then we had better stay at the bottom," Frits said, looking at me, "or we will never again want to meet anybody."

I agreed but added that I had thought of someone who might reconcile us with the human race.

"Who?" Frits inquired.

"The Buddha," I told him.

"That old holy man! He was kindhearted enough, but he was not exactly what you would call amusing, was he?" said Jimmie.

"No," I answered, "but he was so very human and so extremely decent. We shall need him to take yesterday night's bad taste out of our mouth."

"I should say so," Frits replied. "I've tried strong coffee, but it doesn't work."

That evening the name of the Buddha was placed underneath the faithful old lion of the town hall.

As I was very tired, I put off thinking about what we could possibly offer him by way of food until the next afternoon. But early in the morning Kaatje, our second maid, brought me a large, foreign-looking envelope. "I found this in the hall, underneath the door," she announced. "I don't know who left it, but I am sure it was not the postman."

I opened the document. It contained a picture, and something was scrawled underneath a gay arrangement of flowers and fruit. I could not read it. I knew just enough to realize that it was Sanskrit.

I took it to our beloved old dominie, a person of vast erudition. He translated it for me. This is what it said:

The Buddha is deeply grateful to you for your very kind and courteous invitation. He would honor himself by accepting it. Unfortunately he left fifty-seven years ago for a century of meditation and therefore will be unable to attend.

CHAPTER XI

SAINT FRANCIS, H. C. ANDERSEN, and MOZART Come, But They Do Not Come Alone

I TRIED to get Frits on the long-distance, but he had left Amsterdam to visit his family in Zalt-Bommel and would not be back until late that evening. I therefore was obliged to choose our next guests without consulting him. There were three people I had always wanted to meet—Saint Francis, Mozart, and Hans Christian Andersen. I now invited them. They had lived at different periods in history, and one of them had been a preacher, one a musician, and the third one a teller of tales. But in many respects they had had so much in common that I felt they would like and appreciate one another. For one thing, they had all been in love with life, they all had cared for children and animals, and all of them had known how to laugh. This is the letter about them I sent to Frits by special delivery late the next afternoon.

Francesco Bernardone was born in the year 1181 or 1182 in the town of Assisi. Assisi is situated in Umbria, and Umbria is a hilly district north of Rome and east of Florence. Geographically, it is part of the Apennine Mountains, which are the geological backbone of Italy, running all the way from the valley of the Po in the north down to the tip and heel of the boot in the south.

Hilly countries—or rather, regions of low, rolling hills—seem to have an excellent influence upon the development of the poetic streak in human nature. Some day a historian will perhaps give us a list of the world's slender output of geniuses, tabulated according to their geographical background. It will then be shown, I think, that low, rolling hills, as we have them in Connecticut and in England and in southern and central Germany and in northern Italy, are the ideal breeding ground for people with poetic tendencies.

The father of little Francesco (from now on I had better just call him Francis) owned a cloth shop and was a tailor, probably the best tailor in town and therefore a man of some importance. Francis expected to succeed him in the business. Everything was fine, for the son cared more for worldly pleasures than for learning and, although he could read and write, he was not fond of books and hated school. All of which proves exactly nothing, except that he was a perfectly normal boy of the twelfth, the twentieth, or the twenty-thousandth century.

Assisi was not quite a metropolis, but in the year 1181 two thousand inhabitants gave an overgrown village the right to call itself a town. Furthermore, it had walls and towers and all the other attributes of a regular city, including a foreign policy of its own where its neighbors were concerned. Occasionally, this foreign policy, like all foreign policies, big or small, had to be backed up by a show of arms. Such an incident happened just when Francis was recovering from a serious illness. I could find out, I suppose, what the fighting was all about, but it does not seem important enough to take the trouble. During the Middle Ages such encounters between little cities and even villages were the equivalent of our modern baseball games. As a rule they were just as harmless, too, in their final results—a few sprained ankles and dislocated shoulder blades and, in extreme cases, a sock on the jaw from one of the players who so far forgot himself as to resort to personal violence. Should he have come home with a broken nose, Francis would not have minded, but his recent sickness had so exhausted him that he was obliged to return to his father's home before he had been more than a few days on the warpath. Being the town's Beau Brummell was

very nice, but perhaps, so he began to suspect, it was not the
role God wanted him to play.

Suddenly the "war" was over. The young volunteers hastened
back to Assisi. There was a grand celebration. Francis was urged
to come. In this way his more vigorous friends hoped to make
him forget his recent disappointment. He was crowned their
king, and they set forth to awaken the town with a torchlight
parade. But Francis slipped quietly away and when, at last,
he was found, he was like a man in a trance. When he came
back from this visit to distant and unknown regions, the old
Francis Bernardone no longer existed. Brother Francis had
taken his place and, as the poorest of the poor, he was to go
through life until, some twenty-four years later, he was to
descend into his pauper's grave, his body worn out long before
its appointed time by a life of labor and want, his soul living
on in all of us who put our faith in the laughing wisdom of the
"divine fool" rather than in the teachings of the duly belet-
tered doctor of theology.

It is not easy, after so many centuries, to get a very clear idea
of what Francis Bernardone was trying to accomplish, what he
actually believed, and the sort of impression he made upon his
contemporaries. We have not had anyone quite like him for a
long time, and it would take almost superhuman courage to
play the role of a Francis in our era of practical achievements.
Thoreau comes perhaps nearest to him on our own side of the
ocean. Tolstoy during his last years imitated, or tried to imitate,
the private-poverty paragraph of the Franciscan program. But
Thoreau was lacking in one of the most essential qualities of
Francis' character. He was, and remained, an honest Yankee
with a desire to function. He did not care to function as his
cousins of State Street did, but within his little wooden cabin
there had to be order and neatness. Even if it cost him only a
hundred dollars a year to pay for his physical upkeep, he meant
to get that hundred dollars by the sweat of his own brow—no
other Waldenite was going to hold it against him that he had
failed to pay his grocer or the man who had sold him the

graphite for his pencils. As for Tolstoy, his belated descent
into the hell of misery was about as important as the washing of
the feet which the Austrian emperors used to perform once a
year when a dozen old Viennese men and women, having been
duly scrubbed, used to be brought before them that His Majesty, by this act of humility (touching their feet with a wet
towel), might give evidence of a proper Christian spirit.

So let me think a moment how I can make it clear to you what
the good saint means to me.

Saint Francis was no social-service worker as we have come to
know the breed. There most certainly was nothing in him of
the modern evangelist, though he preached to larger multitudes than almost any other man either before or after him. He
was not deeply interested in the literary appeal of religion, although he was the author of some of the most spiritual songs
of all time. He was not desirous of establishing a new school of
thought. So many people wished to follow him that they had
to be gathered together into some kind of definite organization,
but Francis was not very well fitted for that sort of work and he
had to leave it to others with greater personal ambitions and
greater executive abilities.

He was not much of a diplomat, either, although he once did
what no one else had done and survived to tell the tale. He actually went to the Holy Land and called on the sultan to inform
the greatly surprised (and greatly amused) infidel that he was
all wrong in believing what he did and that he had better
change his opinions before it was too late, and, therefore, let his
visitor baptize him into the Christian faith.

Imagine anyone today going to Berchtesgaden to tell Hitler
that he is bound for hell and should forthwith give Germany a
democratic constitution on pain of everlasting punishment! But
then try to think of a modern person blessing the instrument
that is to be used (without benefit of anesthetic) in an operation
on one of his limbs and forgiving it for the torture it will cause.
And yet that is precisely what is told of Saint Francis in his later
days.

I know that we always have had a few "exalted" people around us, that quite often we read about them in the papers (photographs and all), and that they are forever founding strange new cults which promise to save the world by means of eating hay or by denying the existence of matter or by insisting that cholera microbes can be destroyed and broken legs can be healed by some kind of spiritual legerdemain. But, in order to understand the difference between these very doubtful prophets and the little brother of every living being, we need only ask ourselves what the reaction of Francis would have been had such creatures come to him asking to be admitted to his fellowship. He would at once have sensed that no common bond could ever bind them together and would have asked them to be gone. For Francis, in spite of his meekness, was an expert psychologist. An unconscious one, of course, but how he did understand his fellow men and how he knew how to penetrate into the most hidden chambers of their souls and how he was able there to kindle a little light that would never be extinguished as long as they lived!

How do I know? Because for many years my life was thrown with just such a person, and whatever there is good in me—intrinsically good, not just good on the surface (for I am a fairly bright person and can play many roles)—but whatever there is in my heart that I can some day present to God Almighty as an excuse for all the years I have spent on His earth—all that I got from this one man. And so deeply did he impress his wishes upon me that I shall never break faith with him by revealing his name. Among other gifts, he presented me with the key to the only saint who survived the Reformation when all his colleagues, with the exception, of course, of the good Saint Nicholas, fared very badly indeed at the hands of the Protestants. But then Saint Nicholas exists primarily in the memory of children, and children have never been very much interested in revolutions, except as an excuse for inventing a few new games.

Today, though I may be mistaken in this opinion, Francis

seems to be even more popular among the Protestants than among the Catholics. At least, I feel that we Protestants understand him a little better. We accept him as a typical representative of the medieval mentality and therefore can overlook what would otherwise disgust us—his unreasoning acceptance of disease and filth and all other kinds of afflictions which can so easily be avoided and even eradicated by the application of just a little soap and common sense. And we do not have to worry our heads about the question whether he actually suffered the stigmata in his hands and his feet after his visit to Mount Alverno or whether these were the hallucinations of a man exhausted by years of fasting and of nights spent in sleepless prayer. We relegate this problem to the department of psychopathology and then forget about it, having gradually learned that it is just as futile and foolish to discuss questions of pure faith as to engage our grandchildren in a debate about the truth or lack of truth of their best-beloved fairy story.

Finally, we do not need any manifestations of supernatural grace in the picture we have made ourselves of this saint. He existed. He lived the life he lived. That is enough for us.

What became of the order that bore his name (which, being a human organization with human needs and ambitions, could not very long remain truly Franciscan in its inner spirit) is of no particular consequence to us. Today it is just another order, and we wish it well, and if it should forget its true sphere of influence—a spiritual sphere—we intend to fight it, and as long as it remains within this sphere, we shall do all we can to help it along and encourage it in its work among the poor and disinherited. But we claim our share in the great Franciscan heritage. We want to enjoy the companionship of this strange little bearded man, not particularly attractive-looking and most of the time not in the best of health. We want to be allowed to speak to him occasionally when, some lovely evening of summer, we pass through the fields where he sits underneath a lonely tree, in solitary contemplation of this good earth. When our children afterward ask us about the queer-looking person,

vith his sandaled feet and his shabby-looking brown robe, who
smiled so pleasantly at them that they forgot their shyness and
were forced to smile back, we shall say, "That, my darlings, is
someone you must never forget, for it was he who plucked
flowers for the little Christ when he was no older than you and
then told him all the nice stories which he afterward bequeathed
unto us."

None of our guests of next Saturday would ever have been
asked to go to Hollywood. Two of them were lacking in all
outer glamour, and the camera, as influenced by the box office,
is not supposed to reveal what lies hidden behind the human
eye. It might show up certain qualities which easily could interfere with the principles of sound business. And the third guest,
though he adored fine silks and rich garments and loved to bask
in the favors of lovely women, was much too independent to
take orders from anyone but his equals, and within his own
field of endeavor he had no equals.

Let me first refresh your memory about him whom the Danes
call "Ho Say Andersen," not knowing him by that name so
familiar to us of the western world—Hans Christian Andersen.

Christ is said to have been born in a stable, and as a child I
used to envy him. What a delightful place to be born in! The
smell of new-mown hay and the placid companionship of soft-
eyed cows and an occasional inquisitive goat wandering in and
out and nibbling at the wooden handle of a spade or a rake.
And the soft light coming from way up high through a tiny
window, just below the roof.

I remember the room in which I had seen the light of day,
full of stuffy furniture and unromantic portraits of unromantic
ancestors. And ever again I compared it to the stable of the
Babe of Bethlehem, about whom my grandmother had told me
and about whom one of my uncles had given me a book, full of
pictures. And always I silently regretted that I too had not been
born in a stable, getting the smell of the earth in my nostrils
instead of the odor of the wet tea leaves with which, in those

antediluvian times, the floors of all Dutch rooms were swept at least twice each week.

But what of the pathetic little house in the sleepy little Danish town of Odense, on the island of Fyn, where Hans Christian uttered his first uncertain cries? One room to hold a father—a cobbler—and a mother and a whole brood of children. Such hopeless poverty that, instead of a sheet, a leftover scrap from a piece of cloth used shortly before to cover a nobleman's coffin had to serve as a bed cloth.

The great event (great to us) happened on April 2, 1805. Eleven years later, the shoemaker's weak lungs gave up their hopeless struggle. The mother remained alone. Her burdens were heavy, and she sought and found consolation, and finally oblivion, in those bottles of schnapps upon which she spent the money kindhearted neighbors contributed occasionally toward the support of her family.

But the divine spark, dormant in the soul of that little boy, could not be denied, for those whom the good Lord has touched will fulfill their destiny in spite of all handicaps and indignities. In the midst of his desperate poverty, he was forever constructing little puppet theaters wherein he would re-enact the plays of Shakespeare and of his fellow Dane, the famous Ludvig Holberg, not inaptly known as the Scandinavian Molière.

At a very early age came the necessity of making a living. It was intended to apprentice Hans Christian to a tailor, for the world would always need tailors, and it was as good or as bad a way of making a living as any other. But the boy refused. He was going to be an opera singer—nothing less than that!—an opera singer. Odense laughed. The Danes are rather given to laughing, not only at their own neighbors but at the world in general. They are a small nation, and it may be their way of protecting themselves against their enemies, and every country in Europe which goes its own quiet way and tends peacefully to its own affairs is apt to have a great many enemies.

When the child actually walked to the national capital to present himself and his ambitions at the stage door of the Royal

Theater, he became more than a joke. He was considered a lunatic. A harmless kind of fool but one who should not be left at large. He withdrew to a garret. He starved but he continued to sing until his voice changed. Then even he had to realize that a career on the boards was out of the question.

He therefore decided to try his luck with the other end of his grotesque body and to let his feet express what the vocal cords refused to do.

As a dancer, Hans Christian proved as much of a failure as he had done as a tenor. There seemed to be no other way out except the tailor's table. Copenhagen, however, especially in those days, was still a *Kleinstadt,* and a boy with Andersen's queer looks and aspirations easily became a matter of public curiosity. King Frederick VI, who then probably knew half of his faithful Copenhageners by sight, took an interest in him. He sent the lad to school that he might get some kind of education.

Did he thereupon apply himself diligently to his studies and learn his *amo, amas, amat*? Far from it. He became the despair of his teachers, paid but very little attention to his lessons, and wasted his time writing a very bad novel, bearing the weird title of *The Ghost at Palnatoke's Grave.*

In 1829 Andersen was back in Copenhagen, still starving but occasionally enjoying a square meal at the house of a well-disposed rich merchant, a certain Jonas Collin (the names of such rare benefactors of the human race should be preserved), who, ever since Andersen's first appearance in the capital, had "seen something in that boy." Collin remained his friend throughout life, in spite of some of Hans Christian's exasperating habits and enraging characteristics, and he was to see the day when the world had to confess that he had been right. There was a great deal more to this son of the tubercular Odense shoemaker and his tipsy wife than anyone had ever suspected. For after one or two more rather worthless novels and a lot of private tomfoolery and making a clown of himself, Hans Christian finally succeeded in finagling a small sum of money out of a rich patron that he might go forth to see this world and learn about his fellow men.

This scholarship was absurdly small. Compared to it, a modern Guggenheim means riches, but somehow or other these few hundred thalers produced a richer reward for their original investor than all the millions we now waste upon that ambition without talent which seems to be a by-product of every well-regulated democracy. For shortly after his return from his wanderings (which had carried him as far as Rome), there appeared a slender volume containing a collection of fairy tales. At first, they were almost completely overlooked. Then, here and there a few people began to ask each other, "Have you read about the Goose Girl and the Ugly Duckling and about the King who went walking without his pants?" Soon the book was in everybody's hands, and suddenly all Europe heard of Denmark because Denmark had produced that rarest of literary geniuses—a man capable of turning out "true fairy stories."

The rest of his incredible career is known to everybody. His own people continued to be hilariously funny about their "famous" poet. Small nations are never very kind to their great men, and Ho Say Andersen got his share of coffeehouse derision. Fortunately, there was a streak of naïve self-contentment in Andersen which saved him from realizing his actual position. He took this public derision for granted, as he took his own genius for granted and all the honors that now began to come to him. For example, he was pleased and deeply gratified but not particularly surprised that at the end of his visit to England in the year 1847 no one less than Charles Dickens—in person—bade him Godspeed. He went to partake of the afternoon *Kaffee-klatschen* of an endless number of small German princelings and listened to the praise of their dowdy wives and accepted their orders and medals, but he was not at all astonished that this should have happened to him. All his life long he had believed in Santa Claus. What of it if the good saint should have been a little late in arriving?

And so Andersen spent the rest of his days contentedly smoking his long porcelain pipe, frightened by every new invention that upset the peaceful world he had known and loved as a child, turning out novels he himself considered highly superior to his fairy-story stuff, and being cordially welcomed in all the most delightful homes of that most charming and civilized of cities. For all I know, he might have continued doing it until he was a hundred years old, but, unfortunately, at the age of only sixty-seven, he fell out of bed, hurt himself quite badly, and died three years later without ever having regained his health.

There are two kinds of so-called "simple people" in the world. There are those who are simple because they are utterly devoid of inner complications. They were born simple and stay that way until the end of their lives, performing, if they are also honest, sober, and willing to work, simple tasks in simple ways and gaining the respect and not infrequently the affection of their fellow men because they are excellent servants or fishermen or part of the animated furniture of a countinghouse. But there are also those who seem simple because they are so hopelessly complicated that that is the only way the rest of us can ever hope to explain them. They are the men and women who are most apt to move the world out of its humdrum and commonplace existence and to do so with infinitely more far-reaching results than the great conquerors who destroy and found empires.

Both Saint Francis and Saint Hans Christian belonged to the latter category. They were entirely different in their approach toward life, but, fortunately, the good Lord needs all sorts of people his miracles to perform. And in this case he used these two extremes for a similar purpose. The one by his actions, the other by his words, revealed unto us an imaginary world which was but the spiritual reflection of the sort of existence they deemed desirable for their fellow men in order that they should achieve true happiness.

Saint Francis preached to the birds and to the animals of the fields because no one else was at first interested in what he had to say, and any audience was better than none. Until the crowds, slightly ashamed of such an absurd state of affairs, decided they too had better come and listen and catch a glimpse of the truth as seen by this strange prophet.

Hans Christian Andersen, born into the materialism of the early nineteenth century and still smarting under the miseries he had suffered during the days of his youth, created a realm of the imagination in which those same animals of the fields that had been the early friends of Saint Francis played the roles of human beings and behaved with all the greed and cunning, all the charm and tenderheartedness, of real human beings, yet remained consistently within the confines of the animal kingdom.

All this leads up to a fine moral lesson which sometime, when I have a lot of leisure on my hands, I may undertake to point out to you. But not today, for there still is our third guest, and I love him too, and it will be very difficult to dismiss him with just a few lines.

Joannes Chrysostomus Wolfgangus Theophilus were the Christian names by which the offspring of *Herr Kapellmeister* Leopold Mozart was registered when the happy father came to announce the birth of his one and only son. But the boy never used the Joannes or the Chrysostomus. He translated Theophilus into Amadeus (rather than into the slightly ponderous Teutonic Gottlieb) and afterward, for the sake of convenience and with an eye to the box office, he usually Italianized everything into Wolfgango Amadeo, just as he would dedicate his quartet to his beloved Giuseppe Haydn, though his neighbors knew that great and good man as Josef or Pepi. But there was no pose in this during the end of the eighteenth century. It was a matter of sheer necessity.

The Vienna of the latter half of the eighteenth century was not unlike the New York of a few years ago, or the London of the seventies of the last century. Native talent was suspected to be lacking in those qualities of virtuosity which were the birthright of every *bambino* from across the Alps, and even when native talent happened to be a thousand times brighter and cleverer than the imported Italian article, it was by far the better policy to let Heinrich Schmidt sing under the name of Enrico Manescalco, and honest Johann Müller was invariably featured on the programs as Giovanni Mugnaio. It was absurd, but in this world of rococo make-believe, there was very little that made sense and *Erzbischöffliche Hofkapellmeisters* had to live.

When this particular one, to his delighted surprise, discovered that his beloved wife (Maria Anna Pertl, from the near-by lake district) had presented him with a son who could play the harpsichord long before he was able to talk and who composed agreeable little minuets while still in his diapers (in those days, little boys used to wear them until they were three; girls were easier), he decided that luck had at long last knocked at the door of the Mozart family and that it was up to him to make the best of his marvelous opportunity. So, when little Wolfgang had reached the age of six and his sister was eleven years old, Papa took them both on tour. Billed as Nannerl and Wolferl, Maria Anna and Wolfgang Amadeus were dragged from one small German court to the next and then again to the next and then again, sleepy and tired, to still another town, though occasionally they fell ill and were allowed to recuperate for a few weeks in hired lodgings. Old Leopold Mozart had been for too long a time familiar with poverty not to welcome this unexpected chance to acquire a few thousand extra ducats, but at heart he was a kind and good man who dearly loved his children and who, even if he had been lacking in paternal affection, was much too shrewd to want to kill his little geese who laid such nice golden eggs.

Nannerl, a charming young Austrian girl, was rather pert and quite pretty, but Wolferl was the real attraction of Leopold's troupe of performing harpsichordists. He remained completely unspoiled in an age when most people could only stammer and sputter whenever they found themselves face to face with some

Durchlauchtigste Gnaden, though he might be the world's most insufferable bore and boor. Years after his visit to some court or courtlet, from the mighty Hofburg in Vienna down to the half-ruined Schloss Pfurzheim in Buchswinkel an der Lahn, stories were still being told about this adorable child who had made himself comfortable on the broad lap of that fortress of maternal rectitude, Maria Theresa, and had boldly told the old dragon, "I like you. You are nice."

This particular episode was invariably followed by an account of how the little boy had slipped on the inlaid floor of Schönbrunn and how he was just on the point of starting to cry, when one of the imperial princesses, the same one who had been born on the disastrous day of Lisbon's terrible earthquake, had picked him up and had consoled him until little Wolferl, the innocent darling, had kissed her and had told her, "I love you and when I grow up I shall marry you." Quite a number of people lived long enough to be present on the day when this same princess was driven to the guillotine amidst the howls and catcalls of her former subjects, and they may well have wondered whether the poor girl would not have been a good deal happier as Marie Antoinette Mozart than as Marie Antoinette of France, now known as the widow Capet and about to lose her head.

The story of Mozart's rise to fame and his sad and premature death has been told so often that I had rather leave his artistic life to the minute scholarship of Dr. Ludwig Köchel's painstaking catalogue and to the tender care of his widow's second husband, who spent the last years of his own life gathering together all the facts available about his predecessor and presenting them to the world in a spirit of unexpected and most refreshing fairness.

Here are a few necessary vital statistics about Mozart. Born January 27, 1756. Between the ages of six and seven, two tours of the Continent, singing, playing the piano, playing the violin (Papa Leopold was the author of an excellent and still-useful textbook on fiddling), and playing the clown. For the little boy was full of fun, and let it be said before we accuse dear Papa of being merely interested in the financial results of these *tournées*—let it be definitely stated that Wolferl took to these trips like a bear to honey and loved performing quite as much as most trained seals seem to do when catching fish and balancing soup plates on their noses.

Not that we should think of the child as taking his musical work *en bagatelle*. Far from it. For example, when, at the age of eight, he found himself in The Hague, where in spite of the proverbial unmusicality of the House of Orange, he was the pet of the Stadholder's family, he was told that in the near-by city of Haarlem there was an organ, the work of the great Pieter Sweelinck, unequaled anywhere in this world for its many registers and stops. Whereupon he must hear it and play on it and try out the melodies of an oratorio he had composed during the previous year, when he was only seven.

And while living in stagecoaches and not overcomfortable inns and catching one cold after another and taking care of his beloved Nannerl, Wolfgang managed to pick up as much about counterpoint and composition as ordinary mortals, endowed with great application, may learn during some ten years spent in a conservatory of music with purple practice rooms for Debussy, blue ones for Brahms, and afternoon tea served by maids in waltz time.

Mozart spent only thirty-five years on this earth. At thirty-five most people begin to find themselves, but when Mozart died, his overworked brain had found time to compose 626 separate items, including, besides his never-sufficiently-to-be-praised operas, forty-nine symphonies, twenty-nine string quartets, twenty Masses, and an endless number of sonatas and concertos for the piano, the violin, the oboe, the flute, not to speak of an endless variety of pieces for all kinds and manner of instruments. As good old Papa Haydn once observed, young Wolfgang's string quartets alone would have brought him undying fame, and they formed but a very small part of his output. And let us remember that everything he touched became alive with a charm and grace that shouts "Mozart" at you after only three or four bars and continues to do so till the end.

It was a magnificent life—a most useful existence from the point of view of giving. From the point of view of receiving, it was one of the saddest tragedies of all times. This benefactor of mankind, whose music will carry you through the most horrible experiences of your own career, lived all his life on the verge of bankruptcy, exhausted his body by labors which would have killed six ordinary longshoremen, and finally succumbed to undernourishment and worry and disappointment, disappearing in a pauper's grave at a moment when a regular salary of, let us say, eight hundred dollars a year could have saved him for another quarter of a century of useful production.

And now arises the question: was this merely bad luck, or was it his own fault, some unfortunate kink somewhere in his character, or was it a little of both? Such things are terribly hard to decide with a definite yes or no.

Let us first consider the negative qualities which can be written down against him and which undoubtedly were written down against him by many of his contemporaries while he was alive. He had the misfortune of being obliged to live under the rule of two exceptionally dull and shortsighted members of the House of Hapsburg. Maria Theresa was a narrow-minded prototype of Queen Victoria, if you are able to conceive of such a combination. Music to her existed merely as an adornment of crown and altar. Just as the whole world had been really created for the greater glory of the Hapsburg dynasty, that each of its boys and girls (and Lord! were their women prolific!) could be given a nice little garden of his own with a couple of faithful gardeners to keep their master nicely supplied with fresh flowers and vegetables.

As for Maria Theresa's son, Joseph II, he was intelligent but in the wrong way. He had a clear enough brain but no real wisdom—and no understanding at all of his fellow men made of ordinary human clay. He meant to do well by them. He was sincerely interested in their prosperity and happiness. But there was no one at his court who could say: "Sorry, Your Majesty, but you are starting this whole reform business from the wrong end. You want to turn everything upside down before you have made it clear to your subjects why the present arrangement is wrong. Those faithful subjects are not all of them as bright as you are. They only know how things were done while their fathers and their grandfathers were alive. They can't quite imagine that this world can be run in a different way from that in which it has always been run. Give them time! First of all, explain your plans to them and then go ahead, but please proceed very, very slowly."

That was not Joseph's way of doing things, and as a result he started his reforms as a sort of one-man affair and got precisely nowhere, irritated everybody, turned order into chaos, and got involved in a series of foreign wars which were bound to be disastrous, for nobody trusted his leadership. When, finally, he died, he left his little New Deal suspended in mid-air and his country in a state of apprehensive irritation and resentment so profound and so intense that in any other nation except Austria it would have led to an outburst of rebellion.

This misguided Majesty had a much greater feeling for music than his sainted mother, but, somehow or other, Mozart never managed to put himself into his good graces. Young Mozart, so His Majesty agreed, undoubtedly had talent, but his ability as a composer was offset by certain personal shortcomings which His Majesty, the most illiberal liberal who ever graced an imperial throne, could not overlook in a subject.

Remember that in those days Vienna was still an overgrown village, entirely dominated by its court and its aristocracy; remember that there was one secret-service snooper for every ten inhabitants and that even royal and imperial guests were subject to a police control which would report such interesting items as: "Yesterday, although their father makes only five thalers a month, the daughters of Alois Huber of No. 741 Gotthilfe Strasse were seen to be wearing silk hose"; or "This morning Her Grand-ducal Highness of Württemberg, visiting her daughter the Princess of Lichtenstein, bought a pair of purple dancing slippers."

Now Mozart, in spite of the angelic reputation he somehow acquired after his death, was by no means an example of those civic virtues the Hapsburgs expected in their subjects. Neither was he a drunkard or a profligate. He was always in good taste, whether he composed a *Te Deum* or took a couple of young lady friends to the most expensive candy store in town for one of his beloved ices—that marvelous new dish for which he had acquired such a taste during his last visit to Paris. But he was young and good-looking, his manners were charming, and when you made an unexpected fifty thalers, why not spend them before they fall into the hands of the bailiffs?

Unfortunately, he never quite knew how to stop at those fifty. Invariably he made it fifty-one, when he had only fifty thalers to his name, and, as even a freshman taking Economics 1-A will tell you, that is the surest way of heading for the bankruptcy court. Then, in a short-lived but very acute mood of repentance and despair, he would hasten to some obliging friend and ask for a small loan. As the same bright freshman of the sentence above can tell you, that is the shortest road to the poorhouse. But being almost as much of an optimist as the late Wilkins Micawber, young Mozart very easily regained his good spirits and assured himself that all would be well as soon as he should have obtained some definite position (anything at all—organist in a church, teacher of a choir, *Hofkomponist, Hofkapellmeister*—anything with a fixed income) and, in order to make a good impression upon his future patron, he would borrow another hundred thalers, pay back fifty to the friend from whom he had borrowed seventy-five, and invest the rest in a beautiful scarlet coat (bought, of course, on credit) which gave him quite an air of distinction and made him feel that he was once more sitting on top of the world.

In all this, Mozart was undoubtedly extremely foolish. That is not the way a reasonable person should act. But neither would a reasonable person compose *The Marriage of Figaro,*

Don Giovanni, or *The Magic Flute*. It all depends upon which we think the more important item in the sum total of our civilization—the expert at material acquisition, who turns every venture into a fortunate gamble, or the teller of stories in words or melody, who never has any bank account at all—the man who leaves a fortune to his heirs, or the Christ whose sole possession at the time of his death consists of one shirt.

Of course, I am talking of extremes, and they are the exception. Between them lie the cases of hundreds of millions of average people who, somehow or other, will have to muddle through as best they can and who as a rule do so, even deriving considerable satisfaction from their terrestrial adventures. And then, from this distance at least, it seems incredible that amidst all the wealth of Austria, and Vienna especially, it should have been impossible to find that eight hundred or one thousand thalers that would have prolonged Mozart's life (or Schubert's life, for that matter) by a good many useful years. Only one person ever made a serious effort to help him. Frederick William II of Prussia (nephew to Frederick the Great) asked him to come to Berlin and offered him the position of *Hofkapell-meister* at his court, with an annual income of three thousand thalers, as compared to the eight hundred gulden which was all the Emperor Joseph ever meant to give him. But when this opportunity offered itself Mozart refused. And why? Out of loyalty to his Emperor and to his beloved Viennese. And how did his Emperor and his beloved Viennese repay him for this generous gesture? By allowing the Italians, who had had a monopoly on their music and opera for the last two hundred years, to ruin his *Figaro* by systematically singing off key and by going through their parts in such a way that even so magnificent a work was bound to fail. Here, most likely, you will interrupt me and will ask me what of the story (of that endlessly repeated myth) about Vienna as the natural musical center of the eighteenth and nineteenth centuries, which lived in and by and for music. There undoubtedly were a number of noble families who not only loved music but who also understood it and who opened their homes to everybody of outstanding and, sometimes even, of only mediocre talent. But they could not do everything. The general public was, and remained, indifferent. It would pay good money to hear some famous *castrato* reach high C. It would stand in line to get tickets for still some other Italian novelty in which a lady outcoloraturaed a nightingale. But it refused to give the slightest support to those among their fellow countrymen who insisted that the singers must use the native vernacular. And even when Mozart wrote his works in the familiar Italian, they could not follow this music, which, as the Emperor Joseph once complained, "was much too full of notes to please." As a result, when there was a vacancy in one of the theaters, it was much more apt to go to a foreigner than to a subject of His Imperial and Royal Majesty.

And what about Salzburg, which, ever since the Great War, has been acknowledged as the shrine of the whole musical world? During much of Mozart's lifetime and while his father was still employed by the court, it was ruled over by a man who took a positive delight in humiliating the artists who worked for him, who rejoiced in treating them like servants and letting them wait for hours in the drafty corridors of his episcopal residence while he was busy with "affairs of state."

When the Archbishop of Salzburg heard that Mozart, who was on his pay roll, had made a little extra money out of his *Idomeneo* (performed in Vienna), he reduced the poor fellow's income from five to four hundred gulden per year and forbade him from making up for this loss in revenue by giving concerts or taking pupils. And when he thought himself slighted by the Emperor, who with all his shortcomings was a gentleman and refused to tolerate Hieronymus of Salzburg in his immediate vicinity, he ordered Mozart to pack up and leave Vienna and return to Salzburg at his own expense and never again set foot in the Austrian capital. When Mozart, after this final insult, rebelled and reminded him that a musician knighted by the Pope and an honorary *compositore* of the University of Bologna could not be treated as if he were a butler caught in the act of stealing snuff, His Grace dismissed him in a letter so foully abusive that few of the official lives of Mozart have dared to re-print it in full.

But what of the treatment he received at the hands of the Empress, the wife of Leopold II (who in 1790 had succeeded his brother Joseph), after this daughter of the King of Spain had heard the opera which Mozart had composed in honor of her-self and her husband? This Spanish female, who could hardly spell her name, went into such a fury of disapproval that all she could stammer was this: "Just another piece of German *cochon-nerie!*"

And so it went. There were a great many people who recognized Mozart's genius, but there were even more to whom his music was just a little too new and too unusual to be pleasant to the ear, though they vaguely realized that what they heard was the work of an exceptionally talented artist. Therefore, it would be unfair to claim that he was completely unrecognized during his lifetime. He was both recognized and appreciated, and many of his older and more experienced colleagues were on his side, loved him, did their best to help him, and told the world at large that it should take more interest in the greatest of them all.

But something went wrong just the same. What was it? Why did Mozart never find suitable employment? Why, with all his rich and powerful patrons, did he have to write potboilers until he died from sheer physical exhaustion?

You will notice that I am deliberately marking time and that I am desperately grabbing at all the little straws that come my way. Is that a confession that I do not know the answer? It is.

But my most accurate guess (as far as I can see) lies in a hint I have already made a couple of times before. In every career, no matter what brilliant talents, what industry, what artistic in-tegrity, there also enters the element of luck. Several of Mozart's contemporaries in the musical field were proof of this state-ment. Haydn, for example, had the good fortune to meet a Jewish concert manager (the first of all international concert managers, and what a role they have played since then!) who literally bribed him away from his everlasting Esterházy family (again a case of misguided loyalty) and brought him to London, where old Papa Haydn enjoyed such enormous success that he started a new musical career at the age of sixty and produced the best work of his long and busy life.

But either Dame Fortune never called on poor Wolferl, or, when she did, he was perhaps busy teaching the pianoforte or deportment to his flighty and on the whole rather worthless wife, who meant well but who was the last person in the world to know how to manage the household of the kind of man she had married. Or he was absent on his endless trips to this, or that, or the other little Austrian city, where they had promised him an orchestra of not less than a dozen fiddlers and flute play-ers for his next opera. Or he was busy discussing a new libretto of something that was absolutely bound to "pack them in" and that was to be written by his faithful librettist, the curious Venetian, Lorenzo da Ponte, who, after having provided Mozart with the texts for his *Don Giovanni, Figaro,* and *Così fan tutte,* fell upon such evil days that he had to eke out a living in New York as a grocer and liquor dealer, later starting the first oper-atic venture in America and finally dying, in 1838, as a vener-able professor of Italian at what is now called Columbia Uni-versity.

Here are some of my guesses, but I am afraid that we shall never quite know, and so I had better leave the matter right here. Next Saturday you can perhaps favor me with a solution of your own. And now I shall make another confession.

The older I grew, the more I came to depend upon Mozart. When I was young, there was no one but Beethoven, and after-ward I went through a phase of Wagner. They are still good, but Bach eventually pushed them off first place, and Bach, of course, came to stay. But Mozart, once I had made his acquaint-ance (which was rather late in life), became my favorite. In my book *The Arts,* I have summed him up as follows:

Saint Francis, H. C. Andersen, and Mozart

In the small towns and villages of the Tyrol and Salzkammergut and Carinthia, where the spirits of the north and the south have been blended for so many thousands of years, there live a people who are neither Italian nor German but a curious blend of both races. Their language, their manners, their entire outlook upon life are different from those of their neighbors. They have developed an art of their own. Their churches, regardless of the time when they were built, have a character that is so typical of these valleys that, once seen, they are never forgotten. Their local painters have discovered a way of decorating houses and furniture with patterns that are not found elsewhere in the world. Every village and every town has a market place surrounded by a few stores, an apothecary shop, an old inn. In the middle of the market place stands a fountain that provides the people with their drinking water, pure water from a near-by mountain brook.

All the best efforts of the stonecutter and the blacksmith have been concentrated upon this public fountain which is usually surmounted by an image of the Virgin and the child Jesus, both of them done without the austerity that was so typical of the older Gothic. From early morning till late at night this fountain is the center of the communal life. Teamsters come to water their horses. Small girls and boys gather together to fill the household pitchers. But even when there is no one there, the cheerful sound of the silver-clear water, pouring forth in such generous abundance, fills this tiny market place with a deep sense of worldly security and spiritual well-being. There is no hurry. There is no bustle. The white-domed mountains keep the rest of the world at a safe distance, and the prevailing feeling is one of harmony and peace and quiet and a cheerful acceptance of whatever fate the good Lord in his wisdom will deem fit to bestow upon His loving children.

The music of Mozart is like the water that pours forth from these pleasant fountains. It started somewhere among the lonely tops of the surrounding peaks. It flowed down amidst the forests and pastures of the old familiar hillsides. Then it was taken in hand. It was tamed. It was given form and shape that it might become a blessing unto all mankind, a source of everlasting inspiration and joy, for those who have not yet forgotten the laughter and the simple pleasures of their childhood days.

I have nothing to add to that. The little fountain goes on splashing, and when life becomes too much for us, as is apt to happen quite often these days, we can sit down on the stone wall and close our eyes and listen and once more we begin to feel that life was meant to be good and beautiful.

The music for our evening's entertainment was easy, for Mozart, who never had had an adequate orchestra at his disposal during his own lifetime and who not infrequently was obliged to give his performances without having had time to conduct a single rehearsal (and that with musicians playing from hastily and badly copied sheets of manuscript), would, of course, be delighted to hear his works performed by some of our modern maestros, provided they did not indulge in the luxury of playing one of his minuets with an orchestra of one hundred and fifty musicians. I therefore sent a telegram to Frits in Amsterdam and asked him to bring me the following Mozart records: The symphonies in G minor and D and the "Jupiter" Symphony, the Quartet for Flute and Strings in D, the Variations on a Theme by Gluck, the *Requiem* in D minor, and as much as he could get from *The Marriage of Figaro, The Magic Flute, Don Giovanni,* and *Così fan tutte.* That was much too much music for one short evening, but we had no way of knowing what he wanted to hear, and, anyway, nobody can ever have too many Mozart records.

But the dinner—that was no easy matter!

Of one thing I was certain. We must have Mozart's beloved ice cream for dessert, and I wrote to The Hague for a pineapple so that we could have pineapple ice cream or *glace à l'ananas,* as it was to be called on our written menu. (I always drew rather pretty menus so that our guests could take them along as souvenirs, and out of habit I stuck to the French names, which have so much more fascinating a sound than their English equivalents—who would eat Brussels sprouts when he could get *choux de Bruxelles?*)

But what of the rest? I felt that I need not worry about Hans Christian. Although he had always loved good food, he had gone hungry so many years of his life that he would eat anything that was set before him—the richer the better. Saint Francis was in a different category. He too had gone hungry, but out of choice and not out of necessity, for, had he wished to do so, he could have lived as well as the Pope. Then I again remembered Rita Bonsal's recipe for spoon bread—the recipe she had inherited from that intelligent gourmet, Thomas Jefferson, and which I was going to save for the night we hoped to have the author of the Declaration of Independence with us. That would be just the thing for the good Francis, and I translated the original into Dutch so that Jo could understand it.

But how about the serious part of the meal? It should be a little more elaborate than usual. Well, there was the *crème gentilhomme,* a thick soup using artichokes as its base and with a plentiful addition of almond purée (very thin of course) and some of that chicken bouillon which Jo knew how to make so well. I had discovered it in an old copy of the *Almanach de Cocagne* and, although it was more reminiscent of the Middle Ages than of the era of the rococo, I thought that it would do quite well for this occasion.

Next, a fine old Dutch dish—boiled turbot with boiled potatoes and hollandaise sauce. This ought to be particularly pleasing to Hans Christian, who came from a country where they know how to do more wonderful things to a fish than anywhere else.

For our main course, another Dutch dish—*Carbonnades de boeuf à la flamande*—small boiled potatoes, and a green salad made with hard-boiled eggs, tarragon (the raw herbs, as well as a few spoonfuls of tarragon vinegar), a whole leek, well cut up, and a slight touch of onion and mustard.

The ice cream we had already decided upon, and this time Jo was not to place the cream in the cellar, where the neighbor's cat could get at it.

And then, of course, coffee and cognac, for not only had H.C. been an inveterate coffee drinker, but Mozart, whenever he had to finish a rush order, had worked all night long while his dear Constanze brought him more and more cups of coffee.

As for wine, I had to confess that I was too unfamiliar with the Austrian wines to know my way about. I felt it safer to stick to Moselle, so I telephoned my wine dealer, the one I had inherited from my great-grandfather, and asked him to send me six bottles of one of his best Moselle products. He answered that he had just what I wanted, a very mild Riesling 1915, which in some mysterious way had survived the war and of which he had been able to get twenty bottles at a recent sale. Very expensive? No more than a good Liebfraumilch. I told him to go ahead, bade him farewell, and went to see Jo to impress upon her the importance of our next party.

"For goodness sake," she asked, "you're not going to have that slut again—the one with the painted hair who carried on so disgustingly with my Hein?"

"Poor Hein!"

"Poor Hein indeed!" she answered. "It will be a long time before he hears the last of that little episode."

"But it wasn't his fault," I protested.

"I know," she laughed, "he hated the old scarecrow. But it's such fun to have something on him at last."

"At last?"

"Yes, at last, for Hein always was so careful!"

I whispered the Dutch equivalent of "Oh yeah?"

"What is that?"

"Nothing," I told her. "I was just thinking of something."

And now for the most entertaining, amazing, brilliant, and happiest evening we had had so far. Both Frits and I were at home when Erasmus arrived. He had dropped into a regular routine. He used to come at half-past six and then have a glass of mild sherry and a bit of toasted herring, for his dislike of fish did not extend to our domestic herring. We occasionally joined him with his curious hors d'oeuvre, but more out of politeness than from a real love for that humble member of the Clupea family which had laid the foundation for our nation's prosperity.

Our three guests arrived simultaneously, and that boded well for the success of the evening. No difficulty either this time in recognizing them. They looked exactly like their portraits and wore what we had expected them to wear. Saint Francis was garbed in his brown robe. Hans Christian Andersen appeared in his Inverness cape, and his shiny old hat was as badly brushed as it should have been. Wolfgang Amadeus had his hair neatly powdered and had taken out his best red coat for this festive occasion. He carried his little tricornered hat in his hand, and some very handsome white lace was visible around his neck.

We begged them to come in and not stand on any ceremony. "But of course, the good father goes first," Mozart said. "Our beloved Franciscus must go first, of course he must," Hans Christian repeated, and with these few words he betrayed his Danish origin, for all Danes speak as if they had just submitted to an operation for the removal of their adenoids. Erasmus uttered a few polite Latin phrases of welcome, and everything was very simple and very pleasant, and after five minutes we felt as if we had known each other all our lives.

The conversation that evening flowed like a mountain brook in spring. The Italian of Saint Francis was easier to understand than I had anticipated. But his Latin, so Erasmus told me, was not very good. He knew the more familiar passages from the Scriptures by heart, but the fourth-century idiom of Saint Jerome came more easily to him than the classical elegance of Cicero and Virgil.

Mozart spoke both Italian and German fluently, but he dropped so constantly into Viennese and Austrian colloquialisms that Frits, who had not spent as many years in that part of the world as I, often experienced a certain difficulty in following him. Mozart, however, was so delighted to have someone with whom he could at last talk his own dialect that he spent most of the evening addressing himself directly to me and roaring with laughter whenever I used a rather salty Salzkammergut peasant expression to describe someone whom he had known personally but whom I had met only in the pages of my history books.

As for Hans Christian, he spoke both French and German fluently, and my modest knowledge of Swedish made it possible for me to indulge in an occasional lapse into what in America we call "Scandinavian," whereupon he broke forth into many delighted "Ah so's" and "Ja so's" and asked for another tiny *Schluck* of our excellent Riesling.

But it was not what anybody said that made that evening so interesting. It was what happened. It began a few minutes after

Mozart's dog was a most amiable little pooch.

our visitors had arrived. There was a soft scratching at the door. Frits opened it, and there were two unexpected guests, a small dog and a big swan.

"Hello, pooch," Frits began, "what do you want?"

But it was clear enough what the animal wanted, for with one leap he was in Mozart's lap, going through all sorts of contortions to express his delight at being reunited with his master, until in the end he was almost standing on his head in a sheer paroxysm of joy.

"He's always been with me," Mozart said, "ever since that day I was buried and it rained so hard that my friends had to go back at the city gate. He was the only one who then followed

The birds had come to hear Saint Francis preach.

me to my grave. He's been with me ever since, but I did not quite know whether I dared bring him tonight."

"We love dogs in this house," Frits told him.

"How about swans?" Hans Christian asked.

"Swans, too, but pardon my asking: is that your swan?"

"It is my Ugly Duckling—The Ugly Duckling that made me who I am or who I was. I don't quite know this evening. It is all so strange."

"Is that really your Ugly Duckling?" Frits asked. "Then he is even more welcome, and we will leave the door to the garden open in case the room gets too warm for him."

"He would like that."

"But what does he eat?"

"Oh, anything at all. A bit of stale bread."

"And how about the little pooch?"

"Perhaps you have a bit of meat for him."

"Or a bone?"

"I am afraid that his teeth are a little old for a bone."

"Well, we will give him a veal chop, a whole one, and a bone, too. Then he can decide for himself."

"That would be wonderful," and Frits and the dog walked contentedly into the kitchen where Hein and Jo apparently made him so happy that he did not return until after we had finished our own dinner, when he curled up at Mozart's feet and slept the restless sleep of very old dogs who, whenever they

The Mozart dog went back to sleep.

459

dream, seem to be chasing cats or indulging in some other pastime of their youth.

As for the swan, he was no trouble at all. He gobbled down a copious meal of stale bread, then paid a visit to the garden, and, after he had waddled back into the room, he was given a large

H. C. Andersen's Ugly Duckling takes a swim.

tin washtub in which he happily disported himself until it was time for his master to go.

And now from the floor above came the strains of the overture to *The Marriage of Figaro,* as it had been played at the Glyndebourne Festival conducted by Fritz Busch. I saw Mozart's startled look when the familiar melody flowed softly down upon us.

"*Lieber Herr Gott noch a'mal!*" he said in his best Austrian. "I know that, I know it well!"

"You should know it, my dear Wolfgang Amadeus," I answered, "for it is you who gave it to us."

"But not that way," he protested. "I never suspected that it could sound like that if it were really well played. Why has no one ever told me? But they tell us very, very little, don't they, *mein liebes Hundl?* Oh, I forgot. He is having his dinner in the kitchen."

The overture to *The Marriage of Figaro* was followed by the

"Jupiter" Symphony, and once again Mozart was speechless when he heard what tremendous advances orchestral music had made since his day. The "Jupiter" Symphony was followed by a quartet (I forget which one), but that did not strike him as being much better than when he had last heard it, almost a century and a half before. "The strings in this piece are about as they always were," he remarked, "but the brasses and the flutes, they are truly magnificent. When I think of how horribly out of tune they were even when our best players handled them—and as for the piano I just heard! Of course I had to get accustomed to it for a moment, but what a range, what possibilities! If I had had an instrument like that, what couldn't I have done! For example, in my Piano Concerto in C minor where it goes tatee-tee-tum-tee-ta . . .."

"Dinner is ready," Jo announced.

"That is even better than music," Mozart observed.

"And better than literature," Hans Christian added. But the good saint only made the sign of the cross and recited a short invocation.

"Amen," Erasmus said at the end, and Frits and I, both noble heathens, added a little amen of our own. One somehow did when Saint Francis recited a prayer.

We took our seats, and the experiment with our artichoke soup seemed to be quite a success, when Frits, turning to me, asked, "Do you hear what I hear?"

I listened.

"What does it sound like to you?"

"Like the birdhouse in the Amsterdam zoo."

"So it does to me. We must be crazy!"

At that moment Hein came running out of the kitchen. "For God's sake," he shouted. "Come quick—come quickly—and look out of the window!"

We dropped our napkins and rushed into the kitchen. The old pear tree in the garden was full of birds, of all kinds of birds. There was even one which looked like a pelican.

"What next?" Jo asked, who thought a tame swan in her kitchen was enough for one evening.

But Saint Francis was running toward the door that led into the garden. "I think I know," he told us. "They will do that sometimes. They mean no harm. They merely want to hear me say a few words to them. Then they will go away again. But they like it when I speak to them, even if it is only a few words," and he stepped out on the grass and started:

"My little brothers and sisters, you know how much I love you. But tonight some kind people have invited me for dinner. You will see for yourselves that it would not be polite on my part if I were to upset all their plans by talking to you so long that the food their excellent cook has prepared for us would be spoiled. And so will you now please—all of you—go back to your nests? It is time for you to go to sleep anyway, and some of you must have traveled quite a long distance. Good night, my little brothers and sisters, I love you very dearly, but that must be all for this evening."

Whereupon the garden was suddenly filled with a cloud of colored feathers while these beautiful creatures rose into the air, with the exception of a very large one who looked as if he expected something.

"He is an old friend of mine," Saint Francis explained. "I usually give him something to eat. He should not be so greedy, but after all, he is only a bird and lives very far away."

"Would bread do?"

"Just a tiny piece."

Jo handed him a whole slice of bread. Saint Francis knelt down by the side of the bird and fed him. Then he said, "And now, not another piece—and then to bed with you!"

A moment later Frits' little garden once more lay deserted. We went back into the house, and Jo brought Saint Francis his spoon bread, and we had our fish, of which the saint was persuaded to try a small piece, which he munched contentedly with his spoon bread.

I had hopes that we would now perhaps have a few minutes'

rest, but hardly had Jo passed the potatoes than we noticed quite a number of people passing in front of our window (an unusual occurrence in Veere at that time of night), and almost immediately afterward—yes—no—yes—it was the *Kleine Nachtmusik* that came to us from the market place.

Mozart shook his head. "And this must happen just when I am enjoying the only good turbot I have had since I left Paris. Now I suppose I will have to go and tell these good people how grateful I am. Meanwhile, please tell the cook to keep my plate warm for me."

Again, that rather intense interest in their food I had observed among so many of our guests—that fear of missing something with which I was familiar from the last war, when we often fed soldiers who had escaped from a German prison camp, where they had been systematically starved for two or three years. I had occasionally dropped a few discreet hints about this to Erasmus, who seemed an absolutely different person from the one he had been the first time he had visited us. I knew enough to avoid the subject of his present whereabouts, but once in a while, when it seemed entirely natural to do so, I would drop a remark which bore more or less directly upon the problems of his everyday existence since he had left this earth. And on a few occasions he had answered me, but his replies were always rather evasive.

Tonight, however, perhaps under the influence of his congenial companions or perhaps because he was devoting all his attention to the serenade outside, he let a remark slip which was very significant.

"The food used to be much better, I am told, before I arrived. Then it was handled entirely by members of the old faith. But after the Reformation the Protestants claimed that they too should be consulted in the management of our establishment, and ever since there has been a kind of insistence upon 'plain living and high thinking.' It has made everybody rather uncomfortable, and the thinking most certainly has not improved, but . . ." (suddenly he seemed to become aware of what he was saying) "but that music is lovely. Hadn't we better join Herr Mozart on the stoop? At least for a few moments, for I don't want to risk another attack of my rheumatism, and I am forever catching colds."

We stepped out of the door and there found Wolfgang Amadeus hugely enjoying himself, for one by one he was recognizing old friends who had belonged to the Viennese musical world when he himself had been part of it and whom he had often joined when they went forth to pay their musical compliments to some distinguished fellow citizen to celebrate his marriage or his seventieth birthday. He was only waiting for the end of his *Nachtmusik* to rush forth and embrace them, but when the last note died down, behold! the market place lay deserted. The musicians were gone, and what made this little intermezzo even more mysterious was the fact that no one else in the village seemed to have noticed or heard what had happened. Not a single window had been opened. Our village policeman, who ever after that unpleasant experience with the two holy men from Nicaea had made it a point to remain on duty Saturday evenings, was, as we could notice, smoking his pipe and reading his *Middelburgsche Courant* in his small office off the main entrance of the town hall. And so the whole thing might just as well have been a dream, except that all of us had seen and heard it with our own eyes and ears—had seen it as clearly as we had seen the birds that had come to call upon Saint Francis—just as we even then were hearing the soft snoring of Mozart's faithful dog sleeping in front of the fire.

Some day, I knew, I would probably want to tell all that happened to us in that wonderful fall and winter to my grandchildren, and they would listen patiently, and they would say, "We love you, Grandpa, especially when you are telling us fairy stories." And I would insist that I was not telling them fairy stories but the truth, and they would answer me, "We don't believe a word of what you say, but what is the difference as long as we love it?" Wherein they would show greater wisdom than was ever the share of their grandfather, who never quite rid

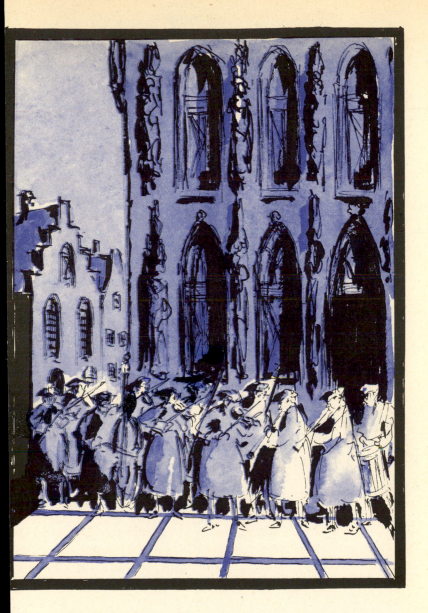

They were playing Mozart's KLEINE NACHTMUSIK.

himself of the notion hammered into his head by his history teachers that he must try and find out the real truth. As if any of us could bear to live in a world of unadulterated truth! The New Englanders came nearest to doing this, and look at the results!

While Jo was removing the plates after our *carbonnades à la flamande,* she whispered into my ear, "I have a surprise for you. Something I read about in that new cookbook you gave me."

"What is it?" I asked.

"Wait and see. But please blow out all candles."

I blew them out and waited. Then came Jo's surprise! She had somehow discovered that when you poured brandy over ice cream, it would burn for a short while without making the ice cream melt. I hated to think of that excellent product of the *fine bois* go up in flames, for really good cognac is getting extremely scarce, now that the whole world has fallen for the fake of a "true brandy of Napoleon." But the effect upon our visitors was delightful, and even Saint Francis was as pleased as a child. We watched the pretty blue flames as they played around the high tower of the ice cream, then slowly died down, flickered up once more, throwing strange shadows upon the ceiling, and finally went out altogether.

The sudden darkness caused two incidents. The Ugly Duckling woke up and, frightened by his uncustomary surroundings, emitted two loud honk-honks, and Jo stepped on the tail of Mozart's dog, who had followed her into the kitchen in search of something more to eat and who now yelped as if he were being murdered. However, the moment the candles had been relighted, the "right atmosphere" returned. The pooch and the Ugly Duckling went back to sleep, and we had our pineapple ice cream.

I had read a great deal about Mozart's physical delicacy. I had never had any reason to doubt the truth of that statement, but when the rest of us noticed how immensely he enjoyed his *Gefrorenes* the family "went slow" on the ice when it was passed to us a second time, and our saintly friend barely touched a spoonful—he had never eaten it before and complained to us, laughingly, that it made him feel frozen all over his insides. But that evening we watched Wolfgang Amadeus Mozart and

Jo entered, carrying her flaming dish.

Hans Christian Andersen get away with three entire quarts of pineapple ice cream. I had heard of such feats in newspaper stories about ice-cream-eating contests in the Middle West, but here I saw it happen before my own eyes.

"Oh well," said Frits afterward to Jo and Hein, who had been looking on, "perhaps they needed a few extra vitamins or something."

"I'm afraid that most of those people you ask never get enough to eat," the compassionate Jo answered. "They sure wolf their food when they come!"

"They live on holiness," Hein told her.

"Give me a good Dutch steak," was Jo's reply, "and I can do without the holiness."

Frits held up both hands. "Children," he remonstrated, "are those the sorts of things that should be said in this house to-night? Think of our guest."

But Jo was unconvinced. "I know," she answered, "and he's a lovely man even if he is a papist, but there! I don't want to be narrow-minded—he's as nice a man as I have ever met. But, poor fellow, if he had only taken care of himself and had paid a little attention to the things he ate, think of what he might have done!"

"It seems to me," I interrupted, "that he did fairly well, even if he never had a square meal. What more do you think he should have done?"

"Never mind," said Jo. "I am no—what do you call it?—I am no philosopher. But I have my own opinions on such subjects." And no matter how hard I tried afterward to make her commit herself on this subject, I never got any further answer out of her. Food was a serious matter to her. Indeed, to her the enjoyment of a good meal was the nearest thing to saintliness. Perhaps it even came ahead.

Is there any greater pleasure in this world than to sit around a table with people you really like, with whom you are tuned in on the same emotional and spiritual wave length, so that there never is any static, and with whom you agree so fully upon all matters of real significance that you can disagree just as heartily upon the nonessentials? We have by far too little of that sort of thing in America. We seem to feel that we should always be doing something. Just to sit and talk or, even worse, just to sit and do nothing at all, not even talk, is held to be a waste of time. How one can waste something that does not really exist, I never have been able to understand, but I do think that it would be of the greatest benefit to us as a nation if we could learn to spend at least half an hour after every meal sitting quietly around the dinner table. If the maid has to go to the movies, let her go, and wash the dishes yourself. Play with a few nuts or pieces of candy, drink a few drops of cognac (for cognac is the soul of wine, and in a sober glass of wine there lies much wisdom), and contemplate the delightful disorder of the dinner table, for it will bring order into your brain which has been somewhat shaken up by the events of the day.

I think it was Vauvenargues who gave us that lovely sentence: "All really great thoughts come out of the heart." I belong to a later and more prosaic generation. I do not want to discard that bit of Vauvenarguesian philosophy—we need it and need it badly. But I would like to make a contribution of my own to this effect: that a great many bright ideas also arise from a cheerful and well-balanced meal.

Some day I shall write a book about this, and by tens of thousands of well-authenticated cases I shall prove that lack of a good digestion has been responsible for at least seventy-five per cent of all the world's great crimes and for most of the great criminals—the Napoleons, the Hitlers, the Ivans the Terrible, or whatever their names. They were always too busy to waste a few minutes of their time just sitting pleasantly around a dinner table, passing the chocolate peppermints and eating oranges. They gobbled their food and went back to their blueprints and their statistics and their plans for further mayhem upon their fellow men.

Whereas Kant, who gave us our categorical imperative, used to keep his friends around him for at least an hour and a half after his midday dinners, whereas Spinoza used to join his landlord's family for a while after their noon meal and smoke a pipe with them while discussing the simple affairs of their very simple lives, and whereas Thomas Jefferson, when his guests threatened to leave him, sent down for an extra bottle of very, very special port that he might partake of their company a little while longer. Yes, there is enough material here for at least three volumes, but I must not start them right now, for I still have to tell you how we spent the evening with our three strange musketeers.

When we finally left the table, it was quite late. The week before, we had praised the good Lord that by putting the clock

ahead a couple of hours Erasmus had set us free from our unwelcome companions. Now we hoped that he would put the
clock back by at least four hours. As for the conversation itself,
good conversation is like good dialogue in a book you are reading. It will fulfill its purpose so quietly and efficiently that you
won't notice it.

Quite naturally, Erasmus spent most of the evening talking
to our saint. For a moment I had feared that the friction that
always existed between the Dominicans and their rivals, the
Franciscans, might have made them a little wary of each other,
but they got along beautifully. I mentioned my fears afterward
to Erasmus, and he smiled. "Of course not," he said. "Such
things never make any difference among civilized human beings. A brown robe—a black robe—what does it matter as long
as underneath we understand each other?"

Also, quite naturally, I had drifted toward Mozart, who was
specially pleased when I told him that when I was very young—
six or seven—my fiddle teacher had for a short while taught me
out of his father's *Violin Schule*. "Dear Papa," he said, "he was
a good craftsman, none ever better than he, and I owe him
much. Perhaps it would have been better for me if I had not
been dragged around from court to court when I was quite so
young. But I am sure dear Papa meant well, and Nannerl and
I really rather enjoyed meeting all those fine ladies and gentlemen. Nannerl was a sweet girl.

"And isn't it wonderful that Nissen should have written my
life! It isn't every man who would spend his days writing the
life of his wife's first husband. Yes, it was a good world. I only
wish it had lasted a bit longer. . . . And now I will tell you what
you can do for me—I would love to hear my *Voi che sapete* once
more, but in German this time. I want to find out whether it
really sounds as terrible as the critics used to say."

Eleven o'clock. Half-past eleven. A quarter to twelve. We had
had almost an hour of music (most of it arias from his operas)
when Mozart said, "That seems about enough. I don't want to

be selfish. I want to give my other friends a chance. Now let us sit down and hear what our Danish friend has to say. He was a storyteller, wasn't he?"

Hans Christian bowed. "I never thought very much of those little fairy tales of mine," he remarked, "but they were such small trouble, and they gave other people so much happiness, I rather felt it my duty to go on writing them."

"Isn't there one you remember which you never told when you were alive?" Mozart asked with more shrewdness than I had expected from him.

"There is," Andersen answered. "Would you like to hear it?"

There was a chorus of assent from all of us, and even Saint Francis, after Erasmus had translated the question, expressed his pleasure with a staccato of *benissime*'s.

Frits, who always thought of everything, had remembered that Hans Christian used to smoke a pipe with a large china bowl. He had dug one up in an Amsterdam tobacco shop, and all evening long our beloved Dane had been contentedly puffing at his new acquisition, remarking from time to time upon those handy little "tindersticks" which would ignite themselves when struck against the side of their box.

"In my days," he told us, "we had the devil of a time to keep our pipes going. We needed a hot brick, and all day long we were rolling up bits of paper to keep our tobacco burning. Yes, I like this invention, and if you don't mind, I will take some of them with me as a souvenir. And now, may I bother you for a little more of that excellent tobacco in the old blue jar. Herr Guldberg, our great poet, had one exactly like it. He used to tell me that it had originally belonged to Herr Holberg, our great dramatist. Thank you, and now if you will come a little closer to me, I will tell you the one fairy story I never told anyone else before.

"Once upon a time, the good Lord decided that He had been just a little lax in the attention He had paid to the human race and that He ought to go on a short tour of inspection. So He went to Saint Peter to ask him about the best method of reaching the earth, for there had been so many changes in the course of the planets since He had last visited that particular part of the stellar system that He was afraid He might lose His way or get hurt, and He wanted to refresh His memory. To His great surprise, He found Saint Peter none too enthusiastic about the idea, and He asked him what was on his mind that he offered so many objections.

" 'Dear Lord,' good Saint Peter answered, 'it is, after all, none of my business what You do or don't do. I only work here, and You are the boss, as I used to say to James and John in the olden days when I worked for them on the sea of Galilee. But will You allow me to ask You a question?'

" 'Of course, I will,' the good Lord replied.

" 'Well, then, You remember, when You created that particular little planet You called the earth, how You said it was going to be your "great experiment" and how You meant to make it as beautiful and lovely as You could and how You were going to create a new kind of being—You meant to call him "man" —and he and his fellow men were not only going to be given full possession of that delightful garden in which You intended that they should spend their days, but You were going to do something You had never done before. Those so-called men were going to be endowed with a will of their own—"free will" was the expression You used, I think—and they were not going to be bound by any hard and fast rules, but they were going to be allowed to act according to what they themselves thought the right way to act.

" 'Of course, all that was long before my time, but You often told me about it when I came here first and when You seemed very much depressed and said that You had just experienced the worst disappointment of all eternity.'

" 'You are perfectly correct, my dear Peter,' the Lord answered. 'All that is exactly as you say.'

"Saint Peter stroked his long white beard a couple of times before he was ready to go on.

" 'Well, then, dear Lord,' he continued, 'here is the question

I always wanted to ask You, but I never had a chance before. It might have seemed an impertinence on my part, but this gives me a good excuse.'

"The good Lord had not the slightest idea what His faithful old gatekeeper was driving at, but as He always had felt a very warm liking for this plain-spoken old fisherman, He told him, 'Go ahead, beloved friend, go ahead and ask Me anything you want.' Once more Saint Peter ran his hand down his beard, and then he asked his question.

" 'Dear Lord,' he said, 'we have known each other for a great many years now, and when one loves a person as I love You, one comes to know a great many things about him he never thinks you have even guessed at, for everybody is always sure that he can hide his thoughts by frowning or looking solemn or smiling or something.'

" 'I know,' the Lord replied, 'that was one of my cleverest ideas, and I am very proud of it—that ability I bestowed upon people to hide their thoughts.'

" 'And You think, Lord, that You yourself are any good at it?' asked Peter, who had not been born to be a yes man.

" 'Yes, I rather do!'

" 'Well, then, I am afraid, Lord, that You have another guess coming, which, of course, is not the way I should talk to You, but that is what I feel.'

" 'Forget it,' said the Lord. 'We are old friends. We can speak our minds. Forget it and ask your question. What is it?'

" 'Well, then, good Lord, since You insist. I know what great hopes You had set on that famous experiment of Yours on that little planet, and how You were full of hope for the future, for now at last You had created a being after Your own image and had given him a fine place of residence and an abundance of free will. That was a combination that must succeed—that could not possibly go wrong.'

"This time it was the turn of the Lord to stroke His beard. 'I remember,' He answered.

" 'Well, then, what I have always wanted to ask You but

never had a chance to do so until now, when You want to go
back there . . .'

" 'Yes, yes,' the Lord interrupted him, 'what is it?'

" 'What I wanted to ask You is this. If You had to do it all
over again—this experiment with this strange biped created after
Your own image and endowed with a will of his own which he
could use for either good or evil—would You do it again?' "

Hans Christian paused. I used the opportunity to look at my
wrist watch—one more minute.

"Go on," I begged him. "Tell us the rest."

"Yes, but my pipe has gone out, and I lost my little tindersticks."

I lit a match and held it over his pipe in such a hurry that I
almost burned his long nose. Hans Christian was a very deliberate fellow when it came to lighting his pipe. Finally it was done.
He took a deep puff.

"Please go on," I told him, "what did the Lord answer? Go
on—we have only a few seconds."

One more pull—a minute before midnight. Then he said,
"The Lord took quite a while, for this was a very important
question—the most important one He had ever been asked—and
then He answered, 'You ask Me whether I would do it again—
create an animate being after my own image and endowed with
that freedom of choice between evil and good which is part of
my own omniscience, but without that wisdom and experience
which I have acquired during an eternity of thoughtful contemplation and practical application.' "

Two more seconds to go.

" 'It is very difficult to give you a direct yes or no' "—
one more second—" 'but on the whole, I feel inclined to say
that . . .' "

BANG said the clock outside. The room was plunged into
darkness, and our guests were gone.

When we cleaned up the table I found a little card stuck up
against a small bunch of flowers and kept from slipping down

by a tiny figure out of one of Hans Christian Andersen's fairy tales. It bore the signature of Wolfgang Amadeus Mozart. A little farther below, Hans Christian had scrawled two words in Danish, *Mange tak*—"Thank you," and at the top, almost illegible, *Carissimi fratelli,* with a cross and his blessed name, Francesco.

On some previous occasions, Erasmus had tarried for a short while after the others had taken their departure. This time, he too was gone. Frits and I were left alone for a few moments, until I got up and waved him a silent good night. Then I stepped out into the dark street. The village was already asleep. In the distance the light of the West Kapelle lighthouse was sweeping its blinding rays across the earth and the heavens. Two short flashes—a long one—ten seconds of darkness—two short flashes—a long one—ten seconds of darkness—two short flashes—a long one—ten seconds of darkness. I walked to the top of the dike, and there I stood for quite a long while, looking at the dark sea in the distance. Two short flashes, when the horizon seemed to have caught fire—a long one—and again the earth was as it had been before creation.

Mozart, Hans Christian Andersen, and Saint Francis—three short flashes—then darkness again.

A curious arrangement, yet one which enabled many a weary mariner to find his way across the turbulent waters of the ocean of life.

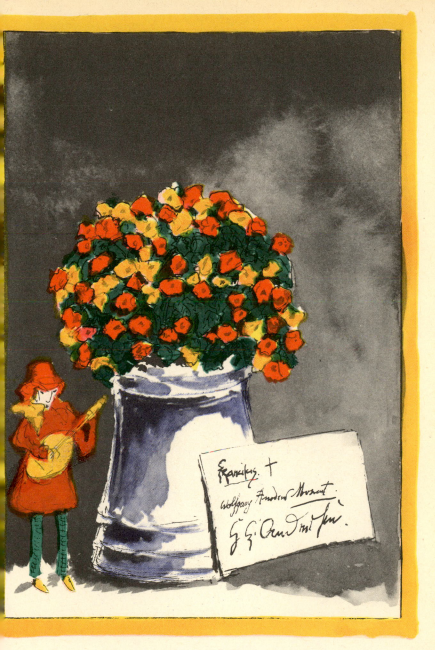

Our guests had left us a little souvenir.

CHAPTER XII

We Entertain BEETHOVEN, NAPOLEON, and My Own GREAT-GREAT-GRANDFATHER and Listen to a Long Monologue

"SHALL I TELL you something funny?" Erasmus asked me the next time I visited him in his sunlit room among his ancient folios. "Something quite amusing, but at the same time a little pathetic."

"What is it?"

"I heard that someone is very jealous of us."

"Of whom?"

"Of *us!* Of those of us who have been invited to your dinners."

"But how does anyone know? We have been very discreet. We have done our best to keep our secret well guarded."

"That I realize. But where I am now it is not really so very different in some respects from life on earth. Curiosity is one human trait that seems to survive even in death. Curiosity and jealousy."

"And now the Elysian Fields are filled with stories about our parties, and others feel hurt because they have not been invited?"

"Everybody seems to know all about your dinners up to the last details: how Mozart and Hans Christian ate all the ice cream and how scandalously those two bishops behaved and what a marvel your cook is at roasting chickens. But now something funny has happened."

475

"Tell me, please. I'm getting curious."

"Well, this is the way I heard it. Most of us, when we bid farewell to this earth, are quite satisfied that our time has come. What with all the troubles and tribulations we have seen, the unnecessary cruelty, the endless stupidities and disappointments, we are more than ready to go. Many of us are more than satisfied when God's dark angel touches us and tells us to be prepared to follow him. But now and then, somebody is born who can never have enough, who is insatiable, who has reached out for everything, who has had everything, yet wants more."

"A horrible thought!"

"The most horrible thought in the world."

"And outside of it, too!"

"I stand corrected—and outside of it, too."

"And who is the unfortunate soul who feels jealous of all our other guests?"

"You could probably guess his name."

"I would rather let you tell me."

"His name is Napoleon. He is said to have been—though I cannot vouch for it, as it happened long after my time—but he is said to have been Emperor of the French, and at one moment it appears he came very close to ruling the whole world."

"We know him well and we don't like him! That is to say, Frits and I and our sort of people don't like him, but there are others who do."

"Why?"

"I am not quite sure, but they claim that he was a very great man."

"Why?"

"Because he got things done."

"What sort of things?"

"He caused more people to be killed than anyone else."

"And they admire him for that?"

"Not for that alone."

"Then for what else?"

"Because, as I said, he got things done."

"That sounds mysterious."

"And it is mysterious, but now that you have mentioned him, it might not be a bad idea to ask him."

"Because he murdered so many people?"

"No, that will make it very difficult for us to sit in the same room with him. But he seems to have been able to cast quite a spell upon everyone who came in contact with him."

"How do you know? Did you read it in a book?"

"No," I answered, "my grandmother told me. Her own father was one of his victims."

"Did he get killed, too?"

"Not exactly. All he lost was his health and his property, two of his sons, and three of his toes."

"Yet your own grandpa loved him?"

"He worshiped the ground he trod on."

"In spite of his two sons and everything else?"

"In spite of it."

Erasmus looked at me in surprise. "You almost make me curious to meet him."

"You will, and very soon, too."

We had planned to ask two women for our next dinner, for we did not want to make our parties too one-sided. But I put Catherine of Russia and Marie Antoinette off until some other Saturday (in the end they never came), and when in the evening I stole forth to visit my faithful old lion, three names appeared on my slip of paper. They were that of the Emperor Napoleon, that of my own great-great-grandfather, a simple corporal of the Grenadier Guards and volunteer for the ill-fated expedition against Russia of 1812, and, as an afterthought, that of the man who had also for a great many years fallen under the Corsican's spell but who had recovered and had forever cast him out of his life—Ludwig van Beethoven.

Frits was delighted when I told him. "I hate that dreadful little Italian," he said, "I loathe the very name of him. But I would like to meet him. And it would be marvelous to make

old Ludwig go after him! I hope he is in one of his ferocious
moods. That would be magnificent!"

Late at night I used to bring the invitations to the town hall.

The problem of food! The Emperor detested long meals.
Fifteen minutes was all he ever cared to spend at the table. I
decided to make him stay for at least two hours. He was a
monotonous feeder—a cold leg of chicken for breakfast, the
same for luncheon (on those rare occasions when he bothered
to eat that meal), and roast chicken for dinner. Anything outside of that was apt to be sent back to the kitchen. Very well,
there would be no chicken that evening. We would give him
fish, which he detested. He drank nothing but a very light
claret. There would be only champagne at our meal. Never
mind the expense! There would be enough champagne to float
Hein's boat, and we would both of us fill the room with smoke
for he detested tobacco. As for the box of snuff which we had
bought a few months before, when we entertained Emerson
we would hide it so carefully that no one could find it, should
the Emperor ask for a pinch of his beloved Copenhagen rappee

It was, perhaps, not a very dignified way of getting even with the little Corsican, but it was better than not getting even at all. And then there was our chance to make his ears suffer. He had despised music. Military bands and a few pieces by Grétry were all he had ever cared to listen to. We still had all those lovely records of Mozart. These would irritate him beyond words, and Hein got instructions to play them the whole evening. Beethoven was too deaf to care, and even if he caught an occasional snatch, he had a great admiration for his older contemporary and therefore would not mind. All that remained to be done was to find dishes of which even the names would cause the Emperor unpleasant recollections, Russian names and Spanish names, reminding him of the defeats he had suffered in those two countries.

Here is the menu I composed. Soup—*potage Condé*. The Condés belonged to the Bourbon family, and the Duke d'Enghien, whom he had murdered, had been a Bourbon. That ought to annoy the Emperor, even if in the end, by marrying the niece of the wife of one of them, he had become a relative by marriage of the late Louis XVI. The French recipe says that "red string beans" are the base of this soup, but I don't know what "red string beans" are. Must ask. Or shall we have *potage Bagration?* Piotr Ivanovich Bagration was the Russian general who had fought Napoleon to a standstill at Borodino in 1812. Perhaps we had better stick to the *potage Condé,* as we shall have other Russian dishes. If I can get it, we might start the dinner with caviar, though, as far as I am concerned, I would just as soon suck a piece of black cotton drenched in salt water.

Entreé—*gigot de mouton à la moscovite*. I suppose it is called *à la moscovite* because it has gin in it. That will make it pretty terrible, but the rest of us can always have something else beforehand. But why gin should be added to mutton is a puzzle to me. However, if the recipe of 1739 says so, we might as well try it.

Vegetables—there I had my choice between *pommes de terre à l'anglaise* (mashed) or *pommes de terre Chateaubriand* (fried in olive oil and with a lot of finely cut parsley). Come to think of it, he must have had lots of potatoes *à l'anglaise* on St. Helena. I shall take the potatoes fried *à la Chateaubriand*. That, too, ought to irritate him, for Chateaubriand was one of his most successful literary enemies and was forever nagging him about the murder of the Duke d'Enghien.

For dessert, how about small *pots de crème* with that angel-food cake which, for some strange reason, the Dutch call "Muscovite cake"? This rather leaves Beethoven and Grandpa out of the picture, but Beethoven was a most careless eater (both as to hours and substance) and my honored ancestor will be much too excited at meeting his Emperor either to know or care what he gets. With the coffee, let's have cooking brandy, or shall we waste a little money on a cordial he will detest when he sees the name: Danziger Goldwasser?

And now a short report upon His Majesty, for he insisted upon briefness in all communications sent to him. This was only natural, as reports came to him all day long—reports from Madrid and Rome and Amsterdam and Hamburg and Warsaw and Berlin and from every corner of the world, including the new one, until he sold us his American holdings for several million dollars. But few communications ever reached him, from London, until the year 1815, when a brief note addressed to the commander of the *Bellerophon* gave orders to remove General Bonaparte to H.M.S. *Northumberland* and take him for safekeeping to the island of St. Helena. Napoleon must have known about that island. In one of his schoolbooks that have been preserved (I think it is in Genoa) he had noted down: "St. Helena, a little and very lonely island in the southern half of the Atlantic Ocean." He had six endless years in which to find out how true that was—six years of being buried alive after twenty-six years into which he had packed more activity and more glory than have ever come to any other man. I don't like him, but I confess that it was a pretty stiff sentence. On the other hand, suppose I had been the British government, what else would I have done? What else could any government have done that wanted to rid the world of a human being who was a volcano, who had more energy than a hundred million ordinary human beings, who had fewer scruples than the lowest type of highwayman, who had more power over his fellow men than anybody else of whom the record has survived, who could do more work in a shorter space of time than two dozen ordinary statesmen, and whose ego was so great that he needed an entire planet as a background for his ambitions and his vanity?

But I must make this brief and, above all things, precise, for that is the way to do things in the truly Napoleonic style. Very well, here I go!

Napoleone Buonaparte was born in 1769, a year after his native island of Corsica had been incorporated into the kingdom of France. An important item, this, for it was to influence all the days of his youth and, until he was in his early twenties, he was not really a Frenchman but a violent Corsican patriot and a rebel with a dream of a liberated and independent Corsican nation and with—who could tell?—a king of its own—His Majesty Napoleone I.

These patriotic sentiments he had inherited from his parents —most of all from his mother. For the father, Carlo Buonaparte, was just another rather shiftless scion of an old Italian family which could pride itself upon a noble Tuscan origin, as two centuries before it had moved from the mainland to this rude and backward island belonging to the Republic of Genoa. Since then, they had lived in the capital city of Ajaccio. They had never done very well. But neither had they entirely slipped out of their own class. Carlo Buonaparte was a lawyer, a small-scale landowner, and a rather prominent local patriot.

Far different the mother! She belonged to the tribe of the Ramolinos, and her first name was Letizia. We shall meet her on every page of her famous son's history—a shadowy figure to the outside world, for Madame Mère, a deeply pious Italian woman of the old style, preferred to remain in the background. But to her *piccolo* Napoleone she was and, until the end of his days, would remain a tower of strength. So much so that she was the only person in the whole wide world of whom he was afraid. For she had a sharp tongue in her head, and he was forever hearing that terrible remark of hers, repeated every time he had gained a new victory and had made himself master of still another country: *Pourvou que ça doure*—if only it lasts!

Letizia Ramolino never learned to speak French correctly. Her Italian accent clung to her until her death. But in this she was not different from the Emperor himself, who never learned to write French without gross grammatical errors. It must have been a Napoleonic trait. His nephew, the third Napoleon, never lost the Swiss accent he had acquired during his years of exile in the Helvetian Confederation.

The people of Corsica were not unlike the Alsatians, who have never yet been able to make up their minds whether they want to be German or French. While they were Genoese, the Corsicans wanted to be French. After they had become French, they wanted to be Genoese again. To settle the problem, one of them, a certain Pasquale Paoli, had started a movement of "Corsica for the Corsicans." It was during this rebellion that Napoleon was conceived. His mother carried him under her heart (as the expression used to be in more modest times than ours) while accompanying her husband on his campaigns in the wilderness. The revolution fizzled out. Paoli was defeated and in May, 1769, the liberator fled to England.

In August of the same year, Napoleone was born. By that time the family was back in Ajaccio, picking up the pieces as best they could. Carlo Buonaparte contemplated the future. No use being in the opposition, now that the cause of Corsican freedom had been lost for good. Might as well get on the right side of the new masters. He had a raft of children. The sons could make their own way, but the daughters had to be provided for. He made himself useful to the French governor. In 1779 the governor felt the need of sending a trusted emissary to Versailles to consult the home government. Carlo Buonaparte was chosen for this mission. He asked leave to take his second son, Napoleone, then ten years old and (as boys of his age are apt to be) a dangerous rebel, every inch a Corsican patriot.

That was the beginning of Napoleone's career as a Frenchman.

He was not a particularly attractive child. He was as pale as a sheet, as thin as a rail, and terribly awkward. He wore ill-fitting clothes and in everything he said or did proclaimed himself a provincial. But he had a pair of eyes no one ever forgot. Also, he had terrible attacks of temper which occasionally led to such outbursts of fury that people suspected epileptic fits. But that was not true. Bismarck, too, was apt to break forth into uncontrollable paroxysms of weeping whenever he was crossed, but no one ever accused him of being an epileptic, like Caesar, Saint Paul, and Mohammed.

For the rest, nothing very remarkable either as a student or, afterward, as a young officer. Except the dreadfully serious way in which he took everything connected with his own person and his family. Papa Carlo died when Napoleone was sixteen, and he then became the head of the family. His elder brother, Joseph, did not amount to much. It was up to little Napoleone to look after his mother and to provide for his sisters.

In this respect he showed himself a perfect Italian. He took care of all his relations and heaped favors upon them as long as he had any favors to bestow. They repaid him in the usual way. They were never satisfied. They were always clamoring for just a little more. When his luck turned, they suddenly were very busy with their own concerns. Except old Letizia. She remained faithful, even after it had been proved that she had been right and that it could not really last.

After having learned the elements of his future trade at the military school of Brienne, Napoleone Buonaparte did a year of postgraduate work at the École Militaire in Paris. He therefore was given the best training the old French kingdom could bestow upon its future officers. In 1785 he became an under-lieutenant, if that is the way to translate the French title of *sous-lieutenant*.

Then came the Revolution, and Napoleon found his second father. For it was the French Revolution that sired the Emperor of the French.

Allons, enfants de la patrie! The people of France were on their way. So was Lieutenant Bonaparte, for together with his Corsican ambitions he was thinking of shedding the Italian spelling of his name. In short, Lieutenant Napoleon Bonaparte was ready to begin his career. And the world was setting the stage on which he would be able to play his role to the best of his unlimited abilities.

If I continue even in this meager detail I shall need a chapter of six hundred pages to follow him through all his adventures, and I promised you that I would be brief.

We begin, therefore, with the year 1785, when Napoleon gets his first appointment. Good King Louis has been on his throne eleven years. He has been married to the lovely Marie Antoinette of Austria for fifteen years. His beautiful Queen, at first adored by her subjects, has done everything possible to destroy her popularity. There is nothing wicked about her, nothing evil, nothing immoral even at a court where the word "morality" has been out of the local vernacular these last one hundred and fifty years. Suppose we just say that she did not "understand" the world in which she lived and let it go at that. She is always getting the wrong publicity. She considers herself so far removed from the ordinary run of humanity that she does not have to care what people say. But in this she is very much mistaken as she will soon find out.

The great of this earth are like little candles stuck way up high in a church, right underneath the rafters. That is the reason they seem to shed so much more light than they actually do. They are up so high. But by the same token, they are terribly conspicuous—at times, almost indecently so. The moment they begin to flicker in a draft, everybody says, "Oh look! There is something wrong with our little candle!"

The old French monarchy, badly in need of repairs, made all the candles within the walls of its ancient edifice smoke. Grease was dribbling all over the Holy of Holies. Everybody felt uncomfortable. At any moment an accident might happen. Should the building catch fire, it was sure to burn down to the ground. The fate of France was in the balance.

King Louis XVI is a good man. His chief weakness is that he is almost too good-natured and too kindly disposed toward everybody. And his Queen, the beauteous Marie Antoinette, is an Austrian and a Hapsburg. She has been brought up far away from ordinary common humanity. She does not know the world in which she lives. Therefore, she is forever being taken in by all sorts of clever scoundrels. Just now a couple of notorious crooks have used her name to swindle several million francs' worth of diamonds out of the absurd Cardinal de Rohan. They have used the Queen's name to lead him on and make him believe that the Queen will accept him as her lover. Now they are safe in London, trying to dispose of their plunder. When the plot is at last discovered, it is definitely established that the Queen is in no way involved, has not even the slightest idea what it is all about. But the talk of the town makes her little candle, way up there in the big hall of Versailles, flicker and sputter so violently that it is almost extinguished. The crown of France can no longer stand that sort of thing. The country is bankrupt. The country has been bankrupt for quite a long time now. The people are starving. The army has become restless. One financial wizard after the other is pushed forward to try his luck and pull billions out of an empty treasure chest. When he is not successful right away, the Queen curls her pretty lips in a disdainful way. As an Austrian Hapsburg, she is above worrying about such foolish details as money and credit. The money should be there no matter what happens, and the credit should be unlimited. Get rid of the latest miracle man, who apparently does not know how to handle the philosopher's stone, and get a new one. Or don't get anybody at all, and just let events take their course.

But it is only the year 1785, and the French are still profoundly loyal to their anointed sovereigns. Four entire years will have to elapse before the representatives of the people will be called together to advise (in the humblest of spirits) their royal master how he may save the country from a financial and political catastrophe. During those four years, Lieutenant Bonaparte wanders from garrison to garrison, spends his vacations in the old home town to help straighten out the family affairs, is once more tempted to dabble in local Corsican politics, but in the end thinks the better of it and returns to his post in Auxonne or Valence or wherever his regiment happens to be stationed. He also has certain literary plans, and at one time, when his funds are very low, he peddles books on the installment plan. Then back once more to Corsica, where Pasquale Paoli, the liberator, has reappeared, this time backed up by English warships and English money.

The moment has come at last to make a definite choice. On the one hand, France, full of new ideas, is rushing forward to the new order of things as it stands explained in the books of the great contemporary philosophers. On the other hand, a quasi independence under the suzerainty of England, which represents reaction, which believes in government by the few, and which denounces the new creed of liberty, equality, and fraternity as an invention of the Devil.

Lieutenant Bonaparte still loves his native island, but he also has become a fairly good Frenchman. If that is the policy Paoli wants to follow, he is sorry, but it can never be his way. Then there is no other choice but to leave Corsica forever—he and his family—his mother, his brothers and sisters, and Uncle Fesch.

Uncle Giuseppe Fesch is not really an uncle. His father's second wife was the widowed mother of Napoleon's own mother, and that makes him—but figure it out for yourself. However, according to the tribal instincts of these half-savage Corsicans, that is enough of a relationship to make Giuseppe Fesch a member of the Buonaparte clan, and Uncle Joseph comes along when the family sails for Toulon, leaving his deanery behind, to become Archbishop of Lyons, to be offered the archbishopric of Paris (which he modestly refuses), and finally to be elevated to the rank of cardinal.

But of course everything tangible has to be left behind, and so, when the expedition finally sets foot on French soil, there is no other source of revenue than what that dutiful second son, Napoleone, can make by his sword and what (but this is mere speculation) the handsome sisters will be able to make by their looks in catching rich husbands.

The Reign of Terror is now in full swing. Lieutenant Bonaparte (Buonaparte is now on its way out; the use of it by a few careless correspondents soon causes resentment) has not taken an active part in politics, but he is known to be a good deal of a Jacobin—a Red, as we would say today. He has even written a pamphlet defending the radical republican point of view. Robespierre's brother has met him when he visited the army as a commissar for the revolutionary dictatorship and has liked him for his civic virtues.

Just then the town of Toulon is the great menace to the safety of the Republic, for Toulon is situated on the sea, and the sea belongs to the British, and as long as they have access to the harbor of Toulon, Paris must face the possibility of a surprise attack from the south. All military men agree that this is a job for the artillery, for it is impossible to use infantry (let alone cavalry) among the steep rocks surrounding Toulon. Captain Bonaparte drops discreet hints that he thinks he can do it, that he has an idea and would like to be allowed to try it out.

He is a pale-looking young Corsican of vague antecedents and said to be a bit queer. But this is a golden age for queer people. The crazier the merrier, for after the mess the so-called intelligentsia has made of this world, let the other kind try—the butchers promoted to be generals, the barbers turned colonels, the *valets de chambre* now foreign ministers or envoys extraordinary and ministers plenipotentiary, the ex-ladies' maids who dominate the salons of Paris. Let that Corsican scarecrow try. He can't be worse than the ex-artist now in command. If he does what he says he will do, we will make him a colonel or a general. And if he fails, he will be brought before a court-martial and shot.

The Corsican scarecrow tries and succeeds. Toulon is taken. The British sail away, and the citizens who cannot find room on one of their transports are executed. Napoleon is not shot. He becomes a brigadier general, when another incident occurs which might easily have cost him his life. In Paris, the Reign of Terror has now come to an end. Robespierre has been decapitated. Then the people begin to ask questions. Did not Robespierre have a favorite in the army, a young artilleryman who is said to have taken Toulon? Letters from Napoleon to both the Robespierres are found among their correspondence and the new brigadier general is imprisoned and told to await trial. Before it comes off, the need for competent officers has made itself so sorely felt that Carnot, creating his armies out of fresh air and enthusiasm, insists upon his being released, but others declare that that is letting him escape a little too easily for a former friend of the tyrant, and Napoleon is dismissed.

Then follows a year of misery and poverty. Napoleon is forced to pawn his watch and sell his books. The Café de la Régence no longer sees him for his daily game of chess. He no longer has the price of a cup of coffee. He is thinking seriously of taking service with some foreign power. The Sultan of Turkey is said to be reorganizing his armies. Why not go to Turkey and see what can be done there, for anything is better than Paris when you have not a sou in your pockets and must support a family of hungry brothers and sisters.

Politics? They would be all right if one knew beforehand who was going to come out on top. Otherwise, they are too dangerous. So there is nothing to do but wait. For it stands written in the stars that this particular young man will succeed beyond his boldest expectations, and the stars are never wrong. In proof whereof here comes a messenger bearing a note from one of the leading men in the Convention, Citizen Barras.

Citizen Barras is really Comte Paul François Nicolas de Barras. Seeing the way the wind is blowing, he has joined the Revolution almost from the beginning and by systematically betraying everybody he has managed to keep his own head on his shoulders. Nobody likes him, and nobody trusts him, but at least he has inherited the habit of giving orders. He now proposes that Bonaparte be entrusted with the command of the troops loyal to the Convention. Nothing can suit General Bonaparte better than that. He hastily accepts, for he is a man of law and order and hates to see Paris being run by the rabble, whether it be the rabble of the right or of the left.

On October 5, 1795—the 13 Vendémiaire, according to the new style—the mob is going to find out who is to be the real master and who will run the capital and the nation. The Convention has forbidden all public demonstrations. Early in the morning, crowds are beginning to move down on the Convention. They suddenly find themselves faced by several batteries placed in front of the church of Saint-Roch. The yellow-faced young man in charge (malaria in Italy has made him turn yellow) tells them to go back or he will shoot. The crowd has heard that before, but nothing has ever happened. They laugh at the yellow-faced young man, bid him shoot his toy cannon, and push on. He does shoot his toy cannon. A large number of people are killed. Many more are wounded. The rest run as fast as they can, and that evening the French Revolution is over.

From 1795 until 1799, France is ruled by the Directory. During those four years, the citizen armies of the Republic defeat, destroy, and annihilate all the subject armies of the old dynasties. Austria is the worst sufferer, for Austria has to fight General Bonaparte, who now maneuvers in Italy as if he were playing a game of croquet in his own garden. When the shooting is over, Austria has lost Belgium and a large part of her possessions in Italy. The west bank of the Rhine has been ceded to France, and a number of newly founded republics are starting upon the inspiring though difficult experiment of self-government.

Everything is wonderful. France, so it looks to the outside world, has triumphed on every front except her own domestic one. For it is one of the few demonstrable axioms of history that a democracy, the moment it has achieved victory, runs the greatest risk of defeating itself.

But there must be no philosophizing in this report. Philosophy is not a popular subject with Napoleon. Nor is God. He will soon enough need God in his own business as a sort of super-Emperor and then he will show Him a few occasional favors. In exchange for these he feels that he has the right to expect fair and, if possible, preferential treatment. Whenever that part of the bargain is not kept, the party of the second part has a right to show his displeasure. But since the party of the first part is out of his reach, the only possible way to give evidence of his wrath is by taking it out on the terrestrial representatives of the party of the first part, as the Pope and the high French (Spanish, Italian, and Austrian) clergy will soon discover to their own great dismay and discomfort.

But plain, ordinary philosophers, such as have been responsible for the Declaration of the Rights of Man and similar nonsense—he has as little use for them as he has for musicians and actors. Actresses are something else again. They may—if they are that kind—amuse him with the passing pleasure of a few pleasant nights when he can be himself and need not play the role of the Great Man. After that you give them a nice brooch with diamonds (but not too expensive, for the honor of having shared his couch should be enough in itself) and forget about them. As for the philosophers, let them starve, unless they also happen to be good mathematicians, in which case they may come in handy for the study of problems connected with ballistics or aeronautics, for their captive balloons have proved to be quite handy in some of the battles in Belgium. But deprive them of all power to think or act independently, for that may lead up to another revolution, and what the world wants and needs just now beyond all other things is peace and quiet and a chance to make some money out of legitimate business ventures. Therefore, all the philosophers who may be really "effective" should be organized into an Academy of Science, which should be subject to official supervision like any army battalion, ready to function at a moment's notice or to be kept quietly in their barracks when not needed. As for the others, tell your police to keep them under observation and forget about them.

Again I am wandering, but this man is not a man. He is as complicated as a mountain range. Before one reaches the highest point, there are endless valleys to be traversed and at least four dozen minor peaks to be conquered.

Let us see—where was I? It is the year 1799, and General Bonaparte has knocked the rest of Europe into a cocked hat. Since he has proved himself the ablest man in France (not to say the whole world), why shouldn't he be given the chance to rule the whole of France and as much of the rest of the Continent as can be forced to submit to his will? Have not all the great philosophers, from Confucius and Plato down to Rousseau, proclaimed that the best form of government is that in which the ablest man is put in charge of affairs? "Every philosopher a king and every king a philosopher." Who said that? Never mind. It may look all right on paper, but it should not be taken too seriously in practical life, and in the meantime, my friends, let us be practical and, above all things, let us "function," for "functioning effectively" is the most important thing in life.

It is too bad that one cannot work twenty-four hours a day. It is worse that there are interruptions from another side. Passion is apt to make awful fools of ordinary people, and when it has them in its power there is little to choose between the commonest of his soldiers and their glorious commander in chief. If only he had never met this Creole woman with her

Caribbean knowledge of how to bewitch men! It was the fatal Barras who had brought them together. She was a widow at that moment, having lost her noble husband, the Vicomte de Beauharnais, on the scaffold. Not because he had been lacking in "civic qualities," but because he had allowed the Austrians to beat him—and during that great emergency an unsuccessful revolutionary general lost both his command and his head.

And now Napoleon must have that woman with him always, for she has got into his blood, and he is an Italian and wants what he wants when he wants it—if it has anything to do with women. Too bad that she is six years older than he and has two grown-up children, but that is the way it is with women from the tropics. Too bad, too, that no matter how much money he gives her, she will always spend thrice that amount. Too bad her teeth are in such a shocking condition. But when he sees her he forgets about the hundred pairs of silk stockings she had made him pay for out of his slender army wages. He also forgets the contemptible crowd of gigolos with whom she likes to surround herself. He forgets that, according to rather substantial information, she has had a great many lovers (how about that useless Barras himself, to whom he is indebted for so many favors?). He only knows that he must have this woman or that he will go crazy. The woman realizes this too. She is much older than that poor little Corsican boy (he has come back from his latest campaign in Italy with all his hair gone, as the result of some kind of skin disease which he had caught in camp) and she is so completely not in love with him that she can make him go through his paces like an organ-grinder's trained monkey.

Josephine then decides that it would be folly to throw away such a magnificent opportunity to become rich and provide for her two children. So she marries the man of the hour, who, after one single night of bliss, rushes off to Italy to send her glowing accounts of his incredible victories and to tell her how he loves her, adores her, wants her, needs her, and lives to have news from her. News, by the way, which takes the form of a very occasional little billet, for as a child, Marie Rose Josephine

Tascher de la Pagerie had been too indolent to bother about such a small matter as spelling words correctly. Besides, her absurd young husband bores her. He is forever talking in terms of empires, of army divisions, of the hundreds of millions of francs of loot that can be taken out of Italy to improve the roads of France, the harbors of France, to build that navy of France which will have to destroy the one power that still defies her—England.

How much more restful to go out for dinner with a good-looking young hussar who does not wear his clothes as if they had been blown on him by a hurricane, but who is so well dressed that all the other women will look at her when he conducts his guest ceremoniously to the table he has reserved in the most fashionable restaurant of the hour. Afterward, he can accompany her for a moment to her apartment, for her little dog has not yet been given his final evening airing. And if, after that spoiled little beast has been tucked away in her bed (her husband has sent her the loveliest silk sheets from Milan, and how she loves silk!), if then he takes her in his arms and whispers how he envies that little beast, well, a woman is only a woman, and if her husband, instead of staying with her, insists (and on the very morning after their wedding!) on rushing off to his smelly soldiers that he may conquer new worlds which he will place at her adorable little feet, then, after all, that is his lookout. Besides, he is such a clod—so inexperienced in the ways of the world (Josephine's world, Barras' world)—that he will never hear a word about his wife's goings-on.

That is what she thinks, but she is very much mistaken. Her husband knows everything that happens. He writes her furious letters. Then he tears them up and crawls before her like a lovesick boy, asking her, beseeching her, for at least a few drops of her favor. He is lost. He no longer can help himself.

And now Josephine hears that Napoleon plans to start forth upon even more idiotic adventures which may take him away from France—from Europe even—for God knows how long. For if this woman has got into his blood, England has got on his nerves. No use trying to attack the island kingdom by way of the sea. It can't be done. Just once he will be given a chance to do it, when an American, by the name of Robert Fulton, will request him to come to the Seine and watch the steam-propelled boat he has been working on until it has become completely independent of the winds and the currents and, if properly armed, can sink the whole of the British navy.

But when opportunity offers itself, his mind, too definitely set in its own unmechanical ways, will fail to grasp the military possibilities of this smoke-belching scow. He will curtly dismiss the Yankee's invention and will go back to his plans to attack England in a way all his own.

The General loves maps, and on his maps he has been tracing the route he proposes to take when the final assault comes. First from southern France to Egypt. From Egypt by way of Asia to the Indus River, and then a sudden plunge into the heart of India itself. In that way the British government will be deprived of its wealth, it will no longer be able to support every European power bold enough to defy the armies of the Revolution, and soon the opposition on the Continent will collapse automatically, and England will be on her knees, suing for peace and begging for mercy.

A fine plan on paper and perfectly feasible—on paper.

In May of the year 1798 the General, accompanied by thirty-five thousand men, disappears from Toulon in a cloud of spray. A few weeks later, news reaches Paris that he has taken Malta. On July 1, he disembarks at Alexandria and three weeks later has destroyed the army of the sultan in a battle fought at the foot of the Pyramids. The road to the East lies open.

From now on, fantastic stories come back about still further victories, until, on August 1, Nelson destroys the French navy, which is waiting for orders at the mouth of the Nile. After that, darkness but many harassing rumors—how, after all, the world seemed to be a great deal bigger than the maps had indicated—how the Turks (aided and abetted by those perfidious Britons) were putting up a much better fight than had been expected—

how the French had been caught in a sort of cul-de-sac—and how their General had even been forced to put his wounded soldiers out of their misery lest they fall into the hands of the infidels, those heathen Moslems who cannot forgive him for having murdered twelve hundred prisoners whose lives he had promised to spare.

Then a year of almost no news at all, while at home one disaster follows upon the other, and the French are held in such disrespect that the oldest of all laws—the inviolability of diplomatic representatives—has been violated, and their delegates to the peace conference at Rastadt have been hacked to pieces by a squad of Hungarian hussars.

Until it is October of the year 1799, and Paris is startled by the news, "He has come back and will be in Paris within five days."

Poor Josephine! Can't that man ever do anything like ordinary normal people? Is she doomed to spend all her days expecting surprises? This latest rumor is very disturbing, what with lovers who have to be packed off and creditors who have to be told to wait just a few days more, because they will be getting their share as soon as her husband comes home.

In less time than anybody has expected, the great man is back in Paris. Then there are mysterious midnight meetings at the houses of a few of his friends. The Directory knows that something is being planned against its own safety, but the Directory is so divided against itself that it is unable to act.

On November 9, 1799—the 18 Brumaire (Fog Month)—the soldiers of General Bonaparte surround the meeting hall of the Directory at Saint-Cloud. Angry words are heard, as on that occasion, five years before, when Robespierre was deprived of power, but this time the bayonets of Napoleon quickly settle the argument. The Directory ceases to exist, and its place is taken by the Consulate, consisting of three members. There is a First Consul, elected for ten years, who is to act as the regent of France. His name is Napoleon Bonaparte. There are two other members with only mild advisory power. They have names too, but why mention them? They will be as completely forgotten as if they had never existed—and maybe they never did!

That is all there is to this story. For further details I refer you to Plato, who predicted this sort of thing quite accurately more than two thousand years before it happened. He did not call it the "eternal circle," but that is what it was.

First of all, a king gets too much power, abuses it, and is pushed off his throne by the common people, who thereupon get too much power and abuse it until all the other classes of society combine against them from fear of what may happen to their own heads. Then the whole performance is once more repeated, and we find the nation dominated by a strong man on horseback who gets too much power, abuses it, and is removed from office by the discontented masses who get too much power, who abuse their power until they in turn—and so on and so forth, world without end, amen.

Here I drop the present tense. In the first place, it is too easy, and in the second place, you may think that I have been reading too much Carlyle since I came to Veere. Besides, by now you probably have begun to understand what sort of young man this is I am holding up for your inspection.

The first thing the French needed after Napoleon had become First Consul was peace abroad and order at home. Their new ruler gave them both and even concluded a peace treaty with England. Then he paid his respects to God by concluding a peace treaty with the Pope, a compromise which returned to the Catholic Church most of its former rights and privileges. Next, a new universal code of law for the whole of France and Louisiana, where it prevails until this day.

In August, 1802, Napoleon became Consul for life. Two years later, he dropped all pretense and crowned himself Emperor of the French, with Pope Pius VII standing by and unable to play the role his predecessor had enacted at the coronation of Charlemagne in the year 800. For on that occasion it was the Pope who had crowned the Emperor. This time the Emperor took the crown into his own hands and placed it firmly upon his own brow. After that public insult, the Pope was allowed to return to Rome and there await further instructions.

The rest of the story is known to every schoolboy. This salesman of the enlightened ideas and ideals of revolutionary France, everywhere welcomed as such, suddenly went in for an entirely different line of goods and thereafter only sold himself. For by now he had got delusions of grandeur. He divorced the woman for whom he had made a fool of himself, because she had failed to give him an heir to the throne, and married an Austrian princess who was to bestow upon his dynasty a slight touch of respectability and legitimacy.

That was the beginning of the end, for gradually the Emperor lost all touch with reality and came to believe in the role he was playing, as if it were something ordained by God instead of being the result of a happy combination of genius and luck. I am not belittling his talents. No sensible historian can deny his superhuman abilities (just as no one can deny that Lindbergh actually flew across the ocean), but a perspective of almost a century and a half allows us to see how much of the Napoleonic success was due to good timing.

In all such meteoric careers of revolutionary origin, correct timing plays a very important role. But in the case of Napoleon, the timing was mostly the work of Providence. He realized this himself and was honest enough to say so.

Dictating his memoirs on St. Helena to the Comte de Las Cases, he confessed that many centuries would have to go by before the unique combination of events that allowed his career would recur in the case of another person.

Good luck, however, will last just so long and no longer. The moment Napoleon ceased to play the role which had made him truly great—as prophet and apostle of the revolutionary ideas— he was doomed. From then on, the timing went against him. In the end, even nature herself turned against him. His armies froze to death in Russia. A final effort, made after his return from Elba, to regain everything by one bold throw of the dice failed. It failed because he had not timed his final battle correctly. He had frittered away several hours of the morning at Waterloo, sitting in a chair, doing nothing at all or scrawling large capital *N*'s on little slips of paper. This delay made it possible for Blücher to appear upon the scene just when Wellington's center was beginning to give in. The battle should have been a French victory by three o'clock in the afternoon. At five o'clock the word Waterloo had been added to the dictionaries of all civilized nations as an ultimate expression for defeat. And a tired and broken man was fleeing for his life, followed by a few thousand stragglers and the curses of millions of mothers.

After that, the living tomb of St. Helena—and death. Modern science knows the cause of Napoleon's demise. The man who had known all the names of all his subordinate officers, who at any moment had been able to recite the number of horses and caissons attached to any particular regiment, and who had been a walking dictionary of detail had overlooked one item which, after years of ghastly suffering, carried him to his untimely end at the age of only fifty-two. He had never paid any attention to his meals. Hence the agony of gastric ulcers. Hence those hemorrhoids which had made it so painful for him to sit on his horse at Waterloo and which had forced him to put off beginning the battle until it was too late.

I am sorry to be quite so clinical, but stomach-aches and headaches and sluggish bowels are apt to play a much greater role in history than most people ever seem to suspect. I recommend this approach to the history of our fellow men to all future students of the historical sciences. Pascal was responsible for the famous statement that if the nose of Cleopatra had been a tenth of an inch longer or shorter, the whole history of the human race would have been different. There was much truth in this statement as far as it went. But that learned Frenchman might have gone a little further. He might have added—as I do it for him here and now—that if, for example, John Calvin or Adolf Hitler had not been such constipated . . . but finish that sentence for yourself. And don't think that I am merely trying to be funny, for I was never so serious in all my life.

And now, let me tell you something about another victim of his own genius and his own irregular habits—but what a difference in the results achieved by the two men! For Beethoven wasted and exhausted himself trying to bestow upon the world such beauty as it had never heard before. And while Napoleon's entire career had been dominated by the first person singular, Beethoven's whole existence was centered around the second person plural. It was "I" against "you," and in the end, the "you" won out.

Today, Beethoven has become one of our secular saints, whereas the name Napoleon survives in a rather rich and unwholesome sort of pastry. The mills of the gods grind slowly but they grind exceedingly fine.

Beethoven's father was a tipsy tenor employed as a singer by the archbishop-elector of Cologne. His mother, Maria Magdalena Laym, had worked for that same dignitary, washing dishes in his kitchen. The family lived in Bonn, where their master spent most of his time. The child's full name was Ludwig van Beethoven—not *von* Beethoven as it is so frequently spelled in many of the editions of his works by German publishers. The Beethovens were of Dutch-Flemish origin. They had little German blood in their veins—a detail which today would fill old Ludwig's heart with great satisfaction. For he was a firm believer in human rights. Indeed, we might call him an out-and-out radical when it came to anything connected with social inequalities.

How Beethoven survived in the antediluvian atmosphere of the old world of the Hapsburgs will ever remain one of history's best-guarded secrets. But Gibraltar still stands, in spite of a million years of storms and hurricanes, and when it came to strength of character, Beethoven was worth a dozen Gibraltars.

At the age of five Ludwig began his musical career, not because he felt the urge to spend hours and hours every day scraping on his little fiddle, but because his father, who was always in need of money for his taproom bills, had somehow heard of the fortune Leopold Mozart had made out of exploiting his children. What Leopold Mozart could do, Ludwig van Beethoven's father could also do. It was all a matter of the right kind of training. But also it appeared to be a matter of personality. Little Ludwig was no Wolferl. He was an ugly and unattractive child, headstrong and obstinate to a degree, and whereas young Wolfgang had adored his dear papa, young Ludwig most cordially detested the boozy author of his being.

Furthermore, Leopold Mozart had been quite a personage and an excellent impresario with a fine feeling for setting the stage upon which his two little darlings were to perform. But one shudders to think of what would have happened if Old Man Beethoven had ever undertaken to play such a role. Nothing, therefore, came of the plan, but as it seemed a pity in view of all the time and money that had already been spent upon his son's musical education, the father decided to continue it as best he could and to prepare young Ludwig to follow in his own footsteps, that eventually he too might become a court singer or organist.

Young Ludwig started on his life's work as a serious musician at the age of thirteen, when he was told to play the cembalo in the electoral orchestra. The position was not very well paid, but every penny counted in the parental household. Then, when he had just turned seventeen, he was offered a chance to go to Vienna. Who paid for the trip we·do not know, but this visit is a historical fact, and it has also been established that he was presented to Mozart, who asked him to improvise for him and who, gracious as always, undertook to give him a few lessons free of charge. Ludwig now seemed fairly well set on his career, when he received news about his mother's serious state of health. He returned to Bonn just in time to watch his mother die, and to assume complete responsibility for the support of what remained of his family. His father by now had become completely irresponsible, and his habits were so uncertain that henceforth his salary was paid out to his son. Otherwise, as everybody in Bonn knew, the money would immediately have been wasted in the nearest wineshop.

Under those circumstances, what future was there for this boy in a small city like Bonn? More than we might at first feel inclined to expect. The eighteenth century was an age of widespread cultural interests. People still lived leisurely lives. Music was part of their daily existence. A surprisingly large number of men and women were good amateur musicians or painters. And in every town—almost in every village—there were several homes where the parents and the children would play trios and quartets for the sole purpose of spending a pleasant evening doing what they liked to do and without any expectations of ever qualifying as musical geniuses.

Also, they still had time in which to be interested in their less fortunate neighbors. And their kindness did not merely express itself in acts of charity—pots of soup for the wife of a day laborer who had just had her seventeenth child and knitted woolen sweaters for her other brats. No, they did something that was much harder to do. Whenever they discovered a child who gave evidence of being exceptionally talented (regardless of along what lines) they would seek him (or her) out, invite him into their homes, and try and give him enough social polish that his subsequent career might be a little less difficult.

The people of the eighteenth century had a profound respect for talent and for genius too, whenever they happened to recognize it—a most difficult thing to do. But they also believed in that Discipline (with a capital *D*) which is the basis of all art—the art of living included. And they were convinced that good manners had never yet prevented anyone from becoming a great musician or painter or author. Therefore, they provided the manners, while the child looked after his daily exercises on the clavichord or the blackboard. On the whole, the results bore them out in their contention that this was the best way to educate a youngster.

Today, young Beethoven would have been at a tremendous disadvantage. He was both shy and overbearing. He was very proud and as sensitive as *Mimosa pudica*. He was a bad mixer. He was an ungracious receiver of gifts, and Dale Carnegie would have predicted a dire future for one who so deeply disregarded the necessity of making friends and influencing people. But the good city of Bonn of a hundred and fifty years ago was kind to this uncommonly gifted boy, in spite of himself, in spite of his rude outbursts of uncontrollable anger, in spite of his awkwardness when in the presence of women, and his unpleasant way of insisting upon a general recognition of his genius.

And so, notwithstanding all his manifest handicaps, the son of the tipsy court singer somehow managed to scrape together an education. He never became a shining light of fashion. All his livelong days he remained inexcusably careless about his outward appearance. At table he usually behaved like Dr. Johnson. His unconquerable shyness made him commit acts of gross incivility like that famous episode when he refused to lift his hat to a mere king. Let the mere king salute him first. For was he not the Jupiter of music? But again, in spite of all this, he had been polished up sufficiently during these years in Bonn to be able to hold his own in almost any kind of society. And when occasionally he fell from grace, the mighty ones of this earth and their friends were sufficiently impressed by his talents to overlook these very painful outbreaks of bad manners. After all, he was a poor devil who had enjoyed very few advantages, so why not take him as he was? There were enough people in Vienna who knew how to hand a grand duchess a cup of chocolate with just the right kind of bow and the appropriate compliment. But could they write sonatas and symphonies and concertos like this clodhopper from the other side of the Rhine? They could not! And therefore Vienna (in so far as it was interested at all) smiled and forgot what could not be helped.

Beethoven, Napoleon, and Great-great-grandfather

The world these last three thousand years has accepted Job as the outstanding example of a citizen bearing up bravely under adversity. If there ever is any need for another candidate for this particular honor, I would like to suggest the name of Ludwig van Beethoven.

I am not merely thinking of his dreadful relatives who spent thirty years making his life a hell on earth. I am willing to overlook that worthless nephew upon whom the poor man centered all his affections and who, being a most commonplace and irresponsible creature without the slightest understanding for his uncle's greatness, accepted his favors as something that was his due and never did anything in return. Nor am I referring to those desperate outbursts of passion for at least half a dozen women which at intervals tore Beethoven's heart to pieces and never brought him the slightest satisfaction. Such unhappy experiences have come to many other people, who yet managed to derive at least a certain modest amount of comfort from the business of being alive.

But what happened to Beethoven was so outrageous that it offends our sense of justice, which, God knows, has been sorely enough tried in this age of ours when cruel and unusual punishments have become the incidents of the day. For what more hideous and cruel thing could possibly happen to a composer than that he should grow deaf? Not just a little hard of hearing, which must often be a blessing to a musician, but stone-deaf—so deaf that he could not even hear himself when trying something out on his pianoforte.

It was in the year 1798, when he was only twenty-eight years old, that Beethoven discovered the first symptoms of his affliction. He thought that they were the result of a cold. That was perfectly possible. He was so careless in his mode of living that he often forgot to light his stove, and most of the rooms he rented (he was a restless person who moved thirty times during the years he spent in Vienna) were ill-ventilated and drafty. Ear trouble, therefore, was one of the regular ailments in that town where tuberculosis was responsible for half of the death rate.

But as the weeks and months went by, the deafness increased, and Beethoven became panic-stricken. He thereupon did what most panic-stricken people will do under such circumstances. He first visited all the regular doctors who were said to know something about ears and, when they failed to bring him relief, he began to consult the local quacks. But his deafness, as was shown by a post-mortem, was not a local matter. It was due to his general condition of health, and it seems fairly certain now that this had been affected by a disease for which there was to be no cure until more than a hundred years later. And so the poor man was left to the mercies of any mountebank who advertised that he had a definite cure for deafness.

Did Beethoven himself suspect the real reason? I feel inclined to say yes. Otherwise he would never have written those heart-breaking words in his so-called "will"—a document found after his death and addressed to his brother. Therein he expresses the fervent wish that posterity will not share the opinion of so many of his own contemporaries who think of him as an old grouch, as a hermit who hates his neighbors and shuns their society. How could they ever come to think of him in that light, he exclaims in despair, of him, Ludwig van Beethoven, whose love for his fellow men included not only mankind but creation itself? *("Seit umschlungen Millionen, Einen Kuss der ganzen Welt!")* How was it possible even to suspect him of such feelings when he, more than anyone else, wanted to penetrate to the very soul of the human race and bring it nearer to Almighty God by the music he wrote?

For there was another curious side to his character which I have already mentioned but which has often been overlooked —his deep piety. Because of his interest in the nobler principles of the French Revolution as laid down in the Rights of Man, he has often been suspected of Jacobinism, of Bolshevism— while his admiration for Napoleon's genius has caused others to infer that he was at heart a totalitarian, a tyrant-worshiper.

Neither accusation contains a grain of truth. Beethoven, being profoundly interested in everything affecting the human race, went through the same spiritual development through which almost all sensitive persons have passed since the end of the last great war. He was horrified by the senseless cruelty of the Reign of Terror, and his erasure, in the Third Symphony, of that dedication to "the Hero" (and when he wrote it there was only one hero with a capital *H*) shows how he felt about Napoleon after he had betrayed his own past and had proved himself the worst despot of all. And I can't see anything at all in these accusations of radicalism except the thoughtless utterances of people who will call everybody a Red who does not share their own view that the world, having reached its final state of perfection when they themselves were born, must now be left *in statu quo* and must never again be changed.

Beethoven's lack of hearing cut him almost completely off from the companionship of his fellow men. In the year 1824 he tried for the last time to conduct a concert, but had to give up in the middle of the performance as he had no idea what his musicians were doing. After that, he could only communicate with the outside world by means of little slips of paper on which he scribbled his questions when he met his friends at his regular coffeehouse. A large number of these scraps of paper have been preserved. They are among the most pathetic and, at the same time, the most sublime manifestations of human courage.

Imagine Rembrandt having gone blind and you will have an analogy to the situation in which Beethoven found himself. Let us do for a moment what the movies do and go back to a century and a quarter ago. The scene is a coffeehouse in Vienna. In one corner a table reserved for the man whom all the people in the capital, from street cleaner to Emperor, have come to recognize as one of the most important of their fellow citizens. Three or four understanding friends sitting by his side, trying to divert him with cheerful little bits of gossip, with anecdotes about some well-known character, realizing all the time that their efforts are in vain—that their companion now only lives inside of himself, that he has done with life except in so far as it exists within that terrific brain of his.

And then back to his cheerless quarters, still accompanied by some of his faithful friends lest he be run down in the street and killed. Back to a lonely and disorderly room full of pianos (some of them especially constructed for a deaf man—one of them without its legs, to allow him to play lying down on his tummy), stacks of music, dirty dishes on the chairs and on the floor, a washbowl that had not been emptied for days, an unkempt bed. In the midst of this chaos, Ludwig van Beethoven died on March 26, 1827, six years after his erstwhile Hero had mumbled his *tête d'armée* and had given up the ghost on that little lonely island at the other end of the world.

People had reason to remember that day. For just as the great master was slipping into his eternal sleep, a thunderstorm accompanied by a hurricane, the like of which no one had ever experienced before, broke loose over Vienna. Amidst the blinding flashes of lightning and the peals of thunder, the good Lord wrote finis to an opus of which even He had every reason to feel proud.

When old Ludwig was carried to his grave, both sides of the streets through which the funeral procession passed were lined with soldiers. Even the House of Hapsburg felt obliged to pay homage to this strange man who in his way had been a greater iconoclast and a more dangerous rebel than any other subject of the double-headed eagle.

As for the third of our guests, my great-great-grandfather, I thought it would be a nice idea to include him because he would at last be given a chance to stand face to face with the man who had been the inspiration of his younger days and the cause of his ruin. For not only did he lose his health during the retreat from Moscow (he was lucky to come back alive at all), but financially, too, it meant his ruin. His business was gone, and he was obliged to begin all over again, and the struggle to make a living for his family in a country completely exhausted by

Great-great-grandfather had been a soldier with Napoleon in Russia.

twenty years of French domination, and from which every movable piece of valuable property had been taken away by the conquerors, proved too much for him. It took three generations to win back what had been lost. Yet until the very end, so my grandmother told me, the old man had remained loyal to the memory of his hero. He was happy to see his native land regain its independence. Occasionally, he would even criticize the Emperor severely for the mistakes he had made during the latter half of his career. But he would always insist that if he were given the chance again, he would do exactly what he had done the first time.

"The Emperor knew best," he used to say, "but sometimes he was badly advised. He was betrayed by those who were supposed to be his friends. And he should have known moderation. But what will you? He was the Emperor!"

I knew this mysterious ancestor only from hearsay. All that was left of him were the buttons of the uniform he had worn when, broken in body, he had finally found his way back to his native village, not far from Rotterdam, and had settled down to his old profession of a watchmaker. And so we were to meet one who had worshiped but had repented and one who had remained faithful unto the end.

A strange combination—the Emperor Napoleon, Ludwig van Beethoven, and a very humble link in the chain that connects me with one of those hundreds of ancestors whose dust has long since mingled with that of the land in which I was born.

Two of our guests arrived punctually. The third one (I need not tell you who) came a few minutes late, excused himself, looked at the familiar little figure in the worn-out old overcoat, but without any outward sign of respect, and said in his best Viennese, *"Gn'Abend, Majestät."*

As for poor Grandpa, he had dressed up for the occasion in his best corporal's uniform, very much the worse for a century of moths. But he had somehow succeeded in patching up the worst holes, and his gun (God knows why he brought it, but he did!) shone as if he had been called out for an imperial inspection.

I wondered what Grandpa would do when he found himself under the same roof with the Emperor. I had been rather afraid that there would be a scene, that he would weep or shout "Hooray!" or something like that. But Grandpa behaved with great dignity. He presented arms and waited until he was spoken to. The Emperor, too, immediately fell into his old role.

"What is your name, *mon brave*?" he asked.

The name was given.

"What regiment?"

The name of the regiment was given.

"What battalion?" The name of the battalion was given.

"Then you must have been at Borodino!"

"Yes, Your Majesty."

"On the right flank?"

"Yes, Your Majesty."

"Did you get wounded?"

"A shot through the left arm, Your Majesty, but it amounted to nothing!"

"And you came back safely?"

"Yes, Your Majesty. I lost three fingers of my left hand."

He held his hand out for the Emperor's inspection. Napoleon took it in both of his and said softly, "It is the hand of a brave man."

"Thank you, Your Majesty. It is ready to fight for him again."

And that was all.

During the rest of the evening, Napoleon treated the old soldier as one of his comrades in arms, addressed him as *mon corporal,* and even drank his health after we had sat down. Whereupon Grandpa (who proved to be really a very nice if somewhat simple person) lifted up his glass and said, "To the day of our revenge, Your Majesty!"

It came as somewhat of a shock to meet such devotion in a person who had been dead for more than a century. It gave me cause to think. But then, the whole of that evening upset so many of my former ideas that I shall never forget it. For during the next five hours I was to learn more about the so-called psychology of history than I had done during the previous forty years which I had spent with my nose buried in my books. I shall now relate what happened that others may profit by my own experience.

We started out with a piece by Grétry, but we soon sent up word to Hein to stop the phonograph, for Napoleon paid absolutely no attention, and Beethoven apparently did not hear a note. In the beginning, we had tried to talk to him, pretending we knew nothing about his deafness. But soon this proved to be hopeless, whereafter we resorted to short written communications during which I made myself popular with poor Ludwig by my ability to render in pictures what others were obliged to express in words. But first of all, something about the dinner.

The meal was on the table, but Napoleon showed no interest in his food, and the only remark he made was about the dessert, the *petits pots de crème à la duc d'Enghien*. I had invented that dish in order to annoy him, but he failed to take it that way. On the contrary, he looked rather contrite when he saw that name.

"Poor Enghien," he said, looking straight at Frits and me. "I suppose I should not have shot him. Even at the time I felt that I was making rather a mistake. The world has never forgiven me. People have forgotten the hundreds of thousands of men who were killed in my campaigns, but they always harp on that one instance of my killing a young prince. And perhaps they are right. It was an error of judgment on my part. But when it happened I was so exasperated by the eternal plotting against my life by all these exiled royalists that I felt that some sort of countermeasure had to be taken to put an end to this nonsense. As usual, it was an innocent person who paid for the crimes of the guilty. But—*que voulez-vous?* That is past history now, and nothing can be done about it, but tell me, how do your people over here in the Low Countries feel about me today? I was their Emperor, too, for a good many years. Have they forgotten me?"

I told him that that would have hardly been possible in view of the tremendous damage he had done to the commerce of the Netherlands. For a moment he sat still, moving his knife up and down and this way and that, which seemed to be a habit with him, and then he answered, "Like everything else, it is one of those questions which cannot be answered without first answering a great many others. But let me show you." Whereupon he arranged the dishes of the table until we began to notice the outline of the map of Europe. This, of course, upset our dinner, but he did not seem to notice it.

"Look," he said, pointing at the fruit bowl. "This is France. And now look at that" (pointing to the potatoes). "That is England. And that little butter dish here is your own country. All the rest of Europe I had organized until it did my bidding. England was deprived of all revenue because it could not export a franc's worth of raw materials to the Continent. You might call it a sort of inverted blockade, but it worked. In order to make it work one hundred per cent there must be no loopholes. Your ancestors provided the English with those loopholes. They absolutely refused to see the benefits that would come to them once England should have been destroyed, and they could have taken its place, for I give you my word, the first thing I would have done would have been to reconquer their colonial possessions and to return them to my Dutch subjects. Had they only let me do this, today they would have been the richest people on earth."

I knew that he was lying, but somehow or other I did not quite find the courage to tell him so. Frits too was fascinated, and so we both sat very quietly as the Emperor continued his monologue. For the whole of that evening developed into an endless harangue by the Emperor. Beethoven was too deaf to follow the conversation, and Great-great-grandpa was too far gone in his admiration to say anything but an occasional: "How true that all is!"

Soon the table looked like a battlefield. Not a dish was in its place. For the Continental blockade was followed by the Emperor's campaign in the east, which had led to the destruction of Prussia. And after Prussia (to the despair of Jo, who no sooner had placed a dish on the table than it became Italy or Poland), we had to be shown how Wellington had failed to understand the situation in Spain and how the collapse of the French in Spain had been entirely due to the incompetence of brother Joseph, who had been pretty good at diplomacy but had been completely lacking in those administrative qualities which alone would have enabled him to dominate a people as difficult as the Spaniards.

Then followed a discussion of the wickedness of the English in bombarding and destroying the city of Copenhagen. The wickedness of perfidious Albion seemed to be his favorite theme, for it occurred again and again and it was only interrupted by sneering remarks about the stupidity of Czar Alexander, who, if he had only known what was good for him, would have joined hands with the French Emperor, in which case the two of them, as Napoleon felt convinced, could have divided the whole of the planet between them.

And so it went while the food grew cold. Beethoven, despairing of getting anything more to eat, withdrew more and more into himself and began to wave his arms as if he were conducting an orchestra, and Frits and I sat speechless, for here we were learning our history (or, at least, one version of it) from the man who had been directly responsible for almost twenty years of bloodshed and destruction.

Finally, as there seemed no other way of putting an end to this deluge of words, Frits suggested that we have our coffee in front of the fire, but this did not do the slightest good. The moment we had made ourselves comfortable, the Emperor helped himself to the pewter mugs and plates that were standing all over the room and used these to demonstrate the plans he had made for the good of Europe and for the ultimate benefit of all mankind.

It was a strange evening—a very strange evening. For shortly after eleven o'clock we at last had reached the subject of Russia. There, as we discovered, the Emperor was in his element. "What a fool I was!" he shouted. *"Che coglione!"* (he often

The Emperor Napoleon explaining the battle of Borodino on the dining-room floor.

trailed off into his native Italian) "what an idiot I was ever to have trusted the reports of my ambassador in St. Petersburg. But my diplomatic representatives—*O Dio mio*—these fellows were the weak spot of my whole administration. Most of them belonged to the old royalist party. I had to use them because they knew how to ingratiate themselves with those insipid imperial and royal highnesses who still were to be found in so many parts of the Continent. Those imbeciles refused to receive my so-called 'new men,' claiming that they had no manners and that they had been responsible for the death of some of their relatives or had deprived them of a few square miles of territory. As if knowing how to handle a cup of chocolate is the beginning and the end of all wisdom! My new men learned that trick fast enough whenever they had to and, besides, they had a way with the women which greatly appealed to the wives and daughters of those exalted gentlemen with their sixteen quarterings who were forever reproaching me for having made my own way by my sword and some of the gray matter in my skull.

"How utterly stupid of me to have put any confidence in the reports of my ambassadors!

"Of course, one of the main troubles was that I always had much too much to do. When I fought in Italy, in Egypt, in Germany, I did not have to run an empire. I was merely a general in command of a few hundred thousand men. I had time to study my maps. Before I started on a campaign I knew every road, every river, the number of houses in every village. I knew where my heavy artillery could go. I knew where I could take care of my wounded. When I got to a place, even some God-forsaken hamlet in Poland, the whole terrain was as familiar to me as the streets of Ajaccio.

"In 1812 I had to leave that part of the campaign to others. That's why I lost. Why hadn't my embassy in Petersburg told me about those Russian roads? I should have remembered what Metternich once told me. He was a scoundrel, but a clever one. I should have pried him loose from my dear father-in-law in Austria. Then I would have won, and there never would have been a Waterloo. I would have won at Leipzig, and my great-great-grandson would now be on the throne of France.

"But, no, the Prince must stick to his silly old Vienna. He probably liked the Viennese women better than the Parisian ones, for which I don't blame him. But it was Metternich—I am sure it was he—who once told me—I have forgotten when or where, but I distinctly remember what he said. I was talking about Europe. I was explaining my plans for Europe, and he smiled (he thought that he could make me uncomfortable by his superior way of smiling) and answered, 'Europe, Your Majesty! What is Europe? A little bit of land that stops where the post roads end.' And he was right. Ten miles east of Vienna the post roads came to an end. What lay beyond was Asia.

"Still, I should have known better. I used to beat my enemies because always I knew just a little more than they did. I
was grossly careless about Russia. I should have found out that
the roads are mere ruts and that those ruts were a meter and a
half apart. My wheel bases were some fifteen centimeters wider,
so they never fitted into those ruts. The horses had to do twice
as much work. They tired twice as fast. The fodder they had to
eat was always wet, for the dew is heavy in that part of the
world. They sickened and died. The wheels got bent and
broken, and we had no spare parts. We should have had! We
had no wheelwrights. We should have had them! Everything
got slowed down, and I, who had always timed everything so
perfectly, was three months late. Had I been in Moscow in
July, the war would have been over in August. Alexander could
not have held out that long. My armies would have been back
in Germany in October, and I would not have lost a hundred
thousand men. As it was, I had to fight both nature and man.
I defeated man, but nature defeated me."

Here Napoleon paused and looked at us with the appealing
eyes of a very small boy who has just tried to explain that, honest to goodness, he didn't mean to smash that window he had
broken with his baseball, that it was not really his fault, that
something had gone wrong, but please don't blame him, for he
thought that he would miss that window by at least ten yards.

Then back again to Russia, with details about the battle of
Borodino and long appeals to Great-great-grandfather, who had
been there and could bear witness to the accuracy with which
the Grand Army had functioned in taking its positions on that
day, the bravery it had shown in maintaining those positions
against overwhelming odds, and how the Emperor himself at
noon, by taking the initiative at the right moment, etc., etc.

Then a few very uncomplimentary remarks about that tavernkeeper's son from Pau, who, having betrayed the man who
had made him, who had given him glory and riches, was now a
king on a throne of his own. "King of Sweden," the Emperor
said, holding his nose as if someone had just thrown a handful

These old soldiers had arisen from their graves to protect their Emperor.

of feathers into the kitchen stove, "but how did he get there except by going back on his word and selling out to the British? Well, I wish him joy with his lovely Désirée and I could tell him something, too, about that lovely Désirée! I knew her—I knew her well—in the old days in Marseille. Before she was Countess of Ponte Corvo. I wish him joy, and if it had not been for his damnable Swedes at Leipzig, I would very likely have won. I know. We were friends once. Great friends too! But when the crash came, how many of those good friends had I left? Just one. My mother!"

The Emperor closed his eyes and sank his head on his chest. He trembled all over. He seemed to be on the point of bursting into tears. Frits and I looked on, completely fascinated. Here was acting in the grand old tradition. Talma would have been proud of his pupil, could he have watched this commonplace scene being elevated into something à la Hamlet with a final reference to the dear old mother. But it was very effective, and we now understood his success with an audience of simple people. Grandpa was completely taken in. As for Beethoven, he just sat there and never said a word. Occasionally we noticed that he took an old piece of music paper out of his pocket, examined a few lines on it, then put it once more back in the inside pocket of his badly fitting blue coat, which not only showed signs of many former repasts but also a few souvenirs from the meal of which he had just partaken.

I have no space for the rest of the story. For two solid hours the little man with the yellow face held forth. For two solid hours he acted the role he had so carefully studied those six agonizing years on St. Helena, though at the time he must have known that it would never be anything but a paper role. For two solid hours he lied to us and didn't know it, for he had dramatized himself to such a point that he no longer was able to disassociate himself from the character he was enacting.

But the Emperor reached the highest point of his act when he turned from Hamlet to King Lear. Then we heard a story of such woe as had never been recited before. Everything that had gone wrong had been the fault of his enemies, who were also the enemies of mankind. He had loved the human race. He, who had caused the death of so many millions of his fellow men, had never intended to hurt a fly. He shuddered at the thought of the ruined cities in the wake of his armies. The destruction of Moscow haunted him. Such a magnificent city, too, and sacrificed by malicious hands upon the altar of a misguided patriotism! What wouldn't he have done to set the Russian people free from their sad plight as willful slaves of an Asiatic despotism! He would have given them liberty. He would have made them prosperous. He would have built schools for their children, hospitals for their women.

And then there was Europe! Poor old Europe, forever divided against itself! He would have turned it into a confederation, something like that experiment of General Washington on the other side of the ocean. This plan too had been spoiled by perfidious Albion. And so we were back at the point at which we had started, and Wellington and Pitt were dragged out of their graves to stand before the bar of history and give an account of themselves.

It was at this point that Beethoven once more took that old piece of musical manuscript out of his pocket, asked Frits for a pencil, and scrawled something at the bottom of one of the sheets.

As for Erasmus, he had been singularly silent all during the whole of the evening, but he now got up and excused himself. "I need some fresh air," he explained. "I shall step into the garden for a moment." Then the relentless clock across the street struck the hour of departure. Frits and I remained alone in the dark.

"Oof!" Frits said.

"Oof *là là!*" I answered, showing that I too knew my French.

But neither of us felt the need of any further conversation, and I slipped out and took the way for home. It had begun to rain, for the fall was now well under way, and the weather was turning bad. The village lay asleep, but in the distance I saw a

Beethoven had forgotten his hat and an old manuscript.

group of people hurrying down the road to Flushing. I took a side street that was a short cut to the old cobblestoned highway which, a hundred and thirty years before, Napoleon had caused to be built so as to move his troops from one end of our island to the other, in case of an English invasion. I hid myself behind the wall of a barn and waited. The little man with the cocked hat was walking rapidly in the direction of Middelburg. He was no longer alone. He was marching at the head of quite a procession. His old grenadiers who had died on our island while fighting the British were following in his footsteps. They had crept out of their graves to escort their Emperor!

When I came to Frits' house early in the morning (for I had been much too excited to sleep), I found the dining room as I had left it the night before. The table had not been touched, and the half-empty dishes and the empty glasses were standing in the same disorder in which they had been placed by the Emperor in his geographical and political demonstrations.

"I'm glad you came," Frits said. "I wanted you to look at something." He pointed to an object almost completely hidden by soiled napkins and two half-empty bottles of wine. "The old gentleman must have forgotten it when he left," Frits explained, "and I thought that you ought to be here when we look at that mysterious manuscript which seemed to worry him so much during the evening."

He picked up Ludwig van Beethoven's dilapidated high hat, as shabby a piece of headgear as either of us had ever seen on any human being, but so much a part of the man that we touched it most reverently. Then we spread the manuscript out on the table. It was part of the Third Symphony, the famous one known as the "Eroica."

On the page that attracted our special attention we noticed two lines of script. The handwriting of the master was like his music. Thought had run away with action. With the help of a magnifying glass we finally deciphered what had been put down in the year 1804, when Beethoven still believed in the destiny of Napoleon, the Hero who was to be the liberator of mankind, as he himself was to be the liberator of music from the bondage of outlived tradition. This is what we read:

"Composita per festeggiare il sovvenire d'un grand' uomo"— Composed to celebrate the memory of a great man.

That great man had been Napoleon. We knew that when Napoleon crowned himself emperor, Beethoven, in an attack of fury, had struck out this dedication.

Then we noticed a few other words which, the night before, he had scribbled down on this piece of paper with the pencil he had borrowed from Frits. It took us half an hour to make out what they meant, but this is what they said in a mixture of German and Italian.

"I see no reason to revise my second opinion. *Non è veramente grande*—he was not really a great man."

CHAPTER XIII

THE GREATEST INVENTOR OF ALL TIME Puts Us to Considerable Inconvenience

FRITS SAID it was my fault, and I said it was his fault. We left the final decision to Jimmie, and she remarked, "Oh well, I suppose it was just one of those things. If I were you I would forget about it. But the next time you should be a little more careful and not quite so romantic."

As a matter of fact, I don't think that it was a romantic streak which had got us into this unpleasant experience. Rather, I would call it some sudden impulse to be a little more modern— a little more up to date than we had been until then—that had made us send out this invitation we had addressed to the Greatest Inventor of All Time.

I know it sounded very boy-scoutish, but we had been entirely sincere when we expressed the wish to meet the man who, in the eyes of one better fitted to judge than we, had contributed most of all to the progress of the human race.

We had not the slightest idea who would knock at our door that next Saturday evening. We talked about it and did a little guessing. We even mentioned a few names—Edison and Barthold Schwartz, who by inventing gunpowder had given the average man of the Middle Ages a chance to hold his own against the ironclad warriors of the feudal castle. There had been other candidates, such as Marconi, who gave us wireless, and Wilbur Wright, who, together with his brother Orville, had enabled us to fly. We even had thought that Leonardo da

Vinci might give us the pleasure of his company, although we feared that most of his inventions had been of a theoretical rather than a practical nature. But when Saturday came, we really had not the slightest idea whom we were going to meet.

Well, the joke was on us, and it was a pretty costly joke, for we had to pay for a lot of crockery and had to settle a not-insignificant bill for broken furniture.

As we had sometimes been able to meet our guests along the harbor or on the streets of Veere, Frits and I had decided that we would leave the house at half-past six and saunter forth to see what we would see. But Veere looked very much as it always did on a Saturday night in the fall when the wind and occasional gusts of rain made most people prefer the warm comfort of the inside of their homes to the cold gloom of the big out-of-doors.

And so we went back to Frits' house that we might be there when our guest arrived. When we turned the corner of the market, we saw Jo and Hein standing on the stoop gesticulating wildly. "Hurry up!" Hein shouted. "Hurry up and help us turn the creature out before he ruins everything. And don't let the doctor come in. He would murder the old gentleman."

"What is it?" we called back, starting to run.

"Come and see for yourselves," Jo told us, moving a little farther away from the stoop.

Now neither Frits nor I are exactly what you might call "heroes," but as we knew both Jo and Hein to be the sort of people that did not easily get rattled, we realized that it must be something very serious and also, on account of our position in the community, we felt it our duty to show that we had a high conception of our duties as defenders of law and order.

What met our eyes the moment we entered the house was about as absurd a situation as either of us had ever witnessed. Practically all the chairs had been upset. The bottles on the table ditto. Wine had been spilled all over the floor. Several of our best dishes had been broken, and one of the candles had landed in a bunch of flowers and the leaves were smoldering,

The greatest inventor of all time had a most healthy appetite.

causing the room to be filled with a most unpleasant smell. At first, however, we saw no signs of any human presence, but Hein, who had followed us, pointed to the other side of the table and said, "Look! There it is!"

Indeed, there "it" was, and at first we had no idea what "it" might be. It looked somewhat like a cross between a human being and one of the higher kinds of apes, but on the whole, the human traits predominated. It undoubtedly had a nose rather than a snout, but the forehead was as low as that of an orangutan, and the whole of the face was covered with hair. So was that part of the body which was visible. As for the hands, they were claws rather than hands. We studied them with a sort of horrible fascination just as the creature reached upward, grabbed a leg of chicken (we had decided upon a simple chicken dinner for that evening, not knowing who was to come), and with a greedy gesture stuck it into its jaws.

As neither Frits nor I had any idea what language "it" would speak, we stuck to Dutch, realizing that it would probably understand that tongue as little as any other, but we had to say something, and Dutch came easiest.

The only answer we got was an incomprehensible grunt and a rather sheepish smile which made it clear that our unwelcome guest was not only hungry but had also been very busy quenching his thirst. As evidence whereof we observed that a bottle of cognac which Frits had placed on the table just before we had started on our walk was now completely empty.

"What are you going to do?" Jo asked, who was hiding behind us.

"Damned if I know," said Frits.

"Nor me neither," I added, being too much preoccupied with the situation to bother about such a detail as grammar.

Then Frits did a foolish thing. He picked up a heavy cane I had left at the house a few nights before—a beloved keepsake, for it once had belonged to that most generous of men, Richard Harding Davis, whose daughter had given it to me. He now waved it in the air and threatened the creature with it. At once the monster jumped to its feet and, making a horrible noise, he picked up a sharply polished piece of stone which must have been lying by his side and made ready to grab Frits by the throat. But like a young dog it seemed unable to focus its attention upon any given problem for more than a few seconds, and in the midst of its warlike preparations it noticed the chocolate cake that Jo had prepared for our dessert. The creature grabbed as much of it as its left hand would hold and squeezed it into its mouth.

Then it once more changed its mind, took hold of the table-cloth, pulled it down from the table, shook it so that this time all the dishes rolled across the floor, dragged it over its body as if it were a bed sheet, and went to sleep. A few minutes later it was snoring away for dear life.

I had no idea what would happen next, for we were absolutely helpless. Once before, we had been obliged to call in the police and we did not want to do that again. It might lead to a lot of gossip, and we knew that the village was already beginning to talk about those strange goings-on in Frits' house on Saturday nights. Soon the authorities would begin to ask questions, and that, of course, would mean an end to our delightful dinner parties, for scandal is the one thing heaven will not allow. Experience has shown that it cannot afford to do so.

Therefore our joy was great when, at the height of this crisis, the familiar figure of Erasmus appeared in the door. What did not quite please us was the happy mood in which he greeted us.

"My poor, foolish friends," he said. "I hope that this will be a lesson to you and that from now on you will be a little more specific when you send out your invitations."

"But, Doctor," Frits answered, "how could we have known that this would happen? We had merely asked for the greatest inventor of all times."

"Well, you got him."

"What! That thing that lies there, snoring like a drunken longshoreman?"

"Yes."

"What did *he* ever invent?"

"A mere trifle, but the one thing that gave us our chance to hold our own against the rest of creation."

"What was that?"

"That bit of polished stone with which he almost cut your throat. He invented the knife."

Do you want to know how the evening ended? Well, first of all, the three of us sat down in front of the fire while Jo sent Hein out to get their own Sunday steak that we should not famish and might regain our nerves by having some solid food in our tummies. After Hein had come back, we gathered around the kitchen table and had our meal. It was an uncomfortable sort of feast, for all of us ate with one eye firmly fixed upon the front room where the creature lay amidst the debris of our lovely china and slept and snored and snored and slept. At last, after an hour or so, the thing stirred. Then it got up, scratched itself, looked at us from under its bushy eyebrows, relieved itself against the curtains, and slowly walked out of the house. Exit our earliest ancestor.

We vowed that we would follow Erasmus' advice. There was to be no more guesswork. From now on, we would not only give the family names of our guests, but their Christian names as well, and, if possible, the dates of their birth.

"And why not add their titles too?" Frits suggested.

I promised him that it would be done just that way, and at half-past twelve I was home and in bed. But for the first and last time, during all the many years I lived in Veere, I locked our front door.

CHAPTER XIV

PLATO and CONFUCIUS May Seem to Make Strange
Dinner Companions, But They Got Along Very
Nicely and Seemed to Enjoy Themselves
and Each Other

I HAD promised Erasmus that from then on I would add the
Christian names of our guests when I sent out our invitations.
But the very first time I tried to do so, I had all sorts of trouble,
for neither Plato nor Confucius had been Christians, and even
after a most diligent examination of a great many learned tomes
I remained uncertain as to by what names their mothers had
addressed them when they told them to come in, wash their
hands and faces, and get ready for dinner.

No harm, however, was done by this omission. Everything
came off as it should have, and this time there was no reason to
shout for the police. Apparently there had been only one Plato
and one Confucius in all of history, and we got the right people,
as we knew the moment they came into the room.

Both our guests were familiar to us, Plato from his statues
and Confucius from his pictures, but even without such concrete advance information we could never have been mistaken
in their identity, for both men seemed the incarnation of dignity.

But let me stick to my regular routine and first tell you what
kind of meal we ordered for these strange guests.

I would hate to be a cook in heaven. So many people from

so many parts of the world (decent heathens, too, are allowed in my kind of heaven), and running all the way from cave men to penthouse dwellers, must be hard to satisfy, for what is Dutch *gehakt* to one is Philadelphia scrapple to another.

So far, we had been rather fortunate in satisfying the tastes of all our guests, but I did not know how long our luck would hold out. Of the Chinese I knew nothing except that they are rice eaters—at least those fortunate enough to eat at all. But my friends who have been in the Orient tell me that I must discard all my ideas about Chinese cooking in so far as these may have been derived from eating in chop-suey places in America. The Chinese have never heard of chop suey.

"Well, then," I used to ask, "what do they eat?"

"They eat messy stuff."

"Always?"

"Always."

"Like the rest of the East?"

"Exactly."

However, on the occasion of a more or less formal dinner given to one of the most formal of men who ever lived, I could not just open a lot of tin cans I had ordered from the Java store in Amsterdam and say, "Here you are, buddies—help yourselves." After a great deal of thumbing of my culinary library, I finally came upon a dish that seemed perfect.

A pilau is one of the few blessings the Turks have bestowed upon the West. It can be made out of almost any kind of meat or fowl, and the rice would be just the thing for Confucius. I had no idea about Plato's preferences, but, being a Greek of the fourth century B.C., he would undoubtedly be a very abstemious sort of person, and we would have plenty of olives for him in case the pilau was not satisfactory. When Jo asked what to put into the pilau, I told her to use chicken. For I happen to prefer chicken to beef and veal. I hate lamb in every shape and form, and I am not allowed to eat pork. In this way, I would be certain that I myself would get what I wanted, and that is about as good a principle for a host to follow as any other I can think of.

Celery seemed to suggest itself as the most logical of vegetables for an occasion of this sort. *Apium graveolens* is a harmless kind of weed which rarely provokes man's passions into the violence caused by mentioning either spinach or cauliflower. Furthermore, it was held in high esteem by the ancients as a mild aphrodisiac. This might not recommend it to Plato, who, according to his most trustworthy contemporaries, was too deeply engrossed in his political, scientific, and social contemplations to have any spare time for studying the interesting problems connected with applied biology.

There was to be no regular dessert, but I intended to have the table full of small dishes filled with all the rather messy things we could buy at any store dealing in Oriental candies, bits of nougat, Turkish delight, Algerian sweetmeats, and whatever else we could find that was highly sugary. Wines? I had no idea. But neither of our guests would be conscious of the pressed grapes, and we had a lot of odds and ends of bottles bought for previous occasions. In this way we would be able to save some money, and these dinners, as we were beginning to notice, would run into much higher figures than we had expected. Not that we minded. They were the best investments both Frits and I had ever made, and when the crash came (as it did shortly afterward) we at least had had something for our money.

Problem No. III. How about music?

Of Greek music I knew nothing, and the Chinese music I had heard in the East had always made me feel as if someone had been filing saws. But I remembered that both Plato and Confucius had greatly stressed the importance of music in their respective systems of education and that they had preferred flutes to all other instruments. I did not want to experiment with pipes of Pan and other instruments used in supposedly "classical" records with which the market had been flooded recently by a number of German professors who at last had "discovered" how Greek music should be played. I had heard the *Hymn to Helios* and the *Hymn to Kalliopeia,* but they had not struck me as the sort of thing to which a person with a more or less cultivated ear would like to listen for more than a few minutes. In which, of course, I merely showed the arrogance of modern man, who forgets that the music which makes us weep in 1942 may impress our descendants of 2942 as unfavorably as the music which made the people of the year 942 swoon with delight happens to affect us.

Not that I have the slightest objection to the flute, which is a noble instrument in the hands of an expert (and there are about a dozen of them in the world). On the contrary, the flute, when kept within reasonable bounds, is a joy to the ear, and an orchestra without a couple of good flutes would be as flat as soup without salt. Its literature is decidedly limited, of course, but there are lovely flute parts in several of Mozart's quintets and sonatas, and both he and Bach have written flute concertos which have a delightful and quite refreshing quality. I ordered some of these from Amsterdam, together with the "Brandenburg" Concerto No. 5, in D major, in which a little, very high-pitched kind of flute, now usually replaced by a trumpet, plays hide-and-seek with the melody and manages to do this with such humor and gaiety that I have adopted that record as my special remedy against those fits of melancholia which are the result of reading the latest news from the dark hinterland of Nazi Europe.

And then came the moment when I had to sit down and play Plutarch and write something about our next guests. I did not find it easy. Like most supposedly educated Europeans, I knew practically nothing about the man who for the last two thousand years has given what are in some way the wisest people on earth that philosophy of life which has enabled them to exist with a fair degree of happiness in the midst of an accumulation of miseries and indignities such as has never been experienced by any other nation. As for Plato, I had gone through so many ups and downs in my feelings toward the founder of the science of statecraft that I never quite knew where I stood or what I could answer when someone said, "Ah, yes! Plato!"

At times I have liked him enormously and have admired him as the most important thinker of the ages, but there also have been intervals when he was nothing more to me than a clever weaver of words and a not very heroic exponent of certain theories of government which had no connection whatsoever with the world as it happened to be. But my peaceful years in Veere had put me into a sort of contemplative mood in which I was better able to understand what Plato had tried to prove.

It should be remembered that the Plato we know was much more appreciated during the Middle Ages and Renaissance than during the centuries following immediately upon his death. For Greece had ceased to exist as an independent nation. The Greek people had deliberately committed suicide by their everlasting quarreling among themselves and by their attempts to establish a working democracy in a society of which ninety per cent of the population were slaves.

Plato, therefore, was not unlike those modern European students of statecraft who spin their yarns about an ideal state, with one eye on the Gestapo and the other on the nearest exit to the Lisbon clipper and the U.S.A. Five hundred years from today we may discover their books in the places where they now lie hidden and then we will be astonished at the brilliant way in which those moderns had discussed the methods by which it might have been possible to save European civilization. But we will also know that nothing came of their beautiful dreams because reality overtook them before they had finished their tasks and had thrown them into those concentration camps from which they were never again to emerge and in which they died of neglect, brutality, and starvation.

Plato, too, wrote his guidebook to applied politics at the very moment it could no longer be of any practical use to anyone. Shortly after his death, the great tyrant from the north gobbled up the whole of the eastern world, and Greece was reduced to the rank of a seventh-rate province and an insignificant part of that vast Macedonian empire which, a few years later, was to reach from the Danube to the Indus. Plato therefore worked in a void. The glory of the age of Pericles, when Athens had dominated the ancient world, was still vividly remembered, but so was the shame of the years immediately afterward, when the barbarians from Sparta, who had always believed in converting their butter into spear points, deliberately destroyed what the Athenians had so painfully built up and left the city, once presided over by Pallas Athene, a mere shambles, its walls gone, its public buildings ruined, and its population decimated by the plague.

But while it had been possible to destroy the physical part of the city which for four long centuries had been the center of ancient civilization, it had proved much more difficult to extinguish that beacon of "enlightenment through actual observation" which the Athenian scientists and philosophers had erected on the shores of the Aegean Sea. And while Athens ceased to exist as an independent political unit, it continued to be the most important center of education of the Old World. From all over the Mediterranean bright young men in search of the best pedagogical opportunities would sooner or later find their way to the city on the Bay of Aegina and for centuries after the Athenians had ceased to function as an international power and a commercial metropolis, eager students from Europe, Asia, and Africa would travel to the land of Attica, that in one of its many academies of learning they might prepare themselves for the difficult business of living.

Universities, in our sense of the word, were not to make their appearance until many centuries later. Teaching was still very much a matter of Mark Hopkins sitting at one side of a log and a student at the other. Except that the scholars, who had often been obliged to acquire the necessary sums of money for their tuition at great sacrifice, were serious young men who knew exactly what they wanted and who came to Athens not merely to get a degree and thereby qualify themselves for membership in the University Club after their return to Rome or Alexandria. They went to Athens in search of the best products then available on the educational market and shopped around until at last they found what they were looking for. After they reached their destination they paid a very considerable sum for the privilege of being allowed to follow the lectures of the *magister* who presided over the establishment of their choice and they sat at his feet to listen and to ask questions and to debate with him upon every possible subject beneath the heavens and earth, until in the end they too might perhaps catch sight of a few of those eternal verities which only reveal themselves by the light of the sparks that are struck by a conflict of first-rate brains.

No attempt was made by these Athenian pedagogues to put together what God had put asunder, and if a student lacked the natural talent which was believed to be a prerequisite for successful work within the realm of the arts and sciences, he was not tolerated for very long. His teachers might feel sorry for him, but if the boy lacked the necessary gray matter, he was told to become a good, reliable carpenter or stonemason but not to strive after a worthless Ph.D.

I suppose that, being human, they would occasionally allow the not overly brilliant son of a rich Roman war profiteer to bribe his way into their schools. But this permitted them to bestow free scholarships upon poor boys in whom they had detected exceptional ability, and so no great harm was done, for the standards were never lowered until much later, when the world had been made safe for the meek and the humble and when the proud of spirit were made to feel that there was no longer any room for them in this world.

Now let me give you a few dates to fix Plato's activities definitely on your mind. He was born in or about the year 427 B.C., two years before the death of Pericles. In 404, Athens, after a war of almost thirty years, surrendered to Sparta and lost its walls and its navy and its leading position among the small nations that went to make up ancient Hellas. In the year 400 Xenophon wrote his dullish book which all little boys who have studied Greek these last twenty-three hundred years have had to read and which I mention only to show how far the Greeks had fallen from their former high estate. Ten thousand Greeks were obliged to hire out to the Persians as mercenaries. A hundred years before, they themselves would have done the hiring.

Meanwhile Athens was passing rapidly through all sorts and kinds of government, from a not very happy experiment with a short-lived oligarchy to an even more disastrous interval of pure democracy, when the fair name of Athens was forever disgraced by the judicial murder of Socrates.

That happened in the year 399, and Socrates of course was the teacher of Plato. Use this year 399 as the peg on which to hang the whole development of Plato.

Plato made three trips to Syracuse to which he was called as a consultant in political matters by the tyrant who was then at the head of the government of this old Carthaginian settlement. At that time Plato still seemed to have lived under the delusion that sometime—somewhere—some great leader would arise who would send for him in a letter, reading about as follows:

My dear professor:

You are supposed to know more about government than any other living human being. I have everything under control here. I run this town, and everybody knows that I am the boss. No rich businessman can put anything over on me because he has bought up the local legislators, as there is no legislature which can be bought. No cheap demagogue can so much as open his mouth or grab a few millions by forcing himself upon the local labor unions, for I don't allow any. I see to it that the workingman gets decent wages and is fairly treated, and therefore he needs no organization to force the employers into doing the right thing by him. We have an army and a navy, but any officer who ever is seen to talk to one of our former politicians is hanged right away.

As for our women, they enjoy the same rights as the men.

The bright ones are not held in any greater respect than their less intelligent menfolk merely because they happen to be women. We recognize the necessity of continuing the population, but we take motherhood for granted as something that is part of nature, like rain or sunshine or the duty of the respectable citizens of the male persuasion to shave themselves every day.

As for the children, you will, of course, be expected to devote a great deal of your time here to a study of our schools. We want to make them the best possible training schools for life, both from a practical and a theoretical point of view. But in giving every child its chance, we do not want to favor the duller pupils at the expense of their brighter classmates. Even I, the tyrant of this town (which I think you will find greatly improved since your last visit, as we have got rid of all tenements and have hanged all racketeers)—even I realize that all people are born equal. The only trouble is that they never stay equal for more than a few hours or days. After that, as far as I am concerned, each one must follow his own destiny, for I do not want to be brighter than the gods who seem to have predestined some of our poorest and least favored infants to rise to unexpected heights, while others, who came into this world with every possible advantage, remain numskulls all their livelong days and die on the gallows or in the poorhouse.

I therefore expect you to rearrange our school system upon such a basis that every one of my subjects will be given a chance to function to the best of his or her abilities and may derive the greatest possible amount of satisfaction from his residence on this earth and will be able to do so without cluttering up the road of progress by futile efforts to do more than he can do, merely because such a course of action satisfies his own vanity.

There are many other problems but these I hope to discuss with you when you reach Syracuse. I shall, however, mention a few—public health, some kind of system that will prevent the mentally and physically unfit from breeding like rabbits and filling our lunatic asylums and poorhouses with a cargo of humanity which the ship of state is by no means able to carry. But of these things—as I just said—I will speak after your arrival, and in the meantime I remain your well-disposed

DIONYSIOS, TYRANT

Some such letter may actually have been written, for Plato, as I told you, paid three visits to Syracuse. But he had to suffer the same disappointment as Confucius when, two centuries before, that good and wise man had gone forth in quest of his own "intelligent prince."

On paper, the schemes of both philosophers looked entirely plausible. But when it came to a practical realization of their plans, the human race obstinately refused to live up to all such parchment theories. It went its own sweet way regardless of the logic of the philosophers, and Plato, forever haunted by the fate of his beloved Socrates (the most intelligent of all Athenians, ruthlessly destroyed by the lowest elements of society), and not being much of a hero, decided to refrain from all direct action and to devote himself exclusively to training a few choice disciples in the science of statecraft.

He lived to be almost eighty years old, but he spent the latter half of his life as the head of a private school and never got himself mixed up with local politics.

This institute of the higher learning was situated in a grove near Athens. This grove was consecrated to the memory of Academus, the Greek hero who, according to legend, had told Castor and Pollux where Theseus had hidden Helen. Outside of his academic labors, Plato found time to write the thirteen epistles and the thirty-five dialogues in which he discussed every possible problem of life (and therefore of politics and statecraft) which for one reason or another struck him as a fit subject for debate with his students.

The esteem in which these "conversations" were held is perhaps best demonstrated by the fact that practically all of them have survived. Whereas the greater part of ancient literature has been irredeemably lost (including some of the holy books of

541

the early Christians), the works of Plato were always most carefully preserved. Even during those chaotic centuries which followed in the wake of the fall of Rome, when the new creed not
merely murdered some of the most distinguished exponents of
the old Platonic philosophy but also burned their books wherever they found them, there were always a sufficient number of
faithful Platonic scholars to hide at least enough copies of these
priceless treasures to save them for posterity.

As a result, we are thoroughly familiar with the ideas of this
greatest of the writers of antiquity, and there never has been a
moment during the twenty-three centuries which separate us
from Plato when he has failed to influence at least a few of the
brighter spirits of our race. For example, we find traces of
Plato in the writings of most of the founding fathers of the
Church. The medieval scholastics, in spite of their devotion to
Aristotle, were very apt to be influenced by Plato, and the
eighteenth century, the great age of universal enlightenment,
was thoroughly Platonic, in spite of its endlessly repeated love
for the average man. Today, amidst the fury of conflicts let loose
by that antithesis of Plato's ideal of the true leader (I am sorry,
but I have to refer once more to Adolf Hitler), the name of the
great Athenian has been somewhat eclipsed by the prophets of
violence and cruelty who now seem to be in full command of
the situation. But watch my words! The moment some semblance of reason returns to our unfortunate planet, Plato will
again come into his own.

It is true that at times he will exasperate us by being entirely
too academic and by behaving as if he lived in a vacuum and
had never heard of the human race. But that is merely one of
the "defects of his qualities," and his qualities are so great that
we can easily overlook a few of the defects, for it is those qualities which have kept Plato's books alive and fresh for more than
twenty-three centuries. Homer, of course, goes back still farther,
but otherwise how very few writers there are (especially upon
philosophical subjects) who are not hopelessly dated after the
passing of a single generation! Whereas Plato, when he really

There, at the foot of the Acropolis, Plato had done his teaching.

lets go and is able to forget for a few moments that Socrates was put to death for much less than he is telling his pupils, sounds as if he were writing from Washington, D. C., or some other modern capital and were writing today instead of in 370 B.C.

Take certain passages in his *Republic,* which was really a kind of Utopia before the Utopias had been invented as a form of political criticism. Having just lived through the terrible experience of seeing his beloved Athens go to ruin (and entirely through its own fault), he has Socrates, who is the hero of so many of his dialogues, discuss the vicious circle which makes it apparently impossible for mankind to escape from the bondage of its own political follies.

Here is part of the story. The old stonecutter (for that was the trade which Socrates had learned from his father) has just paid his compliments to the plutocracy which has come to power when Athens became the richest city of the ancient world. "These new men of business," so he says, "keep up the pretense of never noticing those whom they have already ruined and they contrive to insert their sting—which in their case is their money—into anybody who is not constantly on guard against them. But by this method they succeed in recovering their original investment every time while at the same time they make drones and paupers of everybody outside their own class. They will continue doing this until the people at last see the danger that threatens them. Their despair gives them courage. They arise against their oppressors and triumphantly declare the victory of Democracy over Tyranny and Plutocracy.

"In the first flush of victory they kill many of their opponents, send a few more into exile, and then settle down to show the survivors how the world should really be governed. But soon the democrats turn out to be as the plutocrats and the tyrants had been before them. They use the power of their numbers to get a majority at every election and then they do as they please because whatever they decree is based upon a 'legal majority.' Therefore they are entirely within the law when they divide all offices among themselves and when they keep the people happy by a constantly increasing number of doles.

"Of course, in order to retain the good will of the masses, they are obliged to do something the tyrants and the oligarchs can dispense with. They must flatter the mob, and as a result all standards are debased by an increasing amount of vulgarity. Manners too are coarsened because there is no one to show them any better, and soon it becomes apparent that just as the mad pursuit of wealth must eventually destroy oligarchy, in the same way the excess of liberty must destroy democracy. And then there is another period of decline, for, in such a state, anarchy gains until it presently finds its way into all private houses and even ends by getting hold of the animals. Fathers get accustomed to descend to the level of their sons, and the sons behave with insolence toward their fathers, as they no longer have any fear of them. The teacher begins to stand in awe of his pupils, and as a result the pupils despise their teachers. From that moment on, young and old are equal, and the young are ready to compete with the old both in word and deed, while the old feebly imitate the young. In the end, all horses and donkeys begin to march along with the rights and dignities of freemen, and everything is just ready to burst with liberty.

"And what is the result?

"That the excessive increase of this so-called liberty causes a reaction in the opposite direction, for an excess of liberty, whether in nations or in individuals, seems duly to pass into slavery, and the most aggravated form of tyranny arises invariably out of the most extreme form of liberty, for the moment liberty becomes license, dictatorship is near. The rich, afraid that the prevailing democracy will rob them of their last cent, begin to think of ways and means to overthrow their enemies, and at that moment some enterprising leader is apt to seize power. He does this by promising everything to the poor. Then he surrounds himself with an army, kills first his opponents and next those of his friends who might be dangerous. Having purged the state, he establishes himself as tyrant—as sole ruler.

"And under such conditions," as Plato (in the role of Socrates) is careful to point out, "there is no longer any room for the philosopher who preaches moderation and mutual understanding. The poor philosopher is now like a man fallen among the wild beasts and, if he is wise, he will retire, while there is still time, and take shelter under a wall while the storm passes by."

And there you have the leitmotiv of Plato's whole career. While the storm is raging, there is nothing the man of a contemplative turn of mind can do. Let him take shelter and there prepare for the day when the people will perhaps listen to reason. He emphasizes the "perhaps," for like Confucius he is not quite certain whether that day will ever come. But don't go out on the ramparts and take an active part in the battle. Any well-trained gladiator—some half-witted but strong-armed barbarian carefully trained to the use of arms—will be infinitely better at the business of fighting and killing than a man who has spent all his life playing with ideas instead of bombs. It is not cowardice that makes the philosopher take this step. It is his sense of the fitness of things, for he realizes that, being a doctor of the soul, he is in a way not unlike the doctor of the body, who is also found behind the lines and not in the front ranks.

Having settled those matters to his own satisfaction and finding that his ideas worked (at least on paper), Plato concentrated all his efforts upon trying to discover how the human race could be made to behave according to the laws of reason, by what methods those elements which might be dangerous to such a development could be eradicated, and how the perfect state could be established in very much the same way as a better breed of horses or cows or pigs or sheep or bees or grain could be developed out of the inferior varieties with which the world was only too familiar.

A most noble and most praiseworthy idea! And one with which the greatest minds of all times have occupied themselves at some period of their lives. Some of them approached it from the solemn and dignified angle, which was so characteristic of

Plato. Others, like the carpenter-teacher from Nazareth, tried to solve the difficulty by placing the human race under the direct superintendence of God. Still others, like Voltaire and Dean Swift, chose satire as their mode of attack. Thomas More thought he could do most good by putting a sort of china egg into mankind's nest—a china egg he called Utopia. Descartes endeavored to give us a solution by an application of pure mathematics. Spinoza gave it an ethical twist. Karl Marx took economics as his particular field of research. Rabelais clowned everything in a world of his own making. And there have been all sorts of philosophers, sages, and masterminds (genuine and not quite so genuine) of the in-between variety who starved in garrets and died in cellars, that they might bestow upon their fellow men a blueprint of salvation, searching heaven and hell for an answer to the all-important question, "How can we possibly save mankind from itself?"

But in the end they were like Omar the Tentmaker (one of the most interesting and stimulating of all the seekers after truth), who summed up his own lifelong investigations in this simple quatrain:

> *Myself when young did eagerly frequent*
> *Doctor and Saint, and heard great Argument*
> *About it and about: but evermore*
> *Came out by the same Door as in I went.*

Ever since I began to interest myself in the men who fought so violently to take mankind definitely out of the class of the animals by providing it with a code of conduct based upon some principle that would be foolproof, I have been struck by the fact how deeply every one of them was influenced by his own political and social background. Spinoza, although brought up in the atmosphere of a very strict Judaism, took the government of the Dutch Republic as the norm for his ideal state. Voltaire, when he made Candide utter what was really his own creed, "Let us cultivate our own garden," revealed himself as a good

Frenchman. Plato, in giving us his ideal republic, basically revived the Athenian commonwealth as it had been carried to its highest degree of perfection by Pericles. For when we come down to the core of the Platonic system, what do we find?

Plato believes that it is possible to evolve a state which will be happy and prosperous and able to live in peace with all its neighbors if every citizen can be persuaded to "do his part" to the best of his own abilities. In that way, the nation will acquire a basis of justice and righteousness upon which everything else can then be firmly founded.

He realizes that such a conception was a little too vague and therefore gives us a definite four-point program for the attainment of his brand of civic virtue. That four-point program sounds as follows: every citizen must be imbued with a sense of justice, a sense of piety, a sense of reasonableness, and a feeling of courage that when the occasion arises he will fight bravely to maintain the safety of the common country. Once he has acquired those four civic virtues, the citizen can no longer go wrong. He will be like Immanuel Kant, standing ready to meet all the vicissitudes of life, with the starry heavens above him and a copy of the categorical imperative in his hand.

Plato, like all the other philosophers of antiquity, including the Jewish ones, almost never shows any serious interest in the economic aspects of life. His physical needs, like those of all Greeks, Romans, Jews, and the other peoples of the Mediterranean, were few. An adobe house offered him all the shelter he needed. He could teach underneath the branches of some spreading olive trees, for it was never sufficiently cold to drive him and his pupils inside a steam-heated lecture hall, just as Jesus was able to address his fellow men from any convenient hillside. Again, like all other Greeks, he could eat sparingly because he lived in a warm climate and was not obliged to stoke up, like a teacher in some New England college. Clothes, too, were not a heavy item of expense. But even more important than that, the existence of an almost unlimited and extremely cheap labor supply, consisting of slaves who, once they had been bought, cost next to nothing for their further upkeep, made it possible for the few thousand Greek freemen to devote themselves entirely to the service of the state.

But what would become of the leisure which made it possible for them to do this—to exist free from all economic cares—what would become of it when a new tide set in and deprived them of their economic security? Plato never even seems to have considered such a possibility, and that, it seems to me, was his greatest weakness. Even in his own little world (and, after all, it was a very small world compared to what was to follow), where it would have been comparatively easy to educate the few thousand free people who made up a Greek state, war and violence had been the order of the day. What would happen when Christianity, having preached the doctrine of human equality, should rid the world of slavery (even if it took some nineteen centuries to do so) and when hundreds of millions of other men and women should feel the necessity of some actual participation in affairs of state?

American history throws a very illuminating light upon this problem. As long as we were merely thirteen small colonies in which practically everybody could know everybody else, it was possible for a small group of leaders, animated by the four Platonic virtues, to run the republic. The Washingtons, the Adamses, the Jeffersons, and the Madisons had been deeply influenced by the philosophy of Plato. All of them were still profoundly conscious of their duty toward the state. From childhood on, it had been hammered into their heads that since they had been born with certain advantages over their fellow men, they were also expected to exert themselves more than these other less fortunate ones and that they therefore must become shining examples of courage, justice, reasonableness, and piety— in the broadest sense of that oft-misused word. In short, each one was not only aware of the Bill of Rights, which was part of the law of the land, but also of an unwritten Bill of Duties, which was an inseparable part of his own code of ethics. And

Standing there, like Immanuel Kant, with the starry hea

bove us and the categorical imperative in our hearts.

because they moved and had their being in small communities it was possible for their neighbors to weigh them carefully on the scales of public opinion and to accept them or reject them as they deemed fit and necessary.

Therein, I believe, lies the greatest weakness of all the Platos from the fourth century B.C. until about a hundred years ago. Conditions have changed so completely that there is no longer any safe basis for comparison. But there is another Plato, less well known to most people and often entirely unsuspected. That is the Plato who, having studied individual men and having observed them as they react to certain political and social stimuli, thereupon goes behind and beyond them and tries to come to some understanding of the invisible forces which have made them what they are, who finally tries to reduce these many forces to a single source—to God.

As a small boy I was taught that the Jews, and after them the Christians, were the only people who had ever believed in a single God and that therefore they were superior to the followers of every other creed, including even the noblest of the old philosophical systems. I accepted it as most children will accept almost everything they are taught. Not because they feel very strongly either one way or the other (how could they with their limited experience?), but because they have at least learned this bit of wisdom: "Why argue with grownups who never understand anything, anyway?" Since then I have (without ever having felt deeply attracted by any religious subjects) carefully endeavored to find out whether this was really so and whether it was really Jesus who first of all spoke to us about a single heavenly Father.

It is true that the Greeks and the Romans never saw their own Supreme Being in the role of a father, for he was guilty of too many cruelties toward his children to qualify for that role. But they had long since passed beyond the stage where they still took any stock in the stories they had been told as children: how Pallas Athene had stepped forward, full-panoplied, from the brain of Zeus, how Pan loved to frighten lonely wanderers by making disgusting noises in the bushes by the side of the road, how all the gods had taken sides in the Trojan War and had fought in a war which, deprived of the glamour which Homer's name had bestowed upon it, had been nothing more than a highly undignified quarrel about a woman whom one man had stolen from another. They did not proclaim their disbelief in public. No more so than we of today—who feel completely indifferent to such doctrines as infant damnation and transubstantiation and transfiguration—express our opinions upon these subjects except among our own friends. We would merely hurt the feelings of lots of perfectly nice and kind and good people to whom these words still mean life and death, but we would most certainly not be able to make them change their minds by mere arguments. Therefore, in Plato, one does not come across any overt attacks upon the prevailing superstitions of his own time. He mentions them casually but never makes them a point of issue. Instead of which, he follows the much more intelligent course of leaving the gods where they are, living invisible lives on their snow-covered mountaintop, and then he proceeds to erect the image of his own deity on a distant plateau which is so high and inaccessible that few people will ever care to penetrate that far.

Those few are, of course, among the hardiest souls of the community for whom no exertion is too great if it promises to bring them a little closer to the final truth. The rest of humanity may eventually decide to follow these stouthearted pioneers, but Plato is not quite sure whether such a course would be entirely desirable.

Our modern students (judging by quite a number I have met) are apt to call Plato an "intellectual snob" and then dismiss him as one who has no business in our kind of democracy. I cannot agree at all with this point of view. Plato was an artist and therefore an aristocrat, a man to whom the best alone is good enough and who will accept no compromises in the matter of life's essentials. In an era when to most people the second best is good enough, Plato will suffer a temporary eclipse, but his hour will come again, though neither you nor I, my beloved friend, will be here to see it.

And now to faraway places and a land that is a complete mystery to most of us, myself very much included. I have never been to China, but that does not mean that I have never met any Chinese. Indeed I have, and I have found the poorer ones admirable in their industry and their good-natured cheerfulness. I hear that when they go bad, they do so in a great big way, but those I have known well were as a rule possessed of certain qualities of patience and application which put them shoulder-high above their white and brown and black neighbors, especially the white ones. As for the educated ones, they were so far beyond me in every respect that they made me feel ashamed of myself.

What I liked in the Chinese more than anything else were their truly Erasmian spirit of tolerance, their resemblance to Montaigne in his most delightful contemplative mood, and their wit (ribald or otherwise) which gave everything they said or wrote a pleasant Rabelaisian touch. And finally they had a very delicate feeling for the inner sense of things and were rarely guilty of those gaucheries which Western people so often confuse with honesty. My friends who were thoroughly familiar with China and the Chinese never cease to tell me that this picture is much too flattering. They inform me that the Chinese are also possessed of a high degree of low cunning, that they are apt to be grossly materialistic in their approach toward their daily existence, that they can be very cruel and entirely indifferent about the suffering of their fellow men, and that their outward calm does not at all correspond to that inner peace of soul which we suspect behind their gaily smiling eyes.

All of which may be perfectly true. The Pacific paradise in which I had always believed from the circumstantial evidence left behind by the early travelers and some of the fugitives from our own civilization did not exactly come up to the sad truth I beheld with my own eyes when, a great many years later, I was able to visit that incredibly lovely part of our planet. But when I set foot on Tahiti and Hawaii and saw the hideous things civilization had done to these benighted natives, I forced myself to remember that for a century and a half these poor creatures had been exposed to the tender ministrations of the white whaler, the white trader, and the Christian missionaries, not to mention the white sailors and marines of those European nations which have grabbed those islands as military outposts for their own predatory purposes. And therefore, as far as the Chinese are concerned, I shall, until I learn better, stick to my original opinion that the average Chinese (unless spoiled by his white and Christian environment) is touched by something—a philosophy of life rather than a religious system—which makes it possible for him to derive more satisfaction and contentment from his earthly existence than the members of those other races with whom I have spent most of my days on this planet.

Quite naturally, I then felt it necessary to answer the question: what exactly had made the Chinese what they were and are? Why did they click as they clicked, and what had they got which we Westerners had not got? The only way I could find out was by reading a great many books, and in every volume dealing with the Chinese enigma I sooner or later came across one man, a prophet, or a philosopher (he was called by all sorts of names), who was said to be chiefly responsible for having made the Chinese what they are and for having made them click the way they have been doing these last twenty-five hundred years.

His name was K'ung-fu-tse, but when Europe finally heard about him (a couple of thousand years after his death), his name was Latinized into Confucius, and as such he has been known ever since.

K'ung-fu-tse was born in the year 551 B.C. and he came of an old and distinguished family. It makes us Westerners look a bit silly! Are we really as young as all that? Five hundred years before the birth of Christ, my native land did not yet exist. Nebuchadnezzar had just disappeared from the shores of Babylon, and Jerusalem's first big Temple had been destroyed only a few years before. Solon had just died. The Acropolis still had to wait a century before it was to be crowned with the Parthenon. As for Rome, it was still a small country town struggling desperately to maintain itself against its rivals, the Etruscans, and four hundred more years were to go by before it could lay any claim to being called the center of an empire.

We people of the West, therefore, were still savages who lived in mud huts and painted our faces sky-blue when the Chinese already had learned to eat from their beautiful porcelain dishes and to ornament the walls of their houses with pictures of such exquisite workmanship that they have never been surpassed by any modern artist and had already given the world of eastern Asia a prophet of such profound wisdom that he was able to provide several hundred million people with an understandable and workable philosophy of life which was to influence them in their daily existence for the next twenty-five hundred years and which, at this moment, seems to be as vital as ever.

I am sorry that I can only give you secondhand information about this famous sage, for the Chinese language is a closed book to me, and I am now much too old to learn it.

At the age of twenty, K'ung-fu-tse entered on his career as a government official and was appointed manager of the gardens and public fields of the province which today is called Shantung. That means, incidentally, that the Chinese government was already interested in a planned economy at a time when our own ancestors were still nomads and lived that hand-to-mouth existence which kept them forever on the brink of starvation.

A regular career in the civil service does not seem to have appealed very greatly to young K'ung, and soon afterward he resigned to become a schoolteacher. He was twenty-two years old when he took that step. He had been married three years and had one son. This son begat other sons, and I am informed by my Chinese friends that the story of there still being direct descendants of the great sage is true. The K'ung family there-fore has succeeded in maintaining itself in the direct line for some sixty generations, and that in itself is considerable of a record, for we have not a single Italian family that goes back to the days of ancient Rome, and a western European family that can trace its genealogy back beyond the fifteenth century is as rare as a really warm day in England.

And so at the age of twenty-two we find our hero heading a school of his own, but a very peculiar institute of learning, for it did not teach the usual curriculum but specialized in making its pupils conscious of the existence of good and evil and under-took to instruct them in how to acquire virtue and how to avoid vice. The only conditions of admission (that, too, was rather unusual from our modern point of view) were a serious desire for wisdom and an industrious application to one's studies. There were no fees. Those who came from rich homes were expected to pay for the upkeep of the poor scholars who brought nothing with them but the clothes on their backs and a wooden bowl from which to eat their frugal meals of rice.

The school attracted widespread attention. Two sons of one of the princely houses in the province of Lu were sent by their parents to sit at the feet of this strange young master. When their families suggested that their tutor accompany them on their grand tour (this smacks of the Europe of the eighteenth century), he accepted the offer and used this unexpected oppor-tunity to perfect himself in the knowledge of the Chinese lan-guage and its music. According to legend, it was on this occa-sion that he met the famous Lao-tse, a man considerably older than himself and the founder of Taoism.

What did Taoism mean in the time of Confucius? And what does it mean today? Again I must plead ignorance. As near as I can make out it was a philosophy of life which taught that true happiness could only be accomplished by scrupulously obeying the Law. And the Law, to Lao-tse, seems to have meant the collection of ancient ceremonials which had been handed down from father to son for the last five thousand years. In addition to this respect for the past, Taoism preached the greatest possible simplicity both in thought and action, and in this way it agreed with the conclusions of all the great sages of all times.

Confucius appears to have been deeply impressed by Lao-tse, who from his side does not seem to have been in the least interested in his visitor or to have felt the slightest sympathy for his troubles. Yet troubles he had, and a great many of them. During his absence from home there had been an outbreak of revolution in his native country, and it had led to the expulsion of the ruling dynasty. Confucius, the incarnation of law and order, could not possibly approve of such an act of violence, and when the legitimate prince was driven into exile, he and his disciples followed him voluntarily rather than accept the domination of a usurper.

From that time on, K'ung-fu-tse led the existence of a wandering philosopher. Somewhere he felt there must be a wise and far-seeing leader who would want to avail himself of the services of a true man of learning. But such superior potentates have always been exceedingly scarce. The last example we had of the combination of a great administrator and a very wise human being occurred almost two centuries ago, when Frederick the Great came to the throne of Prussia. He actually did what Plato and Confucius had always hoped for. He sent for the most famous philosopher then alive and asked him to come and live at his court. But the experiment was far from successful and only led to a very painful break between Frederick and Voltaire. Since then, governments have availed themselves of experts on health and animal husbandry and forest preservation, but we have never heard of the Washington government sending for William James or George Santayana, and I very much doubt whether the political leaders of the fifties and sixties of the last century were even aware of the existence of a certain Ralph Waldo Emerson.

Confucius therefore was never able to settle down anywhere for any length of time, except on few and very rare occasions.

One of these came about when he was fifty-two years old. An enlightened prince sent for him and appointed him his minister of justice. So well did the sage acquit himself of his task that the whole of the nation soon became aware of his presence. Then the inevitable happened. Those who formerly had prospered by the unsettled state of affairs (the racketeers and politicians, as we would call them today) were finding themselves out of their jobs and they promptly combined against this over-honest reformer. Rather than fight this rabble, K'ung quietly withdrew and spent the last fifteen years of his life peacefully living in his native province; where he increased the number of his disciples until there were over three thousand of them. Some eighty of these, according to his own testimony, were men of more than outstanding ability and really understood what their teacher meant.

Confucius died at the age of seventy-three, two years after the battle of Salamis, which saved Europe from the invasion of the Persians. According to the disciples who were with him at the moment of his demise, he anticipated his end with great dignity and without any apprehension of a future in which, by the way, he had never believed, for as Confucianism never became a religion, it had no need of either heaven or hell to keep its followers in line. The old gentleman simply withdrew from life when he had grown tired of waiting for that invitation that never came. No great prince, so he was now forced to realize, would ever ask him to become his prime minister and give him his chance to show how a country should be ruled with intelligence and honesty. Just before he sank into his last sleep he composed one of those short and descriptive poems of which the Chinese have always been so extraordinarily fond. It has been preserved and reads almost the same as the quatrain I quoted at the end of my little story about Plato.

The great mountain must crumble,
The strong beam must break,
The wise man must wither away like a plant.

The author of Ecclesiastes also was interested in this subject, though he expressed it in a slightly different form. *Vanitas vanitatum—et omnia vanitas*, but the sense is about the same: "Vanity of vanities—all is vanity."

Webster sums Confucianism up as follows: "As a philosophical system·it is the basis of much of Chinese ethics, education, statecraft, and religion. Filial piety, benevolence, justice, propriety, intelligence, and fidelity are cardinal virtues." A most exalted code of behavior and one of which every sensible man must approve.

Christianity has also been actively preaching such a program for some two thousand years, but these twenty centuries have been an era of violence and cruelty and wholesale murder and theft—of crusades which killed enemy and friend alike—of assault with machine guns upon natives armed with bows and arrows and of pious padres blessing those horrible feats of valor with an appeal to that Man of Sorrows who had preached the law, "Love ye one another."

Then what, as I already asked a moment ago, has the Chinese laundryman around the corner got that allows him to survive under circumstances that would kill any other human being in less than half a dozen years, that enables him to bear up with the sort of white people among whom he is obliged to live on account of his poverty and yet makes it possible for him to turn his children into well-mannered and well-behaved little citizens, in sharp contrast to the offspring of his supposedly Christian neighbors? Yes indeed, what has he got? Did old K'ung bestow upon this world some sort of philosophical compass by which every one of his disciples is able to steer his little leaky craft safely across any part of the map and in any kind of weather? Or had the Chinese character already been definitely "set" long before Confucius was born, and had the sage merely crystallized parts of it for the benefit of his fellow countrymen who were too busy with their daily affairs to be able to study the works of the ancient philosophers for themselves?

There we are back again at the problem of the chicken and the egg. Was the religion of the Dutch people of the sixteenth century the religion of Erasmus, or was Erasmus the expression of the religious feelings of the Dutch people of the sixteenth century? Did Descartes give the French of the seventeenth century a new approach to life, or was he himself the final product of those ideas which had already existed among them for hundreds of years? I don't know and I am very much afraid that I shall never find out. But I suspect that it was the personality of Confucius rather than his works (as revealed by the books of his disciples) which put its stamp upon the Chinese character.

The "characteristic sayings" credited to Confucius are on a par with the short paragraphs one finds in many small-town newspapers and which have no other purpose than to fill up the editorial page on days when there is not any real news. Most of them are pretty commonplace, and few of them come up to the heritage of wisdom which the late Abe Martin bestowed upon the readers of *The Indianapolis News*. Here are two examples taken at random from the literary remains of K'ung-fu-tse and Kin Hubbard.

Says the Chinese sage: "A poor man who does not indulge in flattery and a rich man who is not proud are praisable characters, but they are not equal to the poor who are always cheerful and the rich who yet love the rules of propriety." The Hoosier philosopher settles such problems by the remarks that while it's no disgrace to be poor, it might just as well be and: "Th' world gets better ever' day—then wuss agin in th' evening."

If I ever decide to follow the example of Montaigne and take out my brush and paint inspiring texts all over my grandchildren's schoolroom, I am sure that I shall give them both Kin and Con. That would then make Confucius a sort of Chinese Abe Martin and Abe Martin a Hoosier Chinese. And why not? For it is their "homey" quality, in the best sense of the word, that accounts for their popularity with the masses of plain, ordinary people and for the fact that they succeeded in doing what the much more eloquent philosophers have invariably failed to do. Both of them were country folk, familiar with the people who lived on and of and by the good earth, and both of them were therefore natural philosophers, for no one who is on an intimate footing with nature, who watches the seasons and the tides, and who is dependent for his living upon sunshine and rain can help becoming a kind of village sage. Unless the local witch doctors get him, in which case he is lost and becomes that most hateful of all of God's creatures, a small-town fanatic.

Now not even the worst enemies of Confucius—those rulers who hated him so much that as soon as he had died they ordered all his books to be burned—have ever accused him of that. Bigotry and meddlesome officiousness were abhorrent to him. He was all for the policy of live and let-live. And he was so enthusiastic about the idea of let-live that he sat himself down in his humble but neat and harmonious little house, took out brush and ink box, and asked himself the question, "How and in what manner can I teach my people to go through life with a minimum of suffering and a maximum of contentment?"

Other philosophers and other faith founders have done the same thing, but none of them have been quite as successful, because Confucius was the only one who had always one eye firmly fixed on that soil he knew so well from his own experience and out of which grew his ideas as well as his cabbages.

The accusation often made that the Confucian creed is lacking in spiritual qualities is undoubtedly true. Confucius was not overspiritual. He did not deny that there might be a world hereafter, but he felt that the evidence in favor of such a heavenly home and a future life among the blessed was rather vague and depended entirely upon the hearsay of people who had never been there.

On the other hand, the world in which Confucius lived was very much of a tangible fact. Nobody could deny its existence, because it was there for all to see and hear and smell. People could even sit down on it and touch it and, if they were hungry enough (as often happened in China), they could eat it and in that way prolong life for a few more miserable days. As reasonable and intelligent human beings, so Confucius taught, it was up to the human race to make the best of its bad bargain, for with a little reason and intelligence a great many things could be accomplished.

It sometimes happened, so he taught, that during a journey one was obliged to spend a few days in a poverty-stricken village, waiting for a bridge to be repaired or for a train of pack horses to come along and carry one's luggage. What would an intelligent and reasonable man do under those circumstances? He would examine the situation, take stock of his assets, and make his plans accordingly. He would not expect to find porterhouse steak in a place where nobody was sufficiently rich to keep a cow. Then what was there to eat and how could a few bony chops be prepared in such a way as to make a tolerably good meal? There were no vegetables except turnips. Was there any method by which a turnip could be turned into a dish fit for human consumption? There was no tavern. But somewhere there might be a half-ruined temple which could be turned into quite a comfortable shelter for at least a few nights. And so on and so forth. One might even, by means of a diligent search, discover a few amusing or quaint characters among the villagers and pass a pleasant evening listening to their stories about wild animals that had haunted the neighborhood or to their playing of the flute, for in such remote hamlets there often were old codgers who still remembered tunes long since disappeared from every other part of the land. And best of all, one could make friends or at least get oneself respected by the countryfolk for the civility of one's manners, the elegance of one's address, and the courtesy of one's deportment.

Change this scene from a small village in the hinterland to a big city on one of the large rivers or the coast of a powerful province, and while the people with whom one would have to deal would be slightly different, the manner of one's dealing with them would be exactly the same. Until it was possible to lay down a pretty concrete code of behavior which would work everywhere and under all circumstances and which would make it possible for both the poorest of coolies and the richest of merchants or warriors to spend their short residence on this earth with that maximum of contentment and that minimum of pain after which every intelligent man would quite naturally strive.

Let me give you a few examples from this idea code which I have extracted out of the bale of books I have read upon the general subject of Confucius and Confucianism:

Politeness is the oil of the social machinery. Therefore, train yourself to be polite under all circumstances, even the most painful ones. All men, women, and children will do much more for you if you approach them with a smile than if you come to them with a frown. Therefore, be sure to smile, even if you have a tummy-ache and feel much more like cursing than showing evidences of a cheerful spirit.

The older members of the community are apt to dominate the social and economic life of any city or village, because they have the money. Furthermore, unless they are complete fools, they are bound to have acquired a certain amount of practical wisdom during their long residence on this earth. Therefore, show the older people that you respect them. That will make them like you, and then in turn you will probably come to like them, and that will establish a good understanding, beneficial to both old and young.

A family will never get anywhere if it is a debating society in which little Lin will contradict his father and will tell his mother that she is talking nonsense. Therefore, encourage the children to be polite and courteous to their parents and let the parents treat their children with understanding and forbearance, for that will make life within the circle of the family harmonious, and it will turn the home into a place in which all of them like to dwell.

A stranger who has never met you before will judge you by your personal appearance. You may have a heart of gold, but that will not be noticeable at first sight, whereas last week's scrambled eggs on the lapel of your coat will be spotted immediately. Therefore, try to look neat. Your clothes may be old and worn but they can at least be well brushed.

You may, for a time at least, get away with a certain amount of dishonesty in dealing with your fellow merchants. But in the end your neighbors will find you out, and then there is an end to your commercial career. Therefore, be honest in all your business dealings. If by nature you are inclined to indulge in a little sly crookedness, suppress that instinct, for honesty pays in the end, and you are out to make a living, aren't you?

Often the saint goes about disguised as a beggar. Therefore, be agreeable to beggars, for you may be entertaining a saint.

I might go on for several pages more, but this will give you an idea of my notions about Confucius and what he taught. I know that many of his popular sayings got petrified as time went on, for that seems to be the habit of all maxims. I have also been told that I am much too lenient in my judgment on the old gentleman. At heart, so I am told, he was a good deal of a conservative and even a reactionary who played beautifully into the hands of the ruling classes, who most heartily approved of his insistence upon that respect which all young men should show their elders and upon the subservient attitude with which all subjects should approach their masters. I am inclined to feel that that objection is well taken.

But the same holds good for our own religion. The Christ who is worshiped in St. Peter's in Rome is a very different person from the Christ I once met in a poor Lapp church where the dogs lay around the altar because no one had the heart to turn them out when the temperature outside stood at thirty below zero. It also goes for the perverted and degenerate kind of Buddhism which spread all over India and China five hundred years after the founder of that purest and noblest of all faiths had fulfilled his self-predicted fourscore years and had left this earth for parts unknown. I think it is even safe to say that it also holds true for a great deal of our science, especially our medical science, which in the hands of mediocre disciples is apt to become something very different from what it had been intended to be by the original discoverers of some great new method of bringing relief to their ailing fellow men.

And it is a fact, sadly observed by all those who are in a position to do so, that music and painting also have a tendency to get so set in their mode of expression that they lose all direct contact with real life and have to be thrown on the ash heap, even as Beckmesser's pedantic versifications had to be laughed out of existence by a younger generation of cheerful Nuremberg boys and girls.

For all these reasons I have just mentioned, and even in the face of a great deal of adverse criticism, I still remain a sincere admirer of old K'ung-fu-tse, for without any supernatural pretensions and with a minimum of hocus-pocus he was able to give hundreds of millions of people a practical and workable philosophy of life which has made it possible for them, without any hope of a subsequent reward, to do the best they could under the most terrible of circumstances, to keep cheerful under all kinds of inexcusable provocations, to remain industrious when there was no reason to exert themselves, and to keep smiling when they had every reason to weep.

Wherefore, when he comes to our house next Saturday, I shall accord Confucius the three ceremonial bows to which he is entitled by reason of his having been a state official of the first class with the green peacock feather. And I shall do my best to hide from him the sacrilege we have committed with his name. I always wonder what the Europeans in China would have said if some Chinese columnists had started being very funny about their Saviour. "Jesus Christ—he say . . ."

But then, that sort of bad taste is so entirely foreign to the nature of those who were brought up in the school of the best-mannered of all spiritual teachers that we cannot even contemplate the possibility of its ever having taken place. Or if it should occur, it probably would be the work of some bright boys or girls who had been given the benefits of a Western education.

Saturday came and with it a sudden uncomfortable feeling—how were we going to converse with our friend from beyond Lake Baikal? Plato would be easy enough, for though the Greek spoke no Latin, Erasmus knew enough Greek to be able to translate at least the most important parts of our conversation if there were to be any kind of exchange of ideas—something we could never predict. But Confucius spoke the Lu dialect of the sixth century B.C. No use asking one of our many Dutch friends who knew Chinese to come and help us out that evening, for he probably would no more understand the old philosopher than a Chinese from the extreme north can make sense of what is being said by his cousin from the extreme south. Of course, there was always the possibility of drawing pictures, and I made sure that there would be a plentiful supply of paper and I took out the Chinese fountain pen Dwight Franklin had once given me (a curious contraption—made out of a brush and a small piece of Chinese ink, kept moist by a little sponge) and I practiced up on my strokes and I prayed for that inspiration without which a European trying his hand at Chinese art is bound to express himself almost as clumsily as an Oriental trying to paint in the Western fashion.

Saturday evening, half-past six. Everything is ready, and Frits and I are sitting in front of the fire, waiting for still another chapter to commence in that incredible experience which has now been ours for almost four months. At a quarter of seven, Erasmus slips in, greets us, goes, as is his habit, into the kitchen to address a few kind words to the cook and her husband, and joins us for a small glass of Moselle, which he prefers to the gin which is the common Dutch drink just before dinner. We ask him whether he has brushed up on his Plato, and he says yes—that is exactly what he has been doing these last five days.

"I've caught you at last!" I say. "You always pretend that you have no idea about whom we intend to invite."

He laughs and answers. "Oh, well, one goes places and one sometimes hears things."

It was Confucius, who had just arrived for dinner.

As he has not been, as far as we know, out of his study in the town hall, we wonder what "places" he means, but we think that it is better not to touch upon this delicate subject. We want these dinners to continue and do not want to incur any disapproval for an act of unintentional indiscretion.

Three minutes of seven.

There is a knock at the door. Frits' house still has the old-fashioned Dutch door divided into two parts—a practical arrangement, for in summer it allows you to have a draft in the house while preventing the children from running out into the street. Now the upper part of that door slowly opens, and there stands Confucius. It is easy to recognize him, for he looks exactly like his pictures. Then the lower part of the door too is opened as if by invisible hands, and Confucius enters. He does not offer to shake hands, but to each one of us he bows slowly—once, twice, three times. We answer his salutation in the same way. By means of gestures we beg him to sit down, which he does.

Then we notice that he is being followed by a young Chinese in ordinary civilian clothes. He too bows three times to each of us and then explains why he is there. "I am a descendant of Confucius," he tells us. "I believe that I am his grandson in the forty-second degree, but," and with a sly smile, "we may of course have lost count, for it has been a very long time. I was a student at Cornell, in the agricultural department, when the Japanese invaded our country. I went back home and took service with our army. I'm afraid that I was not a very good soldier. I was lacking in caution. I got shot through the heart. It was a painless death. Tonight my honored ancestor suggested that I accompany him to act as his interpreter. I do not always understand him—it takes a little patience. You know how difficult it would be for you to talk with Chaucer, and he lived only a few hundred years ago. But we are of the same blood and"—another smile—"we get along very nicely."

He now talks rapidly in Chinese. He seems to repeat the last part of his sentence, for the old gentleman looks at him in an affectionate way and pats his back in that unaffected manner which is neither Oriental nor Occidental but just universally human. We tell our unexpected guest how very welcome he is. Then we ask him to repeat this message to his distinguished kinsman.

I notice that a change has come over us. Quite unconsciously we sober-minded and exceedingly unceremonious Dutchmen have suddenly dropped our rather free and easy manners and are proceeding with measured tread in everything we say and do. Frits too has observed this and gives me a knowing wink. Then Jo comes in with the plates for the first course, and a miracle happens.

The average Dutchman or Dutch woman could not possibly be hired to curtsy to anyone, and with all the respect they feel toward their Queen, they prefer not to go to court rather than make themselves ridiculous by going through certain ceremonials they somehow associate with setting-up exercises. But without being told what to do, our cook curtsies deeply before our unusual guest. When I ask her afterward where she has learned it, she answers me, "Of course I never learned it, but it seemed the right thing to do."

Then we notice that Plato has arrived. He looks exactly like his bust in the Vatican, at Rome. He has a heavy black beard, slightly touched up with oil, and his hair drops down over his high forehead. He has a strong nose and a much more sensitive mouth than we had expected.

Him Erasmus welcomes with a few polite phrases in his best university Greek. At first Plato looks puzzled. Then he catches on and repeats to himself what Erasmus has just said. We notice that it sounds very different from the Greek we had learned at school.

As for the two guests of honor, they too now exchange a few complimentary phrases. This takes time, for they have to make use of two interpreters. Then from the upper floor there come the soft notes of a Mozart andante for the flute, and both Plato and Confucius listen with evident delight. When the air has come to an end, they indicate by gestures that they would like to hear some more of the same sort, and I call up to Hein to play Mozart's Quartet for Flute and Strings. Then the moment has come to go to dinner. An extra plate has been set for Confucius' grandson, forty-two times removed, and dinner is served.

The meal, I am glad to say, seems to be entirely satisfactory to our guests, and Plato finds special pleasure in the size of our California olives, which, he tells Erasmus, are almost twice as large as they used to be in his own time, "when," as he adds, "the gods provided us with our meals, for whenever one of my students got hungry, he plucked himself a few fruits from the trees underneath which I used to teach, and we were not forced to interrupt our discussions."

I tell him that is hardly the way we do our teaching nowadays. "Why not?" asks Plato, via Erasmus. "Are not your students interested?"

"Yes," I answer, "but in a different way."

"Is there a different way?" Plato continues his inquiry.

But I prefer to change the conversation. It might lead up to rather painful confessions about the attitude our modern students take toward all problems of learning not immediately connected with the practical purpose of making a living. Jo saves the situation. She has improvised some kind of dessert, and that too is received favorably. Fortunately, Frits has had the bright idea of ordering after-dinner tea instead of coffee. Jo serves it in our best old blue Delft cups, and Confucius notices them, examines them carefully, and tells us that they compare very favorably with some cups he used to have when he lived with the Marquis of Ts'i. Then he adds as a sort of afterthought: "That was in the days when I was still full of hope that I might at last find one ruler willing to give me a chance to put my ideas into actual practice, my ideas about government based directly upon the principles of righteousness and virtue. But the invitation never came. Circumstances were too strong for me. I had only one chance. But the prince soon grew tired, and I was obliged to withdraw."

After our meal, as the night was rather cool, we withdrew to the comforts of the open fire. Erasmus sat in his favorite chair, in which some day we feared he would be roasted alive. Next to him sat Confucius, and next to Confucius, Plato. Frits and I had the other two seats. The grandson placed himself discreetly behind his progenitor. He was full of consideration for the old gentleman, and his translating was done so rapidly and so unobtrusively that it was like talking to our beloved Helen Keller. The unknown tongue seemed to flow quietly into its linguistic equivalent. There was a true "meeting of the souls"—for verily those people were tuned in on the same intellectual wave length.

During the next three hours I consumed more tea than I had ever thought any human being could do in so short a time. Jo had put our largest kettle on the fire and kept it boiling, and tea has the same characteristic as the loaves and fishes of the Sermon on the Mount. It can perpetuate itself ad infinitum. All you need is a little hot water.

And now I come to the hardest part of the evening. I mean the hardest part for me, who am obliged to give an account of what we talked about. At first the conversation was kept on a pretty general basis, but soon it took a more definite turn. For there was one subject that seemed to be uppermost in the minds of these two men who, each in his own way, had given the subject of government as much attention as any other human beings who ever lived.

That was the question of how to put government into the hands of those best equipped for this difficult task.

They were, of course, thoroughly familiar with every scheme that had ever been devised to safeguard a nation against tyranny from either above or below. Democracy, totalitarianism, authoritarianism, dictatorship, out-and-out tyranny, and despotism, representative forms of government, experiments with socialism—all these proved to be problems not merely of our own day and age, but as old as the human race itself. Confucius would give us examples that went back more than twenty-five centuries. Plato would answer with some of his own experiences during the fifth century before the beginning of the Christian era. Erasmus would talk of the difficulties his beloved student, the great Emperor Charles, had encountered four hundred years before. Frits and I would modestly bring up some of the perplexing puzzles of our own time. But to tell you the truth, we got nowhere at all. Invariably we returned to the question, "How can we possibly prevent a single man or a minority from forcing its will upon the majority? And how can we be sure that those best fitted to rule will do the actual ruling?"

Finally, toward the end of the evening, we seemed to be reaching a conclusion. Both Confucius and Plato agreed that a reasonable form of government, equally satisfactory to all people, would never be possible until, first of all, the whole of mankind should have been taught to accept a "moral basis" for its behavior, not merely as private citizens but also as members of the community.

And how could this be brought about?

This could only be done by substituting a love for the good of the community at large for the old attitude that man was primarily a predatory animal, forever in search of his own gain and ready to trample down whosoever came in his way while he was in search of food and lodging and a few extra luxuries (as many as possible) for his own family.

There was no disagreement upon this subject. None at all. But the moment we had reached this conclusion, there we were once more face to face with that perplexing question, "Was there such a moral basis, and if there was, how could a sufficient number of people be persuaded to accept it and to fight for its maintenance with their lives?"

Religion? It had been tried and found wanting.

Education? We had educated and educated and educated, and how much good had it done? It had disseminated a lot of heterogeneous and quite useless information, but it had not noticeably added to the wisdom of the populace.

And so we went on until the hour for departure came.

But this time there was no sudden lowering of the lights, no sudden darkness, no sudden disappearance. Confucius seemed to anticipate that soon the moment would come for us to bid each other good-by. Some ten minutes before the clock was to strike the hour of midnight, he got up and through his grandson (who had proved to be a most delightful and charming companion) he assured us that it was many centuries since he had enjoyed so delightful an evening. Plato did likewise, though in less flowery language, and even Erasmus was moved to confess that the evening had been almost as pleasant as a night spent at the home of his beloved Thomas More.

Then there were ceremonial bows between all of us. Then the clock struck. Then the candles went out, and Frits and I were left behind with some more delightful memories.

We finished our final cup of tea and looked at each other. "Well," Frits said, "the problem still seems as far removed from a final and successful solution as ever before. What shall we do?"

"Work," I answered. "Work until we find a way out, for otherwise . . ."

"Yes, otherwise?"

"Otherwise there soon won't be any human race left to worry about."

In the kitchen Jo and Hein had turned on the radio. The news from London was coming in. Under a Berlin date line, the British Broadcasting Company informed us that Adolf Hitler might in the near future become the undisputed leader of the German people.

Both Frits and I shuddered.

"Good God!" he said, tossing his last cigarette into the fire. "What next?"

I had no answer to give. There was no answer. There was only dumb despair.

"This may be the solution," Frits said, to break the terrible silence that had followed the sound of the bells of Big Ben.

"Yes," I answered him. "The solution of chaos and death."

CHAPTER XV

PETER THE GREAT and CHARLES XII OF SWEDEN Are Invited, and VOLTAIRE Comes Anyway, But Is, of Course, a Most Welcome Guest

WOULD WE ever have another evening like the last one? We doubted it. Not that anything very special had been said or that we had solved a single one of the world's great problems. We had come out by the same door as in we went. Yet we had learned one very important lesson. We had been made to realize that as long as there would be men like the two we had met the night before, willing to give the whole of their lives and all of their brilliant minds toward an effort to make this planet fit for human habitation—we need not worry, for then it was merely a question of time and patience for the secret to reveal itself.

It might take a thousand years or ten thousand years, but that was of no concern to nature, with all eternity at its disposal. It was our own incessant quest for the Holy Grail that mattered. The rest was "detail" as the French would have it. We had now come in close personal contact with two of the noblest knights who had led the search for a reasonable solution and we had been deeply impressed. It was not easy to think of other guests who could possibly come up to the standard that had been set on that ever-memorable evening when we played hosts to Plato and Confucius.

Frits confessed himself to be at a complete loss, and I too had no idea where to turn for even the vaguest kind of suggestion.

I had just acquired the famous Blaeu Atlas, printed in Amsterdam during the middle of the seventeenth century and a joy forever to anyone with a love for fine craftsmanship. The volume containing Europe was on my desk, and, opening it at random, I found myself gazing at a page showing the Baltic.

I have always had a great affection for the countries of northern Europe. I love the landscape of my native land, but I find myself much more at home among the people of Scandinavia. And before I die, I hope to spend one more winter in Norway, one more spring in Denmark, one more summer in Stockholm, and one more fall in Lapland, with a side trip to Finland if there still is a Finland after Russia has once more failed to find an outlet in the south and must content itself with one of the ice-free harbors of the north.

Maps are more apt to give me ideas than any other kind of intellectual stimulants—pictures, letters, or contemporary documents.

"Wait a moment, Frits," I said. "I think that I've got something."

"I hope that it's something good."

"I rather think so. Suppose we ask Charles of Sweden and Peter of Russia. There you have a conflict between two entirely different civilizations. And it is beautifully dramatized by these two strong personalities. Last week we dealt with politics in the abstract. Suppose that next week we have a taste of concrete politics. The contrast should be interesting, to say the least. Provided these two hotheads do not decide to fight it out in your dining room. I once tried on a coat that had belonged to Peter the Great. I looked like one of my grandchildren putting on Grandpa's hat. I was lost in it, though I am well over six feet two.

"Charles, on the other hand, was a little fellow. I have seen his buff and yellow uniform in Stockholm. Not much over five feet three, I would say, but he was one of the bravest and most relentless fighters of the whole of the eighteenth century, which rather specialized in that type of fire-eater and swordsman, and

I hate to think of what would happen to your lovely china if the two crazy fellows choose your room for a final battle."

"Anyway, they could not behave as badly as the holy boys from Nicaea, no matter how hard they tried," Frits answered, "so go ahead and ask them."

Charles of Sweden was born in 1682. Peter of Russia was ten years older. They therefore had been contemporaries, and that made it easy for us to feed them. Not that either of them would have cared much what they were given. Peter was born a barbarian and remained so until the end of his days, eating like one of his own peasants, a habit which caused great perplexities to the rulers of the West when they were obliged to entertain this imperial savage during those journeys he undertook to obtain firsthand information about the civilization of Europe. As for Charles, he had been a monomaniac, so completely dominated by his desire to destroy the growing power of Russia that nothing interested him except his army, his soldiers, his navy, everything connected with his eastern campaign and his Swedish empire. As far as we know, no woman ever played any kind of role in his life. He had a large number of almost pathetically loyal followers but not a single friend, for there was not a man whose life he would not gladly sacrifice if by so doing he could score another victory over the hated Muscovite or the equally detested King of Poland. He merely ate to keep alive, without ever noticing what he put into his mouth, for the business of dining was apt to keep him away (for a few moments, at least) from his maps and his plans, and therefore he could not bother about it.

Charles could not even give himself time enough to get well after he had been wounded in battle and as he was always in the midst of the fray, he stopped many a bullet during his nineteen years in the field. That is a long time to spend in the open, sleeping in tents or smoky peasant huts, but that is his record, and a very remarkable one it is, for Hannibal (who is his runner-up) returned home after only fifteen years in Italy, while Napoleon, although he was forever at war with somebody during the twenty-two years of his active career, believed in short campaigns and hastened back to Paris as soon as he had defeated whoever had been on his list.

Our guests therefore would not be very particular about the food we placed before them, but we intended to do as well by them as we could, for both of them were unpredictable characters, accustomed to have everything their own way. That particular evening, of all the evenings of their lives, might prove to be the one they had expected to devote to the pleasures of the table, and heaven help us if then we should have been found wanting! They had been brought up in an atmosphere of "yes men" and they would let us know in unmistakable terms what they thought about our hospitality.

And so here was the menu upon which, by the way, we could spend all the money appropriated for this party, for we would not be under any necessity to buy new records. Neither of our guests, as far as we knew, had ever shown the slightest interest in music. Perhaps they had liked to listen occasionally to a little military music, but military bands, as we know them today, did not come into existence until the Napoleonic wars, and I would not have known where to get records of eighteenth-century bands that would have sounded like the bugle corps which had accompanied the armies of Peter and Charles. Peter, of course, must have been familiar with Russian church music, but he had never shown the slightest interest in that aspect of the services, which was entirely too cultural for his primitive tastes.

I decided not to waste any money on new records, but instead, I ordered something that is both rare and expensive in the Low Countries—a venison steak. We could get one by telegraphing to Amsterdam, and I asked Jo to follow our old recipe for *Rouelles de cerf à la Saint-Hubert,* which has the venison boiled in bouillon and red wine with a liberal admixture of prunes and laurel leaves, giving it a decided taste of *Hasenpfeffer.*

With this I asked our good cook to serve a purée of potatoes

One tower still guarded the entrance to our harbor.

mixed with string beans, and I thought that brown beans with a heavy gravy would turn this into a stout masculine meal. I decided to dispense with the *smörgåsbord* as it is served today, realizing that, although usually associated with the kitchen of Sweden, it is a comparatively recent innovation. Instead of the familiar *smörgåsbord*, we would have a small wooden keg of fresh Dutch herring and several cans of sardines and anchovies to be eaten with that heavy Dutch peasant bread which has changed but little from the days of the seventeenth century— and lots and lots of unsalted butter.

As for soup, well, there we might see what Peter thought of the modern version of borsch. I am not particularly fond of cabbage and beet soup, which I feel should be served with a chaser of bicarbonate of soda. So, using Erasmus' weak stomach as an excuse, I asked Jo to give him and me a plate of simple Dutch vegetable soup, but to make up for this bit of cheating, I told her to serve the men their borsch with slices of Bologna to take the place of croutons. I thought that this Bologna would appeal to our two simple guests, especially if we could get the original Italian variety with a lot of garlic in it.

All that would seem like quite a meal to a modern person, but realizing that we would have to deal with the hearty if un- cultivated appetites of man hunters, I also ordered a course of cold lobster with mayonnaise to be served immediately after the venison. Neither Peter nor Charles would ever have tasted mayonnaise, for it had been invented by the Duc de Richelieu, who flourished long after their time and who had called this famous sauce after the victory the French fleet had won at Port Mahon in Minorca while he happened to be secretary of the navy to King Louis XV.

Then for dessert, *beignets à la mariée*—apple dumplings with a sauce of orange blossoms—which was a highly cherished dish at the court of France during the latter half of the eighteenth century and which recurs repeatedly in Menon's volume on the suppers of the French monarchs, published in the year 1755.

Wine? Oh, any wine would do for these two old campaigners,

as Frits observed, but there should be several bottles of vodka and aquavit, for when Russians and Swedes get together, they can absorb incredible quantities of these deadly distillations without showing the slightest signs of intoxication.

Coffee? Yes! And, of course, a bottle of Liebfraumilch for Erasmus and me. Frits could hold his own with any kind of alcohol and could join the guests when they tackled their native beverages and could probably outdrink them with ease and elegance.

All those details having been settled, I could now give Frits a short statement about these two extraordinary historical figures who had spent all their days continuing a quarrel which had begun almost a thousand years before their own time and which even today has by no means been settled.

To understand what I mean, please take out your atlas and look at the map of northeastern Europe. An immense plain reaches from the Arctic Ocean down to the Black Sea. It is crossed by many rivers which have their origin in the low hills in the center of the plain and which flow either toward the north or toward the south. In the northwest this plain is bordered by the lake and forest region of what is now called Finland, and west of Finland lies the Scandinavian peninsula, which would be as cold and inhospitable as Labrador except for America's greatest gift to Europe—the Gulf Stream. The warm waters of the Gulf Stream keep the harbors of Scandinavia open for the greater part of the year, but the vast eastern plain has no outlets to the sea that are not covered with ice for six months of the year.

All this enormous tract of land had lain covered underneath a heavy blanket of snow and ice during the last of the great glacial periods. Finally the ice had withdrawn toward the North Pole and the land had gradually become fit for human habitation. Germanic tribes had crossed it and recrossed it until finally they had settled down permanently in western Europe and in Scandinavia. The Finns, a Tartar tribe distantly related to the Hungarians, had somehow found their way into what is now Finland, and the Slavs had at last taken possession of that great eastern plain between the Urals and the mountains of central Europe which today is known as Russia. The Slavs therefore were doomed to remain a landlocked people, a nation of "earth animals," as they were so aptly called by one of our contemporary historians. Not that this mattered as long as they were nomads. And even after they had settled down as farmers, they were still so badly organized and so insignificant in numbers and so backward in civilization that they never felt the need of any direct route of communication with the rest of the world.

But in the ninth century the Russians began to suffer from attacks on the part of their western neighbors. Then at last they felt the need of establishing some kind of order out of the chaos which for so many centuries had prevailed within their domains.

They no longer were heathens. Christian missionaries, hailing from Constantinople and following the rivers which crossed their plains, had taught them a few of the rudiments of civilization. Here and there an energetic tribal chief had established himself as a petty prince. All these princes, however, and all these princelets were forever fighting among each other, and the result was disastrous to the peasants who still dwelled in a state of almost prehistoric poverty and misery.

It was then that the Russians sent word to the hardy men of the West who, as vikings, were beginning to overrun the whole of western Europe and told them, "There are millions of us, but we do not know how to govern ourselves. Please come and do the job for us."

The Norsemen did not have to be told twice. Here was an unlimited chance of easy plunder. They hastened eastward and founded a regular Russian state and as the Ruriki—descendants of a mythical Rurik, a Swedish chieftain who was said to have been the first to arrive on the scene—they administered Russia for almost seven hundred years. Then they died out (seven centuries is a long time for any dynasty to survive), and their place was taken by new rulers of undiluted Slavic origin. Perhaps there was a small admixture of Tartar blood in their veins from those days in the thirteenth century when Russia had been overrun and conquered by the little yellow men from the great plains that lay hidden behind the Ural mountains. But they felt themselves to be Russians and only Russians. The land-locked possessions of the grand dukes of Muscovy were no longer sufficient for their far-reaching ambitions. They must have outlets to the sea. In the north there was the eternal ice. In the south there were the Turks. There was only one exit left, by way of the Baltic. And here we connect with Piotr Aleks-yeevich, better known to us as Peter the Great.

As his name indicates, Peter was the son of Czar Alexius Mikhailovich, and therefore a member of the House of Ro-manov, which had got hold of the Muscovite throne in the year 1613. Alexius Mikhailovich had been married twice. Peter was the son of his second wife, Natalia Naryshkina. There was already a boy in the family, Ivan, but he was such a hopeless imbecile (furthermore suffering from an eye disease which had made him half blind) that even in the unsqueamish Russia of those days it was felt that he must never be allowed to exercise any kind of authority.

The elders of the state came together and appointed Peter to take his place. This led to an insurrection on the part of some of the troops who hoped to benefit by having an idiot on the throne. There was a compromise, and Ivan and Peter were rec-ognized together.

As the boys were supposed to be too young to take a direct share in the government, their sister Sophia (in the case of Peter only a half sister) was told to act as regent until her brothers should have reached their majority. This Sophia was a woman of considerable native ability, but she was very, very Russian in spirit, and the Russians of the seventeenth century were still living in a state of medieval ignorance, filth, and bliss. That would not have mattered so much if Moscow had still been a small Slavic nation. But after the fall of Constantinople, whatever was left of the cultural traditions of Byzantium, of the old Eastern Roman Empire, had been transferred to Moscow, and Moscow had thereupon become the center of a civilization that did not have its counterpart in any other part of the world. For it was an Asiatic despotism, very thinly disguised as a Christian state. The rigid etiquette of the old Byzantine emperors had been moved from the imperial palace of Constantinople to the Kremlin, but for the rest, very little had changed. The peasants in the villages continued to cultivate their lands on a co-operative and communistic basis, holding all the fields in common, just as the Puritans did when they first settled along the coast of the western Atlantic.

This fact has usually been overlooked by the people who have written about the Russia of the last twenty-five years. The Bolshevists did not really do anything new. They merely returned to the days before Peter, when the Russians had been allowed to be Russians and had not yet been forced to behave like imitation Frenchmen, Germans, or Englishmen. To the people of the West, they seemed to be making a nose dive into the future, whereas they were really jumping backward to the days of their earliest youth as a nation, and that probably accounts for the success of their experiments. The Bolshevists therefore continued where Peter had left off.

Here is something else we should remember when we contemplate the almost meteoric rise to power of Czar Peter. He did not have to start from scratch. The Muscovite grand duchy he inherited was already a very considerable empire.

In the year 1480 Ivan III had got rid of the last of the Tartar invaders. Two generations later, another Ivan had conquered Kazan and Astrakhan, and soon afterward Russia had begun its conquest of Siberia. This Herculean task had been performed at such a rate of speed that already by the middle of the seventeenth century the coast of the Pacific had been reached and Russia was beginning to look for additional territory in the New World.

Peter therefore, when he reached the throne, was the ruler of a crude and primitive state but one that could be used as the nucleus for a modern nation, as "modernity" was understood in the seventeenth century. For one thing, there were enough subjects to produce the enormous sums of money necessary for the creation of an army and a navy able to compete with the other European powers. And there were enough young serfs (a much nicer word than slaves, but meaning exactly the same thing) to keep both the army and the navy at par. All that was needed was a man of boundless energy and unhampered by any considerations of conscience to do the necessary organizing and to prepare Russia for the role of a dominant factor in European politics.

Let me now try and show you how I see this wild man who caned his own son to death but who lost his life trying to save that of one of his common soldiers. I have followed his career all over Europe and even through part of Russia. That is the only way you ever learn anything about history. Here, for example, is a discovery I give you for what it is worth. In spite of all we have been told to the contrary, Lenin and Stalin and all their disciples and assistants should not really be considered big bad Communists. They were, and are, merely so many Peters the Great dressed up in modern civilian clothes and with cloth caps instead of tricornered hats. They were, and are, left-wing czars, and the people they rule over are not really modern Communists. They are exactly the same sorts of peasants and serfs as those who lived in the seventeenth century when all this began. The only difference is that today they work in factories instead of sweating behind the plow.

Here is young Peter as I see him. Had he lived today, he would have been the joy of our psychologists—an ideal case for the study of every sort of maladjustment. He had been a neglected child and during his early youth had lived in constant fear of his life. The Kremlin in which he was brought up resembled a Turkish seraglio rather than a respectable Christian palace. But from his mother he seems to have inherited a certain tendency toward "modernism." Although this lady had spent all of her married life in the seclusion of a concubineless harem (the old Russians were strictly monogamous as far as their official wives were concerned), she had as a young girl obtained a little firsthand information about the outside world and she must have contaminated her small son with some of her own enthusiasms for the ways of the West. Otherwise it seems incomprehensible that a young Muscovite prince, brought up in a completely Byzantine atmosphere, should ever have become at least a fifty per cent European. For the only other person with whom Peter came in direct daily contact during his life in the Kremlin was his half-sister Sophia, and she was more than willing to remain as Russian as she always had been, not as much by inclination perhaps as by good sound policy, for she was on top and intended to stay there.

Meanwhile, she had no objections if Peter in his spare time amused himself as best he liked, provided he kept away from all councils of state and did not in any way interfere with the way she and her advisers saw fit to rule the land.

To Peter this was a most satisfactory arrangement. Since he had no regular duties at the court, he could spend all his days wherever he felt most at home. That happened to be that part of Moscow reserved for the foreign element which had gradually found its way to the Russian capital. Like all such foreign settlements, whether in Moscow or Madras, it was filled with a weird and unsavory assortment of human beings. Carl Zuckmayer, who gave us *The Captain of Köpenick* and *The Laughing Vineyard,* should write a play about them. Think of all the strange characters he could mix up into such a hilarious comedy about the scoundrels and swindlers of Moscow's Suburb of the Foreigners. Swiss watchmakers (who had absconded with their masters' funds), German apothecaries (who at home had done a little private poisoning), hard-drinking Dutch mechanics (specializing in ships wherever there was any demand for them and otherwise constructing windmills and water mills), French doctors of doubtful scientific antecedents, Hungarian tailors (who

had cut a little too much of a figure in the Budapest under-
world), Parisian coiffeurs who would guarantee their fat Russian customers (one was not much of a lady, in that happy land,
under two hundred pounds) the exact "arrangement of the
hair" as it was worn by the beautiful Marquise de La Pompe à
l'Eau the last time she had attended the opera in Versailles.

In addition, dour representatives of those English trading
companies which for a great many years had been established at
Archangel on the White Sea, pastry cooks from Brussels, Danish fencing teachers, Amsterdam tobacco dealers (for although
the Russian Church had condemned smoking as one of the
cardinal sins, the habit was taking hold), Turks with no visible
means of support but who knew, in case a young man was interested, where to find him exactly the type of girl for whom he
happened to be looking, French ladies' maids with highfalutin'
names (which they had adopted from their former mistresses)
who were engaged in the same kind of business as the Turks,
Prussian drillmasters who taught gymnastics, cashiered Austrian
officers undertaking to teach the finer points of horsemanship
to anyone with a horse and a solvent father, and Ethiopian
princes selling the elixir of life according to the recipe which
King Solomon had presented to the Queen of Sheba.

In addition (as the society columns have it), the inevitable
French dressmakers (of both genders) and maybe a couple of
very discreet members of the Society of Jesus, nosing around in
their own unobtrusive way to discover whether here and there
—perhaps—they could not catch one of those heathen souls and
save it for their own faith. And furthermore, a number of
Levantines who managed to exist the way only Levantines know
how to exist, and citizens from faraway Cathay, whose tea cara-
vans used to cross the deserts of Asia and who were now trying
very hard to make the Muscovites tea conscious, a task in which
they succeeded beyond all expectations.

Also blackamoors from distant Africa who catered to certain
not so nice interests among the older gentlemen of the local
aristocracy. I even once read of an American Indian who had

found his way to the Suburb of the Foreigners, but what he did there or why he had left his own happy hunting grounds I never was able to find out. John Paul Jones was to be the first bona fide representative of the New World the Russians were to see, but he did not come until much later. And the adventures which befell our great admiral show the sort of life these expatriated citizens lived, once they had ventured forth into the land of the Slavs. If (as we know from Jones' letters) existence was pretty bad and messy in the St. Petersburg of the eighteenth century, what must it have been in the Moscow of the seventeenth?

Yet that was the school which Piotr Aleksyeevich attended and where he got both his A.B. and his Ph.D., and that is where he learned to drink his gin and smoke his pipe. The first was no great sin in the eyes of the good Russians. According to legend, they had only decided in favor of Christianity over the much more practical Mohammedanism because the Prophet had been such a very strict advocate of teetotalism. But tobacco was anathema in the eyes of the Muscovite clerics. A pipe in a man's mouth filled their souls with almost as much horror as the sight of a beardless male face, for the Devil was clean-shaven whereas honest Christians wore beards that reached down to their knees. If this young prince was going to show himself in public "sucking tobacco," as smoking was then called, he might, should he ever come into full control of the government, go as far as to advocate a beardless Russia.

Little did they know what awaited them! The pipe-smoking prince did come to the throne, and immediately afterward his soldiers went through the streets of the capital and stopped every bearded boyar who came along. A quick twist of their sharp scissors—and the whiskers were gone. No use complaining, for if you were a little too loud in your protestations, it might be your head that went next.

Peter's accession to the throne, as I told you a moment ago, had been accompanied by a mutiny of the lifeguards, and this

mutiny had been suppressed in the approved Russian fashion—
the rebellious soldiers had been slaughtered like cattle. Then
there had been seven years during which Sophia had been the
head of the state and during which Piotr of the Russian Kremlin was changed into Peter of the European Suburb. But these
seven years had been no waste of time. On his country estate
(Sophia liked it just as well if her brother kept out of her sight)
Peter was busy drilling the sons of his serfs and on a small lake
he was "playing navy" with a couple of rowboats transformed
into miniature warships.

Came the day—the inevitable day—when the fanatic believers
in the old Russia decided to rid themselves of that walking
menace which was forever talking about a "new" Russia. They
engaged in another conspiracy, but as usual they bungled the
plot, and Peter had his opportunity. He was now seventeen
years old and quite able to take care of himself. He ousted the
regency. Half-sister Sophia was locked up in a nunnery and was
never again seen in the Kremlin. Half-witted half-brother Ivan
was not murdered but allowed to live on in semi-imbecility and
complete retirement. And aided and abetted by a professional
soldier from Switzerland, a clever adventurer by the name of
François Lefort, Peter was off on his self-appointed task of
changing barbaric Russia into a supposedly civilized Western
nation.

The young Czar started upon his new career by turning his
reorganized army against the Turks in the south. He was soon
forced to the conclusion that he was still too weak to handle the
infidel alone and that he would need allies in his crusade against
the unbelievers. Why not try and persuade the rest of Europe
to make common cause with their Russian brethren and start
on a new crusade?

Unfortunately, Europe at that moment was much more worried about the ambitions of King Louis XIV of France than
about those of the great sultan in nebulous and faraway Istan-
bul. All the same, Peter felt that he ought to make the attempt, and so for the first time in history the capitals of western

Europe had a chance to gape at a large number of actual Russians—real Russian nobles with diamonds in their ears and lice in their hair—sweating away underneath their uncomfortable burdens of mink and ermine and making the people of the West wonder what kind of country this might be which was inhabited by such hopeless savages.

But they often failed to notice a gentleman in a simple captain's uniform who cut hardly any figure at all among the other members of the mission in their rich furs and with diamonds in their ears. Had they been sufficiently observant, they might have noticed that it was he who poked his nose into every factory and into every shipyard and print shop and who on the quiet offered nice fat contracts to engineers and architects and munitions makers and shipwrights and surveyors and physicians and apothecaries and carpenters, promising them all excellent wages if for a number of years they were willing to leave their native land and move to distant Moscow and help him reorganize and modernize his country. For this simple captain was no one less than the great Czar himself, and what he had seen during his journey across Europe had made him more determined than ever to start upon the job of rejuvenating Russia—and to start doing it right away.

Yes, he also talked a good deal about a crusade against the Turks, but no Europeans were interested in something so far removed from their own interests. And so, from a political angle, the trip to western Europe was a sad failure. But when Peter returned to Russia he brought not less than five hundred Western experts with him, and while their number was ridiculously small in view of the task that awaited them, it was at least a beginning.

By the way, Peter returned much sooner than he had expected. He had to. The conservatives at home had seen the way the wind was blowing. Soon, they feared, the storm would become a regular hurricane, and once more there had been a mutiny on the part of the old palace guards. Peter, being informed of this new outbreak of rebellion, rode back to Moscow at breakneck speed, and the moment he had arrived in his capital, there was another purge.

This time Peter did his job thoroughly. He himself assisted with the executions of his former soldiers. Only a few of the *streltsy* were left. And after their bodies had been thrown into the river, the work of reform began in all seriousness.

With his own hands Peter clipped the beards of his courtiers. Those who lamented too loudly were given an opportunity to retain their whiskers by paying a heavy ransom—so many thousands of rubles for every inch of hair. Then off with their long Oriental robes, while Hungarian tailors were busy making them their first suits of European clothes, consisting of practical short coats and pantaloons after the best Viennese patterns. And—a terrible shock to all believing Christians—from that time on, the year was supposed to begin on January first, as it did in the rest of the world, and not on September first, when, according to Russian chronology, God had created our planet.

All this sounds rather silly to us, but let us remember that, only a short time before, these same benighted Russians had destroyed a clock which had been erected in the Kremlin because the bell which struck the hours made them think of the voice of the Devil. Also, they had burned down the first print shop in Moscow because books were suspected of being the cause of the spread of dangerous thoughts.

After these preliminary arrangements came the great struggle for a foothold in the north. Without the assistance of Europe, Russia was too weak to tackle the Turks, who held all the southern part of the great European plain. There was only one other way of escape, by means of the Baltic. That was the beginning of the twenty-year struggle with Sweden, the country which then, as now, held the key to the Baltic.

The first battle, that of Narva, ended in an ignominious defeat for the Russians, but Peter, who was just as obstinate as Charles, held on. He quickly reorganized his troops, ruined himself buying the latest cannon that were to be found on the European market, and in the battle of Poltava he annihilated the Swedes.

It was during the next twenty years, when at any moment the Russians might lose all they had thus far gained, that the new Russia came into existence. For now Peter realized that there was no other choice but to go ahead. He must either succeed or perish, and so, as a starter, the grand duchy of Moscow became the Russian Empire.

Once more the title of czar was made to mean what it had meant in the days of the original czars, or Caesars. The cumbersome and antiquated system of government of the old Moscow was abolished, and the road to advancement was placed wide open to talent plus loyalty. The names of the old noble families gradually disappeared from the lists of government functionaries, and the names of new and totally unknown youngsters took their places. It no longer mattered who or what one's father had been. The sons of the commoners and even of liberated serfs could easily mount to the top of the official ladder and sometimes could even stay there, provided they were people of uncommon ability. Corporals were promoted to be colonels. Able-bodied seamen died as admirals. Obscure inkslingers in remote government offices could look forward to ending their careers as members of the senate, now the highest government body in the state, for the only things the Czar demanded were a fair amount of honesty (one could not expect perfection at a moment's notice!) and a knowledge of how to keep books or draw up codes of law or discover a new method by which a few more kopecks could be squeezed out of his subjects.

The patriarch of Moscow, a heavily garbed and golden-crowned dignitary who was very proud of the fact that he administered the Church in exactly the same style as that of six hundred years before, found himself deprived of his office. A Holy Synod, the members of which were appointed directly by the Czar himself, turned the Church into merely another governmental department, like that of the army, navy, justice, the treasury, or the street-cleaning office.

These new men worked like beavers. They were like Lenin's assistants during the first ten years of the great Bolshevik experiment. Many of them died at their desks from sheer exhaustion. Only the Czar himself never showed signs of growing tired. He worked and drank and made life miserable for the women at his court, but mostly he worked, and if he was hard on his subordinates, he was infinitely harder on himself. For now his hands had at last found a new job worthy of his Gargantuan energies and ambitions.

In the year 1702 Peter reconquered the southern shores of what is now called the Gulf of Finland, a deserted piece of territory the Swedes had occupied in the year 1617. There, on the twenty-ninth of June of the year 1703, Peter laid the first stone of the fortress of Peter and Paul, which was to be the citadel and nucleus of his new capital. Less than a year later, there were enough houses ready to move a few families into the city of Peter, which Lenin, who realized Peter's greatness and his essentially Russian character, never wanted to be called after himself, though today it is called Leningrad instead of St. Petersburg.

Then the Czar went after his building program in a great big way. Forty thousand serfs from all over Russia were driven into this marshy region along the shores of the Neva to work on his far-flung projects. These poor creatures died like flies. Malaria, cholera, typhus—all of them were present. Often only half of the poor slaves were well enough to do anything at all. But the job had to be done. In the year 1712 the Czar could move into his first residence, the so-called Summer Palace. A few years later he also had his Winter Palace on the spot where the famous picture gallery of the Hermitage stands today. In 1724 the remains of Saint Alexander Nevsky, the great Russian hero of the wars against the Tartars, were reverently removed from Moscow to the new capital, and in the year in which Peter died, 1725, his city already counted more than seventy-five thousand inhabitants.

The Czar's immediate successors did their best to turn the tide and tried very hard to re-establish Moscow as the national capital. But it could not be done. The tide insisted on running in the opposite direction. St. Petersburg continued to grow and increase just as long as Russia was trying to be a European power. It took the Bolsheviks, with their profound understanding of the true Russian character, to undo what the Romanovs had done and to go back to Moscow. Since then, Peter's "window on the west" has lost all of its imperial glamour. It has, in spite of its vast number of inhabitants, become a provincial town where the grass grows in the streets and where the empty windows of deserted palaces look down in deep despair upon the deserted avenues of what had been the dream of empire-minded Peter.

Peter died on February 7 (January 28 of our calendar) of the year 1725. As happened almost every year, the Neva had passed beyond its banks and had flooded the city. The Czar was in a boat, doing his best to save people who had fled to the roofs of their houses. One of his sailors fell overboard. The Czar jumped after him. He saved the man but caught a cold. The cold developed into pneumonia, and the alcohol-soaked body of the Emperor could offer but little resistance. He died ten days later, amidst the grateful prayers of his subjects.

From a backward, medieval country, Peter had turned Russia into a powerful modern nation. One often hears this question asked: would it not have been better if he had left well enough alone and had not wasted his energies upon so hopeless a task? But when he died, the deed had been done, and it had been the work of one single man. Wherefore I think that I should now put him under my historical microscope, which is a curious instrument that works by the reflected light of several intervening centuries, and study him a little more carefully to find out what kind of creature he really had been.

The first thing I then notice is his absolute—his hundred per cent—Russianism. He might pretend that he loved the civilization of the West, but he cared for it only in so far as it could be of any benefit to his own people. Hence his insistence upon letting the work be done just as much as possible by people of Slavic blood. In the beginning he was of course obliged to hire a great many foreigners. But he did so reluctantly and only on condition that they allow themselves to be Russianized as fast as possible.

Another characteristic that strikes me when I have him a little better focused is his knowledge and understanding of the real Russian soul, to use that rather hackneyed expression once more for lack of a better one. This was and is a very curious development. The man who did more to upset that Russian soul than any other ruler who ever occupied the Muscovite throne understood his subjects much better than any of the so-called typically Russian czars who either preceded or succeeded him.

Peter was, furthermore, completely Slavic in the mystic qualities of his religious conceptions. These did not prevent him from being on several occasions one of the most cruel despots of the last five hundred years. Whenever he met with the slightest opposition to his plans, he knew no mercy, and even his own son—his only son, at that—fell a victim of his father's determination to accomplish his plans regardless of every other consideration.

This boy, Alexius by name, was a pathetic case. While still very young, he had been taken away from his mother. Peter had grown tired of her and had packed her off to a cloister, after first forcing her to become a nun. Left to his own devices, Alexius had made common cause with his father's enemies—the men of the old regime. When the Czar heard of this, he condemned the boy to death. To this day we do not know for sure whether the sentence was actually carried out or in what manner the heir to the throne came to his end. But the best guess, based upon the most reliable evidence, has Alexius dying as the result of a blow from his father's cane. Peter never showed any signs of repentance. He probably felt that a son of his had no right to have such a thin skull.

So much for his truly Slavic characteristics. Un-Russian, on the other hand, were his terrific scientific curiosity and his capacity for steady hard work. But he was entirely Slavic again in his conception of his duties and rights as a divinely anointed autocrat. He was convinced that it was the Almighty Himself who had bestowed his high office upon him, not to use it for his own benefit but that he might the better be able in this way to serve his subjects. Hence his detestation of any kind of abuse of power on the part of his subordinates. If one of his subjects considered himself unfairly treated by an imperial official (be he corporal or minister of state) he could always place his evidence before the Emperor, whose door was wide open, both day and night, to those who wished to approach him on such serious matters. If the petitioner was found to be right, the offending official would be hanged. Did the petitioner fail to prove his point, he himself would suffer a similar fate, for it was up to God's anointed to see that justice be done.

At the same time, this inspired mystic could be guilty of crimes against human decency which make us see him in the light of another Genghis Khan. Like so many Russians (even in our own days), he seems to have been born without nerves. The aspect of human misery never disturbed him in his slumbers, and whether a hundred or a hundred thousand people died building his capital was a matter of no consequence to the man who had drawn up the blueprints.

That lack of any kind of moral equilibrium becomes very evident in the way he treated his peasants. As I just said, he would come down with the full force of his heavy boots upon any landowner who had been unduly cruel to one of his serfs. But that his exaggerated demands for revenue were causing these landowners to work their peasants like dray horses and to keep them going day and night by means of the knout—well, that was something else again and something which never seems to have struck him as somewhat irrational.

It will always be very difficult for a Dutchman or an American to understand a Russian or to be entirely fair to him. There are too many absolutely contradictory elements in the Slavic make-up to give us western Europeans something definite of which we can catch hold. In Peter's case, however, there was one outstanding characteristic we are able to follow throughout his whole career. He worked in superlatives. He did not believe in compromises. There must be no pulling of punches. When Peter cheated, he cheated with all his heart and soul. When he lied, ditto. When he decided to tell the truth, as he did upon a few occasions, one could take him at his word. When he prayed, he meant every word he said, but this would not prevent him, the next moment, from having an entire regiment of rebellious soldiers knouted to death. And when he went empire-building or city-building or palace-building, his empire or his city or his palace must be constructed on a planetary scale—streets three hundred feet wide, market places ten times as large as the Roman Forum, jails for a thousand tenants at a time.

And when, after a short debauch in holiness, Peter decided to go in for the other extreme and wallow for a while in filth and dirt and muck, he then dived right in and with such abandon that he made old Henry VIII look like a Methodist deacon. In short, he was entirely human, only a great deal more so than most people.

A far different person was his lifelong opponent, the austere and ascetic Charles of Sweden. No tender or untender female lips ever touched his, after he had been presented with his first razor. The same held good for alcoholic drinks at a time when Sweden was still proud to be counted among the hardest-drinking countries of the north—Finland included. He evinced some semblance of natural affection for his sister, but outside of this young princess, the human race, as far as he was concerned, did not exist.

That, however, does not mean that we need feel sorry for Charles. For if it be true (I have undoubtedly said this before) that only those people are happy who can play that role which satisfies them most in their own eyes, then Charles was indeed one of the most fortunate of men. Above all other things, this strange despot was an actor, an observation for which, had I made it in his presence, he would have had me shot.

One prima donna in a family (whether it be of royal or common origin) is usually enough to spoil the taste for any more for quite a long time among those who have had to put up with it. The Vasa family had produced that kind of performer when the wife of the great Gustavus Adolphus gave birth to a girl who ought to have been a boy and who arrived in this world so densely covered with hair that, according to the first reports, she was said to be of the male gender. When Charles was born in the year 1682, Cousin Christina was still very much alive, but she had fortunately left her native land a great many years before, after having done about as much harm as any woman has ever done to the state entrusted to her care. She was to return twice, the last time fifteen years before Charles was born. During her final effort in 1667 to regain the throne which she had given up in disgust, she had not even been allowed to get as far as Stockholm. The official excuse for this refusal to let her visit her former home was the fact that she had abjured her Protestant faith and had become a Catholic. The real reason was quite different. The Swedes had grown thoroughly disgusted with the unpleasant publicity which their country had gained in consequence of Her Majesty's desire to keep herself firmly in the limelight.

I have discussed this problem with several learned Swedish historians, who invariably told me that I was wrong and that it was some other queer kink in her character which had made her play the far from edifying role for which she is chiefly remembered. They may be right, but then again we in the New World know a little more about the strange things a bad case of "publicity itch" will do to those afflicted with that unfortunate malady.

Cousin Christina, who had left everything in a hopeless state of confusion (among other little details, she had given away half of the crown domains to her personal friends), had been succeeded by Charles XI. He was only four years old and had therefore been placed under the regency of a council composed of those great nobles who, having helped Gustavus Adolphus make Sweden great, now felt that they were entitled to do a bit of plundering of their own. They were highly successful but not for very long, for when the young King reached the age of twenty he got rid of the whole pack of them and did the only practical thing that could be done if the nation was to be saved from complete ruin—he made himself dictator. Therefore, when Charles XII was born, on June 17, 1682, Sweden was once more on the road to solvency, once more had an efficient army, and was again regarded by the rest of the world as the dominant factor in northern European politics. But of democracy in our sense of the word there was not a vestige, and nobody cared.

The mother of little Charles, Ulrica Leonora, was a princess of Denmark. She therefore came from the country with which the Swedes had fought the bitterest of their wars during the last four hundred years. But the royal union had made Denmark an ally and, as a result, the whole of the Baltic was now in Swedish hands. Russia, of course, always lay in the distance, but it was not considered a serious menace. It was too poor and too badly organized to be of any particular consequence.

As for the young Crown Prince, he was everything a country could have found in its ruler during a crisis. From his father he had inherited a strong love for horses and fast riding, a sport which stood him in good stead later in life when he rode from the Black Sea to the Baltic, straight across Europe, before anyone had even heard of his escape. As soon as he had been able to hold himself in the saddle (he acquired this difficult balancing feat at the age of four), he had accompanied his father the King on all his tours of inspection. He therefore had a firsthand knowledge of all the details of government, such as army posts, dockyards, harbors, stud farms, factories, and storehouses for grain and gunpowder, and he knew about all these things at an age when most children still identify foreign countries with the pictures on their postage stamps.

But Papa, who was a man of strong prejudices and tastes and as conscientious in his duties as any Prussian king of the seventeenth century, had also given his offspring three other avocations. Those were a love for bear hunting, a thorough dislike of everything French, and a profound distrust of anything connected with the art of diplomacy.

Therefore, when Charles XI died (only forty-two years old), it seemed quite natural that this boy of fifteen should succeed him right away, and Charles was promptly elevated to the throne. Already at his coronat on he showed that he intended to be quite as much of an autocrat as his father had been. He did not bother to take the oath connected with the coronation services by which he should have acknowledged himself to be the first servant of the state. Without further ado he put the royal crown upon his own head. His ministers and advisers did not approve of this, but they carefully refrained from asking embarrassing questions. It already had become common knowledge in Stockholm that this young man was exceedingly taciturn by nature and never more reluctant to reveal his opinions than when urged to do so.

Outside of His Majesty's country, these characteristics were less clearly understood. They were mistaken for shyness and weakness of character, and promptly there was a coalition among the loving neighbors of Sweden, each one of whom hoped to regain part of the territories he had lost during the previous fifty years when his armies had been no match for the magnificently drilled troops of great Gustavus Adolphus and his successors. Denmark, Poland (now ruled over by a Saxon), and Russia made common cause and got ready to settle their old scores.

In the year 1700 Frederick Augustus of Saxony began the war by marching against the city of Riga. Charles was then eighteen years old and was supposed to be finishing his education. Instead of which, he forced his unwilling admirals to navigate a certain channel that had never been tried before, landed in Denmark before anyone knew he was on his way, and forced the Danes to sue for peace just before he was ready to storm the walls of Copenhagen.

From Denmark the unexpected conqueror turned eastward

to relieve Riga, but when he heard that Narva was about to fall to the Russians, he gave orders to proceed to that city. Every one of his generals advised against such a move. They told their King that it was a most foolhardy adventure and could lead only to disaster. It was the middle of November, the roads were impassable, and the Russians so greatly outnumbered the Swedes that there was no possible chance of defeating them. On November 19, Charles' army was nine miles away from Narva, and the King ordered fires to be lighted to inform the garrison that help was near. The next morning it snowed. Shortly after the hour of noon the snowstorm changed into a blizzard. At two o'clock, when the visibility was nil, Charles attacked Peter and so completely destroyed his army that, had he cared to do so, he would have been able to take Moscow.

It was a fact well known to the Swedes that Peter was at the height of his unpopularity, that the country was rife with rebellion, and that all the more conservative elements in Russia were eagerly praying for some foreign savior to set them free from their Antichrist. Unfortunately for the Swedes, Charles by now had got it into his obstinate head that he must first of all punish Augustus of Saxony for his treason of the year before. His political advisers and all of his generals begged him to follow up his first success with an immediate attack upon the remnants of Peter's forces. The self-willed young man turned his back upon his ministers and his staff and started on a wild-goose chase after Augustus. Peter, so he said, could wait, for by now the young King was suffering from a victory complex—that unfortunate Narva complex which still affects so many of his modern fellow countrymen. He felt convinced that he could always and under all circumstances beat the Russians, no matter how great the odds, and that is where he was mistaken. For though the Muscovites were still barbarians and individually could not at all compare with the excellently disciplined Swedish privates, commanded by highly trained officers, Charles did not in the least understand the character of his Slavic opponents and he had sadly underrated their power of recuperation.

In consequence whereof, Charles wasted precious years marching up and down the dreary wastes of Poland, and when at last he turned once more against the Russians, it was too late. Peter had used this interval of seven years to reorganize his army and waited for Charles near Poltava. A few days before the battle took place, Charles had been wounded during a reconnaissance. Instead of taking to his bed, as his surgeons had told him, he had a chair rigged up between two horses so that he could take part in the fighting. He seems to have forgotten that a disabled commander with an exhausted and hungry army is not in an ideal position to gain any kind of victory, especially when his opponent has destroyed everything within his path so that there is nothing for either his men or his horses to eat.

At Poltava, Charles tried to repeat the method that had been so successful at Narva, but this time luck was against him. The Cossack reinforcements upon whom he had set such great hopes failed to materialize. Instead of bringing him a hundred thousand cavalrymen as Mazeppa, the Cossack chieftain from southern Russia, had promised, he brought only one thousand, and the reinforcements that had been expected from Sweden had been annihilated by a fourfold force of Russian troops.

Then General Winter appeared upon the scene. The winter of 1708–9 was the worst northern Europe had ever known. Birds, so the old chroniclers relate, were killed by the frost while flying through the air. It was impossible to light fires, for the wood would not ignite in the open. Even the wine froze in its flasks. But Charles, although his army had suffered terrific losses, doggedly stuck to his original plan of a direct attack. The memory of Narva dominated his mind, and as soon as summer had come and the roads were passable again, he hastened to repeat his former success.

Seated in his chair, Charles gave the order of attack. During the first two hours it looked as if the Swedes, by sheer superiority of their fighting spirit, would once again be able to roll up the armies of the Czar. Then fatigue and exhaustion began to tell. Next there was a surprise—a very painful one.

Whereas Charles had wasted his money on his costly and futile campaign against Augustus of Saxony, Peter had spent his subjects' taxes upon the latest and most modern guns that were then being manufactured in Germany and France. His cannon fired four times as fast as those of the Swedes, and soon most of Charles' army was gone. The rest, hopelessly outnumbered, were forced to surrender. Charles was left with less than fifteen hundred horsemen and with those he now took refuge on Turkish territory. There he remained for five full years and during those five years he overcame his former distaste for diplomacy. From his tent in the steppes he kept the whole of Europe agitated about his fate. He also made repeated attempts to persuade the Turkish government in Constantinople to declare war against Russia. Invariably he discovered that the Russians, being much richer than he, had offered the grand vizier a great deal more money to do the exact opposite. In the end, even the Turks grew tired of this absurd comedy. They stormed Charles' camp at Bender and made him a prisoner.

Charles took his new misfortune with his usual superior indifference. He remained where he was for another fifteen months and kept up his diplomatic intrigues as if he were still a free man. He also hoped against hope that fresh troops would reach him from Sweden, in which case he would at last be able to settle his score both with Poland and Russia.

When he realized that the game was up—definitely up—the King mounted his horse and, accompanied by a single aide, rode straightway from Demotika (where he was being held by the Turks) to Stralsund on the Baltic, where he was once more on Swedish territory. (He started on September 20 and arrived on November 11.)

Europe, which had come to regard Charles as something out of a storybook and which held him—the defeated monarch—in such awe that he had by now become the real hero of all his disastrous campaigns, held its breath while Stralsund was slowly being destroyed by the enemy's gunfire. What would come next? In Sweden, the people had long since begun to murmur that by now enough had been done for their country's glory and that the moment had come to talk of peace. An honorable peace was still among the political possibilities, but Charles, with the bit between his teeth, could not be stopped. When Stralsund fell, he crossed the Baltic and, after an absence of fourteen years, he once more set foot on his native soil. Carefully hiding himself in Stockholm, where he remained only a few days, he now carried the war into Norway, which, being then under Danish domination, gave him an opportunity to attack Denmark.

Sweden, exhausted as few countries have ever been, its man power gone, its money spent, its trade ruined, its credit destroyed, had somehow remained loyal. In December of the year 1718 Charles laid siege to the strong Norwegian fortress of Fredriksten. His foremost trench was only eight hundred feet from the walls of the citadel, and Charles (need I tell?) was in the foremost part of this trench. He arose from behind the earthen wall to get a better view of the situation. The next moment he lay dead with a bullet through his brain.

I doubt very much whether we shall ever find out who fired that fatal shot. Almost at once there were ugly rumors that one of his own soldiers had killed the King, so that peace might return to poor, lacerated Sweden. But others who had been on the spot and who had examined His Majesty's body after it had been carried to his tent swore that the bullet had entered the skull from the front and therefore must have been fired by an enemy. Today, of course, the incident has value only as an antiquarian puzzle. The important fact was this—Charles no longer lived, and the Swedes were given a short breathing spell. God knows, they needed it. Within less than twenty years this young man had been able to undo a century of laborious efforts on the part of his ancestors. The dream of empire had been gambled away, and Sweden had been reduced to the rank of a third-rate power, while Russia arose as the dominant factor in northern Europe.

So much for the concrete results of Charles' endless errors.

Yet I can well understand the honor and esteem and affection in which this dashing knight is still held by most Swedes. They lead rather dull and unexciting lives, and Charles adds an element of glamour to their otherwise drab existence, a bit of color which they seem to need almost as much as an occasional glimpse of the warm sun of Italy. Charles, as they will confess, was perhaps a good deal of a fool, but what a magnificent and glorious fool he had been! As a leader of men he was unsurpassed in the loyalty he evoked in those who followed him. Men would stand guard over his tent until they were frozen and they would die without a murmur, as long as they knew that their King was safe. Parents whose sons had disappeared in some Siberian prison camp blessed his name. There were bitter complaints about the sad state of the nation—the general poverty, the loss of territory—but for all these the King's advisers were held to blame while his own memory remained unsullied.

For Charles had been possessed of one quality which the world has always held in such high esteem that it is willing to forgive all sorts of deficiencies and shortcomings on the part of its heroes, provided this one trait of character is present.

Charles was the incarnation of the old ideal of chivalry. For that reason, men will remember him and will revere his memory long after their lesser heroes have become a handful of dust and a date in a schoolbook which little boys must learn by heart if they hope to get an A on their report cards.

Our Russo-Swedish Saturday, too, is one which Frits and I shall always remember. We knew beforehand that we would have two very individualistic gentlemen on our hands (to express it mildly), but we had hardly anticipated to what extremes their individualism would lead them.

It was only six o'clock, but I had called for Frits at the Middelburg station and had not bothered to go home. We never dressed (not quite knowing how those we had invited would be situated in the matter of clothes), and so we always wore dark suits, but nothing very formal. We still had an hour before us

and were talking of this and that and of nothing much in particular. We even wondered whether it would be quite polite
if we had a glass of sherry before our guests arrived, but we
said, "Yes, why not?" And so Frits shouted (electric bells were,
of course, out of the question in Veere), "Oh, Jo-o-o! Bring us
two glasses of sherry, will you-u-u!"

And then a soft voice added, "Make it three, for it is a cold
day, and I could stand a bit of warming cheer."

Without our noticing it, Erasmus had joined us. We were
accustomed to his mysterious comings and goings, but as a rule
he had been so punctual in not arriving too long before any
of our other guests that we were somewhat surprised. He may
have noticed this, for he offered what amounted to an explanation. "It is getting a bit cold these afternoons in that pleasant
room you have given me, and I did not want to have the fire
started, as I was coming over so soon anyway."

Poor Erasmus! He never could get really warm. He had suffered so much from cold when he was young that he had never
caught up, like other people who, having been starved during
the first half of their lives, will go on eating like famished wolves
until the end of their days, not because they need all that extra
fuel but out of sheer force of habit.

I had told Lucie how even in July and with a bit of a fire
going Erasmus would sit in his chair and shiver. "Let me knit
him a sweater," Lucie had suggested immediately. "A nice
heavy fisherman's sweater like the one I made for Hein last
year."

We all had applauded that generous suggestion, but then
Lucie had certain misgivings. "How am I to know his size?"
she asked. "And what does he wear underneath that robe or
cassock, or whatever it is called? As a child, when I saw a picture
of the Pope, I always wanted to know what he wore underneath his long white garments—long trousers or short trousers
or just a pair of running trunks or nothing at all? I suppose
those were not nice thoughts for a little girl whose father was a
general in our respectable Dutch army, but I remember that I

always was curious and I once even asked our dominie, but he was very much shocked and he answered me that he did not know and did not want to know. It was bad enough for someone who was supposed to be a Christian to wear a golden crown and silken garments without going any further. I told him I knew all about the golden crown and the silken garments on the outside, and they were undoubtedly very wicked, but how about the Pope's trousers? I must have been four or five at the most when I started on this line of investigation, but it caused quite a scandal, the general's daughter asking the minister about the Pope's pants. And even today I don't know, though I have spent a lot of time in Rome, for those things are hard to find out, and how am I going to decide the size of a sweater for Erasmus?"

Frits told her he would fix it, and the next time we called on the old gentleman I got very much interested in the Greek manuscript he was examining and meanwhile Frits slipped behind his chair and, using his handkerchief as a tape measure, got the approximate proportions according to which Lucie would have to do her knitting. She was now busy with her wool —a brilliant red wool—a mixture between vermilion and carmine—especially ordered from Paris.

"That will make him feel like a cardinal," Lucie explained, "and of course the color does not matter, for no one will ever see him wear it."

She still needed several weeks to finish her sweater, and that fitted in beautifully with our plans, for then Sint Nikolaas would come around, and we had some very special plans for that day. It would be very difficult to find a suitable present for our learned old friend. A sweater would be just the thing.

But to return to a moment ago—there we were, the three of us, with Erasmus in his beloved chair by the corner of the fire, exchanging pleasant remarks with Jo, who had come to understand his old-fashioned Dutch quite well and could now give as good as she got, for the Dutch are no prudes, and they would have made marvelous officials at the court of Queen Bess.

Then Jo said she must go to her own home and start the vegetables.

"I have to apologize for something I have done," Erasmus began. Frits said that there was nothing in this world which he could think of Erasmus doing for which he would ever have to apologize, "at least to us," he added as an afterthought, "but then, we are no theologians."

"Heaven forbid!" and Erasmus, as was his habit, lifted up both hands. "I am now free from that particular worry, but if you don't mind, I have asked a friend of mine for this evening."

"Wonderful!" said Frits. "Who is it?"

"Well, perhaps I had better not tell you and let him explain himself when he arrives."

"Jo-o-o!" Frits shouted, "make sure there is enough for one extra person and set a plate for him, will you-u-u!"

From the kitchen came the expected *"Ja-a-a!"* and then a very old voice, a bit shaky but still assertive, was heard to remark, *"Ça veut dire 'oui' en hollandais, n'est-ce pas?* In German too, I think, and it was the only word the great Frederick wanted to hear in the mouth of everybody else, but which he himself could not pronounce."

There was no possibility of mistaking the man who had spoken to us. I remembered the definition our witty Lucie had once given of him—"a brain on sticks." The mighty brain was there—a dome as high as that of St. Peter's—and the sticks were there too, for one could no longer call them legs. Like the rest of the body, they seemed to have reached a point where they had ceased to exist for themselves and had but one single purpose left—they must support the brain which was really all that mattered.

But what struck us most was the smile. The mouth was toothless. The ageless face, however, was lit up by a smile that seemed to be made up of pity and understanding. After a lifetime of bitter struggle, of ceaseless warfare upon all that was stupid and cowardly and cruel and lacking in reason and at an age when most people are ready to spend their few remaining years cultivating their little gardens, old Voltaire had once more descended into the arena to espouse the cause of religious liberty. And the last fifteen years of his life (for when he died he was as old as Methuselah!) had been one of the most glorious episodes in man's eternal fight upon the powers of darkness. It was the experiences of those last years which must have given him that insight into the mysterious ways in which the misguided human soul will sometimes work, its misdeeds to perform, and which alone could have been responsible for that wise and understanding smile which seemed to illuminate the whole of our room.

Voltaire bowed to Erasmus and beckoned him not to arise. "I know you, sir," he said, "I know you well. Your *Praise of Folly* has often helped me through difficult hours when nothing else would divert my mind from some fresh disappointment, and although people seem to have been under the impression that I took everything lightly, I assure you that I did not. Only I thought it usually wiser not to show what I felt. I loved that passage in which Folly talks to the King. I have seen her do it in my own day and with the same disastrous results."

"Please have a chair, sir," Frits said.

"But first of all," I begged him, "let me take your hat."

"Thank you. I should have worn my fur coat. It is quite a cool evening."

"It is always cold here," Erasmus complained.

"What would you, my learned Doctor?" Voltaire asked him. "After all, this is a land of water. There are canals wherever you look."

"Yes," I said with some malice, remembering what Voltaire had written when he left The Hague after his unhappy experience there as secretary of the French legation: *"Adieu, canards, canaux, canaille!"*

Voltaire held up both hands. *"Mon cher monsieur,"* he begged. "I said that in a moment of pique and after a very unhappy love affair. Unhappy love affairs do not make one feel very charitable; neither, for that matter, do happy ones!" And to Jo,

Voltaire was merely a brain on sticks.

offering him a glass of sherry, *"Madame est trop aimable,"* and continuing (for he never stopped talking), "I know you, madame. You belong to the one class of women I have always revered above all others."

"Oh yes?" Jo asked, feeling very much flattered, for compliments are rare in Holland. "And who are those?"

"Les cuisinières, madame. The cooks. They surpass even the mothers. For we could undoubtedly have discovered some new way of begetting children, but a well-roasted chicken or a perfectly done dish of string beans—ah, these are something else again!"

"And just for that, you won't get any chicken tonight," said Jo, taking it up for the mothers.

"Then whatever else you are pleased to offer me, but tell me," pointing to the clasp that held her wide band of coral beads which are worn by all the women of Zeeland, "is that real gold?"

"Of course it is! Did you think I had bought them in some cheap French bazaar?"

Voltaire got up on his spindly legs and gave her a most gracious bow. "Madame," he said, "you score, and I am delighted to observe that the spirit of independence in this country has maintained itself so superbly throughout the centuries."

"And there is a lot more of it," said Jo.

"Which I hope you will show me later in the evening, but not in your cooking, for cooking is one of the arts, and the basis of all art is discipline."

I was delighted to hear him say this, for I had preached the same doctrine in all of my books. Then the thought struck me that I might even have stolen it from him, but I decided not to go into the matter any further (at that moment at least), for I noticed that the old Frenchman was looking at me very intently. Having examined me carefully from head to foot, he finally spoke.

"Monsieur," he said, "this is the first time I have the pleasure of meeting you in the flesh."

"And a lot of it," Frits volunteered.

"Oh well," Voltaire told him, "that is the way he was born. Now take me. I have eaten five meals a day every day of my long life. And not an ounce of fat could I put on. I have drunk twenty cups of coffee every day and I have slept like a log every night. It all depends how one is born. But to continue what I was just about to say, I know all about you, my dear sir."

"You don't mean to tell me," I said, "that you have read my books where you are now?"

"Alas, no. They would not last long in that rarefied atmosphere. But these last few years we have been made happy by the arrival of a great many Americans. A marvelous people, and I am glad they have done so well since my day."

"And they told you about me? That hardly seems possible."

"No, they did not. At least, not directly. But they have caused many improvements to be introduced. At least, that is what they call them, though I think the word is open to debate."

"What have those 'improvements' got to do with me?"

"Well, I do not want to divulge any secrets. It is this way. Every so many years we come up for a re-examination of our merits. One of your Americans is now in charge of a large new department—it covers about five thousand blocks in heaven and is entirely filled with tin boxes. In those boxes there are sheets of cardboard. On these cardboards stand revealed what posterity is saying about us."

"Good Lord!" Frits interrupted. "What a hopeless job!"

"Well, you see, we have all the trained help we need. There were always millions of people who loved just that kind of mechanical labor, and as they were too busy to do any harm they went to heaven. But knowing whom I was to have the honor of meeting this evening, I went through my own dossier. At first I could not find it. They are very systematic, your Americans. They had classified me under my original name. And I had to move all the way from the *V* to the *A*—you will remember Arouet. One of the attendants kindly helped me out, for it was a terrible distance—about a day's walk. I then discovered that in your books you have mentioned my name a great many times!"

"Ah," said Erasmus, "that gives me an idea. The next time I am in that neighborhood I shall find out how often my name appears in your books."

"I have already done so," Voltaire told him, beaming happily upon his Dutch friend. "You, my dear Doctor, beat me by one hundred and eighty-two entries. I shall have to make myself very agreeable tonight and perhaps I can add to my score."

Just then the clock struck seven. "Our other guests will be here in a moment now," Frits told us.

"Yes," Voltaire said, "and won't that be marvelous! At last I shall meet that most remarkable young man about whom I wrote with so much enthusiasm."

"Then you never met him before?"

"Of course not. How can one ever write with complete detachment about a person one really knows?"

There was an idea there, and I meant to explore it a little further, but at that moment the door opened and our other two guests arrived. Not only had they arrived, but they passed through the door at exactly the same moment, for neither of them apparently wanted to make room for the other. As they were rather thin, they could do this without causing any damage to our door.

We jumped to our feet, except Erasmus and Voltaire, whom we begged to remain seated.

"But Their Majesties!" Voltaire objected.

"Not tonight," I told him. "Tonight the real Majesties have already come."

We took the hats and coats of our guests. "Shall I take your swords, too?" Frits asked.

Both Peter and Charles shook their heads. "I prefer to keep mine," said Charles, in excellent German.

"So do I," said Peter, in very bad German.

"Then may we present our other guests?" Frits asked, and he mentioned the names of Erasmus and Voltaire.

Charles looked hard at Voltaire. "I seem to remember," he told him in pretty poor French, "having heard that you once wrote something about me."

"I had that honor, Your Majesty."

"Yes, I heard about it. I hope it was better than the stuff they usually write about me."

"But surely, Your Majesty," the Frenchman argued, bowing low and with the perfect grace of the experienced courtier, "one who has himself written such glorious pages in the book of living history need not worry about what we poor scribblers may say about him."

"Rest assured," Charles answered him, "I don't. Besides, I don't like the French."

"Your Majesty, it is our loss."

"It is," said Charles, who never seemed to waste any unnecessary words.

While this passage at arms was going on, Peter had walked to the corner of the room, where he paused before Frits' radio.

"*Wat is?*" he asked, in something that was meant to be Dutch.

"A machine to catch the sounds that fly through the air," I answered, in something that was meant to be Russian.

"You speak our language?"

"Hardly, Your Majesty. I picked it up—just a very little."

"Where?"

"In the city Your Majesty founded."

"Ah, you have been there? Tell me all about it, but first show me how this thing works. I love machinery of every kind."

I turned the radio on. We got London, and someone was teaching children how to speak Italian. "That seems silly," said Peter. "Why don't they teach them how to handle arms? But the invention is interesting. Open the box. I want to see what is inside."

"I am sorry, Your Majesty, but that box is locked, and we have lost the key."

"Oh, that is easily fixed," and pulling his sword out of its scabbard he pried the lid open. Then he put his hand inside and burned his fingers on one of the tubes.

"*Godverdom!*" he swore beautifully in Dutch, "why didn't you warn me?"

"I didn't have time, Your Majesty."

"A feeble excuse! Now tell me how it works."

Being completely devoid of any mechanical sense, I had to confess that I didn't know.

"That is the trouble with you clever people who write books. You have no practical sense. You would have been completely useless to me, but never mind—I will find out for myself," and suiting the action to the word he pulled out a coil of wire, with the result that the radio stopped, damaged beyond repair.

This, however, did not seem to bother Peter the least little bit. For he walked unconcernedly to the table, picked up our bottle of vodka, took out the cork, said, "Wonderful! After all these many years!" and poured half of its contents down his throat. Frits tried to save the situation by asking Charles, who all this time had been sitting in stony silence, whether perhaps he would care for a glass of aquavit.

"*Nej,*" said His Majesty of Sweden, "I am not a drunkard."

Peter did not miss the remark. "It would have been better for you, my dear cousin," he said, "if occasionally you had taken a few drops. It would have reminded you that you are human." Then Peter went to the other corner of the room where Frits' beloved old Frisian clock was hanging from the wall. He clapped his hands, as happy as a child. "I remember those clocks," he shouted. "I had one in Zaandam—just like this one. I took it apart, but I never could quite put it together again. This time I will do better. Take it down and give it to me."

Frits shuddered. "Suppose, Your Majesty," he suggested, "that we wait until after dinner. We don't want to serve you cold food."

"Food! Bah! Who cares about food when he can take a clock apart?" the Czar asked.

"I do," came from Charles.

"That is the first time I heard about it," was Peter's uncomplimentary remark, and Frits and I realized that we were in for some pretty heavy going. But with Voltaire and Erasmus right there to pour oil upon the troubled waters of the Baltic, we felt convinced that somehow or other we would be able to prevent an open outbreak of hostilities, and so we sat down, but we were very careful to separate our two honorable guests. Voltaire was supposed to take care of Charles, while Erasmus was to look after the Russian.

The arrangement worked like a charm. Peter had picked up quite a lot of Dutch during the weeks he had worked in Holland as a plain carpenter in a Zaandam shipyard. Unfortunately, the expressions he used were not exactly those with which Erasmus could possibly be familiar. Even Frits and I, who were often complimented upon our knowledge of the stevedore and coal-heaver vernacular, were occasionally stumped, whereupon Peter laughed so loudly that the candles on the table shook in their holders and he favored us with a few more choice expressions, many of which bore evidence of having been slightly Russified, for they invariably contained references to someone's canine ancestry.

As for Voltaire, I will say that he did his best, but Charles nobly lived up to his reputation for taciturnity. At one moment, trying to make myself very pleasant, I offered some comment in what I hoped was Swedish. Charles gave me a cold stare.

"I dare say that was supposed to be Swedish?" he asked.

"It was, Your Majesty."

"Where did you learn it?"

"In Stockholm, Your Majesty."

"Well, you must have had a very bad teacher," and that was the end of any further efforts on my part to address him in his native tongue.

At that moment there was an interruption. The telephone rang. It was Jimmie, who told me that Horace Liveright had tried to reach me from New York but would call again the next morning.

"Where is New York?" Peter asked.

"In America, Your Majesty."

"And where is America?"

"At the other side of the ocean, Your Majesty."

"I don't believe it," said Peter. "I must look at this contraption for myself. Could you use that 'thing' to talk to my town as well?"

"We could, Your Majesty."

"Then do it."

"We don't know anybody to call up there, Your Majesty."

"Call up the czar. Tell him I want to talk to him. I, Piotr Aleksyeevich."

"There is no longer a czar in Russia, Your Majesty."

"You are a liar. There always will be a czar in Russia. Here, let me have that thing. I will try it out myself." And hastily swallowing the rest of his vodka, Peter got up and went to the telephone, Frits following him with an expression of despair on his face.

As soon as he had left us, Charles suddenly unbent. "Gentlemen," he said, "I must apologize. You must think me a very ill-bred person. I do not, I assure you, intend to repay you for your very generous hospitality by this act of boorishness. But this Russian person—this brute—this savage—has always affected me this way. Even now he gets on my nerves, but let us use this moment's welcome respite to talk of pleasanter things and allow the King of Sweden to drink your very good health," and lifting his glass of wine (he had discovered that Erasmus and Voltaire were having Liebfraumilch), he skoaled us in a most elegant Swedish fashion, a very singular honor, for it is not often that royalty takes the initiative in such matters. After this ceremony he begged my pardon for having spoken so curtly to me.

"I have such an intense dislike for this creature over there," he said, pointing to Peter in the corner, who just then was arguing violently with someone in the Amsterdam central office and insisting that he be given the imperial palace in St. Petersburg, "that it freezes my blood to have to be in the same room with him. But tell me all about Stockholm. I hardly knew the city. I left it when I was quite young and only saw it for a few days after I returned. Has the royal palace been rebuilt and on the same spot?"

I took a pad of paper and quickly sketched those parts of the loveliest of all cities I remembered best. Parts of my pictures he recognized, and he became the most charming of companions, full of that quiet courtesy for which all his companions had praised him during those many and exceedingly trying years he had passed in semicaptivity in Turkey.

At that moment, Peter returned from his telephonic investigations. He had accomplished nothing at all except that he had rolled up a terrific long-distance bill and caused us to be visited two days later by an official of the Royal Netherlands Postal Department with a formal complaint about the "inadmissible language" which had been used over one of Her Majesty's telephones. Peter, however, seemed quite elated and happy, for he had finally heard a few words of genuine Russian at the other end of the line, but Charles immediately dropped back into his mood of gloomy silence and neither ate nor drank, nor did he speak, for the rest of that evening.

The rest of that evening, however, did not last very long. For Peter, amidst much joviality, having just finished his own bottle of vodka and Charles' bottle of aquavit, had now caught sight of the cognac which was supposed to be passed around with the coffee. "Ah!" he said delightedly, "a bottle of that marvelous French wine! I love it. It tastes better than anything else, and one cannot possibly get drunk on it."

He thereupon completely filled one of Frits' Napoleon glasses (which are supposed to be served with about three spoonfuls of the fiery beverage) to the very brim, lifted it to us, shouted, *"Zdorovye!"* poured it down his throat, and promptly passed out of the picture, his head landing on the table with a loud bang.

Charles got up. *"Förbannade fyllesvin,"* was all he said. Then to us, "I am very sorry, gentlemen, but this is too much for me. And so I hope that you will excuse me. Especially you,

Peter the Great, in a drunken stupor, fell down on the table.

my dear Monsieur de Voltaire, and you, most learned Doctor. I deeply regret that this has happened. But it is impossible for me to stay any longer." And taking his hat and his long blue cape, he honored us with a very military click of the heels and walked out of the house.

It was a painful moment, but we could not blame him. Peter's behavior had been abominable. As we could not let him lie there with his head in his plate, we tried to pick him up. He seemed to weigh at least a ton, and we despaired of getting him as far as the sofa. However, the cold air that had rushed into the room the moment Charles had opened the door must have revived him somewhat, for he regained consciousness, looked around him angrily, and shouted, "And so, the little Swede bastard is gone! Then I had better follow him, for if he does not have someone to look after him, he may get lost or walk into one of your canals. Thank you for a nice party. That was first-rate vodka, but I suppose I should not have touched that bottle of cognac. Well, it can't be helped now. Such things will happen, won't they? And now, *goede nacht*," and taking his hat in his hand and rolling up his cape so that he could carry it under his arm, he unsteadily stumbled out of the room.

Voltaire was the first to speak. *"Oh là là!"* he said, "and that is the kind of people who rule the world. And for such people, hundreds of thousands of humble subjects are supposed to give their lives! For such people, whole countries are devastated!"

Erasmus agreed with him. "I should bring out a new edition of my *Praise of Folly*," he told us. "This evening, I have learned a great many new things."

But we still had an hour to spare, and during that hour, Frits and I sat and listened to the brightest and the wittiest and sometimes the wisest conversation we had ever heard or ever expected to hear. With the result that after Voltaire and Erasmus were gone, we remained in our chairs in front of our little open fire and continued to talk for at least two hours, when at last I took my leave and made for home.

It was a dark and stormy night. Wild clouds were racing past a watery moon. I decided to take a short walk, for I felt badly in need of a little fresh air. My road led past the old church, and from there, after crossing the bridge, I found myself among the open fields. By the light of the moon I noticed two figures in a near-by pasture. They had shed their capes and hats, but I recognized them at once. They were engaged in a fast and furious battle of swords. I felt that it was my duty to intervene, but just when I was on the point of making my presence known, the smaller one of the two ran his rapier through the chest of his opponent. The wounded man bellowed like a stricken ox, but only once. Then he fell forward on his face with such violence that the sword of his enemy snapped and broke, the upper part remaining stuck in his chest.

I decided that I had better go home. If there was to be an inquest, I might be called upon as a witness and I did not want to be mixed up in a case of this sort.

But there never was any inquest. I met our policeman the next morning, and after we had commented upon the weather and had told each other that fall was almost over and now it soon would be winter, I asked him whether everything was quiet in the village.

"Never knew it to be so peaceful," he told me. "Not since after that evening when you had those two drunken organ-grinders at Mynheer Frits' house. You remember those wild-looking men who started a fight and hit each other over the head with the wine bottles? And whom I had to put into the clink? Since that evening, nothing at all has happened in our town."

"That's fine," I said, "for that is why we live here. Because nothing ever happens in our little city."

Then I offered him one of my best American cigars, which I carried especially for such occasions, and he, after some urging, took two, and we each went our way, happy that we were allowed to live in a village where nothing ever happened.

Two shadowy figures were dueling in the moonlight.

CHAPTER XVI

DANTE and LEONARDO DA VINCI Come to Dine, the Latter of Whom "Drops In" in the Literal Sense of the Word

"AND NOW," I said to Frits when we met for luncheon on Sunday, "how about a really quiet and peaceful party after all this violence?"

"It would be a pleasant change."

"I think I can arrange it. The people I have in mind would have nothing to quarrel about."

"Who are they?"

"One of them was the final chapter of the Middle Ages. The other was the most interesting chapter of the Renaissance."

"Do they carry swords and do they drink vodka, aquavit, and cognac all at the same time? You should have seen the mess in my dining room this morning!"

"They don't carry swords and as far as I know, neither of them would touch a drop of anything except perhaps a glass or two of their mild Italian wine."

"In that case, go ahead and invite them."

And that is how it came about that the same evening the old lion on the steps of the town hall found himself sitting on a scrap of paper containing the names of Dante Alighieri of Florence and Leonardo from the village of Vinci.

I had only the haziest idea of what I should offer Dante. During the Middle Ages, macaroni and spaghetti were not the common articles of food they are in the Italy of today, and we could not very well offer polenta to a man who during so many years of his life had been dependent for his living upon the mercy of a family called Polenta. I would have to think Dante's menu out and most carefully.

Leonardo, we felt, we could satisfy according to his taste. He had spent a great deal of his time at the court of France, and we had quite a collection of old French cookbooks. But to be on the safe side with Dante, I decided to begin our dinner with a Dutch vegetable soup. After that, there would have to be something muttonish, for veal would have been very rare in medieval Italy. The French cookbooks of that period made quite an ado about something that was then considered a great delicacy— mutton done in butter with tomatoes and olives. That would be a novelty for our guests, as neither Dante nor Leonardo could ever have tasted a tomato. The love apple had been brought to Europe by the early Spanish explorers, but it had been grown only for ornamental purposes until the end of the eighteenth century, being until then considered poisonous and therefore unfit for human consumption. But I decided to take a chance with this pleasant fruit, and Jo was given the recipe for *noisettes de mouton aux tomates* and told not to forget that her slices of tomato must be served with an anchovy rolled on top of each one.

As the people of the Middle Ages (and of the Renaissance too, for that matter) had never been very great vegetable eaters, I thought that Dutch carrots with a plentiful garnishing of parsley would do as well as any other vegetable. Potatoes? Our guests would most probably not care for them, and I thought it safer to order stewed corn. This we imported from America in cans, as the Dutch corn never grows tall enough to be eaten by human beings and is only used to feed the cattle.

For dessert we could have the famous *flamiches* of the sixteenth century, which were a kind of cheese cake. In case our guests did not like these, we would have all sorts of real cheese, for was there ever an Italian who did not take to cheese as a Scotchman takes to haggis?

The wine problem was easily settled. Any kind of "red ink"—any kind of that cheap Chianti which is about the best known of all Italian articles of export—would be satisfactory. A better wine would be a waste of money and effort, for our guests would not notice the difference, being in that respect undoubtedly quite as untrained as the average modern American.

The music had to be chosen carefully, for both our guests were very much interested in this subject. Of Leonardo we knew that he had been a first-rate lute player and had made all sorts of experiments with those instrumental combinations which were so popular during the beginning of the Renaissance. As for Dante, he himself had told about his love for sweet melodies when he described how in Purgatory he had come across Pietro Casella, a famous madrigal writer of the thirteenth century who had been one of his favorite composers.

As there is, however, very little music of that era that has come down to us, and none of it by Casella, I decided to start out with one of the records of Guillaume Dufay which we had played with so much success the night Sir Thomas More called on Erasmus. It was his *Alma Redemptoris Mater*. In addition to this, I sent for Guillaume de Machaut's Credo and Sanctus from the Mass he had composed for the coronation of Charles V of France in the year 1364. The rest would be more specially for Leonardo, and for him I chose Jacopo Peri's *Gioite al canto mio* from his opera *Euridice* and Claudio Monteverdi's *Lasciatemi morire* and two airs from his *Incoronazione di Poppea*. And, in order that we would not run out of records (for what would these two Italians who were so completely different in every respect have to say to each other?), I added Domenico Cimarosa's overture to his *Matrimonio segreto* and Attilio Ariosti's song for soprano and viola d'amore.

We already had most of Segovia's records for the guitar, and these masterpieces of dexterity would delight Leonardo, who had been quite famous in his own right as a guitar player. Should he tire of music, Leonardo, like all good painters, would be perfectly happy with a piece of paper and a pencil and might even be persuaded to follow the example of Giotto and Taddeo Gaddi and give us a good portrait of Dante.

Knowing how much he had liked working in red chalk, I borrowed some of it from Lucie. I felt sure that in this way he would be quite contented, and Dante, if he felt bored, could just sit and brood. We were learning a great deal about the famous ones of this earth. And we had come to the conclusion that it was absolutely impossible to make any predictions about the sort of people they would prove to be. Genius, apparently, could be brilliant, and genius, also, could be extremely dull. We would have to trust to luck.

Here is my report on Dante as I sent it to Amsterdam by special delivery.

Dear Frits: I am afraid that to our younger generation, Dante has become a taste that has to be acquired like a love for figs or scrapple. He is so far removed from our own times that it is very difficult for us to establish any kind of direct contact with this lonely wanderer who, in despair at the world in which he lived, found an escape in a visit to heaven and hell.

I am beginning to feel more and more that there is little use in my sending you long Plutarchian essays upon the lives of people who have been written up (and down) as frequently as those of most of our guests of the last three months. In the case of Dante, there even have been, and there still are, regular chairs of Dantology in many of our universities. These chairs are held by regular professors who do nothing else all their livelong days except explain the great Florentine poet or dig up his old laundry bills and his unpaid grocery accounts. I therefore cannot hope to add much that would be new and, while I like warmed-over dishes, I must confess that I am not very fond of any kind of literary rehash.

The man's name, Dante Alighieri, is a curious one. The Germans, with their delightful habit of modestly claiming every-body who has ever amounted to anything (provided they fit into their scheme of a Nordic *Herren*-race), have tried to prove that his name was of Teutonic origin, and had originally been Aldiger or something like that. Dante himself seems to have been unaware of any Germanic antecedents. Indeed, he con-fessed that he was almost completely ignorant about his own ancestry. While on his famous visit to the nether regions, he stumbled upon one of his great-great-grandfathers who bore the romantic name of Cacciaguida, or something like that. The par-ticular crime or misdemeanor for which this stout warrior and crusader was roasting in hell I do not remember, but there he was, and he and his descendant had quite a pleasant little chat. But it is perfectly possible that Dante, being a poet rather than a historian, had deliberately invented this distinguished pro-genitor, just as I in my *Rembrandt* gave life to the good Dr. Ioannes van Loon, who has since then been honored with a special item in the *General German Pharmaceutical Encyclo-pedia,* although he never existed except in my own brain.

And then there is one other point I want to make right away, so that we do not get things mixed up. Dante did not write his *Inferno* for the purpose of adding to our historical knowledge of the fourteenth century. He wanted to give expression to his private opinion of many of the people with whom he had come in contact during his own political career, and his literary mas-terpiece was his way of getting even with those of his neighbors who had not quite treated him as he thought he had deserved.

The comedy he bestowed upon us is usually known as the "Divine." It was divine from a literary point of view, for few books have been written with so much venom and so much hatred and such profound desire for vengeance as this immortal opus of the gloomy Florentine.

We know very little about Dante's father except that he had married twice and had several other children, but most of them remained obscure and hazy figures who played no particular role in Dante's own life. We have, however, sufficient information about Dante's background to be certain that while he did not belong to the nobility, he was of good family and that his father and his grandfather before him had been men of sound standing in the community, both socially and economically. But when it comes to details about his childhood and the days of his youth, we are again in the dark. His father could afford to give him the best education then available for a commoner and did so. Therefore, the future Columbus of hell was no self-made man within the realm of letters, as has sometimes been claimed. He had learned all that could be learned in a medieval city of the last half of the thirteenth century (he was born in the year 1265), and he was thoroughly familiar with the classics.

The only other incident about this period which has come down to us was the passion which temporarily deprived him of his senses when he first beheld the countenance of the lovely Beatrice Portinari. In spite of his sentiments toward the young lady, he seems never to have met her socially, which need not surprise us, as both of them were nine years old when they first beheld each other in the streets of their native town.

The memory, however, of this frustrated love affair, which had been nothing much more serious than the sort of affliction which occurs to all of us when we are very young and very innocent, assumed truly gigantic proportions in the mind of this highly introspective author. We therefore meet the lovely Beatrice again and again in all of his writings. She, however, did not influence his subsequent career half as much as his decision to go in for politics.

You will remember enough about the history you learned at school to realize that a political career in the Florence of that day was not possible without belonging to one of the two parties which for almost a century had been fighting for the control of the city. Young Dante therefore was obliged to decide first of all whether he would become a Republican or a Democrat, as we would say today.

When Dante was born, all the leading families of Florence

were sharply divided into Ghibellines and Guelphs. As I invariably forget who were the Guelphs and who the Ghibellines, I had better look them up once more. Let me see. The Guelphs (it is easy to remember them from their original German name of the Wolfs—a prominent Saxon family) had for a long time fought the Hohenstaufens, their rivals for the imperial German throne. In Italy the latter had become known as the Ghibellines, which was the way the Italians pronounced the name of one of their largest castles, that of Waiblingen. The original struggle between these two houses in Germany had gradually found its way across the Alps, and there it had led to the formation of two political factions who opposed each other as bitterly as the Guelphs and the Hohenstaufens had done in Germany, but upon a different basis. The Guelphs in Italy were those who wanted the Pope to be the leading power in Italy and who had no use for the German emperor as overlord of their country, whereas the Ghibellines favored the German emperors as the future autocrats of the whole of the Apennine peninsula.

I can perhaps make this explanation a little simpler by saying that the Ghibellines as a rule were the aristocrats, while the Guelphs represented the more democratic element. Not, of course, democratic in our sense of the word, but as representatives of that large middle class which, after a thousand years of an almost total eclipse, was at last beginning to regain some of its old influence upon the government. The rich cities, as need hardly be stressed, were predominantly Guelphic in their sentiments, while the country squires were of the Ghibelline persuasion. In Florence, a stronghold of commerce and manufacturing, the Guelphs had been driven out of power a short time before Dante was born. The feeling, however, between the two parties had been much too strong to have entirely disappeared, and the city, when Dante entered upon his political career, was divided into the so-called Black Guelphs and White Guelphs, or the Blacks and the Whites—as they were called for short. These Blacks and Whites fought each other very much as modern Republicans and Democrats will fight each other in America.

Dante, who from the age of thirty on had been a member of the Florentine city government, happened to belong to the faction of the White Guelphs. Therefore, when still another and altogether unexpected local upheaval had brought the Black Guelphs back into power, he and all the leading members of his party were forced to leave the city on pain of being executed if they should ever again dare to set foot on Florentine territory. That meant that six hundred families of those who had favored the emperor over the Pope were suddenly deprived of all their possessions and were cast upon the generosity of the world at large, without a penny to their name. To many of them it meant the end. Others of a tougher fiber settled down in some near-by White city and supported themselves by doing menial jobs or finding employment in one of the sweatshops which were so characteristic of the Italy of that day. Still others became professional exiles and spent their time plotting for the overthrow of the government in the old home town, while accepting money from anyone foolish enough to let them have it.

Dante was an exception. He must already have enjoyed a certain reputation as a man of letters, for he never lacked at least sufficient cash to pay for his daily needs. These were exceedingly simple. All the same, even a few dollars a week mean an awful lot to a political refugee, and those few dollars Dante always seems to have had at his disposal. And since he was now without any regular employment, he thought it would be a good idea if first of all he saw a little something more of the world than most of his fellow Italians had ever bothered to do and learned a few things about his fellow men.

First of all, he proceeded to Milan, where he paid homage to the newly elected emperor of that Holy Roman Empire of Germanic origin which had been founded by Charlemagne in the year 800. From Milan he wandered all over northern Italy. After that, having enjoyed the temporary hospitality of a great number of Italian princes who supported the Ghibelline or imperial cause, he moved to the little city of Ravenna, where he stayed for the rest of his days under the protection of the

The exile.

local dictator, Guido da Polenta. And there he worked on his great poem and there he died on the fourteenth day of September of the year of grace 1321.

Some years before his death, Dante had been offered an opportunity to return to his native city of Florence. But in order to be forgiven for having belonged to the wrong political clique, he would have been obliged not only to pay a heavy fine but also to go through an act of public penance in one of the churches. He refused to do this in a letter which has been preserved and which reads very much like the noble document in which Thomas Mann answered the obscene Nazi rector of the University of Bonn, who had deprived him of the honorary degree which a few years before had been bestowed upon this most distinguished German man of letters. It makes us admire Dante and occasionally even like him, for few people have ever felt such a fanatical affection for the city of their birth as this unhappy exile. The image of Florence was with him day and night, but as you and I, my dear Frits, are just as absurd in our devotion to our little Veere (which, God knows, is no Florence), we can well understand his attitude of imperishable loyalty. In our case, no matter where we go, we always hope to return to Veere some day. Whereas Dante knew that his sentence was one for life. But it could not be helped. He could not do otherwise. Honor meant more to him than anything else. He could not possibly confess himself guilty when he felt that he had committed no crime. And so he steadfastly refused to ask for a pardon, even if it meant that never again would he see the low hills of his beloved Tuscany and that never again would he stand by the banks of the swift-flowing Arno on the same spot where he had caught his first glimpse of the beloved Beatrice. Rather than so demean himself, he would spend his days in dignified loneliness among the pine forests of Ravenna and would die unforgiven and unforgiving.

Quite naturally, these bitter years of exile were bound to influence his entire outlook upon life, and they were to account for that spirit of all-pervading gloom which often makes the reading of his works a duty rather than a pleasure. But they also were to give that unmistakable touch of nobility to everything he ever wrote, even if he is a most undependable guide when he introduces us to some of the people whom he cast into the deepest pits of hell.

I think this point should be much more stressed than it usually is. The *Inferno* was Dante's apology for his own life. It was his justification for his political activities while he had still been young and full of zeal to serve his country. One would hardly have expected President Wilson, had he ever had time to write his own version of hell, to have given Senator Lodge a prominent place among the saints.

Dante's *Inferno,* therefore, should be taken with many shovelfuls of salt. It is one of the most biased political treatises ever written, and that is what makes it more and more difficult for modern readers to enjoy the book without a great deal of comment. Dante's contemporaries of course got every hint and allusion. In a way, he was their "columnist," except that he went just a little farther than most of his modern colleagues. He did not merely suggest that some of his enemies should spend the rest of their days burning in hell. He actually took them down there and let them burn.

And now let me talk a little about his book, for in the case of Dante, the book is the thing, and the author is only of secondary importance. He lays the opening scene of his famous opus on the Friday before Easter of the year 1300, although the actual date at which he began to do his writing has never yet been decided upon. Neither do we know when he finished it. As for the rest of his output, the *Vita Nuova,* or *New Life,* his tribute to the unforgettable Beatrice, and his *Convivio,* or *Banquet* (*Table Talk,* as he would have called it today), which was a sort of *Book of Knowledge* of the early fourteenth century—all these volumes, while of undoubted merit, never quite enter into the picture. They enjoy about the same rating as the historical plays of Alfred, Lord Tennyson. One would rather do six weeks at hard labor than read one of them.

And now let me see (mostly for my own amusement) whether I can, in as few words as possible, sum up for the defense and state why, in spite of a great many claims to the contrary, it is still possible, after the lapse of so many centuries, to insist that *The Divine Comedy* is good reading and that its author will always remain one of the most important figures of literature.

When I suggested that we invite Dante and Leonardo at the same time, I did so because to me they represent two exceedingly interesting chapters in the history of the human race—the last and final chapter of the Middle Ages and one of the first chapters of the Renaissance, and these are the grounds upon which I shall base my contentions on behalf of Signor Dante.

He was the last of the great medievalists because he was the last man who wrote at a moment when it was still possible for an ordinary human being to be a walking encyclopedia and to know everything that was knowable in his own day and age. As a result, *The Divine Comedy* is not merely a religious poem like *Paradise Lost;* in addition, it is a commentary upon everything the people of the Middle Ages knew or said or thought or did. Indeed, had we been deprived of all our other medieval sources we would, had we saved but a single copy of Dante, be able to reconstruct practically the whole of the life of the Middle Ages out of this one volume.

Modern man can no longer hope to do this. Balzac in his *Comédie humaine* showed us the kind of people who lived in France during the first half of the last century. Zola tried to perform a similar service for those of the last half. But Dante surpassed them both. His field of operations was of course a much less complicated one than that of the two Frenchmen I just mentioned. He lived in an age of basic simplicities. Neither time nor distance had as yet been abolished, and God still ruled over heaven and earth as He had done since the beginning of time. Science was practically nonexistent, and the arts dealt with rather crude materials, for musical instruments and all the modern methods of reproduction, such as oil paints and etching presses and indelible inks, were not to make their appearance until much later.

In order to move from one spot to another, one still walked. If the voyage was to be taken by sea, one sailed by God and by guess, without any very dependable assurance of ever reaching one's destination. Also, there still was a complete lack of even the most rudimentary forms of comfort. Therefore, the prince and the pauper enjoyed very much the same kind of daily existence. The prince might have a thousand horses at his disposal, but he could use only one at a time and therefore could not move much faster than the peasant who had only one mule, provided the mule felt inclined to take a little trip, in which case he might get there a great deal sooner than the royal or imperial stallion.

But even under those favorable circumstances, it remained a marvelous tour de force to reduce the whole of a civilization and a complete cycle of culture to one single volume and to turn that volume not into a dull encyclopedia but to make it a first-rate work of art full of life and color.

Shortly after Dante's death, the Renaissance, then so proudly compared to a rebirth of civilization, swept over Europe with the violence of an artistic hurricane. In the first proud flush of their victory, the men of the Renaissance looked down upon their immediate predecessors with the same contemptuous disdain with which they contemplated the architectural glories of the thirteenth and fourteenth centuries, which they dismissed as too utterly Gothic, too hopelessly barbaric and crude, to be of any real interest to their own refined tastes.

Since then we have learned better. Today most of us prefer the cathedral of Chartres to the church of St. Peter's and we have come to realize that the paper monument which Dante constructed out of the bitterness of his long and undeserved exile towers mightily above all the other creations of medieval man. I know it was not built out of mortar and stone. Paper and ink were the materials the great Florentine used to erect his mighty edifice. But to these he added one other element of paramount importance—that mysterious quality of the soul known as genius.

And now we come to a very different type of person. For while Dante, as a perfect son of the Middle Ages, "knew" and had no doubts, Leonardo "guessed" and never ceased to ask why. In which he was as perfect a representative of the Renaissance mentality as Dante had been of the spirit of the era that had now come to a definite end.

Leonardo was born in 1452. He died in 1519. Let us assume that he needed the first twenty years for his education. That gives him forty-seven years in which to do his life's work. He must have kept very busy when we consider that he was not merely one of the greatest painters of all times but that furthermore he acquired an outstanding reputation as an architect, an engineer, a sculptor, an athlete, a student of physics and ballistics, a poet, a composer, a musician, a philosopher, an inventor, and an expert on military matters.

Now that may seem to be a direct contradiction of what I said a moment ago when I described Dante as the last of the medievalists because he could still gather together all the available knowledge of his time into one single volume. But whereas Dante was the "summer-upper" of all that had been known in the past, Leonardo was the prophet of everything that had to be revealed by the future. As it is much more difficult to "predict" than to "enumerate," Leonardo was the greater of the two, but comparisons are apt to be very futile when they are comparisons between men who were prominent in such completely different fields of endeavor, so I shall drop the discussion right here.

Leonardo was an illegimitate child. His father was a Florentine lawyer. His mother, about whom we know nothing at all, was probably a native of the village of Vinci, and hence the boy's name. His father must have taken an interest in him, for the son received the education of a young gentleman, and showing a definite inclination toward the arts, he was sent to learn his craft from Andrea del Verrocchio, then still quite a young man but already distinguished as a painter, a sculptor, an engineer, and a silversmith.

With Leonardo I am back again at the highly intriguing subject of genius. We have met quite a number of men and women of outstanding ability these last four months, but I am sorry to confess that I don't know very much more about them than I did before they happened to drop in as our dinner guests. I am, however, beginning to suspect that genius is rather like wine, in that there are certain regions which are apt to raise a much better crop of geniuses than others and that there are definite years during which the genius harvest in all parts of the world will be much greater than during other years or numbers of years. I dare not, however, be too dogmatic upon this subject, for quite often an otherwise barren part of the world will suddenly give us a most superior vintage, while other valleys which until then had provided us with the finest annual harvests will suddenly and for no apparent reason become as sterile as the central desert of the Australian continent.

Our specialists in the noble art of winegrowing seem to have some idea why there is apt to be such a great discrepancy between the harvest of one year and another. Unfortunately, the human race, unlike the humble grape, has never yet been subjected to that kind of clinical study, and as a result we know much less about it than we do about the product of our vineyards. Since the exceptional individual has mighty little chance to be made the subject of such an investigation in a world which has made the ordinary individual the center of all his interest, there seems to be little chance of any immediate inquiry into the riddle of genius.

In the meantime and almost in spite of ourselves, we have got hold of a few data, but they only make the problem slightly more complicated. For example, it is easy to understand why a perpetually fertile region, like the valley of the Nile, should have been predestined to become one of the earliest centers of civilization. But why a rocky and barren peninsula like that of Greece should suddenly have risen forth as a beacon of such vast enlightenment that it still illuminates the whole of our cultural landscape remains an unsolved mystery, for there are a great many other rocky peninsulas in this world, and none of them have contributed a pennyworth to the sum total of human progress.

Or let us take another example. Why should the flat meadows of the Low Countries have set an all-high standard for painting, while other flat countries like Denmark never attained anything much higher than pictorial mediocrity? I have no idea. And how about music? Imperial Vienna was undoubtedly a city suffering so severely from every kind of censorship that the available local energy had to find some other kind of outlet than by means of the forbidden politics. In such a case, music has always been an ideal means of escape. But why Vienna should have suddenly burst forth with a Gluck, a Haydn, a Mozart, a Beethoven, a Schubert, a Strauss, and all the others at the moment it did—that again is still a profound mystery. Other nations ruled over by the Hapsburgs were repressed with equal brutality, but their musical output did not noticeably increase. Whenever I discuss this subject (a couple of times a day), I am told that the solution to the Viennese puzzle lies in the fact that the people of Vienna were a hodgepodge of all kinds of races and that such mixtures are invariably productive of great musical talent. Very well, I answer, but if that is true, then why have our own cities with a hundred races so far failed to give us a single first-class composer?

Even more incomprehensible is the problem of why such artistic and spiritual flare-ups, once they have come to an end, can never be rekindled, no matter how hard anyone blows the bellows of local enthusiasm. The recent traveler in modern Italy or Greece will remember (and with a considerable amount of horror) the architectural monstrosities of which these countries have been guilty during the last hundred years. The land of Michelangelo and Bramante has gone Bleecker Street and loves it. The pilgrim to the unknown grave of Mozart will still hear music in Vienna, but it is of the imported variety, for Vienna's native musical genius came to an end with Johann Strauss. Brahms was a foreign import (Hamburg was almost as far removed from Vienna as New York, when Johannes was born), and so were Mahler and Bruckner, and all efforts to revive the city on the muddy Danube as a true center of music have failed as lamentably as the attempt to make Bruges once more a city of commerce by digging a canal that connects it with the North Sea.

There are many more such examples. Holland still paints, but the Rembrandts and the Vermeers are gone, and in the land of Goethe and Heinrich Heine, people today read *Mein Kampf*.

I mention all this merely because the subject fascinates me. I do not expect or even hope to find an answer, but this sort of thinking aloud is a pastime in which all of us should occasionally indulge.

And now back to the Italy of the late Middle Ages and the early Renaissance. The crop of genius which the Italian peninsula raised during the years that lay between the death of Dante and the birth of Leonardo was well-nigh incredible, and it was genius of a very particular sort, genius of the universal type, which is as rare as a good meal in an English country hotel.

That was the blessed era when some obscure professor in Bologna or Padua or Salerno might teach half a dozen different subjects and teach all of them well. That was the age when great painters were employed as ambassadors and made a success of the job, when writers could hold high political office, and when rulers of nations and cities would try their hand at writing, at music, at drawing, and when even a Pope was not held in disesteem because he happened to know the difference between a good picture and a bad one.

Furthermore, it was a paradise in which almost any boy with talent had a chance to find some kind of outlet for his artistic aspirations. For although there was a complete lack of those musical and artistic academies which dot the modern landscape, the quest for men of talent was so widespread and so eagerly pursued that it resembled our own search after promising base-ball or football material. Let it be rumored about that there was a budding painter or sculptor in some distant *villagio* in Tuscany or Umbria, and the art scouts would go after him with the same eagerness with which today they would follow up a clue about a brilliant shortstop or halfback said to be playing in some bush league in Texas or Jersey.

Even social background, that bugaboo of medieval life, counted for nothing. Legitimacy was of course preferred, but illegitimacy was by no means a deterrent. It all came down to Schubert's happy phrase, *"Kann er was?"* or "Does the fellow know anything?" If he did—if he really knew something—he was welcome. Otherwise let him stay where he was and stick to his sheep or his pots and pans or double-entry bookkeeping.

The Renaissance was by no means the last word upon the subject of human perfection. Far from it! The people of the fifteenth and sixteenth centuries remained as indifferent about science as those of the Middle Ages had been. They took no in-terest in those social problems which so seriously occupy us to-day that there is very little room left for anything else. They continued to live quite serenely in a world which stank in the most literal sense of the word. And being indifferent about even the most primitive kind of personal hygiene, those Renais-sance ladies and gentlemen in their beautiful silks and satins tolerated a death rate which makes us shudder when we think of that utterly unnecessary loss of life. But those good people, so far behind us in many things which we consider all-important, were far ahead of us in certain other respects to which we our-selves pay but scant attention.

647

During the Middle Ages, religion had been an integral part of everybody's daily existence. The Church had supervised and regulated everything they did or thought from early morning until the moment it was time to go to bed. Now religion was gradually beginning to lose the hold it had had upon people's imagination, and the arts were taking its place, and after having turned their backs upon the world of the senses for almost ten full centuries, the men and women of the new Europe arose from their long and beautiful dream about the blessings of the life hereafter to discover that existence right here on this planet could also be a most delightful experience. Being still possessed of that sense of wonder which had been so characteristic of the childlike folk who had preceded them, they took to their new toys with whoops of joy and made them as much part of their daily existence as their crucifixes and rosaries had been until only a few years before.

The Florentine and Milanese and Venetian and Paduan and Sienese contemporaries of Leonardo did not go to the theater because the piece that was being given that evening happened to be the rage of the town and because not having seen it would expose them to the superior smiles of their neighbors. They did not storm a church the moment a new painting had been unveiled because to have remained at home might have made them lose out on the conversation the next time they were invited for dinner by their boss. They did not eagerly await the completion of a new opera because going to the opera was the fashionable thing to do, nor did they invite artists to their parties because the presence of those exotic guests would assure them of being mentioned in next Sunday's society columns. A few may have done so, but a much greater number of people than ever before (not even excepting the ancient Greeks) took an active part in all these manifestations of the artistic spirit because they were truly interested and understood what was being done. They knew the output of all their leading maestros by heart in the same way that a citizen of a modern American city will be familiar with the box scores of his favorite players, and they could judge their works on points with the same feeling for technical perfection you will encounter among a group of professional coaches going to attend the annual battle between the Texas Christians and the Southern Methodists.

I seem to be unable to avoid these comparisons borrowed from the field of sport. But that cannot very well be helped, for sport in our own age has taken the place of religion during the Middle Ages, a love for the arts during the Renaissance, a passion for discovery during the sixteenth century, and a love of humanity during the prologue to the French Revolution.

But let me get back to my facts, for I am sure I have now given you enough of a background picture to make you understand why a career such as that of Leonardo was not only possible during the latter half of the fifteenth century but was accepted as something quite normal.

In the year 1472, at the age of twenty, Leonardo was deemed sufficiently well versed in his craft to be allowed to join the painters' guild of Florence. Like all other apprentices of that era, he had often substituted for his teacher, but even in those earliest works of his, we come across evidences of that disastrous habit which would cling to him all through life—the habit of never quite finishing a job. It is easy enough to guess at the cause. Leonardo was primarily an experimenter. He was driven by an insatiable curiosity and a furious desire to find out what made the wheels go round. Nothing else mattered. As soon as he felt that he was on the right track to another discovery, he lost interest in the old problem and turned to something new, and being a true son of the Renaissance in his belief that, being human, he had at his disposal the whole realm of human endeavor, he did not merely dabble in paints and clays but boldly carried his researches into every field of the arts and the sciences.

We usually think of Leonardo as an old man with a generous crop of whiskers, for his self-portrait (in red chalk), which is the best known one, shows him that way. When he was young, he must have looked quite different. All his biographers agree that he owed much of his initial success in life to his good looks, to the charm of his manners, and to the easy grace of behavior which made it possible for him to meet everyone, from queen to chambermaid, on the ground of a common understanding and appreciation.

Here again I could draw a rather interesting analogy between the sixteenth century and our own. Today the artist, if he wants to pay his rent and to provide an occasional ham on rye for his models, must appeal primarily to the women among his prospective customers. And since there are no longer any definite standards of taste (the last of the world-wide cultural patterns having disappeared when the rococo came to an end a hundred and fifty years ago), it is very easy for these modern patrons of the arts to insist that they must be right in their preferences because, while they may not know what is good, they know what they like, a remark which provoked Monet's famous reply, "Yes, madam, just like the cows."

Unfortunately, quite often they don't even really know what they like and they will hire a painter or a composer as they would hire a plumber, by sending for someone who is well recommended but about whose abilities they have no personal or firsthand information. In the case of the plumber they must, of course, practice a certain measure of caution, because a flooded cellar is a terrible nuisance. But a third-rate portrait can always be helped out by giving it the right kind of lighting or a very expensive frame or a fine write-up in the local newspapers. Since most of the admiring guests will be quite as ignorant upon the subject of good portraiture as their hostess, there is little chance that the true value of this wasted piece of canvas will be discovered, at least during the lifetime of the subject.

In Leonardo's day, the men and not the women did the ordering, and therefore the artist was saved the degradation of having to go in for the social life of the community for no other purpose than to establish the right kinds of connections. He probably was just as fond of a free meal as his descendants of today, but he did not have to mix his sales talk with his liquor at a ladies' cocktail party.

In the case of Leonardo, this was all the more fortunate, for he was apparently not interested (or only very moderately so) in the feminine half of the world. He spent most of his life among men, only occasionally painting their wives or using women as models for his Madonnas, but in spite of this they appreciated him sufficiently to keep him employed until the last day he spent on earth. Today, I am afraid, he would have found it very difficult to make a living. Whereas, having been born in the fifteenth century, he died a fairly rich man, and he would have died a very rich man if his royal and princely customers had been a little more regular in the payment of their debts, and if he himself had not wasted so large a part of his income on his everlasting experiments, from submarines to flying machines.

But let me get back to those facts so dearly beloved of all historians and a matter of such complete indifference to most artists. Here is his schedule between the years 1472, when he became a master painter in Florence, and 1519, when he died near Amboise, a small town not far from Paris.

In 1483 Lorenzo de' Medici, the ruler of Florence who not only loved art but (infinitely more important) *knew* it too, sent him as his special representative to Lodovico Sforza, better known as Lodovico il Moro, or Louis the Blackamoor, who at that moment happened to be the political boss of Milan. The purpose of this mission was the gaining of the Moro's good will. Leonardo succeeded so well in making himself popular that, when the time came for him to go back to Florence, the Milanese dictator kept him at his own court for most of the next sixteen years.

During this period, Leonardo started a few pictures that were finished, but a great many more, like his famous *Last Supper,* remained forever in the experimental stage. The rest of his time he worked on the cathedral of Milan, superintended the renovation of the Duke's castle, and drew up the plans for the irrigation of the plains of Lombardy and the digging of the Maremma canal. In his spare hours, he also arranged Il Moro's world-famous pageants, wrote the masques and fables that were given at these parties, and for good measure composed most of the music which was an inevitable part of such mummeries.

Also—I almost forgot—he laid out the plans for the fortifications of the city, finished a treatise on painting, and prepared to enrich Milan with a colossal equestrian statue of Francesco Sforza that was to be twenty-six feet high. This statue, I regret to say, was never finished. The original model was destroyed by some playful soldiers, who, being temporarily in control of the town, used it as a mark for their target practice.

In addition to these trifles, Leonardo also found time to continue his studies of human anatomy, to observe the flight of the birds, to construct a flying machine (which would have flown if he had had some kind of motor), to draw up the plans for a new seat of the municipal government, to collect groups of drunken old crones that he might observe their physiognomies while they were in their cups, to deliver lectures on art in the market place, to show the gilded youth of Milan how one should ride a horse and take a hurdle, to study mathematics with Toscanelli (whose map of the world was used by Columbus during his first voyage across the ocean), to play the lute and write music for this exceedingly complicated instrument, and to act as consulting architect and engineer for those of the near-by political bosses who were on sufficiently friendly terms with Il Moro to borrow his "man of all work" whenever they were planning to do a little fortifying or irrigating of their own.

One of the most famous of these so-called "intervals" when Leonardo was not kept busy at the court of Milan occurred in the year 1502, when Cesare Borgia sent for him to help him solve several big engineering projects in central Italy. One would suppose that, being buried up to his neck in blueprints, Leonardo just then would not have had time for anything else, but it was during the next year—1503—that he began that portrait of the wife of Zanobi del Giocondo, the lady with the mysterious smile who has been familiar to everybody these last four hundred years under the name of *La Gioconda,* or the *Mona Lisa.*

Finally, Leonardo found himself so flooded with orders for all sorts of things that he was obliged to maintain two fully equipped studios, one in Florence and one in Milan, and to these he afterward added still another one in Rome, where his old protectors, the Medici, now occupied the Holy See.

In this way, working and experimenting all the hours of both day and night, he had attained the age of more than sixty at a time when the average expectancy of life was less than forty. Being endowed with an indestructible constitution, Leonardo still enjoyed the best of health, but a new generation had grown up, and younger men like Michelangelo and Raphael were beginning to take the place of prominence he had held until then. He wisely decided that the time had come to retire. Painting and music no longer interested him as much as they used to. He was beginning to become more and more engrossed in his scientific studies. Therefore, when King Francis I of France offered him a quiet position at his own court, where he would be able to do exactly as he pleased, he gratefully accepted. It was just what he wanted to round out his life with dignity.

Francis was as good as his word and, being young and ambitious, he felt that the acquisition of an artist of Leonardo's fame was the greatest achievement of his life. He gave orders that the entire castle of Cloux near Amboise be placed at the master's disposal and earmarked sufficient funds in the royal treasury to pay his greatly honored guest his promised income.

Leonardo bade a leisurely farewell to his native Italy and, together with his retinue of apprentices and workers in clay and iron and his secretaries and his draftsmen and his servants, he moved into his new quarters. Now at last, so he hoped, he would have the opportunity to put some order into those barrels and boxes of notes and scientific observations he had accumulated during the previous forty years and which had been written down in a cipher that no one but the old master himself understood.

But it was too late. He was rapidly losing his strength. Frequent references to his "left-handedness" make us suspect that he had either suffered a slight stroke or had got writer's cramp, that strange malady of the nerves which is so apt to attack musicians, telegraphers, and writers and which, when it affects the legs, has put an end to many a dancer's career. Even today there is no cure for this ailment. The only thing one can do is to learn to write or draw or play with the hand that has remained normal. Judging by the drawings of this later period, that is apparently what Leonardo was obliged to do. He had to become an artistic southpaw.

In the spring of the year 1519, after two and a half years in the employ of the King of France, Leonardo felt that he would not have much longer to live. His mind was still as active as ever. In the spring of the previous year he had arranged for all the festivities in connection with the christening of the heir to the throne. In the fall he had been responsible for the entertainment in honor of the marriage of a Bourbon prince to a princess of the House of Medici. In addition to these activities, he had started elaborate plans for the construction of a canal that was to connect the Loire and the Saône rivers. His pupils were doing their best to relieve the master of all unnecessary details that he might devote himself entirely to the main issues. But when a man has lived the lives of a dozen ordinary mortals, he must expect that sooner or later the engine will show signs of wear and tear and that nothing can be done to restore it to its old efficiency.

On the eve of Easter of the year 1519 Leonardo made his last will and testament, giving evidence of that kindness and generosity of heart which had been so characteristic of him that it had become proverbial. With full premonition of his coming end but without any fear of death, he quietly went to sleep one

beautiful evening in the month of May of the year 1519 and
never woke up.

*As a day well spent gives joyful sleep, so does a life well spent
give joyful death.*

I should, of course, have thought of it, but somehow it had
slipped my mind and it therefore came to me with quite a shock
a few minutes before seven on Saturday night, when I was unexpectedly reminded that we should have prepared for an extra
guest. I was on my way to Frits' house. I had as usual been
working at my *Rembrandt* since early morning and I took the
long way round while going to the market place, and this led
me to the neighborhood of the road to Middelburg, and there I
suddenly beheld a strange procession.

Signor Dante, with stately steps, was approaching the good
city of Veere. But he was not alone. As I should have anticipated
(if I had been just a little brighter), he was accompanied by that
faithful guide who had conducted him on his voyage through
the nether regions. Immediately behind him there walked a
creature that looked like a hog and which carried some kind of
monster on its back. How stupid that I should have forgotten
about Virgil until I actually saw him. Fortunately, there still
was plenty of time to rearrange the seats at our table. I ran back
home, grabbed my bicycle (which, like a cowboy's horse, was
always waiting for the good people of Veere in front of their
houses), and a few minutes later Jo had been given the necessary instructions, and three cups of water had been added to the
soup.

That was the first of our adventures on this strange evening,
and there were to be several others.

Immediately after the last war, Veere had for a short time
been a station of the Dutch flying corps. Being situated on the
Scheldt, it was an ideal spot for seaplanes. But war departments
are fickle institutions, and no sooner had the necessary docks
and hangars been finished than all the plans had been changed

and the fliers had been removed to another part of the country. But once in a while, when the navy held its annual maneuvers near Flushing, a few dozen hydroplanes still came to our town. We were expecting them within a few days, as the fall maneuvers would be held by the beginning of the next week. A young Dutch flier whom we had met through Charles Kingsford-Smith (Charles used to spend practically all his spare time with us while preparing for his flight to America) had arrived a few days before to make the necessary arrangements for the ground crews and the repair men. And as luck or ill luck would have it, he knocked at our door on this evening of all evenings and only a few minutes before our guests were supposed to make their appearance.

When he noticed that we were expecting company, he politely excused himself and said that he must leave immediately, but apparently there was something on his mind which he felt that he must tell us and right away, too.

"I am sorry to disturb you," he said. "I am terribly sorry and, anyway, I can stay only a moment, but I wish you would step out here for just a second and tell me whether I am drunk or something. Just come out here for a second, please, and look at that up there—that spot in the sky. It's the damnedest thing I have ever seen in the air. I have been following it for the last hour and a half but I haven't the slightest idea yet whether it is a glider or a plane or something a kid got for his birthday and that flew away on him. There it goes again! Right there over the mill in front of that dark cloud."

Frits and Hein and I followed his finger and saw that he was right. About a thousand feet or so above us, something resembling a huge bird (but much larger than any birds ever seen in Holland) was rapidly soaring through the air. It made no noise. It apparently had no motor, and the pilot was hanging below the contraption, strapped apparently to the wings and with his feet fastened to the tail.

"I ask you," said the young Dutch officer, even more excited than before, "I ask you, what in God's name is it? Is it some-

Signor Dante and his retinue were slowly walking toward Veere.

thing new the Heinies have just invented? They are said to be making all sorts of queer experiments with gliders. If it is one of their new gliders, I suppose I ought to go up and find out and shoot at it till it goes back home. For that fellow up there has been looking us over for the last hour and a half and in that time he must have been able to photograph every fort in Zeeland. But wait! Wait! Look at him now! S'help me God, he is going to come down! I had better run and see what he is up to, for he may break his neck. Mind if I use your bicycle? I'll bring it back in the morning."

"You'll do nothing of the sort," I answered.

"Why not? What do you want me to do? Take it lying down? Listen, we can't let the Heinies get away with that sort of thing! They should at least realize that we are on the lookout and know what they're up to!"

I took him by the arm and pushed him into the house.

"Take off your spurs," I told him. "You're going to have dinner with us tonight and then you'll find out all about that mysterious flier."

"Then you know who he is? You might tell me, for if I don't do anything about it, I'll get in an awful lot of trouble with the people at The Hague."

I bade him be seated and have a sherry. Then I asked him, "Ever hear of a certain Leonardo da Vinci?"

"You mean that crazy Italian who lived a thousand years ago and who thought that he could fly?"

"Well, perhaps not a thousand years ago. Make it half that time and even a little less. But you are right when you say that he was an Italian and tried to fly."

"That's all very lovely and interesting, but what in heaven's name has it got to do with the Nazi bastard up there who is spying on our forts just now?"

"That's where you are wrong. That isn't a Nazi bastard. That was the old Italian—himself and in person."

"Impossible!"

"In Veere, everything is possible."

"I thought you never touched the stuff! When did you take up drinking?"

"I am as sober as I have been these last fifty years, but if you will sit still for just a moment, I'll tell you something—only promise me that you will never say a word about what you are going to see here tonight."

"Good God! Are you working for the Germans too, and do you want to bribe me to keep my mouth shut by a glass of sherry and a slice of roast beef?"

"Don't be silly," I told him. "We hoped that no one would ever get on to what we have been doing these last four months. You happen to have stumbled on our little secret. We now make you our partner in crime. I have only a few minutes, but here is the story," and I told him about our mysterious dinners.

The young Dutchman absolutely refused to believe me. "The trouble with you," he said, "is that you have been working too hard. You have read too many books. You have gone crazy."

"Remember this is Veere."

"Sure, I know, and I also know that one can get away with a hell of a lot of things in this funny little village. But when you tell me that I am about to have dinner with an Italian who has been dead and buried for the last five hundred years—I tell you, you are cuckoo and I am going home and tell your wife to call for you and bring the doctor. Good night to you all, but I am off!"

And he would have gone too, except that just as he opened the door, he found himself face to face with Leonardo, who in French but with a strong Italian accent asked him whether this was the house where he was expected for dinner that evening. Completely taken aback by this strange meeting, the poor Dutch boy had not the slightest idea what to do. So he clicked his heels in his best military style, gave the new arrival a salute which made me fear that all the buttons of his uniform would snap off, and in his awkward schoolbook French he barked back, *"Oui, monsieur. C'est la maison."*

"Alors, on peut entrer," Leonardo continued, "and I shall be

It was Leonardo, coming down in his glider.

very glad to sit down for a little while. I had not handled my little machine for so many centuries—*on perd l'habitude*—and my back hurts as if I had been painting murals for a couple of months."

I assured him in my not too elegant Italian that a most comfortable chair was awaiting his pleasure then and there, and he was obliging enough to pretend that he understood me and with a sigh of relief he settled down in Erasmus' chair, stretched his legs, showing us the rich rose-colored robe he wore underneath his flying coat, and by clicking his tongue against his palate in the true Italian manner, he gave expression to his feelings of complete satisfaction.

My Dutch friend had followed all this with eyes that almost popped out of his head. At last he found his voice. "This," he whispered to me, "is surely the damnedest thing that has ever happened to me. Tell me once more—is that really old Leonardo?"

"It is."

"O.K. Then I will stay. This is going to be fun!"

"And how!" I answered, "but let me warn you that before the evening is over, the old fellow will have asked you more questions than any living being can hope to answer, and he may know more about flying than you can ever hope to do."

"I don't mind. I've had ten years of flying every kind of crate. I'll hold my own. And now, will you please present me?" For, like all good Dutchmen, he felt that one could not possibly address a stranger without first having been properly introduced.

I asked Leonardo to be allowed to let our friend make his acquaintance. *"E aviatore,"* I added.

"Ecco! un aviatore olandese! Benissimo, benissimo! Parla francese?"

I assured him that he spoke French quite nicely and then I took our flier by the hand, put him next to our Italian guest, and said to him in Dutch, "Now go to it and show him that you know something."

"Won't I though?" and being a pleasant and cheerful young man, he went after his unexpected task with all the eagerness that fliers otherwise reserve for a first assault upon an exceptionally pretty pair of ankles.

Leonardo therefore was off our hands, for after a few agreeable words with Erasmus, who meanwhile had come in by way of the kitchen, he was completely lost in a preliminary bout with the young Dutchman and, as far as I could make out, he was asking him what he thought of the possibility of ever making any extensive flights with gliders. The Dutchman was just about to answer that he thought mighty little of the whole subject of gliders when our two other guests arrived. They did not, however, come in right away. There seemed to be some kind of trouble. It was Virgil who did the explaining and Erasmus who did the translating.

"They don't seem to know quite what to do with their—shall I call them 'companions'?" he explained, and he pointed to the piglike monster I had noticed on the Middelburg road with a little black devil riding on his back.

"What do they want to do with them?" I asked. "They don't want them to come in, I hope."

"No," Erasmus answered, "but they have had a long walk and are tired out. They are wondering whether we could give those creatures something to eat."

"Of course," I said, "just let them tell us what they want. Meat or vegetables or stale bread or milk—or whatever they want."

Erasmus relayed this message to Virgil. Then he turned to Jo, who had joined us to ask what she could get these strange visitors, and said, "I am afraid that none of those would do. Milk and bread are too mild for them, but if you have a few hot coals for them from your kitchen stove and perhaps a little carbolic acid to quench their thirst, that would just about suit them."

"Nothing easier," said our ever-cheerful Jo, and a moment later she returned with a pailful of hot coals from the kitchen

stove and a china bowl full of undiluted carbolic acid which we had bought once upon a time to disinfect an old cesspool in the garden.

Virgil expressed his profound gratitude and said, "Those will be wonderful. The poor things—they are completely exhausted," and a moment later a contented series of grunts and squeaks showed us that Dante's humble companions were enjoying their meal.

Then at last we could introduce everybody to everybody else, and at the same time Hein started the gramophone, but he must have made a mistake, for instead of giving us Jacopo Peri, whom I had chosen for our first number, he started with a Mozart record, *Martern aller Arten* from *Die Entführung aus dem Serail,* sung by Ria Ginster. I was about to go upstairs and correct this error when I caught sight of Leonardo. He seemed so enraptured by the melody that for a moment he had forgotten all about his aviator. Then he looked at Dante, and Dante, for the first time that evening, indulged in a slight movement of the lips which in a normal person would have been called a smile, and both of them were evidently delighted with what they were hearing.

"What was it?" Leonardo asked when the music stopped. I told him. "And who was this Mozart? An Italian?"

"Alas, no. He was merely an Austrian."

"He deserved to have been an Italian," Dante said. "I never heard so lovely a song."

"Neither have I," Leonardo added. "Have you any more of this master's work?"

I assured him that we had enough of Mozart's works to keep him happy for the rest of the evening, but I added that it was about time for dinner.

"Why not combine the two?" Leonardo asked. "We will enjoy our meal all the more if our souls are at peace, listening to these charming melodies. *Che dice il Signor Dante?*"

Il Signor Dante answered that the Signor Leonardo was entirely right. Virgil, too, by way of Erasmus, informed us that he would be delighted, and as for the Dutch flier, we did not bother about him because we knew that he would prefer any kind of American jazz to all the assembled works of Mozart, Beethoven, and Bach. And so we ate our dinner (a meal which, incidentally, greatly pleased our guests) without exchanging more than perhaps a dozen words. But it did not matter, for our guests were having the time of their lives. They listened like men who had been starved for good music during so many years that they were absorbing it like a sun-baked garden which is being drenched by a torrential downpour. Even the Dutch flier seemed slightly impressed.

"Perhaps I never heard enough of that sort of music," he offered by way of apology for nothing in particular. "And I love to look at the faces of those two old men. My! How they are enjoying themselves!"

Music makes for well-regulated meals. At exactly nine o'clock Virgil had consumed the last of the olives, and Dante had absent-mindedly drunk the last drops of our Chianti, and Leonardo had asked a dozen questions about that strange beverage called coffee which Jo had served out of force of habit and which had delighted him as much as it had disgusted Dante.

It was time to rise from the table, and after Erasmus had spoken a short prayer of thanksgiving, followed by an amen on the part of Leonardo and Dante, we moved across the room to the fireplace, and there we made ourselves as comfortable as possible, for outside the first snow was falling, and the house was getting rather chilly. Erasmus, as usual, indulged in his forty winks. He woke up when the aviator dropped the poker with which he had been demonstrating some problem connected with the proper balancing of a modern bomber and, in order to show us that he had not really been asleep ("I merely rested my eyes for a few moments," his usual excuse), he asked Virgil whether he had been doing any writing lately. Virgil said no, he had not done anything really worth while for almost two thousand years. But he now felt like changing some of his *Eclogues* after the rich farms he had seen that afternoon on both sides of the road he and Dante had followed from Middelburg. When Erasmus, thereby flattered by this allusion to Zeeland's richness, returned the compliment by an offhand recital of whole pages from the *Eclogues,* the Latin poet's joy knew no bounds.

"What a delight!" he said, "and what a surprise! After all these many hundreds of years, I am still being remembered? I had never dared to hope for so much fame. When I was told to guide our noble Florentine friend through hell, I felt that I had reached the height of my career. But to discover that you, my most honored pupil, are able to speak my verses and in such pure Latin and after all these many, many years—it is incredible, and I am grateful indeed!"

That, however, was a mere side play, for Leonardo was the star performer of the evening. Having squeezed the Dutch flier so completely dry upon the subject of aeronautics that the poor fellow gasped for air and drank more whiskies and soda than were good for him, he tackled Frits upon the subject of our polders. He wanted to know, first of all, how we had dried the land, next how we kept the water inside the polders at just the right level, how we drained our meadows, how many head of cattle we could feed on how small a piece of land, how we managed our locks, and whether the farms belonged to those who worked them and whether we had the same problem of absentee landlordism which had caused him so much trouble when he was trying to irrigate the plains of Lombardy.

From there Leonardo switched over to music, and it was then that I asked him whether he would be interested in examining a lute which, some twenty years before, I had ordered to be made in Munich, a rather complicated affair with four extra strings— four so-called *Brummer.* He said that he would be delighted, and I went upstairs to get it. I had long since given up trying to learn it seriously. I had found the lute so much more difficult than the violin, especially for the right hand, that it used up all the time I needed for my fiddle, and my fiddling too was rapidly going to pieces, now that I had begun to write those big books to which I owed the fact that I could live in our beloved Veere. I still knew enough about the lute to be able to keep the instrument in tune, and when Leonardo got his hands on it, he found it in perfect working order. He was as pleased as a pianist who, after a long trip in the hinterland, once more puts his feet on the pedals of a Steinway Grand.

"A beautiful piece of craftsmanship," he said, looking tenderly at the long, slender neck. "But tell me, how do you tune these four extra strings."

I explained that they were supposed to be tuned according to the principal chords you intended to use and showed him how it was done.

"You play too?" he asked.

I told him that I had tried to learn it but that I had found it impossible to be faithful to both the lute and to the violin. He answered that he agreed and that the lute, if one wanted to play it well, took all of one's time. Then he asked me whether I had one of my violins in the house, and I said yes. My second-best one. I kept my Santo Serafino at home, where it was much drier than at Frits' place, which was inhabited only two days a week.

"Get your violin, will you?" Leonardo begged me and, after he had carefully inspected it, he asked me to tune it to his lute.

"And now we will play," he said. "We will play something in the old Italian style and we shall play to honor the greatest of our Italian poets. We will play something slow and stately and in keeping with Signor Dante's incomparable style."

Then followed one of those delightful "jam sessions" which make people who are not familiar with music gasp with wonderment, though it is really extremely simple, if you happen to have been born with the gift. Leonardo and I began to improvise. We felt our way around for a moment, then sort of got the "feel" of each other, united on a comfortable key, and off we were.

We kept at it for more than an hour.

I do not remember what we played. Ideas came and ideas went, and sometimes the lute took the lead and sometimes the fiddle, but these changes were achieved by a sort of silent instinctive consent and as soon as one of the members of our audience asked us, "Now give us something French," or "Play that tune the way the old Flemings would have done it," or "Let us have that in the Spanish manner," we did as they bade us do as automatically and easily as well-trained horses going from a trot into a gallop.

To spend an evening doing that sort of thing when we could have talked to the author of *The Divine Comedy* may seem a complete waste of time, but if the author of the greatest poem ever written in any language is tongue-tied and refuses to utter more than a few words every fifteen minutes or so, there is little you can do about it. Apparently the poor exile had been for so long a time accustomed to keep his ideas to himself that he had lost the habit of thinking out loud. Whereas Leonardo, dwelling most of his life in the companionship of one of the princes for whom he worked or spending his days in a studio filled with young and enthusiastic apprentices, was completely at his ease in any kind of company. And being an artist rather than a writer, his emotions could find expression by means of his fingers. Unlike Dante, he was not merely a teller of tales who must write down combinations of words to communicate his ideas to his fellow men. Accustomed to re-create the world by means of a lump of clay or a brush or the entrails of a sheep transformed into a string, he was able to convey an almost endless variety of nuances, shades, accents, and intonations to his audience by everything he said. This, by the way, is a quality I have detected in a great many other painters and sculptors and musicians, who are apt to be much better conversationalists than their colleagues of the goose quill.

The manner of our parting was the usual one. But to our surprise, the young flier excused himself immediately after our guests had disappeared. We urged him to stay for at least one more whisky and soda, but he said no—he was very busy with a number of reports and had to send a call through to the navy department in The Hague. We knew that as it was Saturday, every official of the navy department had left the office hours before. He therefore must have something else on his mind, and as it could not be a girl (Veere was not that kind of village), we were at a loss to account for his haste in bidding us farewell. But after all, he was free, white, and twenty-one, and it was none of our business.

As soon as he had closed the door behind him, Frits found the solution.

"I'll bet you ten guilders to one," he said, "old Leonardo talked him into giving him a ride in his airplane. It is dark, and nobody will be any the wiser."

"I'll take you on. We will ask him tomorrow, for I told him to come for breakfast. Good night and thanks for a most delightful evening. Good night, Jo-o-o-o! Good night, Hein!"

From the kitchen came a cheerful good night—and the remark that one of those two Italians must have been very handsome when he was young.

I stepped out into the dark, for there was supposed to be a full moon, and when the calendar said "full moon," Veere's six street lanterns were not lighted—a matter of economy. The snow was beginning to melt, and it was very slippery. I had to walk carefully. Just before I reached our own house I stopped, struck by a strange noise.

A moment later I knew that I had lost my guilder. High up in the air, a flying machine was gaily looping the loop.

CHAPTER XVII

How We Entertained MONSIEUR MONTAIGNE and
DOCTOR RABELAIS and How Their Visit Almost
Led to a Public Riot in Our Peaceful Village
of Veere

JIMMIE WAS right—something was always happening in Veere.
Frits had just returned from a short trip to Paris, and a friend
of his in The Hague who was going to the Indies had wished a
minni-piano on him. As Frits did not play a note, it was of no
particular use to him, but as a piece of furniture it was entirely
inoffensive, and he therefore had had no good reason to say no.
And, as he sagely observed, "A piano is like a Sanskrit dictionary. It may seem rather useless at first, but you never can tell
when it may come in handy."

Little Minni was therefore placed right underneath the staircase, and a tuner was ordered to come from Middelburg and
put the instrument in order, for untuned pianos are as annoy-
ing as clocks that are not going.

As for the visit to Paris in connection with some loan his
firm happened to be floating just then, while it had been a success from a financial point of view (the boom, remember, was
in full swing, and the public would buy anything), the trip had
been an eye opener to Frits, and he came back with anxious forebodings about the future of France.

"I never saw anything like it," he told us. "I know this will
hurt Lucie's feelings, for she loves the French in spite of everything, but it is really terrible."

"What is terrible?" Lucie asked, who, as every other Sunday, was having a late breakfast with us. Nine o'clock was very late for breakfast in Veere.

"Everything," Frits answered.

"But 'everything' is so vague," Lucie protested. "Give me a few examples."

"Very well, then, here are some of the details. In England they are merely asleep. They never had much imagination, the British, but the crew that is in charge right now is hopeless. They seem to notice nothing of what is happening in Germany. When some of us warn them that in another couple of years this fellow Hitler will be able to lick the whole world, they smile pleasantly and say, 'Let him get strong. He'll use his army to destroy the Bolshies, and that is exactly what we want.' And when you ask them what they think he is building all his sub-marines for and all his tanks and machine guns, they suddenly get up on a very high horse and tell you, 'My dear sir, the Germans have not yet forgotten what happened to their naval ambitions during the last war. They will never repeat that mistake.' That this fellow Hitler also has the strongest army the world has ever seen is a matter of complete indifference to them.

"And then we are off. I ask them to remember that during the Great War, they had the American fleet on their side, but that only makes them mad, and they have their answer ready. 'But of course the Americans will again fight with us.' No use telling them that this time the Americans might refuse to be as obliging as they were in 1917, and that the American people have grown sick and tired of being called Uncle Shylock, and that it will be much more difficult to get them into the next war.

"But in France—God help us! In France they are not only fast asleep when it comes to the present situation, but the whole country is rotten through and through. Everybody is thinking only of himself. Every man and every woman has his or her price. You can buy ministers and, if necessary, you can buy their wives. To get this loan of ours started—why, in England we could have done it for the price of a couple of ads in two or three of the big newspapers. But in France we had to grease everybody's palm, from the minister of finance down to the fellow in a cocked hat who stands in front of the Banque de France."

"That was a nice thing to do," said Lucie, who was going to love the French in spite of everything. "An honest, purehearted little Dutchman bribing French officials!"

"Don't be foolish," Frits told her. "It did not bother my conscience in the least little bit. I never knew anything about it. We employed three French lawyers. They did all the dirty work. They merely sent us the bills, and we paid them after they had showed us a list of the men they had 'approached.' It was that list that frightened me. It made me feel that there was not an honest man left in all of France. And if there should be another war, I am afraid that this time there would not be another Verdun. There won't even be much of a fight. France will blow up like a kid's balloon hit by papa's cigar.

"And worst of all, the brighter Frenchmen seem perfectly aware of this, but they shrug their shoulders and say, 'What can we do? It is the government that is at fault. We now have a democracy, *notre chère démocratie française'!* And they are right. They have their famous French democracy. Every third-rate provincial lawyer considers himself a Danton, every country doctor feels that he is destined to become another Clemenceau. But none of them care a hoot for the country as a whole. On every street corner someone is making a speech. In every café someone is writing out a new constitution. Once upon a time, France was a nation of philosophers. They were a bit vague, these famous men of the eighteenth century, but at least they accomplished something. Today, France is merely a debating society in which everybody talks and nobody listens. How those fellows love to fill the air with words! But to do this, they need a lot of money, and that money they will take from anyone willing to give them a little financial support. In the meantime, the country goes to hell."

This led to a general discussion upon the subject of *la France éternelle,* and the talk finally dwindled down to an inquiry into the state of modern French literature. For reasons known only to the Lord Himself, the world suddenly had got tremendously interested in the works of Marcel Proust. Neither Frits nor I (and in this one respect, even Lucie agreed with us) thought very highly of Proust. We found him unhealthy and attributed his momentary success to the fact that having spent all his life surrounded by superficial and dull people, who thought only of themselves and their own petty interests, the sickly Proust was ideally fitted to be the prophet of a time that had lost all faith in itself.

Jimmie, who never had had much use for the French (for no particular reason except that she just did not like them), soon dropped out of the conversation and started knitting away at a pair of woolen socks she had promised to the captain of the *Nieuw Amsterdam.* Lucie and Frits and I then continued by ourselves until it was time to switch over from breakfast to lunch. This was easily accomplished, for the process consisted in starting a fresh pot of coffee and ordering some more toast. By the time Kaatje had brought the coffee and the toast, Lucie had sufficiently regained her spirits to reaffirm her conviction that no matter what might happen, there always would be a France. Not only that, but she prophesied the coming of a new and brilliant crop of writers who would save the French from themselves and would bring about that "renewal of the spirit" which had never failed to take place in the glorious land of the Gauls whenever they were on the point of being engulfed by either a foreign or a domestic enemy.

It was this discussion (which, by the way, never got anywhere at all, like most such talks) which made me suggest to Frits that we invite the two French men of letters who had always interested me more than any others—Montaigne and Rabelais.

"A queer combination," said Frits, "but an interesting one.

And they will be much more cheerful company than our gloomy friend from hell last week."

I told him that that was hardly the way to talk about the author of *The Divine Comedy,* but he refused to apologize. "Old Leonardo was a grand person," he agreed, "but that long-faced Florentine with the laurel leaves dangling from his cap, who sat and sat and drank our wine and said nothing at all and made Jo feed hot coals and carbolic acid to his pet hog—no, I am afraid he did not impress me very much. But the old painter and inventor—he was wonderful! I hope he got home safely and did not break his neck."

Then and there we decided on our new guests. Next Saturday we would request the honor of the presence of François Rabelais, M.D., of Lyons, France, and Michel de Montaigne, honorary citizen of Rome, Italy.

They had been contemporaries and they had been Frenchmen. Here was a chance to go in for some fancy culinary effects. For once, too, we would have experienced wine drinkers with us, as Montaigne came from Bordeaux, and Rabelais hailed from the Touraine. There was only one wine that was good enough for these true connoisseurs, and by chance I had been offered a dozen bottles of it only a few days before. I refer, of course, to Châteauneuf du Pape and Châteauneuf of the vintage of the year 1921. Neither Frits nor I believed in the theory that a meal can be enjoyed only if you serve a different wine with every course. One kind, either red or white, drunk all through the meal is much more satisfactory, provided it is of outstanding quality, and the sun-baked grapes of the hillsides near the old papal city of Avignon—when they are at their best—no, they have never been surpassed.

The menu was not so easily settled. We intended to do our best, and I felt that I needed Lucie's help if we wanted to surpass all our previous efforts. We spent the whole afternoon on the meal and turned the leaves of my old *Cuisinier français* until both of us were dizzy. Here is what we finally chose.

First of all, a *soupe à l'oignon à la Stanislas*. This was absolutely safe. Every Frenchman seems to have an inborn passion for onion soup, and so we could not possibly go wrong.

Next, *filets de sole à la sauce ravigote,* and as our main course, *faisans à la Périgueux.* The latter would have to be served in the ancient style with their feathers on so as to give them a life-like appearance, a job which Hein, who was the handy man around the house, would love to undertake. The vegetables were to be the inevitable string beans and carrots, for Holland in the fall does not offer much of a choice when it comes to fresh vegetables, and we tried as much as possible to do without canned ones.

After the pheasant, there was to be a huge bowl of salad with hard-boiled eggs and that tiny bit of garlic in the dressing which all Frenchmen and Italians so dearly love. For the benefit of Erasmus and the other Dutchmen, there also must be a small leek cut up in slices, and tarragon vinegar, of course.

And then (for this time we would have guests who knew what a real dinner should be), an extra course right after the bird— a course consisting of cold lobster with mayonnaise (Lucie had offered to make her own special mayonnaise for us that evening), and finally, for dessert, a *macédoine de fruits à la kirsch.* The fruits would have to be preserved ones, but at The Hague we could get the pineapple in which to serve it.

Coffee? Yes—no—yes! Erasmus had come to depend upon his little after-dinner cup, so why not let the others try it too? If they did not like it, they need not drink it.

After dinner, only one liqueur—the last bottle of our 1837 cognac, but, as far as I was concerned, the best was hardly good enough for Montaigne. I owed him a heavy debt of gratitude. When I was quite young, his book had become my Bible, and it has remained so ever since.

I need offer no apologies for my interest in Montaigne. He is one of those perfectly mannered philosophers whom you can safely take with you into any kind of company. Perhaps a word or so beforehand to your hostess, just as an act of civility. "Elizabeth, my dear, do you mind if I bring a very charming Frenchman with me tonight? He won't be any bother, he is an old friend and I am sure you will like him."

"Why, of course not! Bring him by all means, and what did you say his name was?"

"Montaigne—Michel de Montaigne. He is a writer. Several of his books have been translated into English. You may have heard of him."

"Of course I have! The last time we were on the Riviera we met some delightful people by that name—French people from Bordeaux, I think. Perhaps he's related to them?"

"Very likely, and he will be so much interested to hear about his cousins. Thank you for your kindness! You want to see us at about seven—if I remember correctly."

"That is what the invitation said. But I know you are not a drinker. It will probably be eight o'clock before we sit down at table, so suppose you and your friend come at seven-thirty, unless he insists upon a few cocktails."

"I hardly think so. He has the gout. He has to be very careful about what he drinks."

"Fine! Seven-thirty it is, and we'll be delighted to meet your French friend, Monsieur de Montaigne. Good night! My love to Jimmie and Noodle."

"Good night and thank you."

Whereupon you tell Michel that you are sorry you have got to take him out for dinner the night he is coming, but it is Thursday and the servants have that day off. Besides, your friends, the Whoozises, have a lovely house. They also put up a very good table. The husband is perhaps not very exciting, but Elizabeth is very beautiful, if a bit gushing. And Jimmie will pretend that she has a headache and will use that as an excuse to go home early. And then we can sit in the library the rest of the evening and have a glass of hot Swedish punch and talk about the happy days the last time we met in Paris.

Then it is Thursday, and the party is a delightful affair. Your

677

friend Michel is the success of the evening. He has been every-where and he knows everybody and he is terribly good at tell-ing amusing stories, and one of the guests, a college professor, has even read some of his books, though he does not entirely approve of the author's style, and the hostess is delighted and is very grateful to you for having brought that charming and delightful guest.

But Rabelais? He is a different kettle of fish altogether, and the moment you mention his name, your friend raises an in-quiring eyebrow and says, "Rabelais! You surely cannot mean that you would expose us to the man who wrote those horrible stories about a giant—let me see—what was his name? Gar-gantua or something like that—just like the big ape. For if it is he, I will have to rearrange my whole table. I could not very well let him sit next to Aunt Mary, who is going to be with us that night. Her father, you remember, was a bishop. And then John's boss is going to be there too, the president of the bank for which he works, and he is an elder in a Congregational church. He is rather a puritan too, except that he likes his cock-tails, and of course, I don't want to spoil John's chances. I sup-pose, if you insist, I have got to let you bring him, but ask him not to use those dreadful words of which his books are so full. They may be funny to some people, but I never could see why words must be dirty in order to be funny, and so—you won't mind, will you?—but please tell him to be as nice as that other friend of yours, that Monsieur de Montaigne whom you brought that other time. We all loved him!"

Unfortunately, that is more or less the reputation poor Dr. Rabelais has acquired during the last four hundred years. He is now chiefly known as a man who wallowed in dirt for dirt's sake, who created gigantic figures, obscene and grotesque fig-ures, for the sheer joy of having them perform obscene and grotesque acts, and as an author who may have been funny in the eyes of his contemporaries but who today should no longer be tolerated in polite society.

There is an element of truth in this harsh condemnation. Gargantua and Pantagruel are not quite housebroken from the point of view of our modern world. They are a little too earthy for people who live so far removed from the soil. And as for the abbey of Thélème, where everybody was supposed to behave exactly as he liked—no, such an institution too cannot really have been a very happy place in our eyes, and those jokes which made the English of the time of Queen Bess rock with laughter (for Rabelais was the most popular of all Continental writers in the England of the last half of the sixteenth century) —those verbal quips too, which he handled with such fatal facility—are no longer welcome among the kind of people who are on intimate terms with the findings of Professor Freud and his disciples and who now know what it all means.

I realize all this and, as I said a moment ago, I even agree with some of it, but just the same, Rabelais is one of the authors who fills a very prominent niche in my private pantheon of literature. I did not bestow this place of honor upon him on account of his literary abilities. I doubt whether he really wrote very well, and I agree with those who hold that his work is no longer readable. He is almost as much dated as Sir Walter Scott or John Galsworthy.

But there is no use in arranging a man hunt after him, chasing the poor Doctor with the bloodhounds of our watch-and-ward societies and delivering him into the hands of the local magistrates. He is really no longer a menace to the younger generation. The younger generation knows him as the man who wrote that funny book about funny giants who would pull up castles like carrots and then would throw them at their enemies as if they had been pebbles, after the pattern of Dean Swift's Brobdingnagians, and the very young one is only familiar with all the different supermen of the air and the comics, compared to whom Gargantua and his cronies are gentlemen of high moral repute.

Then why did I want to meet Rabelais so much that I asked

him for dinner in preference to hundreds of other more likely candidates?

For one thing, although he may not have given us a book of superior literary value, he did something almost as difficult. Like our friend, Don Miguel de Cervantes, he sat himself down, picked up his pen and his inkhorn, and gave life to a couple of paper characters who not only incorporated themselves into every known tongue but who were so full of vitality and joy of living that they became infinitely more real than hundreds of millions of people who have actually existed.

To succeed in this ambitious enterprise, my good Frits, takes a rare amount of courage and ability. For the author undertakes to set himself up in open competition with the good Lord who, as both the Old and the New Testaments inform us, is not exactly conspicuous for his lack of envy and who only tolerates such rivalry when he fully approves of the efforts of his human contestants. Let me show you what I mean by a concrete example. What does King Henry of France mean to us of today? At best a name and a date, unless we remember His Majesty because he was said to have been the lover of the beautiful Diane de Poitiers, the girl whose statue still delights us when we meet her in the Louvre.

But say Gargantua or Pantagruel, and we find ourselves immediately in the heart of a mysterious land of giants and titans, with King Grangousier making merry war on his neighbor, King Picrochole, and with Friar John—and what a friar!—deliberately and successfully upsetting all the accepted rules of sound pedagogy, while in the distance we behold the abbey of Thélème standing forth in majestic glory and quietly reflecting its high walls and its slender turrets in the blue waves of a lovely mountain lake.

Not that Rabelais was the only writer who ever succeeded in doing this sort of thing. We have already mentioned the author of *Don Quixote*. Then there was the famous case connected with Queen Anne of England. That lady was about as complete a nonentity as ever graced a throne. Talk about Queen Anne, and at best she will remind the average listener of beautiful little tables with very slender legs (not by any means modeled after those of Her Majesty!) and of certain other pieces of furniture that stood in Grandmother's parlor. But mention the two magic words *Robinson Crusoe,* and forthwith a lonely island rises from the placid Pacific and a man with a beard and a funny-looking peaked cap is anxiously studying strange footsteps in the sands of the shore, and we become young once more and we have just built ourselves a hut in the empty lot next door and we are waiting for our own man Friday (our younger brother turned Blackamoor by means of a burnt cork) to come and tell us that he has seen the sails of a ship rapidly approaching our domains, which means that we must make ready to defend our possessions against still another attack of buccaneers.

Or, again, who today still takes the slightest interest in George I or George II, or, for that matter, in the policies of a Walpole or a Pitt? But every one of us is so thoroughly familiar with the land of Lilliput that we would not be in the least surprised if in some hidden corner of New Zealand, a few hundred miles beyond Erewhon, a traveler should suddenly have come upon the last remaining survivors of the tribe of the Lilliputians, living there peacefully in their tiny houses, eating from miniature plates and raising diminutive children who go sailing in nutshells on lakes no larger than a bathtub.

And then—I had almost forgotten him—there was our guest of last week, who gave us an Inferno (which he most surely can never have seen with his own eyes) vastly more convincing to us than all the real countries any of us have ever read about in Baedeker.

One final idea upon this pleasant subject. Were not the men and women and the dogs and cats whom we met in the pages of Hans Christian Andersen's fairy tales infinitely more real than those flesh-and-blood uncles and aunts whom we had to visit every Sunday and of whom we remember nothing except that Uncle Moritz wore a wig and that Aunt Amy had a red nose as the result of a perpetual cold? But was there any doubt about the number of buttons on the coat of Hans Christian's soldier?

As for the life of Rabelais, there really is not very much to tell. He was born about two years before Columbus discovered America. He saw the light of day in Chinon, a small town in the province of Touraine. His father was either an apothecary (most likely) or a tavernkeeper (less likely). While still quite young he was persuaded to enter a Franciscan monastery, but he soon became suspected of heresies, chiefly on account of his preference for the study of the law over that of religion. He was not actually found guilty, but just the same he thought it wiser to bid farewell to his Franciscan brethren and to join the Benedictines, who made a specialty of learning, in contrast to the Franciscans, who went in primarily for preaching and were rather suspicious of the wisdom of this world.

After five more years of a cloistered existence, Rabelais began to feel that he had made a mistake in the choice of his vocation and that he would never make a good monk. He then tried to qualify as a secular priest, but with even less success. As he would have to make some kind of living, he next played with the idea of becoming a physician. He went to the University of Montpellier and at last he had found his true vocation. In less than a year's time he was allowed to deliver lectures on Galen and Hippocrates, the two great oracles upon whose books (written respectively thirteen hundred and nineteen hundred years before) the doctors of that day depended exclusively for their diagnoses and clinical information.

Here and there in Italy a few courageous chirurgeons had reached the bold conclusion that in order to know all about sick people one should with one's own eyes observe and study sick people. But as the Church remained adamant in its opposition to the dissecting of human bodies, anatomy was still in its infancy, and when the physician came to the bedside of his patient, he would look up his symptoms in his copies of Galen and Hippocrates and would then dose him according to the

Montaigne's ivory tower.

somewhat antiquated prescriptions of these ancient worthies. It was not a very satisfactory system from the point of view of the patient, who usually died, but it saved his doctor from being burned at the stake, and the doctors therefore were quite willing to let bad enough alone.

In the year 1532, Rabelais left Montpellier, knowing as much about medicine as could be learned in those days of endless pills and purges, and settled down in the city of Lyons, where he was appointed intern to the town hospital and was allowed to do something so bold that it was considered positively revolutionary. He was given permission to lecture on anatomy with demonstrations from the human body.

It was during his internship in Lyons that Rabelais began to do a little writing, as we would say today. Out of these early attempts grew the gigantic world of Gargantua, Pantagruel, and all their jovial companions. He worked at his books only in his spare time—or at least he said so—but the city fathers, who soon became aware of his literary ambitions, had reasons to doubt this and were not at all pleased. The pride of their hospital was supposed to attend to the business of curing the sick and could not go gallivanting all over the countryside whenever his muse got hold of him. This was a serious matter, for, contrary to all rules, the eminent Dr. Rabelais had got into the habit of taking French leave whenever he tired of his job and on such occasions he was apt to stay away for two or three weeks at a time, only showing up when he had finished a few more chapters and was ready to undergo a little more hospital drudgery.

As a sixteenth-century surgeon was not, as a rule, a rich man, the magistrates at first wondered where their doctor went during those self-granted vacations. Rabelais was more than willing to tell. As a young man he had gained the good will of a very powerful family—that of the du Bellays. When one of the du Bellay sons became a cardinal, Rabelais on several occasions accompanied him to Rome. This token of high clerical favor gave him such an excellent social rating with the Lyons magistrates that instead of fining him, as they would have done any ordinary doctor, or curtly dismissing him, they meekly appointed a substitute whenever their regular house physician chose to play hooky. It was, from their intern's point of view, an almost ideal arrangement and undoubtedly of great benefit to the patients.

Well, the years went by, and the Rabelaisian manuscript increased in size so much that it had attracted the attention of both the court and the Sorbonne. The Sorbonne (ever faithful to its reputation of being an icehouse of reactionary sentiments) gave evidence of its interest in this strange medical cleric by condemning his books and ordering them to be burned by the public hangman. That was a sign to the royal court, then presided over by the amiable and accomplished King Francis I, to show its appreciation of the Doctor's works by reading them, by laughing over them most uproariously, and by giving an unmistakable hint to the theologians of His Majesty's most loyal University of Paris to please mind their own business and allow the favorite author of the King to go on writing as he pleased.

As a further token of his approval, the monarch, in the year 1550, obtained for Dr. Rabelais (via the inevitable du Bellays) two livings which allowed the eminent author to devote himself exclusively to his literary labors, for it is now known that he never officiated in either Meudon or Saint-Christophe de Jambet. He contented himself with pocketing his pay and lived happily, and why not? as it was the custom of the times and no one took offense at a little graft of that sort.

Three years later, Dr. the Reverend Father François Rabelais died, and that is all there is to my story. Just that and nothing more. But as with several of our other guests, the work they had done was far more important than they themselves and, in the case of Rabelais, the book was the thing or, more precisely, the hero of the book, the mysterious giant called Gargantua.

That name had not been invented by Rabelais. Gargantua had already enjoyed several centuries of fame and popularity long before Rabelais was born. He had started his career as a

kind of medieval Paul Bunyan, but he did not really force himself upon the attention of the public at large until Rabelais got
hold of him and gave him the leading role in his famous satire.
As Gargantua, as far as I know, has not yet been put into the
movies, his adventures are probably unknown to the younger
generation which now derives most of its literary and historical
information from the learned pedagogues of Hollywood. It may
therefore not be out of place if I present you with a very brief
synopsis of Gargantua's career.

In volume one, a behemothian baby is born to behemothian
parents. His arrival is celebrated by a colossal feast at which both
the eating and the drinking assume mammoth proportions.
Next the hero goes to school, and this gives Rabelais a chance to
express his opinions upon the subject of contemporary educational methods. The eminent doctor had as little love for the
system of the Schoolmen (who were then still in full control of
all educational establishments) as I have for that under which I
was brought up in my native land fifty years ago. He exposes it
in all its preposterous absurdity. He shows it up for what it is
and then asks why children must be forced to wander for years
through the petrified forest of a dead learning when, with so
much more profit to themselves, they could have been turned
loose into the delectable gardens of the Muses which the hu-
manists had once more made available to the public at large
but from which the younger generation was still excluded by
all sorts of theological *verboten* signs.

Having thus paid his respects to the field of education, the
good doctor then examines the inanities of warfare as practiced in every part of the world, and through the mouth of a
certain Friar John he gives us a circumstantial account of the
violence with which Gargantua's father and his neighbor, King
Picrochole, went after each other, smote their hundreds of
thousands, and left everything exactly as it had been before.

This conflict which settled nothing having come to an end by
means of a peace which settled even less, Gargantua decides to
go in for a short detour which leads him into the field of social

685

service. I am sorry to say that the method he chooses to improve his fellow men and make them conscious of their duties toward each other is not quite according to our modern pattern. There was, of course, nothing new about the idea of building a religious retreat. Monasteries had been going up for more than twelve hundred years. But the abbey of Thélème of which Gargantua became the founder was indeed a unique institution. For whereas, in all other similar establishments, you were supposed to spend your life in sackcloth and ashes, performing highly uncongenial tasks, the rules of Thélème insisted that you do exactly as you please.

In making an arrangement of that sort, Rabelais showed a lamentable lack of understanding of man's true nature. I cannot for the life of me imagine anything more dreadful than to be obliged all day long to do what I want to do. But I think that I know what was actually in the good Doctor's mind. Rabelais lived in an age of repressions and as a physician he realized what too much moral restraint will do to the average normal human being. His abbey, with its gay device of "Do as you please," was really a sort of sixteenth-century sanatorium maintained for the benefit of those who needed a few months' escape from the burdens of everyday life. Our modern psychiatrists might well look into this matter. An abbey of Thélème built right in the heart of many of our more isolated country districts would save hundreds of thousands of poor women from their unavoidable fate and would therefore be a godsend to the taxpayer, one quarter of whose involuntary contributions to the state now go into the pockets of our specialists in charge of our lunatic asylums.

There is a lot more to the chronicle of Gargantua, but these little excerpts will do. They will have shown you that Dr. Rabelais' flight into the realm of fancy was of a very different nature from that of Signor Dante, who also constructed a nonexistent world in order that he might give us his reflections upon its living counterpart. What Dante meant to achieve was so simple

The Abbey of Thélème—the dream of Rabelais' life.

that everybody could understand it. He meant to settle his private score with those who had thwarted him in his political ambitions. But even now, after almost four centuries of careful studies, the friends of Dr. Rabelais are not quite sure what he had in mind when he sent his hero forth upon his strange peregrinations and created his Pantagruelian world to prove—what?

That is what we would like to know but have never yet found out with sufficient certainty to reduce the good Doctor to a single formula.

According to Webster, Pantagruelism is "the theory or practice of Pantagruel; buffoonery or coarse humor with a satirical or serious purpose." Suppose we dismiss the reference to the "coarse humor." You and I, my dear Frits, belong to a race which has its roots so deeply struck into the soil of the Middle Ages that this so-called coarseness is still part of our own nature. We are careful to hide it from strangers, for they would not understand and would merely be embarrassed. But when we are alone with the simple folk of Zeeland or Holland or Flanders, we not only can be very, very Rabelaisian (in the accepted Anglo-Saxon sense of the word), but we find ourselves completely at home in that strange atmosphere of puns, whimsicalities, drolleries, jocosities, quiddities, quirks, and quips which seem to have been the delight of the people of four hundred years ago. To them, the much-decried vulgarity of Rabelais was not at all out of place. It fulfilled a perfectly natural literary function and it was the method by means of which Rabelais hoped to make people take an interest in what he had to say.

The fact that from the King down almost every Frenchman of that era was able to derive a sincere enjoyment from his copy of the *Grandes et inestimables Chroniques* proves that the author had been right in choosing that particular form of approach.

And now one final word, almost inevitable in our age that is so conscious of its social obligations toward its fellow countrymen. Did Rabelais have what nowadays we call a "message"? I doubt it. I find no evidence that he ever thought of himself as a reformer and I am sure that he would have greatly resented being classified among the contemporary uplifters. But in spite of his pretense that he wrote only to please himself, he must have known that there was a great deal more to his book than appeared on the surface.

Rabelais was a bright fellow and apparently a most kind-hearted person. He lived in a world of gross superstition and ignorance, a world in which people were continually committing acts of the most inexcusable cruelty and for no very evident reason. It is undoubtedly true that during the previous century there had been a certain enlightenment among the better situated classes, those who could afford that leisure which is necessary for the development of the graces of life. But the submerged masses were still as hopelessly brutalized as they had always been. They continued to share their grubby existence with their domestic animals. They never had quite enough to eat and were prevented from committing all sorts of abominable acts of lawlessness upon each other only by that fear of hell by means of which the Church had managed to keep its charges within certain rather elementary but highly necessary bounds of decency for at least part of the time.

Rabelais wanted to depict the world in which he lived in such a way that everyone would understand him, and he chose to do this by creating his absurd world of giants. Erasmus (whom Rabelais revered as his master), being a different kind of person, had made his little puppets dance their merry jigs in his *Praise of Folly*. To show his fellow men what he thought of the prevailing state of society, Thomas More had created his *Utopia,* that he might depict the kind of universe of which he dreamed as the ultimate and most desirable place of residence for all men of good will. Cervantes had given form and shape to his preposterous knight that the creature might persuade his fellow Spaniards to take stock of themselves and perhaps mend their ways so that they would no longer be the laughingstock of the rest of the world. I have already mentioned Dean Swift and his Lilliputians and Brobdingnagians who were to make the self-satisfied Georgians conscious of their own foibles and short-comings. Still one century later, Samuel Butler returned from his disastrous sheep-raising adventure in New Zealand with news about *Erewhon,* the Land of Nowhere, which was so wisely administered that it should serve as an example to all others and become the Land of Everywhere.

Rabelais, being a Frenchman of the early half of the sixteenth century, had quite naturally availed himself of that literary form which he knew to be best suited to his own kind of reader. And by sticking to his last, he undoubtedly succeeded in making himself the most brilliant social exponent of his own era. He pretended to be immoderately desirous of life because he felt a deep hatred for the image of death which grinned at him from every corner. He acted the clown that he might hide that hopeless sense of melancholy which was really at the bottom of his sensitive nature and he played the fool because he knew that that was the only way in which he could make his neighbors partake of at least some of his wisdom. To sum it all up in a single sentence, Rabelais, in order to achieve his ultimate purpose, was willing to let himself be condemned for the very vulgarities by means of which he endeavored to cover up his deep and everlasting love for his fellow men.

Wherever I go, my copy of the *Essais* of Michel de Montaigne accompanies me. Not that I read it every morning and evening, as our ancestors used to peruse their Old Testament. I am not obliged to face the odds of a Dutch skipper of the sixteenth century who had set forth to conquer a tropical empire fifty times larger than the homeland and who depended for his safety against hundreds of thousands of natives upon a handful of ex-convicts armed with harquebuses and swords. My tribulations are of a different sort and do not as constantly affect me. But when the whole world seems to be out of gear (as it does these days with ever-increasing regularity), then it is very soothing to have old Michel by the side of your bed and spend half an hour communing with him before you find escape in sleep.

I have been fortunate enough in life to come across quite a few people who were endowed with such delightfully even temperaments that they could take you completely out of yourself and were able to make you forget all the tribulations of the day. But the number of books able to perform this same useful service is very small indeed. I tried to write them all down last night and I could not think of more than half a dozen which qualified for my list of honor, and think of the millions of books that have been printed since old John Gooseflesh, *vulgo* Gutenberg, died in poverty and obscurity!

Now Montaigne is the one man who has never failed me, and for that reason I respect and venerate his name. Sometimes, I must confess, I will skip a few of his classical references, for I was taught Latin and Greek so badly that even after seven years of hard labor among Homer and Virgil they are still picture puzzles to me which have to be solved more by luck than by actual knowledge.

Montaigne, who seems to have absorbed his classics together with his mother's milk, quoted Homer and Ovid as readily as I quote Goethe or Vondel. It meant absolutely nothing to him to slide from French into the tongue of the Romans and the Athenians and then back again into his native French. To me, those lines of Plutarch and Cicero, with which he juggled so elegantly, mean a painful groping for half-forgotten words and completely forgotten rules of syntax, and therefore I usually hasten as quickly as I can through those pages in which the Frenchman indulges in his favorite hobby. That, however, is an easy trick for a fast reader (as any honest book reviewer will confess), and there remains the bulk of the text, which like a mighty mountain stream rushes toward the sea through a landscape of unparalleled charm and loveliness. Let me but spend half an hour on the banks of this river, and all will be well again with me and with the world at large. Wherefore I here and now pay homage to Michel de Montaigne's memory and gratefully proclaim myself his most humble pupil.

Montaigne and Doctor Rabelais

My good teacher was born in February of the year 1533. He therefore was another one of those winter babies who have played such an important role in the history of the world because they were conceived in the spring, the time of year which from the beginning of creation has been the natural mating season for all mammals, including Homo sapiens.

Montaigne's family name was Eyquem, but the Eyquem had been dropped after the family had obtained possession of the castle of Montaigne, not far from the city of Bordeaux in the southern part of France. Michel's father, Pierre Eyquem de Montaigne, had been in trade and so had his grandfather. Those who did not like Michel (and he was by far too witty not to have made himself some very choice enemies) were very apt to hint that this change in name had been the result of a desire to make the public at large forget the very honorable beginnings of the now distinguished family. There may have been some truth in this accusation. The desire for a fine-looking genealogy going back to the days of Caesar and a coat of arms of sixteen quarterings is a perfectly normal one and a very harmless hobby, compared with the foolish ways in which rich people are apt to spend their money. But as Montaigne, in his books at least, gives no evidence whatsoever of any kind of intellectual and political snobbery, we can dismiss this bit of gossip as envy on the part of his less enlightened neighbors.

Today they would probably have attacked him from a somewhat different angle. They would have inquired into his mother's ancestry and then would have given each other a knowing look: "You see? We told you so!" For his mother was undoubtedly of Jewish origin, and that of course explained why her son was so much quicker and so much more cosmopolitan than the ordinary, hundred per cent pure Frenchman.

It sounds familiar, doesn't it? It sounds painfully familiar. And what can we do about it? Not very much, I am afraid, until we shall have changed our entire system of education and shall have cured our children of the belief that there is such a thing as a chosen race, which is as absurd a claim as that of belonging to a superrace.

Yes, Montaigne's mother was undoubtedly Jewish. She belonged to the powerful family of the Louppesses (now modernized into Lopez) which for many centuries had played quite a role in Spanish history. During the government of that doleful couple of fanatics, Ferdinand and Isabella, the Louppesses had been forced to accept baptism. The few drops of holy water sprinkled upon their foreheads may have performed a miracle in the matter of faith, but they had not been able to extinguish the flames of genius which burned so brightly in that extraordinary family, and if Montaigne must be accepted as a typical result of a mixed marriage, then I can only regret that both my parents and all my ancestors were so one-sidedly Dutch.

Montaigne's father too seems to have been a man of more than ordinary ability, a queerish sort of person and saved by his intelligence and common sense from being a freak. He was very original in his educational theories. After Michel became his heir—in consequence of the death of his two older brothers —the father decided that his only surviving son must be given every opportunity to amount to something. Believing that a direct contact with the good earth was essential to every child's physical welfare, old Montaigne sent the infant to be nursed by a peasant woman in a near-by village and insisted that the son of the squire be brought up on a footing of absolute equality with the children of his future retainers. After his preliminary course in the simpler aspects of life, little Michel was brought back to his father's castle. But here he was attended by servants who spoke only Latin (God knows where Papa Montaigne had found them!), and every morning he was awakened by the playing of beautiful music.

This so hastened the intellectual development of the boy that already at the age of six he was ready to go to a public school, which in Europe has always meant a private school—to differentiate it from a clerical school. At thirteen he proceeded from his private school to the university. There he studied law, and

Montaigne and Doctor Rabelais

at the age of twenty-one we find him a member of the town
government of Bordeaux.

Such a career was, of course, only possible for a young gentleman of independent means and with a considerable amount of
political pull. These same fortunate circumstances enabled
Michel to pay frequent visits to the court in Paris. They also accounted for his term of service in the royal army. Otherwise
there is nothing much to report about the first thirty years of
our guest's life.

Montaigne was a very civil young man (as there were thousands of others in the France of that era). He went out into society (as did thousands of other polite young men in France at
that time). But when he had eaten all the dinners that were to
be eaten (although in moderation) and had drunk all the wine
there was to be drunk (see above!) and had made love to all the
charming young women who were there to be made love to
(not quite so moderately, I regret to say), he did something that
none of the other polite young men of France of that time had
ever thought of doing. He not only confessed that his present
mode of existence had greatly begun to pall upon him as an un-
profitable waste of energy, but he also announced that he intended to devote the rest of his days to some useful task and
henceforth would not merely content himself with political
sinecures and the administration of his estate.

The useful task Montaigne thereupon set himself was nothing less than the writing of a book in which, for the first time in
the history of the human race, a man would tell about himself
and his reactions to everything that had ever happened to him
with *absolute honesty*. Let me repeat it—WITH ABSOLUTE
HONESTY.

Montaigne started work on his *Essais* in the year 1577, and
they kept him busy until the day of his death in the year 1592.
Occasionally he still did a bit of traveling, mostly in connection
with his health or on some official mission. But during the
greater part of those last fifteen years he dwelled happily and
contentedly in his famous brick tower, and whenever he was

forced to leave his hermitage, he counted the days until he should be able to return to that quiet spot where he could really be himself and where he could devote all his working hours to the agreeable pursuit of depicting Michel de Montaigne as he actually was and not as he tried to make himself appear in the eyes of his friends and neighbors.

A great many other people have tried to follow his example, but few of them have ever succeeded as brilliantly as this grandson of a French herring merchant and a baptized Spanish Jew.

Montaigne had enjoyed one great friendship during the early half of his life. The name of his beloved companion was Étienne de la Boëtie. It is quite likely that the death of de la Boëtie had affected him so deeply that it contributed to his decision to withdraw from all further worldly pursuits.

This surmise (I have nothing concrete to prove it) is borne out by the fact that Montaigne, before he started work upon his own autobiography (for what else are the essays but the autobiography of a singularly honest man?), had spent considerable time editing the works of his friend, who had already gained some renown as a poet before his unexpected and untimely death.

After this labor of love had been finished, Montaigne took a clean sheet of paper and wrote his famous first sentence. "This, good reader, is a book written in a spirit of complete honesty." I think that it is only fair to say that when he put finis to the last chapter, he had most faithfully lived up to that promise. The essays are indeed the honest revelations of one man's innermost feelings. By sheer good fortune, it so happened that Montaigne was able to contribute the most important of all the many ingredients which are necessary if such a book is to be a success. He not only had character, but in addition he also was a character. And it was undoubtedly the happy combination of these two traits which gave his work that freshness which has made it one of the most obstinate best sellers of the last four centuries.

It is said of my dear friend, Stephen Bonsal, that although he has done more traveling than any other human being and has been in more places than seems quite possible, he never starts forth upon a fresh trip—be it merely to proceed from Washington to Georgetown—without feeling that this is going to be an entirely new and most glorious adventure. Montaigne shared Stephen Bonsal's happy attitude toward life. In the morning he got up, went to Holy Mass (for he was most faithful in the observation of his religious duties), partook of his breakfast, and then took a look out of his lofty tower window. After so many years, he should have known the landscape by heart, but every time it delighted him as much as if he had never seen it before, and whatever caught his eye became thereupon a welcome subject for a short meditative essay.

That everlasting sense of wonder undoubtedly accounts for the delightful and ever-surprising variety among the titles of his chapters. "On Being Sad" precedes a dissertation upon "Philosophy as a Means of Learning How to Die Happily." After he has pondered upon the unfortunate consequences of being a pedant, he discusses the desirability of reading lots of good books. Cannibals attract his attention, but so does male and female dress. Having delivered himself of two short sermons upon "The Art of Going to Sleep" and "The Vanity of Words," he will suddenly ask himself how it is possible "to laugh and cry over the same thing at the same moment."

Drunkenness comes in for some very poignant remarks, but so does abstinence. Friendship and loyalty too are studied as carefully as the ceremonies which prevail at royal courts and the fact that what is caviar to one person is nothing but a dish of oversalty fish eggs to the next one.

This method of writing without design quite naturally divides Montaigne's readers into two hostile camps. Those who believe that we should go through life browsing and that the joy of a journey consists in following every possible detour rather than in reaching the place of your destination in the shortest possible period of time—they will love Montaigne and will find him the best of traveling companions. Whereas the boys and girls who want to get things done and who want to save time (and for what purpose, may I ask?) will call him a hopeless egotist and will refuse to have anything to do with him.

They make no bones about their feelings. "We will wait until the 'Confessions of Raymund de Sabunde' (isn't that the chapter in which he is supposed to explain his own philosophy of life?) has been reduced to three pages," so they will tell you, "and then we will read it in one of our digest magazines (provided we have nothing better to do), but until that shall have been done, the old Frenchman is too wordy for us, he talks too much, he is one of those French bores who will waste a whole afternoon over one single glass of wine, discussing the meaning of a certain line in the latest opus of some long-haired poet who has just starved in a garret on Montparnasse."

Literature in some ways is very much like religion. You either like a certain point of view and accept it unqualifiedly, or you don't like it and there is no use talking about it. The Montaignards will continue to love their teacher, and the anti-Montaignards will go on detesting him, and when they meet, if they are wise, they will talk about the price of eggs or the chances of the Dodgers next year or some other remote subject. But they will leave the *Essais* and their author alone.

Outwardly, as I have already said, Montaigne observed those rules of behavior and deportment which were the accepted code of his time. He was by no means a revolutionary and he did not see any sense in frontal attacks. If the majority of the people believed in honoring the king and obeying the rules of the Church, he was perfectly willing to accept their verdict and had no intention of making himself conspicuous by going hunting when everybody else happened to be in church or by preaching rebellion when the crowd in the street was loudly hurraying for a visiting member of the royal family.

This, however, did not prevent him from having a great many

very definite opinions of his own upon all such subjects as religion and statecraft and the true basis for a happy family life. One may even doubt whether he was at heart a very good son of the Church or even a sincere admirer of the world as he found it—royalty included—for whereas the truly faithful believe and accept without arguing, Montaigne, in everything he ever wrote, was forever asking himself this very important question, "After all, what do I really know?"

Descartes would have advised Montaigne to believe only that which he could observe with his own eyes, but Descartes had not yet made his appearance, and Montaigne was completely lacking in the "scientific approach," as we people of the modern world have come to understand that expression. This did not prevent him from becoming one of the world's greatest specialists in the actions and reactions of the human soul, for in his lonely laboratory he would dissect and study his own and his neighbors' impulses with the complete detachment of a Vesalius, except that he never went quite as far as the man with the scalpel.

But whereas that famous Flemish anatomist reached a great many definite conclusions, Montaigne, just before he reached the final answer to the question he had posed himself, would come to a stop. His inborn and incurable habit of looking at the world from the angle of his skeptical *que scai-je?* ("what can I really ever know?") prevented him from taking definite sides on any question and from dividing the whole of creation too sharply into either white or black. He preferred the intermediary colors and in this he proved that he was a brother under the skin to all other good philosophers from the days of Socrates to William James. They too had come to realize at a certain point in their careers that eternal doubt must be the price of spiritual liberty and that truth, once it has been accepted and has been elevated to the rank of dogma, can be used to crush its former friends and to establish itself as a tyrant, infinitely more cruel and unrelenting than the tyrants it has just helped to crush.

The doubt of which these prophets spoke had something of the divine about it. It did not consist in asking futile and superficial questions, like overbright children trying to make the lives of their Sunday-school teachers miserable by asking, "Please, Miss Jones, what is God?" It was a very humble kind of doubt. It was full of reverence before the very subject it happened to doubt. But it was doubt, nevertheless, a wavering of opinion and a fear of coming to definite conclusions before one could be absolutely certain that all the evidence now at last available was in—that somewhere or other beyond the distant mountain ranges the jealous gods were not still hiding a few scraps of the ultimate verities, which they intended to preserve strictly for themselves as being much too good for mere mortals.

Skepticism, as we understand it today, is the philosophy which claims that outside of the field of science no absolute knowledge is possible and that no fact or truth can be established upon philosophical grounds alone. It therefore preaches the gospel of suspended judgment.

I don't know much about such things (being an artist rather than a historian or a philosopher), but it seems to me that the skeptics who have played a role in history have been about as fine a body of men as ever lived and that on the whole they have been more useful in making our world a little more civilized than any other group of spiritual leaders. From the days of Pythagoras until those of Immanuel Kant, they have been distinguished by their moderation and tolerance, their willingness to listen to both sides of every controversy, and their unwillingness to pass harsh judgments upon those who disagreed with them.

And of none of them can this be said more truthfully than of Michel de Montaigne. He accepted life as he found it. He declared that in his eyes it was neither entirely good nor entirely evil, because everything depended upon the way one approached the problems of everyday existence. Just as in the case of Voltaire, his original skepticism was afterward modified by his conviction that in the end reason would provide a solution for most of our difficulties. Therefore, as Montaigne grew older, he became more and more of a stoic. He did his best to rise superior to both pain and pleasure, but in this he never quite succeeded. He was too essentially healthy in his reactions, too much a product of the fertile soil of France, to set himself as entirely apart from all ordinary human experiences and emotions as the Emperor Marcus Aurelius or the slave Epictetus had tried to do fourteen hundred years before.

At times Montaigne had also interested himself considerably in the ideas of Epicurus, who had taught that pleasure was the only good in this world and should therefore be the end of all our endeavors, but he had too strong a streak of melancholia in his make-up (he himself called it "grousing" rather than "complaining") to find satisfaction in a philosophy which so greatly stressed "happiness" as the ultimate goal of all human endeavor.

However, I am now doing what should never be done. Program notes may serve their purpose for the average composers and philosophers, but they can't be written for either a Beethoven or a Montaigne, because these men were much too complicated and too many-sided ever to be reduced to a few simple outlines. Just the same, I ought to make an attempt at it in the case of Montaigne.

By and large, I feel inclined to say that he was the best-balanced human being whom we encounter within the pages of the past. And being so harmoniously balanced, he can be of immense benefit to people like myself who lack that spiritual equilibrium and who are either on top of the mountains or way down in the cellar.

This very virtue (this co-ordination of all his critical faculties) will forever prevent Montaigne from becoming one of our popular heroes. His talent for discrimination, his love for well-chosen intermediary colors—these will always keep him apart from the majority of his fellow men who will insist upon the extremes of either all white or all black. But that is unavoidable under our present setup.

Progress has always been a question of the few and not of the many. Those who are the leaders realize this and accept their fate. They know that they are condemned to pass a good deal of their time in utter loneliness, but such solitude is unavoidable if they wish to achieve what they have set out to do. No use to bewail their fate. Their reward will consist in the consciousness of having worked for the common good and without any idea of self.

In the year 1565 Montaigne had married a lady by the name of Françoise de la Chassaigne, the daughter of one of his colleagues in the city government of Bordeaux. It had apparently been one of those prearranged French matrimonial alliances which (though we greatly disapprove of them in North America) seem to offer a more substantial basis for a lasting companionship than our own system which is based on that illusory and short-lived attraction which we call romance. The good lady had presented him with a daughter who passed safely through the perils of infancy and whom her father educated according to the best pedagogical precepts of the latter half of the sixteenth century.

The mother and daughter were the only two women who played any kind of role in his life, with the exception of one other person of the female persuasion, whom I shall mention in a moment.

Montaigne was always held in great esteem at the royal court, and his former Gascon neighbor, Henry of Navarre, was forever trying to persuade him to return to Paris. Michel declined His Majesty's flattering invitation as regularly as Spinoza was to decline those of an even-mightier potentate, the great King Louis XIV of France. Both men were grateful for the honor bestowed upon them, but the one thing they valued more than anything else in this world was their personal freedom. They therefore could not permit themselves to be caught in a position where they might be beholden to someone else for their daily bread and butter.

Henry was intelligent enough not to take offense at his subject's rebuff, while Montaigne from his side gave expression to his feeling of loyalty by an occasional visit to the city of Paris. He would then pay homage to his ruler, but as soon as he could do so without giving offense he would return to his ivory tower.

It was during one of those visits to Paris that Montaigne had made the acquaintance of one of the most famous bluestockings of the sixteenth and seventeenth centuries—a certain Mademoiselle Marie de Jars de Gournay. Montaigne seems to have been quite impressed by this learned woman and, being old enough to be her father, he adopted her as a sort of honorary daughter, a *fille d'alliance*. He remained in correspondence with her during the rest of his days, and shortly after his death, the lady, duly chaperoned by her mother, traveled all the way to Bordeaux that she might express to Madame de Montaigne her deep regret at the demise of her never to be forgotten husband.

Not only did the widow of the famous man receive Mlle de Jars de Gournay most graciously, but she also presented her with annotated copies of her late husband's works, both in manuscript and in printed form. The faithful adopted daughter, not to be outdone in her devotion to the memory of her adopted father, then set to work to give the world a perfect edition of the famous *Essais,* with all the quotations correctly translated and made ready for public consumption.

As I pointed out a moment ago, Montaigne will never be very popular among our average readers. The essay form which he invented is the favorite literary dish of all true connoisseurs, but mention the word "essay" to a publisher and he will turn pale, pull his watch out of his pocket, claim that he has got just five minutes in which to catch his train, and that is the last you will see of him until he is definitely informed that you have left the city and have returned to Connecticut. Don't blame the poor man. Essays mean only toil and trouble to all connected with them, and why deliberately invite a loss of good money when there are so many other forms of literature which the readers are only too eager to buy and which the booksellers will promote as if they were four-leaf clovers at the Donnybrook Fair.

Now that I come to think of it, we should have invited Montaigne to come the same evening as Emerson. Then we could have obtained some vital statistics upon the subject of essay distribution and we also would have been allowed to listen to some rather amusing conversation, for the quick-witted Montaigne would undoubtedly have taken the slower-moving Emerson for considerable of a ride. But as this would have been done without any malice, Emerson would never have noticed it, and Montaigne was too good a connoisseur of the human soul not to have realized very quickly that here for once he had struck pure gold and he would have acted accordingly. But it was too late now. There were to be no repeats in the matter of our invitations, and we had to accept whatever was coming, without regrets and without complaint.

Montaigne was the first of our guests to arrive. He explained to us afterward how he had happened to come by boat. "I hadn't had a chance to revisit the scenes of my childhood days," he said, "until now, and so I made the best of my opportunity. I first of all went to Bordeaux, and imagine my joy when I found that my beloved tower was still standing! In Bordeaux I hired a fishing smack, not very different either from those we used to own when we were still in the herring business! and after a few false starts and a few days of seasickness and bad food, those good fellows finally landed me on your little island."

I asked Montaigne where his craft would wait for him, but he told me that all that had been taken care of. He apologized for not being more specific and ended his sentence in the same way so many of our guests did when they spoke of their present whereabouts. "We know so little and we can say even less."

This invited an answer on my part to show him that I had not only read him but could also quote him ad lib., though this particular quotation was easy enough.

Monsieur Montaigne arrives in a fishing smack.

"What you really mean to say, Monsieur de Montaigne, is that you don't know anything at all."

He caught the allusion to his famous motto and smiled. "Yes, I suppose so," he answered. "I am afraid that I shall never be able to live that sentence down. One makes a remark—a mere nothing—a little casual observation such as one probably makes a hundred times a day—and writes it down. The world passes by thousands of other such insignificant observations and forgets them, but then one sticks. And for the rest of his days, the poor author must pose as the brilliant sage who asked the immortal question, 'What do I really know?' All the really serious books upon which he has slaved so hard during a lifetime of unending labor are forgotten or have been cut up into packing paper for sausages or cat meat, but that one commonplace remark goes on forever."

"*Que vous avez raison, monsieur,*" Erasmus said, who had heard most of this monologue and who now indicated that he would like to be presented.

"*Permettez,* Monsieur de Montaigne, this is Dr. Erasmus, the eminent scholar whose works must be familiar to you."

Montaigne eagerly grasped the old Dutchman by both hands. "This is indeed a happy moment! Unfortunately, I was only three years old when you left us, most venerable and erudite Doctor, but had you waited just one more year, I would have been able to read you while you were still present. I have been reading you ever since. I had a great many of your books in my library. And now—what great and good fortune! Now at last I hold the original copy of all this wisdom right here in my own hands!"

Carefully, almost tenderly, guiding Erasmus, he led him to the fireside, took the glass of sherry Frits offered him, lifted it, and said, "To the teacher of all of us." To which Erasmus undoubtedly would have replied with one of his elegant little speeches, done in the best of Ciceronian Latin, if only he had been given the chance. But just when he was about to start on his peroration, our house was shaken as if it had been caught in the aftermath of an earthquake. Tiles came rattling down from the roof, and I had grave fears for our windows.

"That must be Leonardo," said Frits, "come back for a little more flying with his little officer. I am sure he landed on our chimney. God help us all, there it goes!" and he rushed toward the door, but ere he reached it, it swung wide open, and a terrific voice shouted, "What is the idea of making my master wait? Where are your manners, you lazzaroni, you brigands, you blacklegs, you musty, cheese-eating rats?"

Montaigne was delighted. "That sounds familiar," he said. "I know that voice! You do not mean to say that you have perchance asked the good Dr. Rabelais to come here tonight and share our meal with us and bring his beloved Gargantua?"

Frits said, yes, he was right. We had indeed invited the Doctor, but not a word had been said about his bringing anyone with him.

"Don't worry. Even if he has, the Doctor will know how to treat that difficult brain child of his."

True enough! At that very moment we heard the voice of Rabelais, who was in a state of absolute fury and who was apparently berating a third person.

"*Tais-toi,* Gargantua," we heard him shout. "Keep quiet, you monster, did you hear me? I told you to keep quiet. You have caused me enough trouble as it is. I never knew such a day! You have behaved like a badly spoiled child. I am angry with you. I am very angry with you and I don't like you at all!"

Thereupon there followed an outbreak of such weeping and moaning and wailing as none of us had ever heard, and a sad, woebegone voice begged to be forgiven, protesting that no harm had been intended and that everything had been done in a spirit of good, clean fun.

"I know your good, clean fun, my little cabbage, but you have been a most damnable nuisance. And for that, you cannot come in but have to stay outside all night long! Besides, this house would not be big enough for you. So go away—leave us in peace —at least for a little while, and don't bother us any more. I gave you a cold boiled ostrich for your supper before we left. Unless you have already eaten it—and I told you not to—it still must be in your knapsack. Take it and eat it. That will quiet your nerves. After that, leave me alone, I say, for the love of God— *leave me alone!"*

"Then you are no longer angry with me, dear master?" the giant whimpered.

"No, I am no longer angry with you, but only if you promise that from now on you will be good. If you give me any more trouble, I shall leave you home the next time I go out and I shall take Pantagruel."

"I will be very good," Gargantua humbly promised.

"Then go away! *Fiche-moi le camp!* Disappear!"

"Yes, master."

Rabelais entered and, without bothering to shake hands with any of us or giving us so much as a look, he slumped down upon the nearest chair, rubbed his knees, and said with a gesture of despair, "This is absolutely the last time I shall let that idiot accompany me. Every time he promises me most solemnly that he will be good, and always it is the same story.

"You see, these giants are very faithful. They are not very bright, but they are extremely loyal to their masters. Now it so happened that there were some other giants abroad today, and not only giants but dwarfs too, and the dwarfs came upon us in such hordes that they were much more dangerous than the giants. These dwarfs and giants, so I have been told, belong to an Englishman, a certain Meester Sweeft, if I got the name correctly. He lived a century and a half after me, and I think he was a dean in the English church—or something they now call the Church of England. When he started writing books he needed those creatures just as I needed mine when I turned author, and what a lot of trouble I would have saved myself if I had stuck to medicine or religion!

"But those complaints won't do me any good now. And, after all, I am not the only man of letters who had a right to invent such a Noah's ark of numps and oafs, and God knows I bear Meester Sweeft no ill will. The more giants, the merrier, and they are badly needed in our world of twerps. Yes, they are very badly needed. But what happens next? Those hulks are perhaps not as intelligent as they should be, and at the same time they are incurably jealous and pathetically loyal to those of us who created them.

"For some reason, my imbecile elephantine children seem to feel that this Meester Sweeft had no right to invent a few giants of his own. I have told them at least a thousand times that I don't care—that our planet is big enough to hold them all. Does that do any good? It does not! No sooner do my ruffians and those of Meester Sweeft catch sight of each other than there is a battle—a veritable battle of Titans—with Behemoth trying to stick his knife into the eye of Polyphemus while Gog is disemboweling Magog.

"This afternoon, at first, all went wonderfully well. Gargantua, noticing that I was getting a little tired, had picked me up and was carrying me on his shoulder. And then—the Lord only knows where they had been hiding—but suddenly a whole army of Lilliputians—I think that is what they are called—came racing toward us, and they were led by three or four of the largest and toughest Brobdingnagians I have ever seen. The old story—Meester Sweeft's paper children coming after mine, and with murder in their eyes too!

"As soon as he noticed them, Gargantua got so excited that he dropped me. I assure you, it is no bagatelle to fall all the way down from his shoulder! I can still feel the lump on my head.

"For a moment I thought they would sink the whole of your island, they stamped so hard and shouted and shrieked and bellowed, and the little Lilliputians, that miserable rabble, went straight after me and they were climbing all over my arms and legs, hacking at me with their little swords. When suddenly— *voilà—encore un autre géant!* I had never seen him before. He was as tall as my own Gargantua, but he was dressed quite differently. He looked as if he had been born fifty years ago and he

The Lilliputians and the Brobdingnagians were after Gargantua.

wore high leather boots. He was standing by the side of a canal, chewing a straw and taking it all in as if it were a joke. It may have been a joke to him, but it wasn't to me, for Gargantua was getting the worst of it, and badly so. One of Meester Sweeft's giants had my poor Gargantua by the scruff of the neck and another had taken out his knife and was trying to cut his throat and then, suddenly, I saw this new giant bend over the canal near which he was standing, pick up a boat that happened to be sailing past, take aim and—bang!—throw it at that giant of Meester Sweeft who had his dagger at Gargantua's throat. A marvelous shot! That boat hit the Sweeft giant with such force that it cracked his skull, and he fell backward with a horrible howl of pain, and before he could get back to his feet, I saw my small Gargantua pick him up and throw him clear into the sea that lies on the other side of the dunes.

"That evil fellow must have been the leader of the mob, for the moment he was gone, the miserable pack of hyenas turned heel and ran away as fast as they could. Of course, I rushed right over to the gallant fellow who had just saved our lives. I thanked him and asked him for his name because some day I hoped to be able to repay him for his kindness."

"What was his name?" I asked.

"Alas, monsieur, you know how small a gift we Frenchmen have for foreign names, but it was something like Bunion or Bonnion—it rhymed with *oignon*."

"Could it have been Bunyan?"

"It could."

"And his first name?"

"The first name I remember because it was like that of the Apostle Paul."

"Well," I said to Frits, "our island is picking up. Think of Paul Bunyan having come all the way to Holland!"

"Who is he? I never heard of him."

"No, you wouldn't. But he is one of the heroes of our Far West. He is so big that when he goes walking he—Lord God Almighty! What has happened now?" and I jumped from my

chair, for right outside of our house there was a noise as if another earthquake had struck our town. Once more chimneys
were falling down, beams were creaking and breaking. Walls
seemed to be tumbling down, and then there was a sound of
church bells being shaken violently as if by a hurricane.

Rabelais was the first to act. "That idiot again! He will never
learn," he shouted at us, "but this time I will teach him a
lesson. Look what the fool has done now."

He pointed across the market place. Gargantua was sitting on
top of the town hall, leaning contentedly against the tower
(hence the noise of the falling bells) and munching away at his
boiled ostrich.

"Gargantua," Rabelais commanded, "come down here and
come this instant. Come here, I say!"

The giant got up. He looked as sheepish as a small boy who
has done something he vaguely suspects he should not have
done but who is not quite sure what it may have been.

"*Oui, maître,*" he answered, stepping with unusual care over
a couple of houses. "I am coming. Right away!"

"Gargantua, give me that plate. Give me your supper."

"But, dear master, I have not had a bite yet. I spent all that
time looking for a place to sit down."

"Well, you found it," Rabelais said, looking as mad as a
dozen wet hens. "Yes indeed, you found it all right! And now
look at what you have done, you imbecile, you ninny, you oaf,
you dunderpate, you kind of an Englishman!"

Gargantua, following his finger, saw the church bells lying
all over the market place and the street. He drooped his head.
"I am sorry, master," he said, "but I was hungry and I did not
realize."

"No, you never realize. You are always sorry but you never
realize. But this time I shall make you realize. Give me your
plate."

Gargantua handed him the plate containing his meal. Rabelais
took it with both hands and gave it to Hein. "Hide this, if you
please, hide it where this creature won't be able to find it. But

Gargantua had sat down to lunch, on the roof of our town hall.

Paul Bunyan had picked up a boat that happened to be sailing through a near-by canal.

be careful where you put it. He is very clever when he gets hungry. He becomes almost human."

Gargantua was in tears. "Master," he pleaded, "dear, dear master, you don't mean to say that you are going to let me go hungry?"

"I am. Not a morsel of food until tomorrow morning."

"But, master, my beloved master, I will die of hunger!"

"I wish to God you had done so long ago. That would have saved me a lot of bother." Then turning to us, "I suppose the cows are no longer in the pastures?"

"Not in November. They are all in their stables."

"Any sheep left loose?"

"None."

"Any goats?"

"We have only a few, and they are all locked up."

"Very well, then he won't be able to do any harm. And it will be good for him to go hungry for a little while. Maybe it will teach him a lesson, and now, messieurs, I must apologize to you once more, and then perhaps you will give me something to eat. I too am so hungry I could almost eat Gargantua. But perhaps first of all you will introduce me to my fellow guests."

This apparently was to be an evening of surprises. First the incident with Gargantua. But now it was the turn of his master. Rabelais, I noticed, had been casting glances at Erasmus as if he were asking himself, "Where have I seen that face before? Now, where have I seen that face before?"

No sooner had Frits said, "Dr. Rabelais, this is Desiderius Erasmus," than it was the turn of the Frenchman to go through some of the same sorts of antics displayed but a moment before by his pet giant. With much greater agility than one would have expected of a man of his age he threw himself on his knees right before the greatly embarrassed Erasmus. Then he took the old humanist's hands into his own and carried them tenderly to his lips.

"My father," he said, "my revered and deeply beloved father, who is also my mother, the one man in the world to whom I owe more than to anybody else. And so at last I am to meet you!" and he actually wept tears of joy.

All this apparently came as a complete surprise to Erasmus.

"It is undoubtedly flattering to my pride," he began, "to find a stranger bestowing such honor and affection upon me, but I fail to see why I deserve this act of homage. Come on, my good

Rabelais greets Erasmus.

sir, sit down. Sit down quietly by my side and tell me why you feel that way about me. A father? Yes, I suppose I might have been someone's father, but a mother? Even by the widest stretch of the imagination, that is carrying things a little too far, isn't it?"

"I know," Rabelais answered, recovering from his outburst of enthusiasm, "but if only you could feel what you have meant to me! I first discovered some of your works in the library of the du Bellays. They were very much interested in literature and they bought every book that came from the press, and it was there that I met you, and if it had not been for you, I am sure I never would have set pen to paper. It was from your writings that I got my first idea for my own foolish yarns. Afterward I read everything you published. And if you had been my own father, you could not have been closer to me than you were. And now I can see you and touch you, and this is indeed the happiest day of my life, even if it comes four hundred years after my own death," and so on and so forth, for his admiration for Erasmus knew no bounds, and he might have continued for another hour if it had not been for that most welcome announcement that came from the kitchen. "If you gentlemen will please sit down, I can then serve the soup."

This was the seventeenth of our weekly dinner parties. We had now entertained a sufficient number of guests to be able to draw a few general conclusions about the degree of their "interestingness." The statesmen came way down at the bottom of the ladder. Most of them had been very dull, unless, of course, we called Sir Thomas More a statesman, but he had only dabbled in politics as a side line. Those born to the purple had been little better. The theologians—well, we had known what to expect and so had not really been very much disappointed. The scientists had been good enough when given a chance to ride their own hobbies. The purely didactic type of mind, too, had not been exactly stimulating. It had been much too self-conscious, too self-centered, to be able to enter into the mode of thinking of others. Confucius might have proved the most interesting of our guests if we had had a chance to talk to him directly and without an interpreter. Some of the professional philosophers had been too much set in their attitude toward the nonphilosophers to make good table companions.

Then who was the ideal type of person with whom to spend an evening?

Most assuredly he was not the expert, but the many-sided amateur, the intelligent dilettante who had been the cultural ideal of the ancient world. After he had been called back into existence by the Renaissance, he had been returned to his former position of honor during the baroque and had enjoyed another short-lived period of success during the era of the rococo. But he had been rudely and definitely pushed off the stage the moment the so-called expert had made his appearance. Then the all-around man—the highly talented amateur—had been informed that henceforth there was going to be an end to all his dilly-dallying nonsense and that from that moment on the world belonged to "the man who really knew."

How much harm these experts had done to what used to be called a civilized form of living we realized once more during that evening while listening to the talk of Erasmus, Montaigne, and Rabelais. Of these three, Erasmus had been the only one who might have remotely qualified as an expert, for he had been a professional teacher, but only for a short while and not long enough to let his mind become petrified. As soon as he had resigned from his pedagogical duties, he had taken up literature and thereafter had roamed contentedly up and down the slopes of Mount Parnassus, but without any definitely fixed place of abode or any definite purpose. Rabelais had been a theologian and a physician and a private secretary before he became a writer. As for Montaigne, he had done about everything a human being could hope to do. He had been suckled by a peasant woman and had ended his career as the personal friend and trusted counselor of a king. He had had practical experience within the realm of government and was well versed in all those subtler qualities of life one can only learn from one's women friends. Only after he had tasted of every experience within the reach of mortal man had he settled down to become an author. Therefore, that evening we had with us three out-and-out amateurs or, to use a word that is even less popular in our modern world, we had with us three complete dilettantes. I wish we had been able to make a record of what was said, but we had to observe the rules of our silent agreement. Besides, there was no electricity in Veere, and a recording machine would have been out of the question.

As soon as the first part of the meal was over—a most excellent dinner, by the way, and just the right kind of music for the taste of our guests—we steered the conversation in the general direction of politics and, with the assistance of Erasmus, who seemed to have guessed what we were driving at, finally reached a point where we felt that we could risk a definite question. It was Frits who asked it: "Who will ever give us a formula by which we can hope to live like civilized human beings and not like animals in the jungle?"

Both Rabelais and Erasmus bowed to Montaigne as if to indicate that he was the one to give us our answers. He poured himself another small glass of Châteauneuf and said, "I would, if you don't mind, like to hear some more of that music of the young Austrian you played a little while ago. It was most pleasing and soothing, and I can think better when I am listening to soft music. The habit has probably stuck to me from my childhood days."

I gave the message to Jo, who relayed it to Hein. We heard the machine being wound up, and then the voice of Elisabeth Schumann came down to us in the familiar *Voi che sapete*. Montaigne smiled and said, "My dear friends, the answer to that question, what is the right formula for a happy life, was given thousands of years ago. But nobody really wanted to know. It has been repeated ever since and at regular intervals, but nobody ever seems to have cared sufficiently to listen. I have no doubt that a thousand years from now, it will be just the same. The answer will always be there, but what use is even the best of remedies, concocted by the most learned of apothecaries, if the patient throws the mixture out of the window and his physician after it?"

We did not say anything to indicate that we would like to hear him elaborate just a little upon that somewhat cryptic statement; we left it to him to go on. After another sip at his Châteauneuf, he did so.

"Suppose we look at it from this angle," he suggested. "Who rules this world, who created the heavens and the earth, who is the beginning and end of all power, the incarnation of all wisdom?"

"It is God," said Erasmus, crossing himself.

"Amen," said Rabelais, doing likewise.

"Very well. We can all of us agree upon that. The conduct of our universe is in the hands of Him who is best fitted for that high office."

"It is indeed," said Rabelais.

"Immo vero," said Erasmus.

"And to whom do we entrust the care of our spiritual affairs?"

"To the Pope," said Rabelais.

"And also a little perhaps to the emperor," said Erasmus, liking his little joke.

"Again I can only agree," said Montaigne, "but now answer me this question: how do this Pope and this emperor come to hold their power?"

"They get elected," said Rabelais.

"I am sorry," said Montaigne. "I sound like a village priest, driving his little peasants through their catechism, and I beg your pardon, but it is the only way I can prove the point I am trying to make. The Pope and the emperor get elected, the same as I got elected when I became mayor of Bordeaux. And who elected me?"

"I don't know how they run such things in your part of the world," Erasmus told him, "but here in the Low Countries, the aldermen and the sheriffs would have balloted for you, and if you happened to have got more votes than your rivals, you would have been given the office."

"And how did those aldermen and sheriffs come to be installed on the seats of the mighty?"

"Because they were the brightest members of the community," said Erasmus with a great deal of unction in his voice. "I knew many of them well. Some of them could even read and write!"

"Yes," Rabelais added, "and all of them could count and do neat little sums with the ducats piled up in their strongboxes."

Montaigne let these remarks go by without any comment and continued his inquiry in the same quiet manner in which he had begun. "It is a fine system," he said, "at least from a theoretical point of view. Everybody has always agreed that it was the best system. The other day I read about a Chinese philosopher who seems to have lived hundreds of years before the great Plato, and this is what he said, if my translation is correct: 'Let him who is best qualified be in command of his fellow men.' Plato, the most learned of all the ancient sages, did likewise. So did Socrates. So did the great Aristotle. So have all the wise men who since then have given the matter their serious thought. 'Let him who is best qualified be in command.' And what have they actually accomplished?"

"Not very much, I am afraid," said Erasmus.

"That, my honored master," said Rabelais, "is stating the case very mildly."

Then Frits made bold to enter into the conversation. "If that is so, monsieur," he asked, "then what solution do you offer?"

Montaigne shrugged his shoulders with that gesture to which we were rapidly becoming accustomed. "I don't know," he said. "Except that maybe, like so many other problems in life, there may be no solution at all."

Now Erasmus took the floor, figuratively speaking, for once he was comfortably tucked away in his chair, he would hardly move during the entire evening.

"If you will allow me, Monsieur de Montaigne," he began, "and you, my reverend Doctor, if you will allow me to offer a few observations? I never laid claim to any deep sense of piety, but I tried to be a fairly good Christian and, as long as I lived, I was a faithful son of the Church. And while young I had a certain amount of training as a theologian and so perhaps I can speak with some authority. At least, I shall not be far wrong when I quote from Holy Writ, for I know my Scriptures.

"Monsieur de Montaigne told us that we need not wait for still another political prophet to tell us how we can obtain a reasonable and righteous form of government, and we all agreed with him. That point having been decided, we only need devise a workable and practicable method by which we shall be able to find that man who is best fitted to rule and then give him his chance. The difficulty, as I see it, is not in finding that man, for people of extraordinary ability are so rare that they soon enough attract our attention. But how can we arrange matters in such a way that we can get him elected and do not see his place being taken by someone of infinitely inferior abilities but who, for one reason or another, appeals more to the popular taste?

"And now I want to be a little more serious for a moment than I usually am. Let us forget about politics and statecraft for a moment. Let us talk about matters of the spirit. Do we need laws to guide us in our actions of the spirit? I hardly think so. Right here in this most hospitable house I have had the privilege of meeting that distinguished Chinese statesman whom Monsieur de Montaigne mentioned a moment ago. I have, alas, never read anything he wrote, but I have heard a great deal about an Indian sage who was known to his followers as the Buddha.

"Long before the birth of our blessed Saviour, he seems to have taught unto his disciples that love for their fellow men must ever be the guiding principle of all their deeds and thoughts. Socrates, certainly one of the wisest of men who ever drew breath, was forever stressing the necessity of following our daimon, that still, small inner voice we now call our 'conscience' and which tells us automatically whether a course we intend to follow is right or wrong. Most of the Latin and Greek philosophers whom I know from their works—and whom I know fairly well, if I may say so, from Epictetus to Marcus Aurelius—they too—and practically all of them—stressed that same point—that in order to achieve true happiness in the outside world, we must first of all acquire that inner contentment which comes from the knowledge that we have never deliberately done anything of which we knew that some day we might feel heartily ashamed.

"Even the Romans, steeped in the darkness of their brutal pagan creed, instinctively felt this, as you will remember from Horace's *Integer vitae, scelerisque purus*—'The man of life up-

right whose guiltless heart is free from all dishonest deeds'—
a poem worthy of being chanted every day in every church of
the Christian faith.

"And then came our own blessed Saviour, who taught us, as
it is reported by Saint Matthew the publican, that the greatest
of all commandments is this—that we shall love the Lord our
God with all our heart and all our soul and all our mind and
that furthermore we should love our neighbor as ourself. And
now I ask you, my friends, have ever words of greater import
been spoken than these—'love thy neighbor as thyself'?"

"Never," said Montaigne.

"Never indeed," said Rabelais.

Frits and I kept quiet. This was getting a little beyond our
field of observation.

"Then," Erasmus continued, "is it necessary for us to wait
until still another prophet shall appear upon the scene to teach
us still better, when all of us know that at the moment these
sentences were uttered man reached the highest point in his
spiritual and moral development? Haven't we already got the
one incomparable compass by which to steer our course through
life? Why ask for more or better?"

Erasmus took a sip of that mild Moselle which was his usual
evening beverage. He waited a moment before he put his final
question. Then he asked in a low voice, "If all of us are in full
agreement upon this subject, and if it is as simple as all this,
then why have we never seriously tried to do just this?"

"Haven't we ever?" Rabelais asked. "Not even for a moment?"

"Undoubtedly, a few people have tried to do so now and then
and here and there, but their efforts never lasted very long. And
what I meant was this, why, if we are all of us convinced that
salvation lies only in that direction, then why have not all of us
endeavored to obey that law everywhere and all the time? What
answer have you to this, Monsieur de Montaigne, and you, my
other dear friends?"

"Alas," Montaigne replied, "once more I feel obliged to an-

swer that I do not know." As for the rest of us, we said nothing,
for there was nothing to say.

At that moment the clock struck a quarter before twelve, and
all of us realized that soon we would have to bid each other
good-by. I looked at Frits, and Frits looked at me. It had been
another evening of great and good friendship and perfect understanding. We wanted to explore that question a little further,
but we feared that it was too late, and Rabelais, who for quite a
long time had given signs of increasing nervousness, spoiled all
further efforts at conversation by getting up and asking to be
permitted to have a peek outside of our door.

"It is not raining, my dear Doctor," said Frits, who had just
looked at the weather.

"It is not the rain that worries me, but I am afraid that I was
perhaps a little too hard on my poor Gargantua. He does mean
so well, only—like most giants—he is so incurably stupid. But no
one was ever more faithful or more loyal."

With that he opened the door, and there was Gargantua, lying right on the cobblestones with a couple of trees he had torn
out of the ground as his pillow. He was not asleep. His eyes
were wide open and firmly fixed on the door of Frits' house,
very much like those of a Newfoundland dog which has been
waiting outside for his master.

"Well, my poor little one," Rabelais said, his voice almost
trembling with kindness, "and have you been a good boy after
I scolded you?"

"Master, never have I been so good in all my life!"

"And you had nothing to eat or drink all evening long?"

"I have had nothing to eat. But when I got thirsty, I tried to
take a drink out of the harbor. Such horrible stuff! It tasted like
brine. It made me choke. So when I saw a little tin cup full of
water standing just outside of the village, I drank that."

"Good Lord!" said Jo, who had come forward to have a good
look at the giant, "so that is why the water in the sink has
stopped flowing! The fellow must have drunk up our reservoir,

Montaigne walking past our ancient church.

and will you tell me how I am to wash my dishes without any water?"

"Let the dishes wait till tomorrow," Frits told her. "They will fix the water tower soon enough."

"No," said Jo, "our plumber is much too stiff-necked a Calvinist to work on Sunday."

"Then we will send for a few plumbers from Middelburg."

"They are just as bad."

"Then the dishes will just have to stay dirty. Meanwhile, where is Hein? Oh, Hein, have you still got that boiled ostrich or whatever it is?"

"Sure. It was a tough job, but I got it into the cellar just the same. Want it?"

"Yes. Bring it up, will you?"

A moment later Hein was back, dragging the ostrich behind him. Frits turned to Rabelais and said, "Please, my dear Doctor, as a favor to us! We hate to see one of our guests go home hungry. Suppose you forgive your little giant, or let him have at least a drumstick?"

"*Alors!* For this one time," and turning to Gargantua, "*Voilà, mon petit chou-chou.* This kind gentleman has intervened on your behalf. Take your supper and be quick about it, for it is about time for us to leave, though gladly would I stay a few more hours at this delightful Thélème."

In the meantime, Erasmus and Montaigne had been bidding each other a most affectionate farewell. They apparently had enjoyed each other's company most thoroughly. As for Gargantua, it was pathetic to see the way he devoured his food. Nor was he particularly neat about the disposal of the gnawed-off bones. He dropped the greater part of them right into our harbor, where they were found the next day and gave rise to the rumor that the carcass of a whale had been washed up on our shore.

It took the giant exactly four minutes to gulp down his supper. Then he carefully wiped his hands on the roof of Frits' house and announced, "I am ready, master. I am ready any time you want to go."

"Very well," Rabelais told him, "and perhaps Monsieur de Montaigne will give us the pleasure of his company. If I am not mistaken, we are going in the same general direction!"

"I shall be delighted, *mon cher docteur,*" Montaigne answered and, after having thanked us for the most agreeable evening he had had these last four hundred years, he allowed Gargantua to pick him up and to deposit him most carefully in one of the pockets of his jacket.

"We shall be quite comfortable in here," Rabelais shouted down to us after he had joined Montaigne, "unless the creature has been picking onions again. He dotes on onions. And now my little man, let's be on our way. *Bon soir, messieurs, au revoir,* my beloved father Erasmus. I will make a point of looking you up as soon as you return. A thousand thanks to all of you. Especially to the cook. It was a wonderful evening!"

With that Gargantua began to move. And as he turned the corner of the market, the clock struck the hour of midnight.

We found, to our great surprise, that the candles were still burning. We blew them out, and then I bade everybody a cheerful good night and went home. While crossing the market place, I noticed that one more tree was missing. Gargantua apparently had felt the need of a walking stick.

CHAPTER XVIII

And Now a Rather Strange Combination, EMILY DICKINSON and FRÉDÉRIC CHOPIN, But Emily Has the Time of Her Life, and Chopin Shows Us What Can Be Done With a Minni-Piano

"FRITS," I SAID next day at lunch, "what do you know about American poetry?"

"Very little. The usual stuff, *Moby Dick* and Walt Whitman."

"Well, *Moby Dick* is not exactly poetry. I don't really know what it is, for I never have been able to get through it. Walt Whitman too is not one of my favorites. But did you ever hear the name of a certain Emily Dickinson?"

"Dickinson? Emily? No, never heard of her."

"You've missed something."

"What's all this leading up to? Do you want to invite the lady for dinner next week?"

"I would love to. Unless you have a better candidate."

Lucie came in from the kitchen. She had been making *sauce rémoulade,* for we were having cold meat, and *sauce rémoulade* was one of her specialties.

"Did I hear you talk about Emily Dickinson?" she asked.

"Yes, you did."

"I know all about her. Don't you remember? You sent me a book about her a few years ago—the last time you were in America. I loved her poems! Strange bits of sound, they were, but entirely original. I liked her immensely!"

"There now!" I said to Frits. "I have found someone who agrees with me! You tell him about Emily, Lucie."

"I don't know that there is much to tell except that she wrote a most fascinating kind of poetry. She never bothered about either rhyme or meter and I don't think you can compare her verse to anything in any other language. But it was fascinating stuff and entirely new. I would love to meet her."

"I have already thought of that," I told Lucie, "and I would arrange it that way if I only knew how to ask you. I am always afraid that if we do something that is not entirely according to the rules—and what are those rules?—we may find that we can't have any more guests. I think that it was understood that only Frits and I were to be present. Of course, we had that aviator the night of Leonardo, but he could not be helped. He was an accident."

Lucie gave me a pitying look. "Poor man," she said, "can't you see how simple it is? Emily was a very shy creature and, besides, she came from New England. She would never have dreamed of visiting the home of two gentlemen without being duly chaperoned."

"Of course not," said Jimmie, who had never seen a chaperon in all her life.

"Will you come too, James?" Frits asked.

"I am sorry, but it is Noodle's day out and I must stay in. I might stand the female poetess, but you will probably have one of your usual musicians too. No, I had better remain at home and leave the job to Lucie."

And so it was agreed that we would invite Emily Dickinson and that Lucie would be there to play the duenna. That, however, would leave us with only one honest-to-goodness guest, and we had got in the habit of asking several at the same time. It helped with the conversation and it made the party much more cheerful. But who, in the name of all the little Amherst saints, would fit in with Emily? It would be difficult enough to make her feel at her ease with two strange men, but we were, after all, ordinary mortals. Before a famous historical personage who was unknown to her, she would evaporate into nothing at all, so to speak. She would hide in some dark corner of the house and never show herself or open her mouth.

It was Lucie who made the suggestion that seemed most likely to solve our problem.

"That Dickinson girl's poetry is like little scraps of music. Sort of thing Schumann might have written to amuse his friends."

"All right," said Frits. "Then let us invite Schumann."

"God forbid!" Lucie warned. "We would have Clara on our hands and we can do without a jealous wife! But will you let me make a suggestion? I am thinking of someone who often expressed himself in his music *exactly* the way Emily did in her verse."

"Who is that?" Frits asked.

"Chopin," Lucie answered.

"Good for you, Lucie!" we both said. "A marvelous idea! Chopin will fit in better than any other musician."

That evening, shortly after midnight, the names of Emily Dickinson and Frédéric Chopin were duly deposited underneath the lion of the town hall.

To devise a dinner that would at one and the same time satisfy a Pole, who had lived all his life in Paris and who had always "enjoyed a delicate constitution," and the simple and unsophisticated daughter of a New England country lawyer, who probably had never been aware of what she was eating, was rather complicated. It had to be a very neutral meal, but with the help of Jo, whom we found still washing her dishes from the night before, we solved it in a few minutes' time.

On this occasion we would not be obliged to go in for strange, old-fashioned dishes, for the people we had asked were our near-contemporaries, and so a *potage santé* was quite in order, for there was no reason why Emily should not like sorrel soup, and it would be good for Chopin's weak chest, as sorrel is supposed to be very healthful for whatever ails you. After that, a plain roast chicken with mashed potatoes and cauliflower *à la polonaise* (for the benefit of Chopin) would undoubtedly satisfy both parties. At Jo's suggestion, we added a dish of our everlasting string beans. "Cauliflower is too risky," she warned us. "You know what it does to most people."

"You're telling me!" I answered, and the string beans were duly noted down on Jo's shopping list.

The dessert, too, was easy. Jo promised to make us a good old-fashioned bread-and-butter pudding with a lot of whipped cream. As for wine, Emily was sure to drink only water, and Chopin could finish the case of Châteauneuf that had been left over from the previous Saturday.

Our kitchen.

Should we have music? There is a problem that always presents itself when you are entertaining musicians, for as a rule they are not only exceedingly positive in their likes and dislikes, but also very outspoken in their criticisms, should anything fail to please them. Emily, we knew, had not been spoiled as far as music was concerned. She could have heard little that was downright bad but also very little that was of any particular merit. When she was born in the year 1830, Boston had not yet become the center of the musical arts it was to be sixty years later.

We therefore could give Emily almost anything we wanted. Provided it was not too loud, she would not object. But what of Chopin? Berlioz was the one composer who was definitely out. Liszt, too, had never found great favor in his eyes, but that may just have been the traditional dislike between a Pole and a Hungarian, rather than a matter of taste.

Fortunately, the gramophone companies had recently published a whole lot of Schumann recordings, and we telephoned to Amsterdam for the following list: Schumann's Symphony No. 2 in C major, opus 61, his Concerto in A minor for Piano and Orchestra, opus 54, his *Carnaval, Kreisleriana,* and his *Kinderscenen,* in addition to which, we asked for the complete cycle of *Frauenliebe und Leben.* If that was not sufficient or was not appreciated, there were all our Mozart records, and if Mozart too was not wanted, we now had that minni-piano, and Chopin could play whatever he pleased. We felt that all the necessary details had been taken care of, and I could sit down to provide Frits with my report upon our next two visitors.

In the case of Emily Dickinson, there was very little to say. Ten or twelve lines would cover the story of her outer life. But what passed through her heart and mind while living in her old Amherst home—that was something else again and something it would be very difficult to write about. But it had to be done, and it was done—after a fashion.

Emily Dickinson's grandfather, Samuel Fowler Dickinson, the descendant of a Puritan immigrant of the vintage of 1630, had been a true man of God and had moved to this remote part of New England in the early twenties, that the world might be made safe for the Congregational faith by means of a college where young men could be prepared for "the conversion of the whole of mankind." A fairly large order—"the conversion of the whole of mankind"—but entirely in keeping with the spiritual ambitions of the America of a century ago.

In due course of time and long before the world was saved, Grandpa Dickinson begot himself a son who was called Edward. This son in due course of time became the father of three children—one boy and two girls. One of these received the name of Emily after her mother, Emily Norcross, and that was our Emily.

The child went through the regular pedagogical routine of her day. When she was old enough to leave home, she was sent to Mary Lyon's "female seminary" in South Hadley. It was supposed to be one of the best schools of the forties of the last century, but Emily was only bored by the institution. The headmistress, according to Emily's letters to her friends, made it her purpose to cramp, curb, and repress every natural impulse and desire in every one of her charges. In Emily, the old lady met her Waterloo. When she tried to pit her will against that of that shy and innocent-looking pupil from Amherst, she failed most miserably. Emily did exactly as she pleased, and when Mary Lyon objected, she packed her carpetbag and went back home.

That was not the way the New England young ladies of that day were supposed to behave, but Emily was an exception. She was her father's favorite and knew that she could wind him around her little finger. She now began to accompany him on many of his professional errands through the surrounding country districts, for he was not only a lawyer but he also functioned as treasurer of the college his father had founded and, besides, he was a cheerful fellow who loved his fellow men and who was welcomed wherever he went. The witty and—according to her only picture—quite attractive daughter and the dignified father must have made a most pleasing combination. When therefore, in the winter of 1853, Papa was elected to Congress, it was Emily who accompanied him to the national capital.

It was on this occasion that the disaster took place which was to ruin Emily's chance at leading a normal life but which was to be of such inestimable value to American literature.

The early New England settlers had followed the rivers.

Emily Dickinson and Frédéric Chopin

While on their way back from Washington, the Dickinsons stopped over for a few days in Philadelphia. There Emily met a clergyman—a most respectable gentleman with a wife and a child. All those emotions in her which from earliest childhood on had been repressed, curbed, stifled, and cramped suddenly exploded. Such catastrophes have happened before. Indeed, they are said to be as old as the human race itself. As a rule, they do very little damage. They may cause a rather painful detonation and a little puff of smoke, and occasionally, with very bad luck, a pair of pretty eyes may be reddened or a delicate heart will develop a nervous jerk. But when an electric spark is suddenly sent through a charge of dynamite, packed tightly in an old iron box which in turn has been sunk deep into the rock of duty, then everybody had better get out from under, for no one can foretell the havoc that may be caused and how much of the countryside will be turned into a shambles.

When she returned to Amherst after having met her "fate" (as people used to say then), Emily's life, as far as she was concerned, was over, and at the age of twenty-four Emily Dickinson withdrew from a world in which, as she had discovered, a woman could suddenly be placed before the choice of either ruining a sister's chance at happiness or surrendering her own hope for a perfect union. That, at least, is the official and accepted version of the incident which fits in most beautifully with the novels about queer spinsters in ungainly calico dresses who never again were seen by anybody "after Ebenezer had left the farm to marry that city gal." (Lucky Ebenezer!)

I have no more—and certainly no better—information upon the subject than anyone else. But from the secret testimony of Emily's own poems, I would come to a somewhat different conclusion. I once discovered a curious religious institution in a remote part of the Austrian Alps. I never got inside, of course, but I derived my knowledge from a woman who had visited it. She told me that all the inmates of this nunnery, the moment they took their vows, were presented with a small doll, a regular child-Jesus doll, which thereafter they could dress and wash and array in the finest garments that could be bought in the Vienna silk shops. The nuns themselves were never seen again, for being supposed to be completely happy where they were, there was no reason why they should ever return to the wicked world that lay outside. But some of their dolls were preserved in a small museum in the near-by village, and these were shown to the public.

To Emily Dickinson, her poetry was such a child-Jesus doll. She was so bright and understood herself so well that she must have known how totally unfit she was for the business of living a normal life in the community into which she had been born. For generations, the girls of her class had been brought up to believe in something which they called (if ever they dared to speak about it at all) "a pure passion." They might as well have gone in search of "a heatless flame."

It is true that flames can cease to give out heat, but only after they have been extinguished. Most women of Emily's social antecedents humbly accepted their fate because their ministers and the Good Book had taught them that the role they were supposed to play in the scheme of things had thus been ordained by God, and who were they to question the wisdom of the Almighty? Emily Dickinson's relations toward her God were rather particular. They included the right on her part to ask whatever embarrassing questions she meant to put up to Him, and if the good Lord did not come forward with a prompt and satisfactory reply, she herself meant to supply it.

By birth and breeding, Emily was a life member of the Pure Passion League and she knew that she would never be able to escape from her own background. Being also a very great artist and therefore insisting upon perfection, she refused to engage in any kind of activity at which she would never be able to excel. If this were so, would it not be much wiser and much pleasanter to spend one's days as a highly amused spectator of life, peeping through carefully drawn curtains at the strange antics of one's relatives and neighbors, rather than marry a

A quiet country inn somewhere in Massachusetts.

young professor or clergyman and run the risk of once more being tempted by visions of things that could never be? Her two fatal meetings with her handsome dominie from Philadelphia made her see all this very clearly. Her strong sense of duty and her gift of detecting the ludicrous in her fellow men, but most of all in herself, prevented her from going in for dramatics or from doing anything that would make her look conspicuous and therefore silly. Gradually she spent more and more of her time in her own room, until at last she fully withdrew from life and was never again seen by any other human being. Sometimes at night she would leave her virginal chamber to water her beloved flowers in the garden around the paternal home. But from the year 1862 until the hour of her death—May 15, 1886—she worked hard at building up her favorite myth about the silent little woman in white, whose shadowy figure was sometimes observed by a frightened visitor as it hastily fled from the parlor or the kitchen to find safety in her nun's cell upstairs, where she would then spend a delightful evening with her favorite doll, which in her case consisted of tiny bits of verse writ down upon tiny bits of paper held neatly together by gaily colored ribbons and carefully stacked away in the drawers of her chaste little writing desk.

I may of course be entirely mistaken, but I feel inclined to believe that Emily Dickinson in her own queer way got infinitely more out of existence than almost all her contemporaries who lived normal lives. Being in her unobtrusive manner a completely selfish creature, it was not a sense of inferiority that made her insist that after her death all her poems and letters should be burned. Far from it! She had had a marvelous time writing them and felt no need to share her pleasure with others. Let the others wonder and guess. It would be good for their souls, and Emily, in spite of her severe New England exterior, was at heart a good deal of an imp. She loved her little jokes.

Fortunately, her relatives, being people of common sense, understood that they would be committing a sin against literature if they were to destroy so perfect a work of art as the poetry of their departed sister and cousin. It would have been like sneaking into Rembrandt's studio, a few minutes after that melancholy master had expired, and tearing up all his pictures and etchings.

The Dickinson family surrendered most of Emily's private correspondence to the flames of the parlor stove, but they tenderly preserved the neatly tied bundles of her poems and afterward they had them printed and made available to the public at large, or rather to that part of the public capable of understanding them.

On Thursday, immediately after he received this letter, Frits telephoned me from Amsterdam. "Listen," he said, "according to what you have written about this Dickinson girl, she'll never come. She'll be much too shy."

"Don't worry," I told him, "she'll be there, and if Lucie is going to be there too, she will make a grab for Chopin before Lucie can get him. And Lucie, as you know, is no amateur when it comes to the favorite female sport of 'Catch them as you can.' I think we are going to have one of the most interesting evenings we have ever had. It will be a noble contest, and Chopin may wish he had his Mme Sand—his Lucrezia—with him to protect him from these two wild women."

Here follows my private report on our musical guest.

Frédéric Chopin got his French name from his father, Nicolas Chopin. This energetic young man from the city of Nancy, despairing of ever making a decent living in his native land, had gone east in the year 1788 and had found employment in Poland as a wheelwright. A short time afterward, Thaddeus Kosciusko, having learned the trade of arms while serving under General George Washington in America, had tried to bring the blessings of liberty unto his own unfortunate countrymen. Nicolas Chopin had joined him, had fought with him, and had ended his military career as a captain in the Polish revolutionary forces.

After the rebellion had been repressed, it was quite certain that for a long time to come there would be no further roads built by the Russian conquerors, and the wheelwright business having therefore come to an end, Captain Nicolas Chopin had looked for a new way of keeping himself alive.

That proved comparatively easy for a young Frenchman of pleasant address and genteel manners, for every noble Polish family needed a private tutor that its children might learn to express themselves in the language which meant an open-sesame to the civilized world of the West. Hence we soon find Nicolas teaching his own beautiful tongue to the sons and daughters of the Count and Countess Skarbek and marrying the Countess' lady's maid. This young woman, Justina Krzyzanowska, was the daughter of an impoverished Polish nobleman, and most likely it is from her that Chopin inherited the dash and force and glamour of that unfortunate race which has never yet failed to fight most valiantly for every lost cause.

Having taught the young Skarbeks all they needed to know to be an ornament to polite Warsaw society, Nicolas Chopin moved on to Warsaw, became a professor of French, and was able until the day of his death in the year 1844 to maintain his wife and four children in a state of decent if modest comfort.

As he departed this life only five years ahead of his son, Nicolas also had the satisfaction of knowing that he had begotten a genius. For Chopin's life, in spite of a great many difficulties, was on the whole a very successful one. This may have been due to two causes.

Frédéric Chopin was undoubtedly the greatest composer for the pianoforte the world had seen. But other artists, painters, composers, and architects have been equally prominent within their own fields of endeavor, yet have died in the same poverty in which they had been condemned to live. It is not difficult to guess the reason for their failure. They had missed out on two qualifications which had set Chopin apart from the rest of his colleagues. In the first place, he was the only genius produced by the Polish race while it was struggling for its existence as an independent nation, and in the second place, he had a unique chance of standing forth as the living symbol of a lost cause.

The other musicians who did not fare as well as he did were Austrians among other Austrians or Italians among other Italians or Dutchmen among the usual run of the Dutch. They could never hope to become the embodiment of all that was glamorous and heroic among a people in exile. By this I do not mean to detract one single F sharp from the assembled works of this unequaled teller of musical tales. I owe him as much of a debt of gratitude as anyone else who in moments of desperation has found consolation in listening to one of Frédéric Chopin's nocturnes. But without their lost cause and the opportunity to impress themselves upon the rest of the world as the incarnation of all the hopes and aspirations of a nation which had the sympathy and admiration of every civilized human being, neither Frédéric Chopin nor our beloved friend, Ignace Paderewski, would ever have attained those heights of fame they finally attained. Peace be to their ashes, and may they soon find a worthy successor to inspire the rest of us with a love for that utterly adorable, if at times completely exasperating, people known as the Poles.

There is very little sense in my repeating here the outstanding facts in Chopin's musical career. You can find them in every encyclopedia, and they are very simple. The boy played the piano before he could read and write. That piano, by the way, was used for kindling wood by the Cossacks when they suppressed the Polish revolution of 1863, for that was the way in which the Russian usurpers usually gave expression to their interest in the cultural achievements of their subject races. At the age of six, little Frédéric began to compose. His father not only recognized his son's uncanny abilities but he refrained from doing what so many other fathers under similar circumstances have done. He did not exploit his offspring as a musical prodigy, but neither did he threaten to break every bone in his body unless he gave up the idea of becoming a famous piano thumper and prepared himself for a more practical career, such as that of a bookkeeper or a government official with the expectation of a pension at the age of sixty. (I am giving you an offhand quotation from one of the letters of Schubert's father to his son Franz.) He quietly but effectively encouraged his son in his aspirations and all throughout his life he helped him as much as his modest circumstances allowed him to do.

It is true that the boy gave his first public concert at the age of eight, but that was not done for mercenary purposes. It had been arranged that he might bask in the admiration of the beautiful ladies of Warsaw. Chopin, all through his life, would love to do that sort of basking. When the time had come for him to be trained seriously in the rudiments of his craft (I mean music, not basking), he was sent to the best local teachers of the Polish capital and afterward to those in Vienna. Some of these, it appears, were not quite as good as they might have been, and it was due to their faulty methods that Chopin, during the whole of his amazing career, was never able to overcome that technical awkwardness which finally made him decide to withdraw from the concert platform altogether and devote himself exclusively to the business of composing.

While in Vienna he had heard some of the greatest performers of his day, notably Hummel and Paganini. Like every other young artist, he felt convinced, after listening to that sort of playing, that he could do equally well, and for a time it looked that way. He had what it took to attract the crowd, especially the female part of the audience. But aside from a technique which never approached that of Liszt and many of the other great performers of that day, he was also lacking in that physical endurance which is absolutely essential for a concert virtuoso or an operatic prima donna. Chopin was like a brilliant ball-player who begins to show signs of collapse after the seventh inning, and it is the seventh inning that counts.

Then came a series of disasters over which he had no control but which were to have a far-reaching influence upon his subsequent career. Chopin happened to be in Vienna in the year 1830, when another ill-fated revolution broke out in Poland.

He was cut off from his family in Warsaw. He never expected to see them again. He decided to go to England and from there to America to begin a new life. In Stuttgart in September of the year 1831 he heard the news of the fall of Warsaw and the beginning of those wholesale executions with which the old regime of Russia used to "pacify" its most recent territorial acquisitions.

In a state of complete despondency Chopin traveled by slow stages to Paris, but there he gained new courage, for he was welcomed as a conquering hero. The French, still smarting under the defeat of 1812, hated the Russians, and furthermore, Paris had "gone romantic" in a great big way. Chopin's music completely answered the needs of the concertgoing audiences while his Polish passport opened the doors of all the most worthwhile homes of the capital.

In Poland, events took their normal course. Russian gallows were being erected at all crossroads, and the Polish insurgents were in full flight. Soon Paris was chock-full of refugees. Most of them were as poor as church mice and lived in the slums. But a few of the great feudal families had anticipated what was going to happen and had carefully provided for the day when they could no longer dwell on their ancestral estates. They now used Paris as the center from which to prepare their counterattack. Being well aware of the value of publicity, they meant to use every possible opportunity to prove to the world that as a race the Poles were infinitely more cultured than their Russian oppressors.

Overnight young Chopin had become exhibit No. 1 of Polish civilization. Rarely has any artist or author (and you cannot start a successful counterrevolution without either) lived up quite so magnificently and so satisfactorily to what was expected of him—or quite so easily and naturally. For Chopin at that time had all the necessary qualifications to become a popular idol. He was young and very good-looking, but in a delicate sort of way, so that people instinctively felt sorry for the poor boy whose shoulders were already bowed down with grief over the fate of his unhappy fatherland. And when he played one of his own compositions and was so deeply moved by the music that he had to ask someone else to finish it for him—then the tragedy of Poland ceased to be merely something the people had read about in their newspapers. Then it became so real that those in the audience felt like taking up their muskets and rushing to the defense of their beloved Polish friends. But ere they could do this, the jubilant strains of a mazurka or a waltz had broken through the gloom that had settled down upon the hall, and everybody went home feeling that the cause of Polish freedom was not yet lost, that it never could be lost, that Poland would arise once more in all its ancient glory.

It was long before propaganda in the modern sense of the word had been invented. But Chopin and his music were the best propaganda a desperately outraged patriotism ever had. I wish to God he would come back to us right now!

Of course, as the years went by and nothing happened and the world (which has such a very short memory) began to forget the bestialities of the Romanovs in Poland and wherever else they set foot and the bestialities of the Hapsburgs in Italy and all the other bestialities which, these last two hundred years, have been an unavoidable part of what Europe used to call its "foreign policies," Poland too began to bore people and next it dropped out of their minds altogether. Not that this affected Chopin in his artistic career, for he continued to be the most sought-after piano teacher in Paris, and his compositions were published the moment he finished them. But the atmosphere around him was gradually changing, and although he was undoubtedly the most distinguished Pole of his time, when he, a mere pianist, aspired to marry the sister of a boyhood friend, the Countess Marie Wodzinska, her esteemed papa, old Count Wodzinski, let him understand (and in very plain terms, too) that such a match was absolutely out of the question. What with this annoyance and a few others, Chopin once more contemplated that step which he had already wanted to take in the year 1831 and emigrate to America.

His family, his friends, the Polish colony in Paris, his public, and his creditors—they all went down on their knees to prevent him from taking such a dreadful step, which they considered to be the equivalent of a social and musical suicide. Such appeals are of course very flattering, and Chopin let himself be easily persuaded to remain where he was, and more is the pity! For it was in Paris that Frédéric Chopin now met with a fate infinitely worse than falling into the hands of the ferocious redskins of the Far West or the managers of the East.

In what I am about to say, I may seem to be a bit harsh on a distinguished colleague who wrote no fewer than a hundred books. But she really was pretty bad. She was pretty bad because, like certain members of the insect family, this female invariably devoured her males the moment they had surrendered to her charms.

A great many volumes have been written upon the subject of Amandine Lucile Aurore, Baroness Dudevant. After she had spent three years in an English nunnery, had survived matrimony with the Baron Dudevant, and had achieved motherhood, she had been obliged to find some means of support for herself and her two angel children and had thereupon decided to try her hand at professional journalism and popular fiction. Being a bright lass and suffering from very little competition (in those days, ladies did not yet write for a living), she had a lot of leisure for her favorite amatory pursuits. Then one day she met Chopin, and he was hers.

He was at that moment a very sick man. The first symptoms of tuberculosis had just announced themselves. The cause of his beloved Poland was lost. His career as a public performer, so he felt, had come to an end. He badly needed a mother, and George Sand offered to take her place.

I shall lightly skip over that incredible voyage to Majorca, whither Amandine Lucile Aurore took both Frédéric and her ailing son, that the mild climate of this Mediterranean island should cure both of them of their bothersome pulmonary afflictions. Majorca sounded very romantic while you still talked about it in the Rue Pigalle. But after you had disembarked at La Palma, it was Spain, and Spain at its worst, and you were right back in the Middle Ages. There was no hotel in the Majorcan capital. There were no apartments. There was no food fit for human beings, especially those accustomed to the cuisine of Paris. And everywhere you were hounded by suspicious officials. When you sent to Paris for your piano (for her dear Frédéric must go on with his work and must write even more beautiful things than before) it took the customs people six months to allow it to pass. Why should anyone in Majorca want a piano? It looked queer. It smacked of revolution. And when you fell sick and coughed your head off, there was no doctor on the island, but the officials, suspecting that you might have caught some queer kind of pestilence, forced you to leave the city and to withdraw to a home in the country, miles away from everywhere, in an old and damp monastery, where you added bronchitis to your other troubles and almost died of them.

Chopin, however, must have been tougher than he looked. He not only survived Majorca, but also the tender care of his Lucrezia, and he returned to Paris and lived for a good many years to come.

On the whole, these last ones were not very happy. Paris was rushing from one revolution to the next. News from Poland grew increasingly bad. And under those circumstances teaching —even at twenty francs a lesson (an unheard-of price in those days)—was apt to become an intolerable chore. Besides, that bronchitis of Majorca seemed to have come to stay. Chopin was beginning to lose a good deal of blood and often he was so weak that he could hardly move. But he needed money and, like Paderewski in his last days, he painfully dragged himself to his piano stool, that he might make a few more pennies to pay other people's debts and help his poor country, but most of all that he might continue to live up to his reputation of being a really *grand seigneur* who never turned down a request for some slight assistance on the part of a fellow patriot and who would have starved to death before he confessed that he himself had not had anything to eat during the last three days.

Chopin died on October 17 of the year 1849. At his funeral, Mozart's Requiem was played, together with his own Funeral March from the Sonata in B-flat minor and, after that, two of his preludes, the E minor and the B minor. A silver goblet, filled with earth from his beloved fatherland, given him by his friends when he left Poland for good in the year 1830, descended with him into the grave, together with the withered rose Marie Wodzinska had given him when she still hoped that her father might relent and would allow him to marry her.

Today all the actors in this drama are dead and gone. Nothing remains of either the oppressors or the oppressed. The Romanovs, who drove Chopin into his exile, are dead, but they did not have such an impressive funeral, and Polish soil proved more merciful than Bolshevik quicklime. And to be remembered as the man who wrote the Nocturne in E-flat major and the Mazurka in A minor is a happier fate than to survive in people's memories as the despot of the gallows and the knout. I, who am old enough to have seen the merry Cossacks do the bidding of their unspeakable masters, who have lived through those agonizing days when there still was hope for my Polish friends, I here and now offer a heartfelt prayer for the souls of those departed tyrants who destroyed all that was lovely and charming in the fair land of Poland: "May their names be forever cursed!" And the same goes for all their successors, in every part of the world, and in all eternity, amen.

Suddenly winter was upon us. And quite contrary to a Dutch November (which is usually very wet), it snowed for three days and nights, until the whole countryside lay buried underneath a heavy blanket of white. That, by the way, was the time when our island was at its loveliest and when Veere became almost unbearable in its beauty. The kids were having a wonderful time with their little sleds, and I hoped that Emily would not forget to put on her arctics. But being a good New England girl, I knew that she would remember.

Frits had returned from Amsterdam on the mail train to Flushing, and Jimmie had called for him. Jo had reported that everything in the kitchen was under control, and after another day of revising my *Rembrandt,* I felt that a few lungfuls of fresh air were the thing I needed if I wanted to get through the evening without falling asleep.

As usual when the weather was bad, I walked in the direction of Middelburg. After I had crossed the moat which Napoleon had bestowed upon us a hundred-odd years before, I noticed a dark group by the side of the road and not very far away. Some-one was holding up a lantern, and by its light I could see what had happened. An old-fashioned traveling coach had almost slipped into the ditch, but at the last moment it had been caught by a tree, and out of the door on the right which still could be opened, a thin man, dressed in the costume of the eighteen forties, was now being assisted to the street by the coachman, while someone else, who was apparently his valet, was holding up a lantern which threw its feeble rays upon the scene.

From his pictures I recognized the traveler as one of our two guests of the evening. It was Frédéric Chopin. I hastened forward and told him who I was and added the by-now-usual fib that I had walked down the road in the hope of meeting him. He was quite as good a liar as I, for he told me that he had half expected that someone would come and show him the way to our house.

When we reached Frits' place we found considerable excitement, for Jo had to report a curious adventure.

"It was this way," she explained, after I had presented Frits to Chopin. "I was getting the things ready for my pudding, the dinner was on the stove, and I suppose it must have been about half-past six, when suddenly quite an old and rather stout gentleman entered. I thought it must be the piano player about whom you had told me and so I said, 'Monsieur Chopin—that is to say, if you are Mynheer Chopin—won't you sit down and make yourself at home and in a moment Mynheer Frits will be here. Meanwhile I will get you a glass of sherry, or would you rather have port?—for it is a cold night and you must be tired.'

"My French is of course not so very good, but I thought he would be able to understand me. But he only smiled and said, 'And so you mistake me for Frédéric Chopin! Ah, my dear woman, I love you for that, but, alas, I am merely the cook, so show me the kitchen, and I will set to work.' Well, no cook likes to be pushed out of her own kitchen by somebody who has just walked into the house, and so I answered—and I don't suppose that I was any too friendly about it—that no matter who he was, he could not touch my stove, but if he cared to take a chair in the kitchen and wanted to wait until Mynheer Frits came back, he was welcome, but he must not touch my things.

"Well, all this time I was hoping that Mynheer Frits would come back, as I didn't quite know how to handle this stranger. He might, of course, be the famous French chef he claimed to be, but he did not look the part. He looked much more like a musician—sort of wild and none too neat. And then, just when I was getting ready to go into the kitchen and see that he kept his fingers out of my pots and pans, something else happened, and that was even worse.

"The front door suddenly opened and I said to myself, 'Thank God, there is Mynheer Frits now!' but it was a young woman, all bundled up in shawls and scarfs and with a funny-looking fur cap. Fortunately, Mrs. van Dam arrived at the same moment as the old doctor, and I thought that between them they would be able to take care of the girl in the fur cap. But not a chance! For when Mrs. van Dam held out her hand and said how happy she was to meet someone of whom she had heard so much and whose work she admired so much (you know how Mrs. Lucie is, once she gets started on that line), the girl in the cap gave her a pretty ugly look and said, 'My dear madam, I am here because I can't help myself, but please don't think for a moment that I came out of my own free will. However, there is no power on earth can force me to stay in this room

It was Chopin who was coming out of the broken traveling coach.

and meet a lot of strangers. I shall go upstairs—I saw a light there, and there must be some place where I can sit. You can bring me my supper up there and I shall need very little, for I am not at all well and now I bid you a good evening.' And before we could stop her, she was gone—lickety-split—up the stairs, two at a time, as if someone had been chasing her. Then we heard her turn the key of your door and also heard her laugh a little, and after that, not another sound."

At that moment, Frits finally arrived. He had been obliged to go to the post office to mail a special-delivery letter, and that was how he had missed all the excitement. "Never mind," he said, "the rest of us are here, and if Emily feels that way about it, she can have her supper upstairs, and we shall have just as good a time. So won't you please take a chair—all of you—until Jo is ready?"

"Yes," said Jo, pointing to her kitchen, "but how about the fellow in there?" and then, catching a glimpse of her stove, she used a well-known Dutch expression no Dutch woman is ever supposed to use and cried out, "Didn't I tell you! The creature is actually stirring up my gravy!"

This seemed to be carrying things a little too far for a stranger who had not even been invited, and Frits, waxing a bit hot under the collar, shouted out, "*Eh, vous là-bas, monsieur!* What are you doing?"

The fellow in front of the fire turned around sharply, then recognized our guest, threw both his arms around him, and joyfully called him by his name. "*Frédéric, mon cher Frédéric! O, que c'est bon de te revoir. Tu vas bien?*" and Chopin, dropping his serious mien, cried back, "Well, of all people! Dear Papa Rossini! Imagine meeting you again after all these many years!"

Thereupon the two men, the older and the younger one, once more embraced each other most affectionately, until Chopin remembered where he was and, turning around, said, "My un-known hosts, this is my dearly beloved friend Signor Gioachino Rossini, and a very great artist he is, too."

"You mean he was, my dear Frédéric," Rossini answered, "but before we do anything else, let me explain why I am here. I am, I assure you, not in the habit of going to places where I have not been invited. Therefore, I am not here as your guest and I shall not enter your dining room, even if you should ask me to do so. I came here because I had to.

"You see, we sometimes hear about certain things that are happening in the world of the living. When I was told that old Johann Sebastian had been entertained by you, I felt very sorry that I had not been here too, for I had always wanted to meet him surrounded by his sons, some of whom, I am afraid, have gone to the other place. A little later, Herr van Beethoven complained that he had left his hat and a very valuable manuscript behind at a dinner party, and the description he gave me of your home made it clear to me that he too had paid a visit to this charming village.

"Imagine my grief! Here I had had a chance to cook for old Johann Sebastian, whom I revere as if he were God Almighty Himself, and for Beethoven, his greatest disciple! And I had spent both evenings playing backgammon with Olympe! She is a good girl, but she will never learn to play backgammon as well as she does certain other things. And then someone whispered something about Frédéric too having been invited to the same place as Johann Sebastian and old Ludwig. That was too much for me. I walked out with a batch of souls that had just been weighed and had been found wanting. I had a devil of a time getting here, for I would not take a train. I had ridden in one of those contraptions once, and believe me, once was enough, at least for me! And now, if you will kindly explain all this to this charming lady—and what a becoming costume she wears!— I am sure Olympe would want a bodice like that if she knew where to get it—but will you please explain to *madame la cuisinière* that I shall not be the least little bit in her way? I just want to add a few of my own little touches to her gravy, and I think that even she"—with another deep bow to Jo—"will

Rossini was poking around among Jo's saucepans.

agree that while Gioachino Rossini may not have been much good as a cómposer, he did know how to prepare a sauce!"

Of course, after that speech, Jo could no longer bear any resentment. And the upshot of it all was that we persuaded Rossini to take Emily Dickinson's empty place. Jo told him she would call him when it was time to start on his sauce, and all of us sat down and had as pleasant a time as on any previous occasion.

We had not forgotten Emily, but we behaved as if we were not even conscious of her being on the premises, and I explained the situation to Rossini and Chopin and told them that our invisible guest was somewhat of an eccentric who, after an unhappy love affair, had vowed that she would never again come in contact with the human race, except a few of her own relatives.

Rossini looked at me with his mouth wide open. "And all that on account of one teeny-weeny little love affair? Ha-ha-ha! I must tell Olympe! She will die laughing."

"Lucrezia would write a dozen books about it," Chopin added, rather grimly.

"But you must remember that this young lady was an American," Lucie said, not without malice, "and American women are, of course, different."

"Different?" Rossini clapped his hands as he said it. *"Ma chère madame,* in that respect, no women are different. They are all alike." And to Chopin, "Don't you think so too, my dear Frédéric?"

"Of course," said Chopin, coming to the assistance of his friend.

"But you have an example right before you," Lucie continued, pointing to the ceiling. "Right up there above your heads, messieurs, there is a poor girl with a broken heart who has not smiled since she saw the man she wanted to love and could not. What answer can you give to that?"

"What answer? Well, that only proves that American men do

not know how to handle their women. We Poles would know what to do!"

"So would we Italians," Rossini added proudly.

"How?" Lucie asked.

"How?" Chopin answered. "But, my dear lady, it is so very simple!" Then turning to Frits he asked, "Does that instrument in the corner work?"

"It does, if someone plays on it."

"Very well, my dear madam, if you want your answer, I shall now give it to you."

He pushed his chair back, sipped the last of his glass of wine, dropped his napkin on the table, and went over to the little minni-piano which had been wished on Frits and now stood at the foot of the stairs. He opened it and tried a few chords. Then, he made a pretty sour face and said, *"Oh là là!"* tried it once more, and played the opening notes of his Nocturne in G minor, the one that is known as the "Hamlet" Nocturne on account of its bleakness and loneliness. He pitched right in and he played magnificently—much better than I had expected from the descriptions I had read.

When Chopin came to the middle section, which sounds like a chorale, all of us were completely carried away. Even Jo and Hein came out of their kitchen and sat down on the lowest step of the stairs. As for Rossini, his head was thrown back and his eyes were closed, while his body was slowly swaying forward and backward. Erasmus was leaning his chin on his hands, and Lucie seemed to have completely passed out of the picture. I remembered a painting I had seen of those famous evening parties at the house of the Princess Czartoryska, where our guest used to play for his fellow exiles, and then understood the stir the young Chopin must have made among the Polish ladies of a century before.

I don't know why, but it so happened that at a given moment my eyes wandered toward the ceiling, and there, so help me heaven, I noticed that a small square of paper was being carefully pushed through a crack of the floor. It fluttered down like

A bit of paper had come down through a crack in the ceiling.

an autumn leaf and deposited itself among the flowers on the table. I picked it up and in Emily Dickinson's familiar hand-writing, as clear as print, I read:

> *There's a certain slant of light,*
> *On winter afternoons,*
> *That oppresses, like the weight*
> *Of cathedral tunes.*

I reached across the table and handed it to Lucie, who had been watching me. She smiled and put the piece of paper in her lap, picked it up once more, smiled again, this time pointing at Rossini, and returned to her own thoughts.

The nocturne came to an end, but, without waiting for us to catch our breath, Chopin went off into his famous Mazurka in A minor. I wondered what effect that would have upstairs, but I did not have to wait very long. Another smaller piece of paper came fluttering down. It contained only one line:

> *I measure every grief I meet.*

The mazurka stopped with a loud final chord, and Chopin was off on his Barcarolle. This time I had to wait a little longer, but again a bit of paper was being pushed through the crack in the ceiling. And now Emily had written:

> *To stay the homesick, homesick feet*
> *Upon a foreign shore.*

I judged from the way Chopin finished his Barcarolle that this would be his last piece, but by now he had warmed up to his task, and there followed his Ballade in F minor. To which Emily answered:

> *Beauty crowds me till I die.*

After his ballade Chopin got up. "Could I have another cup of coffee, please, madam," he said to Jo, "and perhaps a small glass of cognac? I feel rather exhausted. It is so long since I touched the keys of a piano."

"You might give me one too, for I never tasted it," came a voice from a little higher up on the stairs. "Monsieur Chopin played so beautifully that he made me thirsty."

"Of course," said Jo, now again in control of the situation. "I will bring it up to you in a jiffy."

"Oh, don't bother to do that," Emily begged her in a voice as sweet as honey. "It would be too much trouble. Besides, you might spill some of it. That would be a waste, and we must never waste anything!"

"Then perhaps you had better sit down here," Lucie invited her. "This is a very comfortable chair, right by the fire, and you can go upstairs again as soon as you have finished your coffee."

But Emily never went back to her safe retreat until a few minutes before it was time to go. For with one thing leading to another, we had a more hilarious evening than on any previous occasion. It appeared that Chopin was not only a great composer and virtuoso, but also a most amusing mimic and an excellent actor. Rossini too was in his element. He sat down at the minni and undertook to show us how different famous singers had handled (and sometimes murdered) the *Largo al factotum* in his *Barber of Seville*. And finally—though no true worshiper of the late Emily Dickinson will believe this—our little Emily (no longer so very shy) went to the piano and gave us an imitation of one of her youthful Amherst swains, trying to entertain her with a sentimental love ballad. She had forgotten the words, but she substituted others which she made up as she went along.

Both Rossini and Chopin were delighted and now offered to turn that foolish melody into the sort of thing Mozart would have made of it, and after Mozart came Beethoven, and after Beethoven, Liszt (whom neither of them seemed to have liked very much), and in the end, all three of them were sitting on the same small bench, and the evening's entertainment developed into a regular jam session which did not come to an end until after Emily had given us another imitation, this time of Mary Lyon, the head of the South Hadley Female Seminary, lecturing her girls on "moral depravity." Whereupon Rossini, who having been brought up as a Catholic could afford to do so, gave us his version of a sermon he had once heard an old cardinal preach in the cathedral of Milan, a sermon on "mother love." As the cardinal, according to Rossini, had stammered

Rossini, Emily, and Chopin playing on the little piano.

quite badly, the imitation, though a little painful at first, soon became almost unbearably funny, and it was even improved upon when Chopin sat down at the minni to play an obbligato to Rossini's sanctimonious exhortations.

Meanwhile, it had rapidly grown later, for clocks have a habit of going twice as fast as usual when you are enjoying yourself. Chopin's traveling carriage, repaired by our village blacksmith (who most obligingly had left his warm bed to fix up the broken wheel), was waiting for him in front of the door. We had only a few minutes more. Lucie was sitting in front of the fire in eager conversation with Emily while Chopin and Rossini had withdrawn to the kitchen for a final cup of coffee and brandy.

Erasmus was placidly dozing in his chair, and Frits and I were standing by the table, congratulating each other upon the success of our latest dinner party.

A few minutes before midnight, Lucie took Emily upstairs to help her with her layers of shawls and scarfs, and then we bundled our three guests into the big old coach. Suddenly all of us found ourselves singing *Auld Lang Syne*, but the clock struck the hour of twelve, and the coach rapidly disappeared around the corner of the market place. As we went back into the house, Lucie stopped me and said, "You owe me a new lipstick. Emily borrowed mine, but she never returned it."

CHAPTER XIX

The Sint Nikolaas Party, Given in Honor of the LOST CHILDREN OF HISTORY and Attended by That Noble Old Fellow, BENJAMIN FRANKLIN

"BY THE WAY, Lucie," I asked her at luncheon the next day, "how are you getting along with your sweater for Erasmus?"

"It's almost done," Lucie told me.

"When are you going to give it to him?" I asked.

"At Christmas, I think."

"But why Christmas?" I asked. "Christmas will mean nothing to him."

"When would you suggest?"

"Do you know what day it is next Saturday?"

"I've forgotten."

"Sint Nikolaas' Day."

"So it is!"

"Then why don't we have a party for him? A special party such as he must have had when he was a boy?"

"A marvelous idea!"

"Excellent!" This from Frits. "Why, that is the best idea you have had for a long time! But I want to make a suggestion. Let's make it a children's party."

"For the kids of the village?"

"For those and for the others."

"What others?"

"The youngsters who never had a good time. The unfortunate ones like the little princes in the Tower. Hendrik can tell us about the others. There must have been lots of them."

I thought for a moment and then offered a few more candidates.

"Of course," I said, "there were the little princes in the Tower, those who were murdered by their uncle. And then there was the Dauphin, the son of Marie Antoinette and Louis XVI, the youngster who disappeared in prison. And Virginia Dare, the first white child born in America. You remember? She was lost with all the other colonists. And Kaspar Hauser. That would already make quite a number."

"How about the infants of the Children's Crusade?" Jimmie asked.

"Yes," said Lucie, "and the boys and girls who followed the Pied Piper of Hamelin?"

"But think of my house," Frits warned. "There'd never be room enough for such a mob. Fifteen or twenty is all we could possibly pack in."

"How about hiring van Beveren's hall, where they repair the buoys in spring," Lucie suggested, "and inviting them all? You need not ask every one of the Hamelin boys and girls. I suppose a dozen or fourteen would be enough, and five or six from the Children's Crusade and a dozen or so of our own village children to make the others feel more at home."

That settled next Saturday's party.

We asked van Beveren whether we could have his place for a Sint Nikolaas party for the children of Veere (deeming it wiser not to mention the others), and then we set to work to make it such a party that our unhappy little guests would, for a while at least, forget the terrible things that had happened to them on earth.

Jo was in her element. She knew exactly what we should give this sort of guest. "It will probably be a cold night," she said, "what with the weather we have had so far. It will probably snow. I will therefore start them on Dutch pea soup. The Doctor is forever telling me about the pea soup his mother used to make. I don't see why I can't do just as well! After that, the kids would love some kind of croquettes. They always do—croquettes seem to mean a party to them. Chicken croquettes, if I can get enough chickens, and otherwise plain veal croquettes. And, of course, there must be ice cream, but for such a crowd you will have to order it from Middelburg, for I am afraid that my freezer is not big enough. And *speculaas!* Lots of *speculaas.* I can easily make that too, if I begin early enough. And oranges and apples and candy and those things you call 'pistaches.' You must remember them—we all had them when we were children —but only at very nice parties. They were small rolls of colored paper with a funny cap inside and a funny poem and something at which you would pull and then it would go off with a bang."

"Crackers," Jimmie translated. "We call them crackers or favor holders in America. I never had many of them as a child. My people were too religious to let me go to parties."

"Fine, and paper snowballs, for we won't have to clean up the mess. Van Beveren can do that. And a real Sint Nikolaas and a real Zwarte Piet with a rod for the bad children and presents for all those who have been good."

There followed a very busy week, and I think we had much more fun preparing everything than the children did when the party took place. Especially Jimmie, who used to get terribly fidgety unless she had something to do and who now could drive all day long between Middelburg and Veere to buy everything we needed. As for Frits, he thought it was so much fun that he telephoned his office in Amsterdam that he would not be back for the rest of the week, and he also asked a friend of his, who was an amateur actor, to come down from Amsterdam and be our Sinterklaas. This friend was a newspaperman, but his paper still owed him a few days' vacation, so that he was able to join us on Saturday. Frits offered to play the part of Sinterklaas' black slave, who for some mysterious reason had always been known as Black Pieter, and Lucie knitted away at Erasmus' sweater when she was not at Jo's, helping her make *speculaas* soldiers and sailors and ships and houses and all the other figures children would expect.

Frits and Jimmie also plundered the Middelburg ten-cent stores, and soon we had enough presents for a small army. We did not tell Erasmus anything about what we were doing, for everything that happens on Sint Nikolaas evening must be surrounded by mystery. We merely explained that we had invited rather a larger number of people than usual, so that he must not be astonished if, for this once, we did not dine at Frits' home. We asked him to come to van Beveren's place, which, as we promised him, would be entirely comfortable, since we would start heating it up three days in advance.

As we wanted more than anything else to make Erasmus feel as if he had been in his mother's home, I had gone to the Middelburg library to consult some of the old cookbooks they had there, and I had copied two sixteenth-century recipes for pea soup and *speculaas*. Here they are:

To make *speculaas* you will need:

Of flour—150 grams (about ⅜ lb.)
Of butter—50 grams (about 1/10 lb.)
Of almonds—12½ grams (about ⅛ lb.)
Of powdered clove—2½ grams (one big pinch)
Of powdered cinnamon—½ teaspoon
One small dash of nutmeg
Also 5 grams of succade (candied lemon peel—big spoonful)
Finally, one big soupspoonful of milk
together with 100 grams of brown sugar (¼ lb.)

Dissolve the sugar in the milk, cut the peeled almonds in fairly large chunks, cut the succade up in small strips. Knead all these ingredients into a round ball and press this dough into *speculaas* forms cut into a wooden plank. Take a sharp knife and with this remove the superfluous dough. Put the cookies on a metal tray upon which you have sprinkled some fine, dry flour. Put the tray with the cookies into a fairly hot but not overhot oven until they are beginning to turn a light brown (about fifteen minutes), then let them cool off, and they will be ready to serve. (*North Netherlands Cookbook,* A.D. 1617.)

And here is the recipe for the genuine Dutch pea soup as it was given in the same cookbook, though of a slightly later date (A.D. 1639).

  2 pig's feet
500 grams fresh sausage or 50 grams butter (1 lb. sausage or 1/10
      lb. butter)
 ½ pint dried peas
  4 quarts water
    A bit of salt
  4 leeks
    A handful of celery green
  1 heart of celery

Wash the peas and let them soak overnight in the cold water. Next morning let them simmer over a slow fire for about two hours, until they are thoroughly boiled, but be careful to proceed slowly. Then pass everything through a sieve and add the pig's feet. Let all this boil another hour. Then take the sausages, into which you have previously pricked a great many holes with a fork, and let the whole mess boil once more for about half an hour. Then take the sausages out, until fifteen minutes before serving, when you put the sausages in again, for they are to be eaten with the soup. Then add the vegetables, which in the meantime you have cut up into small pieces, and let everything boil over a slow fire until the meat has separated itself from the bones. In case you think it necessary, you can, from time to time, add a little water, and the soup will be ready as soon as it is no longer in any way lumpy.

That was the recipe. It was a bit complicated and indicated that our ancestors had more time than we, but Jo told us not to worry. She could easily fix it that way.

As one large bowl of that soup was the equivalent of a three-course dinner, we had now provided for the grownups as well as for the children and we dropped our plan of giving them chicken croquettes on top of it.

Thursday morning at breakfast I had an inspiration. Frits had now met several Americans and had found them very pleasant company. Why not ask another American to be with us on this particular evening? Someone who had been known to be fond of children—someone like old Benjamin Franklin, the most civilized American of the eighteenth century, the man whose ready wit and common horse sense had charmed and delighted young and old, kings and peasants—everybody who came in contact with him.

It was rather late to send him an invitation. Not that he would in the least mind being asked as an afterthought. He was not that type of person. But I had not the vaguest idea through what formalities my little slips of paper had to go before they were acted upon. Well, it would do no harm to try, and that evening the wobbly stone lion of the town hall was balancing itself on a slip of paper which bore the name of Benjamin Franklin, inventor of the lightning rod and author of the famous *Project to Arrive at Moral Perfection.*

As most Europeans know less about American history than they do about that of Greenland, I prepared a short *curriculum vitae* of Dr. Franklin for the benefit of my Dutch neighbors who would be present at our Sint Nikolaas party.

Benjamin Franklin was born in the year 1706 (in January, of course) and when he was ten years old, it was perfectly possible for him to have met a few people who had lived through the Cromwellian period and who had seen Charles I step out of the famous window which led to his scaffold. When he died in the year 1790, the Declaration of Independence, which he himself had helped "edit," was already fourteen years old. He therefore was a kind of connecting link between the last stages of European feudalism and the first stages of American democracy.

In the span of time he covered, Franklin was not different from a great many of his neighbors who also reached the three-score and fourteen, but he was entirely unlike these others in

772

his awareness of everything that took place around him and in his tremendous appetite for living. Furthermore, he not only watched what was actually happening, but his quick-thinking brain made it possible for him to see those events in their right perspective. In addition to this, he had been blessed with a glorious sense of humor and a most amiable and realistic view of the universe. All of which made it possible for him to spend sixty years in public life without ever losing faith in his fellow men.

Not that Franklin had any particular reason to love them. At times, his fellow Americans had bestowed a great deal of honor upon him, and especially toward the end of his days he was often treated more like a demigod than an ordinary human being. But he was much too intelligent not to know that the greatest ambition of his life—to keep the Anglo-Saxon world together as a co-operative political unit—had been a failure and could never be revived. His sound philosophical habit of mind training prevented him from wasting useless tears upon that which could not be helped, but he would have been a great deal happier had he achieved his purpose, and the world at large would probably have been spared a couple of dozen wars.

As a rule, when we think of a great man we have a vision of him at one particular moment in his career. I always see Franklin as an old man, when he had done the work of a dozen ordinary mortals and when, under ordinary circumstances, he would have withdrawn from all further activities to await the end. But instead of settling down to that quiet and dignified old age to which he was most assuredly entitled, he had started forth upon still further adventures and had so greatly impressed everyone he met with the vigor of both his body and spirit that many people suspected him of having learned the secret of the life everlasting from his friends, the Indians of the Pennsylvania hinterland.

Ships had improved considerably from the days when his father had first crossed the ocean, but an ocean voyage during the last quarter of the eighteenth century was still far from comfortable, and the chances of reaching one's destination were always doubtful. Just the same, when the call of duty came, old Dr. Franklin was not found wanting and, with his young grandson as his secretary, he sailed for France in search of those funds which were absolutely necessary if the cause of the rebellion were not to collapse through a lack of ready cash.

Arriving at last safely in Paris, but without the slightest idea how he would be able to pay for his board and upkeep, Franklin not only succeeded in getting in touch with the French government, but he actually persuaded this already bankrupt concern to sink fifty million francs (which it did not have) into a cause that seemed about as hopeless as that of a free Czechoslovakia at the beginning of the last great World War.

That was a pretty long sentence, but it sums up the whole situation in less than thirty words. At home, Congress was weak and without sufficient power to enforce its will upon the thirteen colonies, which often hated each other more cordially than they did the common enemy. The soldiers of General Washington were so sadly lacking in the daily necessities of life that they were seriously thinking of going back home and accepting any kind of peace rather than prolong a struggle which offered no possible expectations of victory. As for his colleagues, the other representatives of the sovereign United States of America, who were now wandering across the face of Europe, entrusted with mysterious diplomatic missions, they were so completely lost in their own little plans and ambitions and so hopelessly jealous of each other's success that they spent more time sniping at their Parisian colleague than trying to get those cannon and rifles for which General Washington's starving and freezing volunteers were clamoring with never-diminishing insistence.

To make the picture of his disillusionment perfect, Franklin's only surviving son (upon whom he had set such high hopes) had turned Tory and had joined those who opposed the war against his own country. His wife, with whom he had spent a great many placid and contented years, was dead, and he himself was suffering from that most painful of all maladies, gall-stones.

But Franklin never uttered a word of complaint. Once he had set foot on the soil of France, he proceeded to do what he had set out to do with the same meticulous care and precision with which, half a century earlier, he had founded his Phila-delphia publishing house. Being a past master at handling men, he carefully planned the assault he would have to make on the entrenched bureaucracy of Versailles. He kept away from that madhouse and settled down in near-by Passy. From his modest retreat in that somnolent suburb (in a house lent him by a French banker friend) he so cleverly manipulated his one-man propaganda that ere London had become fully aware of his presence on the other side of the ocean, France had definitely taken the side of the transatlantic rebels, and our war of free-dom was won.

I have made a pilgrimage to that little house at the corner of the Rue Raymond and the Rue Singer (the first French home, by the way, ever to be protected by a lightning rod), and I have sat in the Passy coffeehouses, even as old Benjamin must have done during that long stay of his as our commissioner. I have watched him there, coming down the narrow street, conspicu-ous in the clothes of a bygone generation in the midst of the most fashionable world of his day, wearing his outlandish beaver hat (that beaver hat was to become one of his assets as the repre-sentative of a truly democratic nation) and making himself the living symbol of democratic simplicity in the heart of a country where the word "liberty" had not been heard for the last three centuries.

I have quietly observed Franklin partaking of his cup of chocolate (no coffee, if you please, for a man with gallstones) and munching the nuts which had.come to him by the latest packet just arrived in Bordeaux ("Have a nut, Your Majesty! They're from my own garden in Philadelphia and are sent to me regularly, now that there is no longer any danger from English privateers"), and I have rather indiscreetly stared at him as he put on his big, old-fashioned glasses and started to read his mail (arrived on the same ship as the nuts). And I have wondered what was going on in his mind while he took off his glasses to wipe them clean with a large, old-fashioned handkerchief (old-fashioned things being part of his role as the venerable sage from the New World) to make sure that his eyes did not deceive him and that he actually read what he thought he was reading—an endless tale of blunders and acts of cowardice and narrow-minded selfishness.

And then I have shared his joy when he opened still another document, bearing the private seal of General Washington, and when he learned that all was not yet lost, that the General still stood as a rock of confidence in the midst of a sea of doubt, and that the General, in spite of the treachery and betrayal with which he was surrounded, would continue to fight the battle for liberty until either victory should have been won or he himself should have lost his life.

At such moments I have perhaps wavered a little in my devotion to that other great patriot, Mr. Thomas Jefferson of Albemarle County in Virginia, whom I always considered the leading figure of the Revolution, for I felt that I could bestow just as great an affection upon this old man with his plain face (but elegant manners), his quaint speech (hiding a profound knowledge of the English language), his shambling gait (but with feet that would unerringly carry him to his ultimate destination). Yes, there have been moments when I could actually have loved old Ben, the printer and mail carrier, the diplomat, and one of the half-dozen men directly responsible for the founding of our independent republic.

The sentiment just expressed was by no means shared by all of Dr. Franklin's contemporaries. Those who based their position in life on inherited privilege, those who lived upon the labors of others, those who hoped to get a great deal in return for very little beyond the fact that they had taken the trouble to be born—all of them most cordially detested and feared this dangerous revolutionary rabble-rouser who had tried to deprive the Penn family of their legitimate revenues, who had helped to bring education within reach of everyone by substituting English for Latin as the main object of a gentleman's education, and who had actually preached the pernicious doctrine that candidates for office should be appointed according to their abilities rather than the social and economic status of their families. And all these Tories and reactionaries had called Ben Franklin a Red and a Communist (or whatever was the eighteenth-century equivalent of these words), who was perhaps not without a certain talent but who must be kept in his place, no matter by what means.

But where was the right place for a man who had started life as one of a brood of thirteen children of an impecunious if honorable Boston soap boiler who (horrible thought to most of his neighbors!) had not only been a recent immigrant but also a creature suspected of nonconformist leanings—and that in a Boston still dominated by the old Puritan theocracy? And how could one hope to keep a person within the bounds of social and economic respectability when at the age of twenty-six he had already established himself as the leading printer of the thirteen disunited colonies and had attained such a degree of financial independence that the threat of withdrawing a contract merely made him laugh and might even provoke him into telling you that you had better try elsewhere, for he never again meant to set a line of type on any job you intended to entrust to his care?

In addition to all these reprehensible qualities, the upstart seemed to have been endowed with a very pronounced flair for science, so that (in spite of his never having gone to a respectable college like Harvard or Yale) he had gained world-wide fame as the inventor of the lightning rod; as the inventor of a new kind of stove which for the first time in their career had made it possible for the New England farmers not to spend the winters rolled up in horse blankets, and as the ardent advocate of a public lighting system by which citizens going out for an evening stroll were now saved from breaking their necks by falling over their neighbors' garbage cans. Most important of all, how could you successfully attack one of the cleverest publicists of his day, the author of the best-selling almanac in an age when most people in the New World read only two books—that and God's Bible?

I could continue in this vein for several pages more, but I am not writing a life of Dr. Benjamin Franklin, postmaster general of His Majesty's colonies on the other side of the ocean. ("Damn the fellow! within a year he has turned that service from an everlasting money-loser into a most profitable source of revenue!") I am merely trying to show you the sort of person you are going to meet this coming Saturday.

America until *now* has produced only two universal geniuses. One of them was Benjamin Thompson of the village of Woburn in Massachusetts, and the other was Benjamin Franklin of the village of Boston in the same province. But Benjamin Thompson chose to be on the wrong side of the fence, and when the Revolution broke out he was obliged to escape so as to avoid being tarred and feathered by his own neighbors. After a brilliant career in what he still considered his mother country, he moved to Austria and to Bavaria and in the latter country he had become the benevolent power behind the Bavarian throne, changing that backward country from a state of almost complete medievalism into as modern a nation as was to be found anywhere in the Europe of the Napoleonic era. His success had earned him the title of a count of the Holy Roman Empire, and all future generations should praise him as the man who first of all had the courage to lay down the law that it is a better policy to make hungry people first of all happy by feeding them and then give them a chance to become virtuous, rather than by first trying to make them virtuous by force in the expectation that their newly gained consciousness of moral rectitude would thereupon satisfy the gnawing pains of hunger in their empty entrails.

The other universal genius produced by the New World—

that enlightened citizen who, in spite of all temptations to lure him away from his cause, stuck faithfully to his homeland—was our good Dr. Franklin. And therefore, while we politely salute Benjamin Thompson, Count Rumford, as a most interesting historical phenomenon, we honor and revere Benjamin Franklin, for though he never gained any titles beyond those bestowed upon him by his fellow Freemasons, he gained everlasting renown as one of the real founders of that experiment in self-government which soon may become the last surviving stronghold of democracy and therefore the only hope for a better and more human kind of world.

Kant's far-reaching *Critique of Pure Reason* appeared while Franklin was in France. He may have read it and he may not. He did considerable traveling through Germany, but he never, as far as I know, visited Königsberg. It would have been nice if we could have arranged an evening at which these two interesting men would have had a chance to exchange and expound their views. I even thought for a moment of including Immanuel Kant in our Sint Nikolaas festivities, but I hesitated to invite a professional philosopher to a children's party. Children are apt to ask such embarrassing questions!

Our Sint Nikolaas party, I am delighted to say, was an unqualified success. We had asked Lucie and Jimmie to come and help us, for while we could take care of the little boys, they would know much better than we what to do with the small girls, and we had no idea whether Virginia Dare had lived to a ripe old age or had died in infancy. When she came she proved to be only seven, for having been adopted by an Indian family, she too had succumbed to "a complaint of the chest" (tuberculosis, of course) when the rest of the tribe which had murdered her parents and her fellow settlers had fallen victims to that dreadful disease.

Lucie and Jimmie and Jo had gone straight to the big meeting hall, where Erasmus too had promised to come. But Frits and I were still at his house, busily engaged upon the not so easy task of changing his actor friend into something resembling a bona fide bishop of the fourth century of our era. Poor Frits, who was not familiar with the difficult art of blacking up, had by this time got so much more black on his shirt than on his face that we were obliged to take him out into the garden to get him clean and we had rather stupidly forgotten to watch the clock, until we were suddenly called back to reality by a loud voice which demanded to be informed whether he was at the place where he was supposed to be or whether they expected him somewhere else. It was Benjamin Franklin who had walked in on us and who now stood in front of our open fire and was looking at it with eyes that expressed everything but approval.

Without waiting to be introduced, he poked his cane into the burning pieces of firewood (big logs were not to be had in Veere for love or money) and then said, "My dear young men, don't you see what you are doing? You are wasting half of your heat. More than that, I would say. It may be as much as three quarters. Now if only you would move the logs up a little farther forward and put a curved iron plate behind the fire—but then, of course, you would have to change your chimney too and—oh well, what's the use? You misguided Europeans will never know how to be comfortable!"

Then he sniffed. "What is that peculiar smell?" he asked. "Dampness? Yes, it can't be anything else. How do you manage to survive in this quagmire? And yet there is nothing simpler than to keep a house dry. We had a lot of trouble with damp houses in Philadelphia. The Dutchmen who lived with us were the worst offenders. I don't mean your kind of Dutchman. I mean those immigrants from the Pfalz. They were an obstinate lot, and the way they had built their houses in the old fatherland was the way they must build them even after they had come to America. So I made quite an investigation of the problem. I found that it depended entirely upon the way you had started your cellars. Of course, this house is pretty old, I suppose?"

"It was built in the year 1562."

"That was long before my time, though sometimes I feel as if I were as old as Methuselah. I know that I don't look it! Indeed, I don't look a day over sixty. But that's easy. There's no trick to it. I will tell you how it can be done. Never worry about what may happen tomorrow, for in ninety-nine cases out of a hundred, it won't. And don't take things too seriously, for very few things are worth it.

"And now, please show me where the entrance to your cellar is. I'd like to inspect it and I'm sure I can then tell you how to fix it so that you won't have to live any longer in a cave like this. It is disgusting and—worse than that—it is unnecessary."

I showed him the door to our cellar.

"Oh, there it is! Now, just let me have a candle and I will tell you in a jiffy. I like to be useful around the house. Got the habit from my mother. She came from Nantucket. Ever been in Nantucket?"

I told him I knew the island well.

"That's interesting! Did it stay with the Union or did those obstinate Quakers declare themselves independent in the end? You will remember that they were always threatening to do so."

I assured our guest that the last time I had been there, Nantucket had still been part of the Union.

"That's all to the good, but what a headache they were—all those little villages and those little cities and even some of the smaller provinces. They caused us more trouble than the big ones put together! Each one had his own junto—a useful institution if handled the right way. I started one of my own in Philadelphia when the Quakers and the Dutchmen and the Penns refused to do their share in the wars with the French, but it takes a man who knows what he wants to handle them properly. Whereas in those hamlets the juntos were usually run by a small clique of Hotchkinsons and Wedderburns, eminent Philadelphians whose fathers or grandfathers had stolen themselves rich, cheating one another and the poor Indians.

"When the Revolution began, these families somehow hoped to become the kingpins of the new setup. They never looked any farther than their noses, and most of them were snub-nosed. But they made the mistake of their lives when they called in George Washington to save their necks from the English hang-men.

"Old George, bless him, came to Cambridge and gave them one look, and after that he treated all these little potentates like the dirt under his feet. Of course, he too was a good deal of an autocrat. He loved to be called Your Excellency and to act the part. I am a plain man and don't go in for that sort of nonsense. But in spite of all that, I honored old George. He was a great man. But then, all those slaveholders had an air of 'Yes, my good fellow, and what is it you want?' I suppose it was because they always had had so many Negroes hanging around them, ready to do their bidding. There was only one exception. That was Tom Jefferson. A nice youngster was Tom, and brighter than the rest of us put together. And now let me see"—holding up his candle. "Just as I thought! Your cellar is all wrong, but it can easily be fixed. Let me show you . . ."

But I never discovered how Frits' house could be made as dry as a bone, for Jimmie was yelling to us from the top of the cellar stairs that if we did not want to be much too late for our party, we had better come up right away. So we climbed the stairs, and I introduced Mr. Franklin to Mrs. van Loon as a fellow Pennsylvanian.

"And where were you born, my dear madam?" asked old Benjamin, giving her a bow which showed that he had not wasted his time at the court of Versailles.

"In Harrisburg, sir," said James, who rarely sirred anybody.

"Harrisburg? Let me see. That is where old John Harris had his ferry, wasn't it? I knew John when I first came to Philadelphia. And so that village became a town afterward?"

"It is the state capital now," said Jimmie, with more pride than I had ever seen her take before in her native city.

"That shows that the people of Pennsylvania have at last got a little sense. After the way the Philadelphians let the General's troops starve that winter in Valley Forge, they no longer de-

Benjamin Franklin inspects our cellar.

served to be the capital of a civilized community. And look at what they did to my poor academy! The moment I was looking the other way they turned it from a free school for the poor into a Latin hothouse for the children of the rich. The same old story, and it seems as if they will never learn.

"As for the Reverend William Smith, who spoiled all my lovely plans, that fellow should have been hanged! But I suppose I really had no one to blame but myself. I appointed him. Then he went back on me. Yes, he should have been hanged, though we Freemasons don't believe in capital punishment. Yes, ma'am—at your disposal, ma'am—and what do we do now? I am under the impression that I was to have the pleasure of meeting a few youngsters. No reflection on your age, ma'am. How old are you, anyway?"

"Forty-nine."

"Well, ma'am, you surely don't look it. You must have learned not to worry. You must have read my almanacs. Do they still print them?"

"No, I'm afraid they don't. At least, I have never seen any. Your name now appears on only one magazine published in Philadelphia."

"I have heard about it," Benjamin answered, but offered no further comment, except to look at his big, old-fashioned watch and to remark, "It is late, and one should never let children wait. In the first place, it is not polite and, in the second place, they might break the house down. And so, with your permission, I suppose we had better be off, and I see there is the good Saint!"

For by now the Bishop was at last duly garbed in all his white-and-golden glory while his servant was as black as our kitchen stove, and everything was ready. Most of us were able to find room in Frits' car, which was a great deal larger than our own Chevrolet, but the Saint took up so much room that I preferred to walk. However, it was no distance at all, and when we reached the small hall we had rented for that evening, we found the party already in full swing. The day before, while driving through the Middelburg streets in search of our favor holders (hard to get them in such a small town) I had come upon a fellow playing the accordion in the street. He was a wizard, and then and there he had been hired to come to Veere the next night to play for the children. He had arrived on the seven-o'clock bus and was now warming up. That is what he called it, but I never heard such an avalanche of arpeggios and glissandi, such tremolos and such juggling with notes and chords as came pouring out of his instrument.

Lucie and Erasmus were sitting comfortably in front of the stove, which was red hot. During the afternoon it had once more started snowing quite heavily, and the hall, although ventilated and heated for the last three days, was still quite damp and smelling heavily of tar and paint. I wondered what Franklin would say! But he was too much engrossed with the children to favor us with another lecture on ventilation.

We had declared in favor of candles over kerosene lamps. They were perhaps a little dangerous with so many small boys and girls around, but we had several pails of sand placed in convenient corners and would keep a careful lookout for accidents.

By the light of the candles it was at first a little difficult to see how many youngsters there were. We had invited a dozen of our small neighbors, six boys and six girls. We had been careful to ask such among the girls as still wore the beautiful old Zeeland costume, and they were a joy to the eye in their starched lace caps and with the colored kerchiefs that served as bodices.

They were, quite naturally, a little bit scared of those other strange-looking children who had arrived only a few moments before, and they seemed especially awed by little Virginia Dare, who was dressed entirely in animal skins—"just like a real Indian," as one of the boys whispered to me when we came in, "those Indians you see in the movies!"

One of the little girls, braver than the rest, had already made friends with the little Dauphin, who was dressed very handsomely in black satin and who was a very good-looking boy, bearing a striking resemblance to his mother, though he already

showed a beginning of that slightly puffy chin so characteristic
of his father's family.

The boys and girls from Hamelin (we knew them from the
costumes we had seen on the walls of Hamelin's *Rattenkrug*)
seemed to have established the most cordial relations with the
boys and girls from the Children's Crusade, but the two little
princes from the Tower were a pathetic sight. They looked
miserably scared and were sitting on two pillows, as close as
possible to Lucie, who was patting the head of the older one,
who in turn was holding his small brother's hand.

When we came in, our accordion virtuoso had just been ren-
dering his own version, with many interesting variations, of a
well-known old Dutch melody, the song of Piet Hein who
captured the Spanish treasure fleet, but he stopped when he
noticed us and slipped over into *The Parade March of the
Grenadiers,* a tune known to every Dutch child. As soon as they
heard this, the Veere infants lost their self-consciousness. They
rushed wildly up to the foreign children. Each Veere girl grabbed
the arm of one of the boys, and each Veere boy did likewise
with one of the little girls from abroad, and, without being told,
they formed a regular procession and started marching through
the room. The accordion player (who for the occasion had put
a gay feather in his hat) walked ahead, and the rest of us followed him with the good Saint well in the rear. Behind Sint
Nikolaas walked his black servant, rolling his eyes wildly and
grimacing most savagely at all the children. On his back he carried a heavy burlap bag full of presents which would be distributed afterward. In his right hand he held a light birchwood
stick, and underneath his left arm rested a large book, the volume from which the Saint would read the good and evil deeds
that the children had committed during the previous twelve
months.

The head of the procession had almost reached the place
where Erasmus was sitting, when the door opened, and a very
small boy on crutches came in. Jimmie went up to him and
asked him kindly who he was and what he wanted. The little

boy seemed very much bewildered, as if he felt that he had done something he should not have done. Then, wringing his felt cap with both hands, he suddenly burst forth in tears and buried his head in her skirt.

"Please, gracious lady," he pleaded, "please don't send me back!"

"Of course not," Jimmie assured him, "of course we won't send you back, but we can't let little boys walk all over the village so late at night and all alone, so tell me—who are you and how do you happen to be here?"

He wiped his eyes with the back of his rather grimy hand and then he said, "My name is Johann, and I am from Hamelin. You see, I was the small boy who could not keep up with the others because I had to use crutches. And so I never got into that mountain, for the doors were closed just when I reached it, and I lost all the fun the others had, and then they never came back, and I had no one to play with afterward, for they were all of them inside the mountain and none of them were ever seen again. I have been so terribly lonely all my life long, and the fathers and mothers of the others hated me because, as they told me, I used to remind them of their own children whom they had lost. Sometimes they even beat me, although I had done nothing bad, and I heard that some of the other boys and girls would be here tonight and I wanted so much to see them," and he broke forth into such a deluge of tears that Jo, who was somewhat better suited for such maternal activities than either Lucie or Jimmie, picked him up in her arms and carried him over to the other Hamelin children, who at first looked at the lonely boy as if they could not believe their eyes and then, shouting, "*Johann! das ist unser lieber, kleiner Johann!*" took him by both hands and, regardless of his crutches, dragged him into a wild roundelay which was so contagious that the others at once followed suit and joined in the fray.

The maestro, who was a quick-witted fellow, immediately caught the spirit of the occasion. Dropping his march, he switched over into an old-fashioned polka and, by this stroke of genius,

turned the hall into a complete bedlam in which Benjamin
Franklin hopped and skipped between Jimmie and Jo until
everybody had joined except Erasmus, who sadly shook his head
when Lucie invited him to dance with her, but who immediately afterward changed his mind and performed a *pas seul*
with so much elegance and dexterity that I wondered whether
all those evenings at Sir Thomas' hospitable house had really
(as he always told us) been spent singing madrigals or listening
to serious discussions upon the subject of infant damnation and
transubstantiation.

This, of course, could not go on for very long. We had a
bishop with us, the real, honest-to-goodness Bishop of Myra,
and he was there for a very special purpose. It was about time
we gave His Sanctity a chance to officiate according to the solemn rites of the feast which all these many centuries had been
associated with his name.

I therefore clapped my hands. The troubadour stopped his
playing, and all the Dutch children stood stock-still, for now
they knew that the great moment of the evening had come and,
as Sint Nikolaas is a very mighty personage to them (and quite
as real as their own fathers and uncles), they did not want to
spoil anything by indulging in a little more horseplay.

Jo and Lucie and the other grownups now bade all the youngsters seat themselves in a semicircle. Sint Nikolaas next stepped
forward, and his black slave dropped his heavy bag on the floor,
and the *Musikant* played a fanfare, and the moment for which
all our little Dutch guests had waited had at last arrived.

Our newspaper friend played his role superbly and closely
observed all the best traditions of the true Sint Nikolaas ritual.
First of all he told everybody how happy he was that he had
been able to reach Veere in time. It had not been an easy voyage, for all the roads were covered with snow and so were the
roofs of the houses across which he had been obliged to ride
to find out what present each child wanted him to bring. Yes,
it had been so slippery that he had almost had an accident. His
horse had slipped but it had caught itself in time, and now the

Then I went dutifully through my share of unpacking, but of course I found out that it was really meant for Dr. B. Franklin. Old Benjamin then picked up the scissors, only to discover that, after all, the bundle should have gone to Lucie. Some fifteen minutes went by in this way, the package changing hands a dozen times, until at long last (and now having dwindled greatly in size) it remained in the definite possession of Erasmus, and out of it came that beautiful red woolen sweater which Lucie had knitted for him. He held it up for all to admire and then he said, "But I could not ever wear this, for it would make me a cardinal."

"Why not?" I asked him. "You could have been one if you had wanted to."

"Perhaps so, but then it hardly seemed the right thing for me to do."

"Now it is," Lucie smiled back at him.

"Indeed, and so it is, my dear madam, and I shall ever remember the fair hands that knitted it for me."

But he too remained faithful to the code of Sint Nikolaas evening, that one must never under any circumstances pretend to know who has given you any particular present, and then he excused himself and with Hein went into a small side room and came back a few minutes later with a big bulge underneath his shoulders.

"Well, Doctor," Jo asked him, "and how are you feeling now? Warm at last?"

"Wonderful! I am really and truly warm for the first time in almost four hundred years. And who is getting the next present?"

This time it was the turn of Benjamin Franklin. A few weeks before, while rummaging through Bal's antique shop in Middelburg, I had come across a dozen old blue tiles showing small boys and girls flying kites. As soon as I suspected that Dr. Franklin might be one of our guests, I had telephoned Bal and, as I had found him very reasonable in his prices, I had asked him to have the tiles framed and sent to me. Now Sint Nikolaas

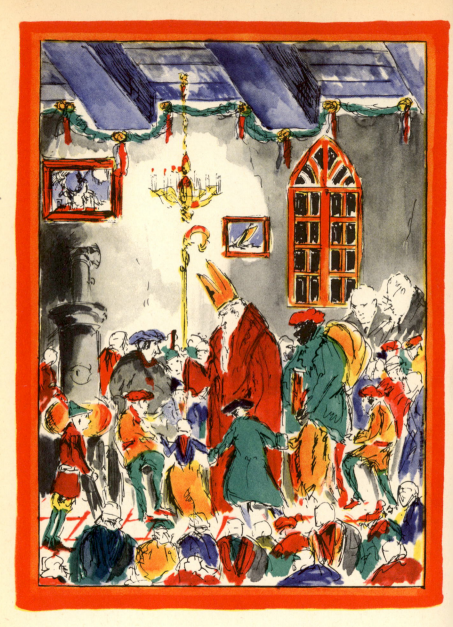

The Sint Nikolaas party was in full swing.

made a very gracious speech about bright little boys who loved to fly kites, and Benjamin Franklin got up and received his gift.

Jo was next. She was asked to step over to the small side room where Erasmus had put on his sweater. There she found a beautiful new gas stove for her own kitchen which Frits and I had bought for her. We felt that we owed her something a little better than what we might have given her in ordinary years, for without her, our dinner parties would never have been the success they had become.

Jo thanked Sint Nikolaas most effusively for his most generous present, for that is something you are allowed to do. You may thank the Saint, but there must be nothing personal in your expressions of gratitude.

Then Black Pieter felt it was his turn to take a hand in the proceedings. He suddenly opened his burlap bag and with a quick gesture threw handfuls of candy among the children. By this time, the little murdered princes had so completely lost their shyness that they rolled as merrily across the floor as the others, and there was a free-for-all which ended in the usual fight when the two smallest of the Veere girls had got hold of the same stick of peppermint at the same moment. Hein settled this controversy by lifting them up as if they had been ill-behaved puppies, and peace and harmony once more returned to the hall.

The grownups had now been taken care of, and the time had come for Sinterklaas to open his big book to find out which of the children had been good enough during the previous year to deserve being remembered and which should be spanked with Black Pieter's birchwood rod. We had somehow feared that some of our small foreign guests might not quite understand this part of the ceremonies and therefore we had slightly changed this chapter. Sinterklaas merely studied his pages for a few minutes and then remarked that, as far as he could see, they had all of them been pretty good. He therefore would leave it up to them to decide what he should do.

"All of you get up," he commanded, "and now tell me—on

your word of honor and cross your heart—have all of you been really good enough to deserve some kind of present?"

The Dutch children answered for their foreign friends.

"Ye-s-s, ye-s-s! Sinterklaas," they shouted in unison. "Cross our hearts and hope to die! We have tried awfully hard to be good." And the little Dauphin got so carried away by the noise they made that he too clapped his hands and said, *"Oui, monsieur l'archevêque, j'ai été un très brave garçon!"*

"And you feel that none of you deserve to be spanked?" the Saint continued.

A thunderous "No-o-o-o-o!" followed this question.

"Et toi, mon prince?" the Saint asked the Dauphin.

"Non, monseigneur, pas du tout!" the boy protested, anxiously looking around him as if he feared that the terrible shoemaker would be there to administer another undeserved lashing.

"Very well, then," said Sinterklaas and, reaching behind him, took the birchwood rod in both hands, broke it across his knees, and threw the pieces among the children, who once more used this opportunity for a grand free-for-all fight which would have gone on for heaven knows how long if the faithful black man had not changed it into a scramble for more candy by emptying the rest of his bag among the little ladies and gentlemen rolling so merrily across the floor of the smelly, paint-stained hall.

That was about the end of the official part of the evening. It was getting late, and the kids were getting hungry. All that still remained to be done was to distribute the presents. We had left it to Lucie and Jimmie to choose them, and they had done a first-rate job. First of all came the Lost Children, and each seemed to be getting what he or she had always hoped for. And then all the little Veerenaars received their share, and Jo told them: "Now get up, children, and we will bring in your table."

Thereupon she and Hein and Benjamin Franklin and I (for Frits must not fall out of his role of Black Pieter) carried in a big table, which had been got ready in the other room, and

Hein brought in a lot of chairs, and the children unrolled their napkins (a funny cap came rolling out of every napkin), and when they beheld the table with a large *speculaas* figure awaiting them at every seat, there was a loud hooray which grew even louder when Hein returned with a large tray and they realized that they were going to have their favorite dish—hot pea soup with pig's knuckles.

After that, silence except for the clicking of the spoons of both children and grownups, but the brew appealed so greatly to Benjamin Franklin that he got up and proposed a toast to the cook who had been responsible for this "piping hot nectar" and asked her for the recipe, for, as he explained, "If we had had that soup for our troops, the war would not have lasted more than a year and, believe me, there never would have been any Valley Forge."

There were fresh outbreaks of joy· when the ice cream was brought in, for each child received a lovely flower in pink or green or yellow, resting elegantly upon a bed of white spun sugar. This sugar at first frightened the two little princes, who thought it was glass until they saw their Dutch friends gulp it down by the spoonful, when they took courage, picked it up in their fingers, and liked it so much that they asked for more.

And what happened after that? I am sorry, but I feel that that should remain a matter about which the world had better not know too much. For the end of the evening was filled with so much sadness, it was so full of unconscious tragedy, that I would rather not talk about it.

No, nothing very startling occurred. The children ate until they could hold no more, but they behaved like lambs. Then Benjamin Franklin told them stories about the time he had been in the army and had fought in the American wilderness and had met real Indians (when he mentioned the Indians, Virginia Dare looked quite proud and very superior), and our newspaper friend, who had once more discarded his regalia and had been duly introduced as another guest just arrived, performed some wonderful tricks with eggs and with burning candles and bowls of water that were suddenly filled with goldfish, and the maestro played all his jolliest tunes on his accordion, and then the boys and girls, although they did not know a word of one another's languages, sang lots and lots of songs, and Jo arranged them in two groups—the boys on one side and the girls on the other—and taught them a number of old-fashioned Dutch kissing games. And then, as if they were obeying a silent signal, the children suddenly grew very sleepy—and that is when gaiety left us and tragedy stalked in.

For those poor little mites seemed to feel that very soon they would have to bid each other farewell and by this time they had grown so fond of each other that they did not want to say goodby. The little Veerenaars had not quite known in the beginning what to make of their strange-looking friends in their outlandish costumes. But they had soon sensed that there was something mysterious about them—that they had gone through certain experiences which had left deep marks upon them—and where (so they whispered to each other) were their fathers and mothers and why couldn't they play like the other children, but had to be encouraged to laugh and to be gay, as if they did not quite understand that they were allowed to dance and be happy to their hearts' content? Why, in the middle of one of those lovely games, where at the end you were allowed to kiss your partner, had they looked with such frightened eyes at the doors as if somebody might come in and hurt them? Why, whenever a plate or a cup had fallen, had they stiffened up as if expecting a sudden blow? And because, childlike, they had felt that those other boys and girls lived in a constant dread of some terrible calamity, they had tried to reach out to them by being very nice to them—much nicer than they ever were to each other— and though they would stoutly have denied it if one had been tactless enough to tell them so, they had actually wrapped little scraps of love around the thin shoulders of their small comrades.

But from their side, too, the Lost Children had undergone

quite a change. They had almost completely lost their former fear and shyness. They were really beginning to enjoy themselves, but they seemed very dejected at the prospect that all this could not last much longer and would very soon come to an end. They clung desperately to the hands of their Dutch playmates. The Dauphin (there the Bourbon blood showed itself!) had chosen the prettiest of the Veere girls to be his particular companion. The two princes were both of them sitting in a large chair with their arms around a small Zeeland girl, too far gone with sleep and food to know or care what was happening. And our little Indian and a Veere boy were contentedly scraping the last of the ice cream (now a lukewarm soup) out of the glass jar into which Jo had dropped the leftovers. But all of them seemed apprehensive of the moment they would have to depart.

It was then that the good Frits, with his great understanding and tact, did one of those things for which everyone who ever met him must also love him.

He climbed onto his chair, clapped his hands, and shouted, "Children, I want to ask you a question. Did you have a nice time?"

A loud hooray showed him how they felt about it.

"Then would you like to have another party like this next year?"

This time I was afraid their noise would lift the roof.

"Very well! Then I will tell you something. I talked to Sinterklaas before he left and he promised me that if he possibly can do so he will meet you here again, not only next year but every year after, and now you may kiss each other good-by and say: 'Till next year,' and then we will all sing one more song."

But that song was never sung. For the relentless clock struck the fatal hour. And when Hein carried in a lamp, the Veere boys and girls found that their newly found friends were gone.

Fortunately, children, to whom the whole of the world is a constant mystery, rarely stay surprised very long. They looked at each other a little sheepishly, hastened to make sure that they would not forget to take home the presents they had received, and, having been bundled into their mufflers and shawls, were all of them packed happily into the car in which Frits was going to drive them home. But suddenly they remembered that they had forgotten something and they came trooping back into the hall. They gave each one of us a very dirty little paw (covered with floor dust, chocolate cake, pea soup, candy, and ice cream), said, "Thank you very much for a very pleasant evening," and returned to the car, satisfied that they had done their duty and now could assure their mothers, "I did what you told me. I said, 'Thank you very much, Mynheer Frits,' and he answered that we had been so good that we could come again next year. Will you let me go, Ma? Please!"

CHAPTER XX

Fridtjof Nansen, Jakob van Heemskerk, Willem Barents, and Surgeon de Veer Are Our Visitors on a Very Cold Night in December

We happened to be talking about the heroes of our childhood days. During the last months we had met so many strange people—famous men and women who had made their mark upon history—that the subject was bound to come up sooner or later.

Both Frits and I were well aware of the small esteem in which our own world held the "exceptional man" and how his place had been taken by the "average man" as the center of public interest. We had often discussed the problem with our guests and had found that all of them agreed with us that a world without adequate and forceful leadership would never succeed in setting the human race free from the slavery of its own fears and ignorance. Not being entirely blind to the things that were happening around us, we also understood why the exceptional people were enjoying such a bad press. In a world filled with the unpleasant noises of a Hitler and a Mussolini, wildly shrieking their belief in their God-given missions and giving loud expression to their hatred and contempt for everybody and everything else, one did not like to hear anything more about "leadership" than could possibly be helped.

"But," as Frits asked quite sensibly, "what do these noisy fellows prove? Of course, they are terrible people, these Duces and Führers. I detest them. I have seen them at work and I loathe them. But what in God's name do they prove? Only one thing.

That they are the wrong heroes and the wrong leaders. It also shows—and very painfully—that we ourselves were flabby and weak because we refused to take them seriously and let them get as far as they have got. We were so busy with our own little affairs—we were fighting so desperately among ourselves for more plunder and for more colonies and to decide which politician or labor leader should run the show—we just had to close our eyes to what all of us knew was coming. And I think that all our indifference was due to our own lack of good leadership. It was old Gresham's law repeating itself for the so many hundredth time. Bad money, unless you watch it like a hawk, will drive out good money, bad manners will drive out good manners, bad music will drive out good music, and bad heroes, unless you get rid of them in time, will drive out good leaders. I apologize for this sermon. We have threshed all this out before —Plato—Confucius—Montaigne; it has become the eternal subject of almost all our dinners. And look at what we have got— the worst mess of all times. And believe me, it is going to be much worse before it gets any better, and I sometimes doubt whether it is not much too late now to do anything about it and whether it will ever get any better."

Frits stopped and looked at us a bit apologetically. But Lucie took up where he had left off. She was somewhat older than the rest of us, and in many ways she belonged to a bygone age— out of preference, for her mind was perpetually young.

"Yes," she said, "it was very different when I was a girl. Everything was so much less complicated. And we were still very simple when it came to our heroes. Of course, we had them and lots of them, too, but we took them for granted, just as we still took it for granted that our parents knew best. Perhaps they didn't always know best. Sometimes they were probably quite wrong. But on the whole, the system seemed to work. God was in His heaven, the king was in his palace, the burgomaster was in the town hall, and when Papa took his nap after a hard day's work, all of us children kept very quiet. My grandchildren go right on doing whatever they happen to be doing when

Grandma puts her palette aside for a moment and tries to catch forty winks. When told to shush, they answer that if it were not for Grandma, they never would have been born, and so Grandma has only herself to blame when her slumbers are interrupted by her grandchildren, or words to that effect. As for the burgomaster and the queen and God, they will ask you, 'Who put them there? We did, didn't we? And therefore we have a right to send them packing when we don't like the way they run things.' I suppose that they are right, and since the whole world has now gone Bolshevik, why not? But I am afraid that it makes life rather complicated for the rest of us, the old ones who were accustomed to the other and simpler arrangement."

Jimmie, being a good conservative of the American school of the nineties of the last century, wasn't particularly interested either one way or the other. She identified "liberalism" with Greenwich Village, where she had spent a great many years of her life, and quite naturally did not like it. It meant people who were careless about shaving and paying their grocery bills. Jimmie paid hers five minutes after they were dropped into her mailbox.

As for myself, as usual I had not been quite able to make up my mind. My old weakness—my love for the middle of the road —was preventing me from taking sides in too definite a way. I was like Erasmus. I felt attracted toward the Lutheran way of thinking, but I wanted to combine the Lutheran way of thinking with the more polished popish way of living, and while I realized that the dear old Mother, Home, and Heaven trinity of thirty years before was no longer taken seriously by most members of the younger generation, I had little love for that philosophy of Myself and Nothing Else which had replaced it. Half a century of digging among the ruins of the past had made me painfully familiar with the feet of clay which were buried deeply in the sands of time and which only too often supported the magnificent superstructure of some of the statues erected to our departed gods and half-gods.

But, on the other hand, where would we have been—yes,

where would we be today—unless occasionally there had been feet of granite, willing and able to carry their owners into the realm of the unknown and find new roads toward progress? The answer was—nowhere at all. We needed those *voortrekkers,* as our South African cousins used to call them. We needed a few stout hearts to do the pioneering. Without those men and women who trekked ahead of the rest of the crowd and either found new grazing fields or died in the attempt, no one of us would ever have got very far. We would have been obliged to stick to the swampy coastal regions, where we had lived and died until then, since the beginning of time, and we would never have known what lay hidden beyond the distant mountain ranges.

Today, of course, the physical world has been thoroughly investigated and opened up, but that was only a beginning. In spite of all our marvelous technical achievements, we are still cave men riding around in little gasoline-driven cars. It is true that we now can soar like the birds, but as long as we still behave toward each other with the brutality of wild animals, we might just as well have stayed where we were. The entire realm of what I would like to call "the human decencies" still remains to be conquered. And in order to give our youngsters the courage needed to continue the work of spiritual exploration, we must show them what some of our physical heroes have been and what they have done. Otherwise (and here old Gresham is back with us again), for lack of good and dependable and trustworthy leaders, the youngsters in their despair may feel tempted to follow the phony heroes who have now got such a hold on their imagination. For youth can no more live without some kind of hero than it can without its daily supply of fresh air and vitamins.

That very morning something in the newspapers had once more brought all this back to my mind and in very vivid terms. For years, the youth of Germany had been organizing itself into so-called "suicide squads" which had undertaken to conquer

Mountaineering, the noblest of all sports.

the Swiss mountains once again, but this time by routes which all honest mountaineers knew to be impassable. However, for Führer and *Vaterland* these poor idiots must do the impossible. Never mind if they were sure to lose their lives in the attempt. Others would follow in their footsteps, inspired with the same desire to conquer or die for their beloved Leader. And the Leader, by offering a special medal (in bronze and retailing at $3.49 a gross), was doing all he could to encourage this lunacy and to keep it going. For what other name could we bestow upon an undertaking that was not only devoid of all practical purpose (there was an easy road to the top of most of those pinnacles and often even some kind of hotel on the top), but one that had long since lost all connection with the noble sport of mountaineering?

But the poor, misguided youngsters had kept on coming, for if one of them should ever succeed, his name would be in all the German papers as another shining example of the do-and-die philosophy of the new and glorious Nazi dispensation.

The story printed that morning in all the papers was an account of four Nazi boys who had started out to scale a perpendicular wall, four thousand feet high and covered entirely with a thin layer of ice. It could only be done by means of iron spikes hammered into the rocks, which thereupon made some kind of ladder. Every Swiss guide had warned against it. Every good and honest mountaineer had denounced it as sheer folly. But the four had departed skyward, singing lustily about Horst Wessel and loudly cheering their beloved hero, Adolf Schicklgruber.

Toward evening, the people in the valley had lifted their eyes toward the mountain and by means of their telescopes they had seen how the four men, for lack of enough space to lie down, had tied themselves to their iron spikes and were preparing to spend the night standing on their feet. A second day and night had been spent the same way. On the morning of the third day, one of the four had slipped. The rope had caught his companion right above him and had almost decapitated the victim. This had thrown the third one off his balance. He had dashed his brains out against the side of the wall, and this had left the fourth one still alive but firmly fastened to the corpses of his former companions.

On the morning of the fourth day, the survivor still seemed to be breathing. A party of Swiss guides had thereupon decided to risk their own necks to bring this fool back to the valley. After Herculean labors they had at last got to a spot from where they could touch him. But just before they could throw him a rope, his strength had given out and, together with his three dead comrades, he had slipped into the abyss.

By great good luck, the Swiss guides had found their way back to the valley. But four young lives had been lost—had been deliberately thrown away—and an almost superhuman amount of strength and energy had been squandered upon an enterprise that not only lacked every practical purpose but which, even by the widest stretch of the imagination, could not possibly be connected with a real sporting venture.

Then why this absurd manifestation of courage of the wrong sort and this reckless playing with human lives? Merely to show the rest of the world that the Germans, the master race, were the *Herrenvolk* to whom nothing was impossible.

And what had actually been accomplished? Were we ordinary mortals impressed? By no means! We were merely disgusted, but our disgust was explained away as a manifestation of "physical softness" and "physical cowardice"—mixed with jealousy at not being endowed with the same spirit of high adventure which was to make the Nazis the rulers of the world.

I had read that story—a well-written story, too—and then I had thought of my good friends of the hospice on top of the pass of the St. Bernard. I had often visited them and had come to know them quite well. Ever since the year 962 these monks had been living there, more than eight thousand feet up in the air, amid their snow-covered peaks in a little sheltered valley on the road from Italy to Europe. A nice place to visit on a pleasant day in August, but a hopelessly bleak and desolate spot during at least eight months of the year. But every year before the digging of the great transalpine tunnels, these good monks had taken care of more than twenty thousand travelers, had fed them and given them a place to sleep, and on countless occasions had saved their lives by digging them out of the avalanches that forever descended upon this ancient mountain pass.

And what was the reward that awaited them after twenty or thirty years spent in this lonely wilderness? I know exactly what awaited these Augustinian fathers, once their strength had given out and their hearts had gone back on them. They were sent back to the valley to die, and after they had been laid out, their bodies would disappear into a nameless grave.

But in spite of these hardships there never had been a lack of eager candidates for this life of self-sacrifice and devotion. During the hundreds of years the monastery of the Great St. Bernard had existed, there always had been a plentiful number of young men willing to give up everything the rest of us consider worth while and bury themselves amidst the snows of the western Alps that they might be of service to their fellow men. And why? Because they, like those four Nazi boys who had been killed in the Berner Oberland, had heeded the voice of a leader. But what a difference whether the name of that Leader was Adolf Hitler or Jesus Christ!

We had continued to talk along this line for almost the whole of the rest of the afternoon and, in the end, we had decided that we would do what we had been talking about earlier in the day. We would invite a few of the heroes of our youth. I had made a bid for Fridtjof Nansen, the great Norwegian explorer, and Frits had asked to be allowed to ask three men, known to every Dutch child—Jakob van Heemskerk, Willem Barents, and Surgeon de Veer, the leaders of the famous Dutch Arctic expedition of the year 1596.

It was easy to think up a meal for these guests. They had

been simple folk, not accustomed to elaborate fare. I shall ever remember that enormous jar—almost a small-sized barrel—of mutton which I had seen standing in the galley of the *Fram,* the last time I was in Oslo.

I have always detested mutton with a most particular horror, but apparently Nansen and his comrades had lived quite happily on a regular diet of seal and, as an occasional delicacy, a bit of this embalmed mutton. Just one or two very small lamb chops—well, those I could tolerate if they were served with a sauce that hid their sheepy taste. But that enormous tin can holding what seemed to me fifty pounds of preserved mutton—it had given me a very clear insight into the hopeless monotony of that endless voyage of those occupants of the *Fram.* And knowing something too about the fare upon which the early Dutch polar explorers had subsisted I felt that almost anything we might serve our guests would be welcome.

Which, of course, did not mean that we, as hosts, should be deficient in the care with which we prepared our meal. But it would be better to keep everything as simple as possible, and this is the menu I gave Jo for the coming Saturday.

First of all, there was to be a bean soup, made according to a recipe of our own Gouverneur Morris, a gentleman of the old school who owed a great deal of his success as a statesman to his knowledge of good food. Here is that recipe as it was given to me by one of his descendants.

Bean Soup à la Gouverneur Morris

Put two cups of beans to soak in water to cover at night. The next morning put them into a pot with one teaspoonful of salt and two quarts of water. Bring to a boil and simmer slowly for an hour. Then add six carrots, two turnips, and one parsnip, scraped and cut into small even pieces. Let the soup simmer for three or four hours, skimming when necessary. When the vegetables are soft, press the whole through a colander and return to the pot. Scrape and cut four stalks of celery into small

The Hospice of St. Bernard amidst the endless snows of winter.

pieces and add to the soup. Let simmer until tender. If the soup gets too thick, add enough boiling water to make of proper consistency. Cut four slices of bread into small pieces, toast, and turn over and over in butter. Pour the soup over this and serve.

After that, just plain, ordinary roast beef, prepared in the regular Dutch style, with a lot of vegetables on the side and plenty of gravy. For dessert, one of Jo's excellent puddings with raspberry sauce and large cups of coffee and all the fresh fruit we could get. There is nothing that makes quite as much for good conversation after a pleasant meal as lots of fresh fruit and an abundance of nuts and candies of all sorts. Not to forget the large jar of ginger which these last two hundred years has always been found on every respectable Dutch dinner table after everything else has been removed.

Music or no music? Would our guests care for it? Jimmie doubted. Frits was neutral. Lucie thought in the affirmative. Then I remembered something else I had noticed on board the *Fram*. In the long room I had seen an old-fashioned music box, one of those tinkly affairs that was worked by means of a metal cylinder and that played three short tunes—three Norwegian melodies.

A few of my readers may remember these curious contraptions from their childhood days—those absurd ka-plink-ka-plankety-plunk doodads, endlessly repeating *Ach, du lieber Augustin, Jeanie with the Light-Brown Hair,* and *Yankee Doodle.* That (or rather the Norwegian equivalent of these popular melodies) was all the people of the *Fram* had had to break the monotony of their long polar nights. All the same, that absurd music box had served its purpose. When the silence of the eternal snows had become unbearable, these plinkety-plank tunes had given them the relief they needed not to fly at each other's throats for some trifling act or word.

I knew, however, that Nansen had been a man of wide cultivation, and any of our Beethoven symphonies would have done for him, except that Beethoven symphonies are not exactly the sort of music one usually serves with the soup. And I thought that it might perhaps be better to start with a few short pieces of the sixteenth and seventeenth centuries. One of them was Johann Kuhnau's "Biblical" Sonata called *David and Goliath's Combat,* of which I had had a private recording made one evening when Castagnetta was playing it for us and when she had made David throw his slingshot with more than usual vigor. For the benefit of the Dutch skippers I added Jan Pieterszoon Sweelinck's *Fantasia in Echo Style,* a piece full of tricks and queer tonal effects but admirably suited to the taste of honest sailors of four hundred years ago. That and Johann Pezel's *Fünff-stimmige blasende Musik* would probably be sufficient. Should they want more, we had by this time such a collection of fifteenth- and sixteenth-century melodies that we could not possibly run short.

Then for Frits' benefit I wrote a short story about the lives of our heroes.

Fridtjof Nansen. The very name depicts the man. It stands out like a Norwegian mountain peak rising abruptly from the snow fields at its base.

Nansen was born near Oslo in October of the year 1861. He went to the local school, did a lot of skiing, and finally enrolled at the University of Oslo to study zoology. He did a lot more skiing and at the age of twenty-one joined a sailing vessel that went to Greenland, getting in this way a bit of firsthand information about life on the ocean and his first glimpse of the Arctic.

After his return to the civilized world Nansen continued his studies, got the inevitable Ph.D., and began to prepare for one of the most fantastic of all polar voyages, at least from the point of view of the late eighties of the last century. He decided to travel on snowshoes and skis from the east coast of Greenland to the west coast, so that at last there would be some definite knowledge about the interior of the great white continent. Together with Otto Sverdrup (who afterward was to command the

Fram), two other scientists, and two Lapps, he sailed for Greenland in May, 1888. In August these men disappeared from view and climbed to the top of the frozen plateau which is the roof of Greenland. After six weeks of trekking through this snow desert at an altitude of almost nine thousand feet, the party safely reached the west coast of Greenland, from where it returned to Norway in the spring of the next year. The problem of Greenland had been settled, and the name of Nansen as a most efficient leader of a polar expedition had been established.

In 1890 Nansen was ready for another walking trip, but this time he was a great deal more ambitious. First of all he intended to build himself a vessel sufficiently strong to withstand the pressure of the polar ice, for he knew that most previous voyages had come to grief because the vessels that had been used had been smashed like walnuts under a giant's heel. Having got hold of such a craft, he would thereupon entrust his floating fortress to the same Arctic current which had carried relics of the ill-fated American *Jeannette* expedition all the way from the New Siberian Islands to the coast of Greenland. First of all he would take his ship to these New Siberian Islands (where the *Jeannette* had foundered, just north of the mouth of the Lena River) and would let nature take its course. If his calculations were right, the vessel would drift pretty close to the Pole and if it should be found that it did not get quite as far northward as he hoped, he intended to hop off at the nearest point to latitude o and do the rest of the voyage on foot. Walking and skiing and climbing had always been his favorite sports, and a couple of hundred miles more or less meant very little to him.

Nansen explained his plan to his Norwegian colleagues and laid it most respectfully before the Royal Geographical Society of London. Without exception the old-school Arctic explorers told him that it could not possibly be done, and greatly encouraged by their doubt, Nansen returned to Christiania (Oslo to us) and began making preparations for his voyage.

He acquired an old whaler, rebaptized it the *Fram* (Forward) and reinforced its inner construction until it was practically ice-proof. Then, as now, money was the beginning and the end of all scientific expeditions. But for this once, the Norwegian parliament (not unaware of the publicity value of such an undertaking) felt inclined to do something to help the good cause along, and the rest of the funds were obtained from the king and a few private individuals.

Otto Sverdrup, Nansen's companion during the trip across Greenland, was chosen to act as master of the *Fram*. Nine other men, consisting of officers, sailors, engineers, and stokers, were put under his command. These Norwegians had been most carefully selected, for it takes not only extraordinary physical strength but tremendous will power to live rationally through so many years in the Arctic, and Nansen figured that he would need at least three years to reach the coast of Greenland.

In June of the year 1893 the *Fram* slowly chug-chugged out of Oslo Fjord. Late in September she was fastened to an ice floe near the New Siberian Islands, and the famous drift began. In March, 1895, two years after it had left Norway, the *Fram* reached its highest latitude. During all this time, not a single square inch of land had been sighted, but constant soundings had proved that the Arctic Ocean was much deeper than had been expected, sometimes going as far down as two thousand fathoms.

Finding that the northward trek of his ship had definitely come to an end, Nansen decided to make his dash for the Pole. As it would not be possible for him to locate his ship in the drifting ice, he told Sverdrup that he would make for Spitsbergen as soon as he had succeeded or had failed in locating the Pole. For his companion he chose the strongest man on board, one with the not-unusual Norse name of Johansen.

On March 14, 1895, the two pilgrims, with their dogs, sledges, skins, and kayaks, left the *Fram* at 84° N, 102° E (look it up on your atlas), and on April 8 they reached 86° 14' N, the nearest spot to the Pole ever before reached by anyone not a bear or a fox.

Nansen was primarily a scientist and, since he was not pro-

Nansen leaves the Fram.

vided with a contract for a syndicated story of *My Dash to the Pole,* he was a free agent. He realized that if he wanted to return to Franz Josef Land before it was too late, he must return at once. And so, within easy walking distance from the Pole, he turned his back upon the object of his desire, which in itself showed greater strength of character than is found in most explorers.

After heartbreaking months spent in the trackless icy wilds surrounding the Pole, the two men finally reached the northernmost island of the Franz Josef group. There they built themselves a snow doghouse, using their silken tent as a roof, and made ready to pass the winter in about as much discomfort as any two human beings have ever experienced for quite such a long period of time. Their food consisted of bear and walrus meat, cooked over a blubber lamp, but somehow they managed to keep alive, and never did they know a day of sickness. Late in the spring of the year 1896 they packed their few remaining belongings on their backs and moved southward.

And now, you will ask, what did all this mean to me and why was I so much interested in the adventures of these two wanderers?

In the year 1896 I was fourteen years old and beginning to outgrow my first hero, the famous minstrel of a Dutch boys' magazine who could do all things and do all of them well. I badly needed someone else to worship—some other outstanding personality who would fill my lonely soul with awe and admiration and who would make me feel that the drab and unimaginative existence of a small and unimaginative Dutch town was not the beginning and the end of existence. And there was this magnificent-looking Norwegian (I was a shrimp in those days, lean from many years of sickness, and very bad at sports and none too good either at my schoolwork), and he and his few companions were somewhere up there—way up north—lost among the endless snow fields of the Arctic. Perhaps they were still alive. More likely they had long since died from hunger and cold, for this was the third year since they had been last heard from, and not a single word had trickled down from the great frozen spaces able to give us the slightest hint about their ultimate fate. Being endowed with a certain amount of imagination and having since early childhood read every book on polar expeditions I could lay my hands on, I could paint myself a pretty accurate picture of the last days and hours of these intrepid explorers. The truth about the ill-fated Franklin expedition (probably the finest piece of British bungling with the exception of the charge of the Light Brigade) had only revealed itself in my father's days, and he still remembered the shock of horror that had swept across the civilized world when it was discovered that every one of that crew of one hundred and twenty-nine officers and men of Sir John Franklin had starved to death, long after they had reached the coast of northern Canada. Being familiar with all the pictures that had been published of the cairns (hiding the last news of the *Erebus* and the *Terror*) and the pots and pans containing the remnants of human bones (for in the end it had become a case of sailor eat sailor), I could now see the men of the *Fram* as they struggled bravely toward the safety of the south, devouring their last dog and finally attacking and killing each other.

And then, in the early part of August of the year 1896, there arrived a brief telegram from Vardö (I shall never forget the name of that little village near the Murmansk peninsula) telling a jubilant world that Nansen was safe and that he and Johansen had been found near Franz Josef Land by an Englishman named Jackson, who had gone to that distant island on a scientific expedition financed by the late Lord Northcliffe. Just in the nick of time, too, for they were on the point of starvation. But they were safe. They were even then on their way to the Norwegian capital on board Jackson's good ship, the *Windward,* but they were full of anxiety about their comrades on the *Fram,* from whom not a word had been heard these last three years.

They could not know it, but on that selfsame day—August 13, 1896—the *Fram* had at last set itself free from the ice floes of the north and was now peacefully sailing southward with every member of its crew in perfect health. A few days later at Tromsö, the old shipmates were once more united and were proceeding to Christiania and to such honors as never before had been bestowed upon a group of men who had long since been given up as lost.

I had lived through all those episodes as if I had been an actual participant in those magnificent adventures, and as soon as Nansen's *Farthest North* had been translated into Dutch, I got hold of it and though I did not understand most of the scientific data with which the two volumes were crammed full, I missed none of the dramatic incidents leading up to that morning when Nansen, realizing that the end was near, had suddenly heard a shot, had climbed to the top of a small knoll of ice, and had found himself face to face with a white man—Frederick Jackson in search of his daily seal steak.

After that, I had lost sight of Nansen for a great many years. I knew that he had continued his scientific career and that he had taken part in a great many other and rather important expeditions, studying ocean depths and currents and suchlike matters which afterward became embalmed in very dull scientific publications, but in the year 1905 his name once more became connected with a human-interest story. That was on the occasion of the separation of Norway from Sweden. After the end of the Napoleonic wars, the King of Sweden, the famous French general Bernadotte, had been rewarded for his betrayal of his former friend, General Bonaparte, by being given the crown of Norway. Norway for the last four centuries had been under Danish domination. Denmark, however, had to be punished for having remained faithful to Napoleon. The King of Sweden had also become King of Norway. The Bernadottes (let this be said to their everlasting credit) had followed a very moderate and sensible course and had been quite successful at their difficult task of running their two kingdoms simultaneously. Gradually, however, the Norwegians had come of age (both economically and politically), until at last they wanted to be masters in their own home and began to clamor for independence. In any other part of the world, such an issue would have led to bloodshed. But these highly civilized nations had sufficiently outgrown their antediluvian instincts to know that a war between them would be worse than wicked—it would be foolish. And so they had bade each other farewell with perhaps a certain amount of personal resentment but without any lasting feeling of mutual ill will.

During this crisis Nansen, the former explorer, had played a most useful role as mediator and counselor of patience. He had summed up the situation with great and good common sense: if, in any such union between two nations, one of them feels that it is not getting quite a square deal—he had argued—then why continue a situation that can only lead to constant friction? Why not separate peacefully and each go his own way?

As soon as the union between Norway and Sweden had been formally dissolved, Nansen had been chosen to represent the new kingdom in London as the first Norwegian minister. Three years later, after things had quieted down, he had gone back to his scientific labors and up to the outbreak of the First World War had been fully occupied with his writing and with occasional expeditions to the northern seas. During the war itself he again had become representative at large of the Norwegian people to the rest of the civilized world. He had gone to America to see to it that Norway received those supplies that were essential to its existence, and as soon as the armistice had been declared, he had accepted a commission from the League of Nations to repatriate half a million prisoners of war which the old czarist government had gradually accumulated in Siberia.

When, immediately after the war, Russia had collapsed, Nansen had established a relief committee (after the Hoover pattern) to feed the hungry Russian millions. At the same time, he had headed that department of the League of Nations which took charge of the people (now turning up in every part of the world) who had lost their citizenship in one country and had not been allowed to acquire it in another. When Mussolini, in an early outburst of megalomania, bombarded the Greek island of Corfu, it was Nansen who had had the courage to protest, in the meetings of the League, against this act of savagery. Indeed, if there had been a dozen Nansens or even half a dozen in Geneva, the ill-starred League might have amounted to something. But Geneva had soon degenerated into a stronghold of dilatoriness and complacency and correct diplomatic behavior, until it collapsed through its own inherent weakness, rather than through any efforts on the part of its enemies.

Even then, Nansen had not given up his indomitable faith in mankind, and returning to Oslo, he had continued his labors for his fellow men, without any thought of self.

Fridtjof Nansen died in May of the year 1930. He had a happy death. He went to sleep and never woke up. That magnificent engine which had so faithfully served him through so many years at last gave out. The little spark which sixty-nine years before had been borrowed from nature's limitless reservoir of energy was once more surrendered to its original source. But the work it had accomplished continues to make itself felt, and in this age of little men (and was there ever such a dearth of truly great leaders as today?) we notice with painful clarity how much we lost when this public-spirited citizen of the world ceased to bother the pinheaded politicians of the postwar era by giving an example of completely unselfish leadership. Fridtjof Nansen was the sort of man who would have been ideally suited to act as the commander not merely of polar expeditions, but of expeditions infinitely more difficult, complicated, and dangerous than those to the frozen north. I refer to those excursions into the realm of applied politics, which so far have rarely produced anything but rank failure because they were entrusted to the wrong kinds of commanders.

And now we are in Amsterdam, and it is early in the month of November of the year of our Lord 1596. The town has at last taken the side of the Prince of Orange and has joined the rebellion against the King of Spain. The city is humming with business, for now one can once more trade wherever and with whomever one wishes. The whole world has become the oyster of these expert fishermen of the North Sea, and pearls are to be found in many of the bivalves which until then have been considered the exclusive property of His Most Catholic Majesty, the sour-faced Philip of evil memory.

Of course, one must accept the good with the bad. Mercurius, a most undependable deity, kept joggling his scales in a most unpredictable manner. Today he would cause the ruin of half a dozen men who until then had been regarded as pillars of the Stock Exchange, and tomorrow he would drop millions into the laps of a brace of fly-by-night speculators who, until then, hadn't had a pot in which to cook their daily porridge. Only last year one of the most promising of ventures—one that seemed to be absolutely foolproof—had turned out to be a sad failure. It was true that most of the money had been provided not by private individuals but by the town of Amsterdam itself, but in the end that was pretty much the same, for the citizens would have to recoup the magistrates for their losses by paying extra taxes. Nobody, however, felt inclined to grumble, for if the expedition had been successful, as the most learned geographers of the day had predicted that it must be, the United Netherlands would have had a route of their own to China and to the Indies and would have been the richest nation in the world.

At that moment, the route to the Indies was still in the hands of the Spaniards and the Portuguese, who brooked no rivalry. But if the Hollanders could discover a passage north of Asia from the Atlantic to the Pacific, the merchants of the Low Countries would no longer be obliged to go to Lisbon for their spices and silks and, instead of being middlemen, they would deal at the source, which often meant a net profit of three or four hundred per cent.

Two ships had therefore been equipped to try the northeastern passage by way of Cape Chelyuskin. That route was fairly well known as far as the strait which separated the island of Novaya Zemlya from the Russian mainland. That strait held a great fascination for the Amsterdam city fathers. For a strait was a narrow opening from one sea into another. Once you had fortified it with a couple of guns, you could close it to all outsiders and you had got hold of a nice little monopoly of your own.

The medieval ideal of monopolistic control as the only sound source of commercial profit still spooked around in the heads of these sixteenth-century traders, and they stocked their two ships well with cannon of different caliber and hopefully put their skippers in charge of a cargo of trade goods which might prove attractive to the heathen Chinese. As the vessel which penetrated farthest north was destroyed, the pieces of ordnance proved a complete loss. But it is typical of the sense of order and loyalty of these old sailors that, shipwrecked as they were, they returned in their open boats with all the merchandise that had been entrusted to their care. They might lose their lives, but business was business, and a trust was a trust.

The two ships selected for this venture were small and not particularly seaworthy, but who wanted to risk new vessels on so hazardous an undertaking? One of them (the smaller one) was under command of Captain Jan Corneliszoon de Rijp. The other was entrusted to Jakob van Heemskerk.

This Jakob van Heemskerk was a man of tried ability. He belonged to an excellent family, and in the year 1595 members of good families rarely took to the sea. It was not considered nice. Heemskerk was the exception. He had been well educated, was as good a scientist as they came in his day; furthermore he already had had some experience in sailing the Arctic sea.

But the real hero of the expedition was a certain Willem Barents. A native of Terschelling, one of the North Sea islands, just north of the province of Holland, he had started life as a cabin boy and had therefore come up the hard way. He had been north twice before and knew more about the coast of Siberia than anyone else whom the Amsterdam burgomasters could have hired.

I imagine him as a rather small man, stockily built, with a

square sailor's beard, and slow but sure in all his movements. A pious and God-fearing old skipper with a strong streak of conservatism in his make-up. This streak of conservatism showed itself when he was proved to be dead wrong in some of his calculations about the return of the sun. During many centuries, this error greatly puzzled the scientific commentators upon the famous voyage of 1596. How could as careful a mathematician as old Willem Barents have been so far amiss in his figuring? Until it dawned upon them that Willem Barents, who had grown up under the so-called "old calendar," had refused to accept the "new calendar" which was then beginning to be accepted by all modern-minded navigators as the only reliable time schedule.

But that same quality of obstinacy proved to be of the greatest value after his ship had been wrecked in the ice of the Kara Sea. Without a leader of his caliber to guide them through their disastrous experiences, it is highly doubtful whether any of his shipmates would ever have lived to tell the tale of their adventures. And so, bless old Willem's stout heart, for though he himself left his bones on Russia's bleak shores, the others got safely home, and that is about the highest praise one can pay to the commander of any expedition that comes to grief.

There was still one other member of the ship's staff who should be mentioned. That was the doctor (or barber-surgeon, as he was then called), a certain Gerrit de Veer. He was a Jack-of-all-trades and, furthermore, a cheerful and optimistic soul who well deserves the fame he gained as the official chronicler of this early invasion of the frozen north. It was he who forced the men to pay at least a minimum of attention to their personal hygiene, and to take daily exercise when they themselves would have preferred to spend the whole of the winter sitting in front of the fire of their little wooden hut. It was he—their doctor— who told them to eat moss when scurvy began to make its dread appearance. Also, being a musician of sorts (he himself played the flute), it was de Veer who organized those amateur theatricals which did so much to keep up the morale of seventeen men forced to spend an entire winter cooped up in a small wooden house and condemned to months of idleness.

Without any difficulty, the two vessels reached the Arctic Ocean. Once there, de Rijp and Barents disagreed upon the course to follow. Barents wanted to go due northeast while de Rijp favored a more western course. When two Dutch skippers disagree firmly upon any point (whether it be a point of the compass or the best way to stow away their barrels of beer or fill a pipe), there is only one thing for them to do—each one must work out his own salvation according to his own best judgment. The two skippers therefore bade each other farewell, de Rijp going northward and Barents holding to that eastern course which after a few weeks' sailing was to make him the discoverer of Spitsbergen, the land of the ragged mountains. From Spitsbergen, Barents and Heemskerk sailed once more in an eastern direction until they reached the coast of Novaya Zemlya. They followed it northward, rounded Cape Mauritius, and counted themselves very fortunate when they beheld the open waters of the Kara Sea. From here, as they had been told by the Amsterdam mapmakers, it would be only a short and easy distance to Cape Chelyuskin, where the Asiatic mainland reached its northernmost point and from where they could sail due south until they reached China.

But once in the Kara Sea, their troubles began. It was now well within the month of August, and the polar winter was at hand. One morning they woke up to find their ship solidly frozen into the ice. Before the days of dynamite (used in 1896 to set the *Fram* free) it was impossible to dig a channel through which a vessel could thereupon proceed to the nearest open water. Heemskerk and Barents discussed the situation and came to the conclusion that they had been trapped. They must prepare to spend the winter in the Arctic and try their luck next spring.

It was the first time the white man had been forced to face the hardships of the long polar night. I think that the most delightful part of the whole voyage lies in the complete co-operation between the two men who headed the expedition. The younger man, in nominal command, tactfully and gracefully conceded to the greater wisdom and experience of his older subordinate. There never was any friction, but such harmonious understanding that in all subsequent accounts of the voyage (and de Veer's book became an international best seller which maintained itself for many centuries) Willem Barents is accepted as the actual leader of the expedition.

They now had to prepare for six months of hibernation. They realized that the ship must be given up as a complete loss. It would be destroyed by the ever-increasing pressure of the ice. Therefore the wood might as well be used for the construction of a house large enough to give shelter to sixteen men. The ship's carpenter (most inconsiderately) died just after the floor had been laid, but in the sixteenth century every sailor was also more or less of a carpenter and could handle an ax or a knife as cleverly as a professional woodworker, and the labor of construction continued.

The vessel had found refuge in a small bay on the northeastern coast of Novaya Zemlya. That seemed as good a spot for the house as any other, and there it was built and there it has remained ever since. There was a plentiful supply of wood, for not only could the ship be dismantled, but the currents running westward from the coast of northern Siberia (the same currents which Nansen used three hundred years later for his dash to the Pole on the *Fram*) had carried a large number of dead trees to the east coast of Novaya Zemlya. It was hard work to drag these from the shore to the inland, and as two of the men were too sick to do any manual labor, the others had to do everything.

The roof offered the greatest difficulties. The sailors solved the problem by constructing a flat frame across which they spread one of the ship's sails. This they weighted down with a layer of sand. Then the Lord obligingly covered the sand with snow. Soon the snow became ice, and the roof remained perfect until the rains of spring melted it away.

They had no stones for a chimney, but most of the men re-membered the peasant farms of their childhood days, when the fire burned in the middle of the floor and when the smoke went up and out through a hole in the roof. They knew enough about air currents to give that hole in the roof greater drawing power by using an old barrel as a chimney pot. But their knowl-edge of ventilation did not go quite far enough. Indeed, on one occasion, during the heavy blizzards of January, some of the brighter lads hit upon the idea of increasing the indoor tem-perature by filling up the chimney with pillows and then using some of the ship's precious coal instead of the usual driftwood to get a hotter kind of fire. As the result, the whole expedition almost was asphyxiated. Fortunately, Chirurgeon de Veer—al-ways on the job—woke up just in time and had sense enough to kick the door open. After that, they never again indulged in such foolish experiments, but lay in their bunks and shivered.

However, from time to time they were made to get up. Their inventive barber had constructed a steam bath out of an old beer barrel, and everybody was obliged to use it at least once a week. The men slept in bunks erected along the southern side of the house. Barents, who was in bad health, was given a spe-cial bed by the side of the fire to the right of their dinner table, which also held the hourglass. In addition to this hourglass, they had a regular clock which showed that the men who had equipped the ship had been quite modern in their ideas. In the year 1596 few ships went to sea carrying a clock. Since one was supposed to sail by God and by guess, a little extra guessing did not really matter, and besides, the poor expeditionary clock soon gave up the ghost. How could it have survived? During half of the day, its innards were roasted and during the other half they were frozen stiff, and no clock then constructed could stand such outrageous treatment. After their clock had given up its ticking ghost, they had to depend upon the hourglass to know what day and what week it was, and one man was con-stantly on guard with no other duty than to turn the glass when it had run its course.

The cabin was illuminated by a single oil lamp suspended from the middle of the ceiling, and a large iron pot full of water was placed in the middle of the fire. This filled the room with a certain amount of moisture and provided the men with hot water for their soup. When everything had been finished, the dwelling was officially baptized the Safe Shelter *(Behouden Huis* in Dutch), and the sailors moved in.

Then the long siege began.

December came with an uninterrupted series of blizzards. Soon the snow drifts outside reached up to the roof, and the men had to tunnel their way outside whenever they wanted to bring in fresh firewood.

At first they were greatly disturbed by the foxes, who, attracted by the pleasant odors of cookery (escaping through the barrel on the roof that served as a chimney), came galloping across the roof. But soon the sailors found that this was a very convenient arrangement, for now they need not go very far outside to set their traps, and within a week they had a plentiful supply of foxskins. They needed these not only for coats and hats but also for footwear. The shoes they had brought with them from Holland had become useless. They had so often been soaking wet and thereupon had so frequently been dried out before the open fire that they had cracked wide open. The sailors, however, were clever with their knives. They carved themselves wooden soles out of driftwood and covered these with fox fur, and, as a result, none of them suffered badly from frozen toes during the whole of that long winter—quite a record for an Arctic expedition, especially one of three hundred years ago.

The climax of their suffering was reached on New Year's Day, when for an entire week such a terrific hurricane swept across the island that no one could go out for driftwood, and the inmates of the Safe Shelter were forced to burn some of their homemade furniture to keep warm.

On January 6, the feast of the Magi, the blizzard stopped, but the morale of the men was at a pretty low ebb and the versa-

Cross section of the "Safe Shelter."

tile ship's barber thought it would be a good idea to have a little party. The first mate was elected King of Novaya Zemlya, and a special dinner was prepared, and all the other festivities connected with Three Kings' Day in the home country were carefully observed. The meal, in case the reader is interested, consisted of pancakes and ship's biscuits soaked in hot wine until they were eatable.

And so the long winter went by until once more there was a short glimmer of light on the distant horizon, and the prisoners knew that the worst part of their period of detention would soon be over, and they could start work on the two boats that were to carry them to safety as soon as the sea should be open.

Work in the open proved a great boon to their health, for they had rarely ventured outside of the house during the long months of winter. In January, one more sailor died. He was the last one to be buried on Novaya Zemlya. Finally, early in March, the ice began to break up, but they had to wait until June before they could actually hoist sail and bid a tearful farewell to that stanch little wooden hut which had been their home for such a long time. Before the door was locked and barricaded against bears and foxes, William Barents wrote three letters, giving an account of their adventures. One of these was placed in a powder horn which was hung in the chimney. It was found there three centuries later, still in a fairly good state of preservation.

Early on the morning of June 13, Willem Barents was carried to the boat, together with one other sailor who was too weak to walk. The course they followed was first of all due north, until they reached the end of their island. From there they went southwest by south until at last they reached the northern coast of Siberia. From that point on, they followed that coast in the hope of reaching the mouth of the White Sea. Barents, although a desperately sick man, now forced to live and sleep in an open boat, never ceased to make the necessary nautical observations. He noted the capes they discovered carefully on his map, and correctly, too, for many of them are to be found to this day under their Dutch names and right there where they should be. After ten more days the sick sailor died, and one morning, old Willem Barents commended his soul to God and quietly slipped off into his final sleep.

At last they reached what must have been the mouth of the White Sea. Their homemade boats leaked very badly. The people in the smaller boat were most of the time sitting waist-deep in water. Their masts had broken, and their rotting sails were full of holes. Whenever they tried to go on shore, they were at once attacked by battalions of hungry polar bears. It was therefore impossible for them to make fires and prepare themselves hot meals. They were all of them on the point of exhaustion, and early in July one more sailor died of what seems to have been pneumonia. A strange detail—even during this desperate flight from death, they still carried those trade goods with them with which they were supposed to have done business with the Chinese, and on the first warm day of summer, by order of Heemskerk, these materials were unpacked and dried that they might be brought back to Amsterdam in as good a condition as possible. Apparently they had never thought of the possibility of using some of this extra baggage to replace their own threadbare wardrobes.

They still had to pass through several other uncomfortable adventures. Due to the presence of the heavy ironclad boxes which were part of their luggage, their compasses had gone haywire, and without reliable maps they only knew the general direction in which they were supposed to sail if they wanted to get back to civilization, but no precise details were available. A few days later, all of them were attacked by scurvy, but on one small island they discovered a lot of scurvy grass *(Cochlearia officinalis)*, and that put them back on their feet in no time at all.

And then, finally and at last, they met their first Russian fishing smacks. The rest of the voyage was comparatively easy, although on one occasion they were still obliged to row for thirty hours at a stretch. In August they reached the Kola Peninsula.

The men of Novaya Zemlya had lived safely through their terrible winter.

There a sudden fog separated the two boats, and for several days they did not know where they were or whether their companions were still alive. The fog lifted, however, before either of the vessels had suffered any serious harm, and together they reached the first Russian settlement, where they were most kindly received and where they ate their first square meal in more than two months.

And now, while recuperating in that Samoyed village, they were most unexpectedly united with Captain de Rijp. After a useless search up and down the Arctic Ocean, he had finally been blown into the White Sea, where he and his men had spent the winter. De Rijp took his former comrades on board his own vessel, and on October 6 they all bade farewell to their kind Russian hosts, leaving them their two leaky boats as a souvenir. Twenty-three days later they were back home.

As they had long since been given up as lost, their unexpected return created a tremendous commotion. What happened to these men afterward, we do not know. Common sailors are apt to lead anonymous lives. They probably went back to sea as soon as nobody was any longer willing to offer them a couple of glasses of ale in return for a lovely yarn about polar bears as big as horses and mountains of ice as high as a church tower. After that—well, a fellow had to live. So it was back to the ocean waves, to live or die as the case might be. And if it had not been for an enterprising publisher who had persuaded Master de Veer to write down an account of their adventures and sufferings, the whole story of that memorable voyage might have been as completely lost as that of many similar trips which were not accompanied by a barber who handled a goose quill as readily as his razor and scalpel.

One more word about Jakob van Heemskerk, who so bravely had led his men through all their tribulations and had safely guided them back to their port of departure. He continued to serve his country as commander of a man-of-war. In the year 1607, during an engagement with the Spaniards off Gibraltar, he was shot through the heart and killed.

We had had strange weather all through the year. A very warm and early spring had been followed by a cold and wet summer. But the fall had been exceptionally warm until almost the last week of November. Then it had turned extremely cold, and we were to experience the hardest winter since 1892. All the canals were frozen over, and even the Scheldt was so densely covered with ice that the ferry service with Noord Beveland had to be suspended, and the few people who insisted upon crossing to the island had to take their chances and go on foot.

As Jimmie insisted on keeping our home in Veere at an even New York temperature, I had escaped from my hothouse study to get my daily modicum of fresh air before I was due at Frits' for dinner. In Veere we did not have much choice when we went out for a short constitutional, and so I wandered toward the canal which connected our town with Middelburg. The locks had not been opened for almost ten days, and the ice on the canal was so solid that people drove their sleighs across it when they wanted to go to town.

There also had been a great deal of skating by the younger part of the population, but it was an exceedingly cold night, and the canal lay deserted. As it was still twenty minutes before seven, I spent a few moments standing on one of the locks, partly to catch my breath (for the temperature was near zero) and also to enjoy the lovely quiet of that frozen evening. Suddenly from behind the bend in the canal I beheld a solitary skater hastening to Veere. He seemed a very powerful man, for although he had to navigate against a strong wind, he proceeded at a rapid clip. His method of skating was not like that of our natives, who had carefully stuck to the old-fashioned and clumsy Frisian skates, which were fine for long distances but did not allow of much speed. The stranger, however, although he wore our own kind of skates (which are fastened to the shoes with leather straps), was going at least twenty miles an hour, and soon he had come close enough for me to recognize him. It was the face I would never forget, the face of the hero of my childhood days, Fridtjof Nansen.

The deserted harbor of our lonely village.

When close to the high steel gates of the locks, he stopped abruptly and then looked around to see where there might be a convenient place for him to set foot on land. As I knew that the lock keepers were apt to keep the water near their locks open in spite of the prevailing temperature and was afraid that the stranger might come to grief, I waved at him and by means of gestures I showed him where it would be safe for him to reach the bank of the canal. He made a gesture to show that he had understood, and a moment later I found him sitting on an old cannon (Holland is full of old cannon, now used for mooring ships), taking off his skates and stamping his feet to restore circulation.

"These skates are all right," he said before I had even had time to welcome him, "but why do people stick to these terrible straps? They cut off all circulation. I think that our Norwegian method of fastening the skates right to the soles of the shoes is a much better one. I hope you won't be offended by my criticism, but I feel as if my feet had been completely frozen."

I answered him that I completely agreed, but I reminded him that we were a people of farmers and fishermen and that farmers and fishermen were apt to be rather conservative.

He smiled as he looked up at me. "My dear sir," he said, "you are telling *me* who have spent most of my life with the men of the sea? I sometimes wonder they have been progressive enough to accept the compass!"

Then he got up. "I think I can walk again," he told me, "and now, since you seem to live here, you can perhaps tell me at which house I am expected for dinner tonight. I do not know the names of my hosts, but I have a description of the house." I assured him that he would not be obliged to make much of a search, for I had come to the canal for the express purpose of meeting him. That evening my little white lie did not go down quite so well.

"That is curious," Nansen said, looking me straight into the eyes, "for I myself had no idea that I would come skating in on you this way. I had expected to walk, but in Middelburg, in a secondhand shop, I saw those skates and they were so reasonable I decided to try and see whether I could still use them. I had no money, but they gave them to me for three of my medals, for where I am now, medals are not of much use, but I carried them in my pocket as a souvenir of happier days."

"Then you are fond of skating?" I asked, none too brightly, I am afraid.

"Skating and skiing and mountaineering have always been my hobby," he answered, "but all that was long ago. They told me that my heart had given out and that I must be very careful and not exert myself. But this moment I feel as well as I ever did, though I must have gone pretty fast the last two miles or so. And now tell me, do you live here the whole year around and is it always as cold in winter as tonight? For this beats Greenland, not to mention Novaya Zemlya, where your ancestors sat and shivered all winter long in their little wooden house and almost died of cold, while if they had only gone out and taken a little normal exercise they would have been as comfortable as we are in Norway."

This remark surprised me, and I asked him, "Then you know about that famous expedition of three centuries ago?"

"Of course I do," he replied. "It was the first regular polar expedition of all times, and I wrote about it in my history of Arctic explorations."

"Then you would be interested in meeting some of the survivors tonight?"

"Of course I would, but how could I? You don't mean to say they are here?"

"Not yet," I said, "at least I have not yet seen them. But we thought it would be rather fun to bring you together, and so we invited three of them. It is now five minutes of seven. In a few minutes we will know whether they could come."

When a moment later I opened the door of Frits' house, I saw that I need not have worried, for all three of our Novaya Zemlya friends were sitting in front of the open fire, enjoying a glass of hot Swedish punch.

It was Nansen who came skating toward Veere.

They got up, when we entered, and bowed most politely. I wondered at their civility, for I knew that they could never have heard of Fridtjof Nansen or his exploits, since they had died many centuries before the Norwegian had appeared upon the scene. But looking up at Nansen, who towered by my side (and I am almost six feet three), I understood. When Nansen entered a room, people got up. Perhaps it was his eyes which compelled this act of involuntary homage. They were the largest eyes I had ever seen, as well as the bluest. Besides, there was something in them that made you feel, "If this man bids me follow him to hell, of course I will follow."

Nansen seemed completely unaware of the impression he made. He walked up to Erasmus and most cordially shook him by the hand. "After Holbein, my dear Doctor," he said, "you need no introduction. I would have recognized you anywhere. And had I lived a few hundred years earlier, you would have given me a special chapter in your *Praise of Folly,* for surely there never has lived a more foolish tribe of men than we people, who wasted all the happy days we might have spent with our families, traveling endlessly through snow and ice to reach a spot which, if ever it is found, will look very much like those snowy fields through which I passed on my way to your village."

Erasmus, answering slowly in his dignified and antiquated German (for Nansen had used High German in addressing him), shook his head a couple of times and then he asked, "Tell me, were you lonely or unhappy when you were out there in the midst of your ice and snow and practically alone?"

"Of course not. I was much too busy trying to keep alive."

"And were you ever unhappy and lonely when you were back in civilization?"

"Very often, and I detest what people call civilization."

"Then," Erasmus concluded, "I don't think I could ever have included you in my little book, for you are a wise man indeed, and now let me present you to your fellow guests. They too were among the wise ones. They came to live in this delightful village."

"But I already know them," said Nansen, with gay eagerness. "You, sir, must be Captain Barents, whose sea I have often crossed on the way to eastern Siberia. And you, sir, must be Captain van Heemskerk. My compliments, sir. You did a most efficient piece of work, bringing your men home safely. And this must be our good Surgeon de Veer, whose book was one of my most cherished possessions when I was a small boy, way back in Christiania. I am only sorry that I could not read it in the original Dutch, but I hope you can at least understand me. A little Plattdeutsch and a bit of Norwegian almost equals Dutch, doesn't it?"

"It does," Barents answered, "and my own Terschelling dialect was not so different from what I learned when once I had a crew, half of whom were Norwegians."

"And there is always English," Heemskerk answered.

"Of course there is," Nansen answered.

"And the rest can be said on the flute," de Veer added. "I have brought mine, and when I can no longer follow you, I will toot the rest."

The evening had started out most happily, and it continued that way until the old Veere chimes struck the unwelcome hour of midnight. For it was one of those nights when everything seemed to click. The music (although we had very little of it) pleased our guests, and Barents and de Veer were so delighted with Kuhnau's *David and Goliath* that we had to ask Hein to repeat it. Especially the scene in which David slays Goliath and in which you hear the whizzing of the stone after it leaves David's slingshot filled their simple hearts with joy, although they derived equal pleasure from some of Sweelinck's *Echoes*.

And then Jo, who had already become great friends with the three men from Novaya Zemlya (it is so easy when you speak the same language), told us that dinner was ready, and we left the fireplace and moved over to the dinner table. None of our guests seemed to be exactly what one might have called gourmets. They had never been in the habit of eating for the sake of eating, but had partaken of food merely to keep alive and had often known the pangs of hunger. But the old-fashioned Dutch meal was very much to their taste, and the three Dutchmen were especially delighted with a large dish of fried potatoes which Jo had added as an afterthought. They had never tasted potatoes before and liked them, but whether it was the potatoes themselves which so greatly appealed to them, or whether it was the way they had been fried, I could not tell. I overheard, however, how de Veer said to Heemskerk, "Captain, if we had had these vegetables just once a week, none of our men would ever have had scurvy." In which he was much nearer to the truth than he could possibly have suspected. For it was not until several hundred years after his own expedition that Captain Cook proved the connection between scurvy and a lack of fresh vegetables. De Veer, however, was a close observer and he may have suspected something about the relationship between fresh fruit and the deadly scourge of all old sea voyages.

The old-style pudding too had been a fine idea, for it reminded the three Dutchmen of their midwinter celebration on Novaya Zemlya, when they had tried to boil a pudding like ours and had been obliged to compromise on pancakes.

But to Frits and me, the most delightful part of the evening came after our guests had had their first taste of a hot cup of coffee (two of them liked it, but Barents complained that it was too bitter for him and asked for another glass of ordinary beer), and when they began to talk shop. There is, of course, nothing more fascinating in the whole wide world than to be present when men who know their jobs well talk shop. It is almost as satisfying as listening to the practicing of a great artist. Nor does it matter in the least whether one knows anything about the subject or not. I have had quite as much fun sitting in on a bull session of football coaches as attending a supper where a couple of astronomers settle down to rearrange the universe. And I shall never forget that evening at the Algonquin when Knute Rockne and Ty Cobb were comparing forward passes and the best way to slide bases. I did not know a thing about either subject, but I had a marvelous time.

It was very much the same at Frits' house when we entertained Nansen and the staff of the Novaya Zemlya expedition. For after the last cup of coffee had been drunk (Barents finally agreeing that with a little practice he might learn to like this strange black liquid), the subject suddenly veered toward tacking. Having once upon a time written a book about ships, I knew in a general way that there was a kind of zigzag sailing known as tacking. But I had never suspected that there were almost as many ways of tacking as there are of preparing eggs. A number of empty plates became polar islands, and a wine bottle—laid on its side—became a sailing vessel, and then the tacking began. Matches indicated the currents that were running between the islands and how one could make headway from the southeast to the northwest with a strong wind blowing from the west and a current running east. When the dinner table proved too small, the dishes and the bottle and the matches were moved to the floor, and Hein joined in, and the famous men, noticing at once that this simple fisherman also knew his business, accepted him as one of their own, and they were having the time of their lives until, with equal rapidity, the conversation switched from tacking to whether one could live on meat exclusively or whether he also needed vegetables.

I was sorry my good friend Stefansson, the great champion of the exclusive meat diet, was not present, for on this occasion the carnivores were in the minority, but meat apparently was only of minor interest to them, and then—again with unexpected abruptness—the talk plunged right into the heart of the subject I wanted to hear discussed most of all—the problem of morale and leadership during a long polar expedition.

Nansen had taken the lead. "A ship's crew," he said, "especially in the Arctic, is exactly like an army. Without discipline, it degenerates immediately into a mob. With too much discipline, it loses all initiative, and the men will sit down in a blizzard and freeze to death rather than find shelter behind some near-by rocks, because no one with a couple of stripes on his sleeve has told them to do so. There have been all sorts of expeditions these last four hundred years, and some came to grief because the sailors stampeded and rushed for the nearest land. Then there was that terrible expedition of Sir John Franklin. I don't think we shall ever know the details, but from the little odds and ends we have found all over King William Island, I feel inclined to say that those poor devils, over a hundred and twenty of them if I remember correctly, were lost because their officers did not know how to assume the right kind of leadership. When you think of where King William Island and Victoria Land are, just beyond the polar circle, why I think I could have spent a winter there with nothing much more than a gun and an umbrella and an extra change of underwear."

I had read a lot about the Franklin disaster and ventured a question. "Wasn't one of the reasons," I asked, "the fact that the officers let the men do all the work?"

Here Heemskerk interrupted me. "That was all wrong," he said. "You should never tell your men to do anything you yourself would not or could not do."

"Of course not," said Nansen. "You don't have to pull a sled all the time if you are an officer—you need your strength for other things that are much more important. But on general principles, the men should realize that you are willing and able to pull your oar or your sled when it happens to be your turn and that you can do as well as the others."

Barents sighed. "I know it," he said, "and if that feeling is in your heart—if it is there really and truly—your men will know it, even if you are sick as I was and too weak to be anything but a burden to the others. I shall never forget how good those boys were to me, even when they themselves could hardly stand on their feet."

Here Frits asked the question that was on the tip of my own tongue. "I wonder," he said, "whether you would tell me—for all of you have had a lot of experience—how do you go about it to make the men do what you want them to do?"

Nansen looked at Heemskerk. "You tell him, Captain," he said, "for I don't know."

Heemskerk looked at Barents. "I don't know either, but Willem here is much older than either of us. Perhaps he knows."

But Barents too shook his head. "Maybe it is God's will," he then replied, "that they should obey you. I have been a good Christian—at least, I tried to be—I humbly tried. I believe that everything that happens in this world is foreordained by God. And I am convinced that God wanted certain of his servants to be leaders and others to be followers, even as our Lord was the leader of the blessed Apostles and as the others were his followers.

"That may seem perhaps a little too simple an explanation. But to me it is perfectly clear. I cannot conceive of a world in which there are no captains and mates and plain sailors. Such a world would not make sense. For just as I was always willing to take orders from those whom God had appointed over me (and I am sure my captain here had never any reason to complain of me), so by the same token I expected obedience from those over whom I had been placed."

We had listened very quietly. The old man had been touching in his sublime simplicity. We no longer saw the world that way, but it was a philosophy of life one could respect. It was a point of view which made sense—as long as that particular philosophy of life had prevailed.

But I was immediately attacked by certain doubts. How about Henry Hudson, surely one of the greatest navigators of all times, but a man who had never been able to exercise any kind of leadership—a skipper who had sailed the Seven Seas in ships that had always been hotbeds of mutiny—a captain who had finally lost his life because he had not even been able to control the evil temper of a member of his own family? And how about those other mutinies on the ships of the sixteenth and seventeenth centuries, that fill some of the most disgraceful chapters in the history of discovery? How about Captain Cook, who was a progressive and liberal and who, during all his endless years in the Pacific, had never found it necessary to flog a single man, while Bligh, a genius at the business of finding his way through uncharted waters, had literally flogged his way through the Pacific and had accomplished nothing but disaster?

I hoped that Nansen would come to my rescue, and he did.

"Master Willem is right," he said. "He is also right when he says that today we no longer find it possible to reduce all these difficult problems to such simple principles. We are, alas, not as devout as our grandfathers used to be. We have got into the habit of asking too many questions. Today we are not merely satisfied with knowing that the clock runs. We also want to understand what makes it tick. But in one respect, our world has not changed."

"In what respect do you mean, sir?" Frits asked.

"In this particular respect—that unless we have a real love for our fellow men—nothing sentimental, if you please, for they would not understand that—but a real interest in their well-being, a real desire to be of service to them (though I have come to hate that word 'service' and so please don't misunderstand me)—in short, unless those entrusted to our care feel that we think of them first and long before we even begin to think of ourselves, well then, everything else we do or fail to do is of no earthly use. The men will immediately sense it, and all control is gone."

"You are undoubtedly right, sir," said Fritz, "but isn't there something more to it than that? There must be, but what is it?"

Nansen smiled at him as a father might smile at a bright boy who asks a foolish question and then he said, "But don't you see that if we knew what that something was, God would have to go out of business?"

"No," Frits answered, "I don't quite see."

"Because then we would also understand the riddle of existence. And where would the good Lord be after we human beings had succeeded in unraveling his most precious secrets?"

I thought of an answer, but I did not give it. It might have hurt old Willem Barents, and that surely was the last thing I wanted to do.

It was well past eleven o'clock before any of us looked at the clock. Barents showed signs of being somewhat fatigued, and as we had pretty nearly exhausted every problem connected with navigation and exploration, there was a lull in the conversation. As had so often happened before, it was Jo who saved us from having to say, "Well, and what now?" by suddenly bringing in half a dozen plates of *poffertjes*. There is no use trying to describe them to outsiders, for *poffertjes* are the one dish that waxes only in the Low Countries. They are a cross between a very small kind of pancake and a fritter and are the main delicacy of the annual village fairs, when special booths are erected to which loving couples can withdraw to devour them by the plateful with lots of butter, sugar, and cinnamon, and a rather primitive form of necking.

It is not easy to fry *poffertjes* in your own kitchen, and you therefore never get them in any private homes. But Jo, with her genius for cooking, had somewhere got hold of an old *poffertje* pan, and there they were as they had been eaten in the Low Countries for the last four centuries. They delighted our Dutch guests, and the Norwegian said they reminded him of something he used to eat as a little boy in Fröen, but whether that was so or whether he merely said it out of politeness, I do not know.

Poffertjes make for good feeling, and we told the cook and her husband to come in and join us, but Jo said no, she could not until after she had brought in the mulled wine which she had dug up out of de Veer's description of the midwinter celebration in the Safe Shelter of Novaya Zemlya. A few minutes later the mulled wine came in, steaming hot, in a lovely old pewter decanter such as had been used in the *Behouden Huis*, and Barents said, "This is wonderful! Now, I feel that I am back home!"

And after the last of the *poffertjes* had been eaten, Surgeon

Our Polar friends go home.

de Veer, whom I had presented with a Dutch edition of my book about his voyage, duly inscribed to my "distinguished fellow author," took out his old wooden flute which he had left with his funny-looking fur coat near the piano and played us the tunes with which he had entertained his fellow travelers during the long Arctic nights, and like all simple music, these cheering melodies carried us back to happier days as nothing else in the world will do. Then the clock started playing our *Hymn of Thanksgiving*, and de Veer added a flute obbligato of his own, though it was difficult to harmonize it correctly with the chimes, which, being very old, were also very much out of tune.

Next the candles began to flicker, and while their dwindling flames threw weird shadows upon the walls and the ceiling, we watched our guests depart in silence.

It was so cold that before going home I dogtrotted to the tower at the end of the harbor to see what the ice was doing and whether there was any danger of the dikes of the near-by Vrouwenpolder breaking through. The moon was shining brightly across the peaceful island of Noord Beveland. There was an eerie light which made every object throw a heavy black shadow. The Scheldt was completely frozen over, but in the distance a small strip of black water showed where it ran into the North Sea where the ice and the water met. I beheld an old-fashioned sailing vessel rocking in the waves of the Roompot. From the pictures in de Veer's book, I recognized it as the ship which had carried Heemskerk and his men to Novaya Zemlya. Four dark figures were walking across the ice in the direction of the tiny craft. Nansen and Heemskerk were supporting Willem Barents. Behind them, as befitted his place in the hierarchy of the sea, walked the faithful surgeon. He carried a halberd. After all, one never could tell. There might be bears or wolves or foxes, and he must be on guard that no harm befall his masters.

When I came home, Jimmie, entirely surrounded by dachshunds (to keep her warm, I suspect), was still up and waiting for me.

"Well," she asked, "did you learn something new tonight?"

"I learned a lot," I answered, "an awful lot." Then I put some more coal on the fire, the dachshunds were dropped into their respective baskets underneath Jimmie's bed and were carefully covered up with several layers of old blankets, and we all went to sleep.

The morning came. It was as glorious and brilliant a day as I had ever seen. Outside, hundreds of seagulls were endlessly soaring up and down, fighting and screeching and altogether looking like a blizzard of feathers while awaiting the moment I should come to the door to give them their daily ration of stale bread. I felt very happy. At last I had approached the secret of true leadership. There was nothing supernatural in these heroes of my childhood days. They were merely "consecrated men" who lived "consecrated lives" in which the idea of self had been completely repressed that they might devote themselves entirely to the task of looking after the happiness and well-being of those entrusted to their care.

CHAPTER XXI

I Get a Cable to Return to America, and So THOMAS JEFFERSON Is the Last of Our Guests as Well as the Most Honored of All

WE DID NOT have our usual luncheon that next Sunday, for Frits, very early, had driven to Rotterdam to catch a train for Berlin. He had been obliged to go there in connection with still another loan his firm was floating, but he hoped to return the following Saturday on the Flushing mail train. To our great surprise he was back on Friday and instead of going first to Amsterdam he had come straightway to Veere, after having telegraphed Jimmie from the frontier, asking her to meet him at Flushing. We had postponed our luncheon so that he could join us. He seemed terribly upset, and, as he was a person who did not easily let himself get worried, we wondered what had happened to have given him such a case of the jitters. He had lunched on the train and so he merely drank a cup of coffee while we had our chipped beef. Meanwhile he told us about his adventures.

"Berlin was a nightmare," he began without any preliminaries. "I knew that I would find the situation changed, but I had never expected to see the things that have happened over there."

"You mean that this fellow Hitler will really come into power?"

"Will come into power? Lord help us all, he is in power right now! There is no longer any opposition. The republic is dead and gone. It never had much life, but even the last little spark has now been put out. Of course, the government goes on, but it no longer means anything. It is as hollow as an old tree. The next gust of wind will bowl it over, and this man Hitler is no longer a gust of wind. He has become a tempest. Soon he will be a hurricane. A hurricane blowing from hell!"

"But surely," said Lucie, who had dropped in to hear the latest news, "it cannot be as bad as all that! France and England will never allow him to come in and take over the government!"

"France and England won't move a finger," Frits answered. "France is in no position to do anything. Besides, what is France? Where is France? As I told you several weeks ago, there is no France left. France today is one large pawnshop run by thousands of small-souled, narrow-minded, pudgy-faced peanut vendors. Whatever business they still do is transacted over the third benedictine after a six-course luncheon and between telephone calls to the lady friends as to where they are to meet them that evening for dinner. The soldiers go about with their elbows out of their coats and their toes sticking out of their shoes, and if war were to come tomorrow, there would not be fifty airplanes fit to fly. France will surrender or, if it fights, it will collapse after a couple of weeks. No, forget all about your beloved France, my dear Lucie. I am sorry to hurt your feelings, but *la France héroïque* no longer exists as a power the Germans need worry about. The French people still do a lot of shouting about their democracy, but that democracy has been so completely sold out that nobody believes in it any more."

"Well, but how about England?" asked Jimmie, who has never got over her notion that the England of today is still that of Rudyard Kipling. "Surely England will never let Germany start another war?"

"My dear James, the crew that now runs England will accept any kind of compromise rather than fight. That old fool with his everlasting umbrella, who is said to be the next Prime Minister, is a small-town fellow with a small-town mind, about as farsighted as a mole. His father and he have sold brass nails until the family has become very rich, and the Chamberlains are now being invited by the best families. To be invited by the best families means something to a hardware dealer from Birmingham. Every night before he goes to sleep the old man looks under his bed to make sure there isn't a Bolshevist there. He and his crowd are much more afraid of the Bolshies than of anybody else in this world, and they hope that the Nazis, if only treated the right way (as they call it), will turn east and lick the pants off the wicked Russians. Then England won't have to do that job herself and can go on growing rich, with the Labour party in its right place and capital on top and the lower classes tipping their caps to their betters."

I felt that it was my turn to add something to this conversation.

"How about America?" I asked.

"Well," Frits answered, "you ought to know more about that than I do. What do you think?"

"I really could not tell."

"Would America care to get mixed up in European affairs after the experience of twenty years ago?"

"It does not seem very likely."

"Well, that leaves me exactly where I began. Nobody will move a finger to stop Hitler if he makes up his mind to go ahead and grab the power in Germany. London and Paris will probably write a few angry letters and next they will tell their people that they have decided to accept the inevitable, that one cannot hope to keep a great nation like Germany down forever, and then they will all go out for lunch. The French will eat well, and the English will eat badly, but they will all drink a lot, while Hitler will merely nibble at a couple of carrots and give orders to build another thousand airplanes and twice as many tanks."

"Is it really as bad as all that?"

"After what I have just seen in Berlin, I would say that it is much worse."

"Is that what made you come rushing back a day early?" Jimmie asked.

"Yes. Also on account of my business, for every cent any of us ever invested in Germany is gone for good and ever. But the main reason I came back was that I wanted to tell Jimmie and Hendrik not to be fools and wait too long. Hendrik has written and has said too many unpleasant things about little Adolf to be safe, and remember little Adolf never forgets."

"What do you mean?" Jimmie asked, instinctively picking up Noodle to protect him against possible harm. "You talk as if we should pack up and leave tonight!"

"Of course not! It will take Adolf a little while to get his airplanes and his tanks and submarines, for this time the Germans are not going to take any risks. They cannot afford another Versailles and they know it, and it will take them two or three years to build the stuff they need before they can strike. But I know how you love Veere and I am afraid that your days here are over. You would not have the chance of a snowball in hell if the Nazis ever invaded Holland, and they will do it—depend upon that—they will do it!"

"But why? The Dutch have not done them any harm!"

"For God's sake, stop talking nonsense! The Nazis are not the sort to worry about such details, and they have long since struck the word 'morals' out of their new dictionary. They will need Flushing for their attack on England and they will turn Veere into an airplane base. A bull-necked Nazi will live in your house, my dear friends, and when we go to Middelburg, we can wave at you when we pass the cemetery and say, 'There they lie! It is too bad. They were such nice people. If only they had left in time!' "

"Perhaps you are right, but this is making it pretty hard for us. What do you want us to do—run away?"

"Of course not, but you told me the other day your publishers wanted you to come to America to see your *Rembrandt* through the press. Why don't you go now and spend a few weeks in America while Jimmie packs up here, for it will take at least two years for Hitler to get ready, and meanwhile, she is perfectly safe. So are you, but you might as well make up your mind that our wonderful days here in Veere are over. There is no hurry, but let us face the facts as they are and get ready for some safe retreat where we can wait until the storm shall have swept across Europe."

"But how about you? Do you think I would leave you and go back to America alone and then live happily ever after, knowing that you were here?"

"Thanks for the compliment, for I know you mean it. And, of course, I may be a little too pessimistic, but after what I saw last week, I don't see how anybody could be otherwise. But don't worry about me. I don't write books. I am not in the public eye. I run my little pawnshop and smoke my pipe and read my newspapers and take Millie and the kid out for rides in the car. All the same, even I, the moment I am back in Amsterdam, I shall make sure that most of my money will be where no Nazi can ever get at it. So that when I join you in America, I won't send you to the poorhouse.

"No, I can perfectly well stay here and I am not exactly telling you either to run away, for you and Jimmie are not the sort. Only, now that they seem to need you in America for that new book of yours, why don't you take a short trip? You can be in New York by Christmas and you can be back here in Veere in February, and then we can go on with our dinner parties. In the meantime, we will know a little more about what is going to happen and we can stay in Veere until Hitler goes on the warpath. When he does, we can take the first boat to England. The Flushing boats get us to England in less than five hours. If the worst comes to the worst, we can take Hein's fishing boat and leave when the Nazis get as far as Middelburg.

"All this sounds pretty sad, but please don't go in for heroics. You can't fight Hitler all alone, and France and England won't lift a finger to stop him. I know that you want to go on fighting him, but you won't be much good after he has plugged a couple of bullets into you. Disappear for a while and do what your publishers asked you to do, and then you come back to us for some more of our dinner parties. In another two or three years, when the little man in the big brown boots actually starts his attack on England and America—and that is the dream of his life—then you lock your front door, and Jimmie takes little Noodle under her arm, and we will all meet in New York. But get accustomed to the idea right now that our happy days in Veere are almost over. So, by the way, are all the happy days in every other part of the world. The Allies made a mistake at the end of the last war, and now it is too late. We might as well be intelligent about it. Europe is doomed. You go to America and you go right away. The sooner you go, the sooner you will be back. In the meantime, whom have you invited for next Saturday?"

"Another American. I hope you don't mind."

"Not in the least. They have been about the nicest of our guests. Old Benjamin Franklin was a grand person and he was wonderful with those kids. And I shall never forget George Washington! I wish we had a dozen of their kind over here, right at this moment, instead of what we have got—third-rate fellows, without any imagination, commonplace hardware salesmen and stockjobbers, each one of them thinking of just one thing: 'Will I be able to save my own precious skin when the deluge comes?' Now, who did you say our next guest was?"

"I think that, by and large, he is the greatest American who ever lived."

"That must be your old friend, Mr. Jefferson. He'll be wonderful!"

"I have already started writing something about him. I hope to have it ready tomorrow evening, but there's so much to say."

"Forget it. I know all about him."

"How come?"

"You gave me a book about him last spring, written by a friend of yours—Nock or some such name."

"I remember. Then I won't have to refresh your memory."

"No, you don't. The book happens to be here, right in my house. I will look through it once more tonight."

The dinner for Mr. Jefferson had to be ordered very carefully. For though this noble Virginian dispensed with all outer formalities when he went to live in the President's house, abolished the title of "Excellency" for the chief executive, removed

the "Honorable" from all letters to high officials, and would hardly stand for a mere "Sir" on the epistles to the lesser dignitaries, he was exceedingly fastidious when it came to his own daily mode of living. It is true that he never smoked, nor did he drink those violent spirits which were so popular in the colonies during the latter half of the eighteenth century, but he well knew the difference between good wine and the inferior sorts, and in the matter of eating it was undoubtedly quite true what Patrick Henry said about him—that he had been abroad so long that he had long since abjured his native victuals in favor of the more delectable viands of the Old World.

Patrick Henry meant to be funny or just nasty when he made this famous statement, but to the democrats ot the Henry variety (plain, two-fisted whisky swillers and snuff sniffers) there was a quality in Mr. Jefferson they never liked. For no matter how simple and unaffected the master of Monticello might be in his personal tastes and how unaffected in his deportment, these brethren of a commoner clay always remained conscious of the fact that intellectually and spiritually their Virginia neighbor was a true aristocrat in that he would either take the best or would do without.

It is true that others with equal pretensions to social prestige were just as much aware of this, as witness Alexander Hamilton's deep dislike for his colleague while he was with him in Washington's cabinet. But Jefferson was "genuine" and Hamilton was not. This may be a somewhat crude way of trying to solve the problem of the antagonism that existed between those two very capable men and which made it impossible for them to co-operate. Just the same, I think that that was the basis for their cordial detestation of each other. Their respective abilities were of the same high quality, but Jefferson was so superior to most of his fellow men that he could afford to treat them as his equals. Whereas Hamilton was obliged to assume a superiority he did not really feel and then became the traditional Englishman who has gone to the wrong school, and this in spite of his Scottish antecedents.

This, too, may account for the cordial detestation in which Thomas Jefferson was held by so many members of the clergy, who never ceased to denounce him as an atheist, an infidel, and an enemy of all established religion. They may have been right in the last of these three accusations, but hardly in the first two. Jefferson, who found it difficult to accept what he used to call "established government," wishing to reduce official interference with the lives of private citizens to a minimum, had little love for any kind of tyranny, whether from the Right or from the Left or even from the Middle. He regarded a man's relationship with the Deity as a purely personal affair between the individual and his Creator. He believed in deeds and not at all in mere verbal expressions of good intentions. Whether a human being was a true disciple of Christ, he said on more

The simple country gentleman of Monticello.

than one occasion, would be shown by his acts and not by the size of the Bible he carried to church on Sunday or the heartiness with which he joined in the responses.

Jefferson had an intense dislike and a great distrust of personal arguments. "No one will ever change his mind on account of a mere argument," he was fond of saying. "A man may change his mind as a result of his own reflections, of what he has read and slowly digested, but debates are a waste of time, as they will never persuade a person to accept a different point of view from that which he happens to hold."

Religious disputations he held in special abomination. His own relations with God Almighty were so simple that few of his neighbors were able either to follow or understand them. His own notion that one should approach the Lord and talk to Him as one gentleman to another had very little chance of being appreciated among the clergy and the laity of the middle of the eighteenth century, and least of all in a part of the country where the general state of education was still as low as in the South.

In the year 1823, being then eighty years old, Jefferson decided that for once and for all he must give some definite and clear expression of his personal attitude toward religion. Until then he had never answered the endless insults and injuries that had been hurled at him for his refusal to take a stand in what were then called "the higher matters." But now, realizing that his days were numbered, he undertook to sum up his private creed in fewer than a hundred words:

"I am a Christian," he wrote, "in the only sense Christ wanted anyone to be His follower. I am sincerely attached to His doctrines in preference to all others. I ascribe to Him every human excellence, believing that He Himself never claimed any others." And in order that his own children and grandchildren should be thoroughly familiar with all that Jesus had said, he collected all the ethical lessons that were to be found in the New Testament, as you can see for yourself if you are ever fortunate enough to lay your hands on a copy of the so-called *Jefferson's Bible*.

All this, however, while no doubt very interesting, had no direct bearing upon the question of what we should offer Mr. Jefferson when he should come for dinner. But, in anticipation of that most happy occasion, I had several months before written to an old friend who was a descendant of his sister Martha, who had married his best friend, Dabney Carr. This woman had inherited not only her great-uncle's easy chair—a lovely chair and big enough for me, for Thomas Jefferson too had been over six feet two—but also his mind and his charm and a great deal of his wisdom and she had told me what dishes Uncle Tom would most likely have asked for. One of those was the spoon bread which we had already served to several of our previous guests. This was the recipe:

> 1 cup of yellow cornmeal
> 1 quart of milk
> 2 eggs
> ¾ teaspoon of salt
> ¾ tablespoon of sugar
> 1 rounded tablespoon of butter

Place the milk in a double boiler on the fire. After it becomes piping hot, sprinkle in lightly all dry mixture, stirring it at the same time and continually stirring it until it becomes thick. Let it cook one hour. After this beat eggs all together and stir them in with the butter. Place in a baking dish and cook thirty minutes in oven (400°) or until brown.

Spoon bread, however, does not a dinner make. I would have to add something a little more substantial and so I had to find out whether there was anyone in Middelburg who could make waffles, for although the Dutch waffle is not at all like its American namesake, being a much thinner and more delicate creature, I thought it would be nice to let Jefferson feel as if he were back in Virginia by serving hot waffles with sugar and cinnamon at about eleven o'clock, a few hours after the regular meal. I asked Jimmie to go to Middelburg and see whether perhaps the people of the Abdij could give her the address of a waffle baker. Meanwhile I was spending the morning in Jo's kitchen, watching her make *hutspot* and trying to get up a menu that could be served as a background for the spoon bread.

Since Jefferson had always been so deeply interested in cheap and popular foodstuffs, I thought that we ought to begin with a *potage à la Camérani*, which would give him both macaroni and Parmesan cheese. Then a few *côtelettes de saumon Dorigny*. We would need some very good Madeira for our salmon, but we could get it in Middelburg. With these slices of salmon, Jo was to serve very small boiled Dutch potatoes. As the *pièce de résistance*, I had thought of duck. A *canard à la broche*—a duck roasted over an open fire—has always seemed to me the best way to prepare that kind of fowl, and Jo could stuff the ducks with chestnuts, champignons, and those olives which had been one of Jefferson's favorite fruits.

Instead of having more potatoes (a good Dutchman will eat potatoes with everything from soup to dessert) we could have spoon bread with the duck, and instead of vegetables there would be a large bowl of fresh lettuce and a plain French dressing made with tarragon vinegar, one hard-boiled egg per person, and some leeks rather than the conventional onion.

For our dessert I ordered a *sabayon chaud au vin de Porto*. That was light and fitted in with Jefferson's preference for light meals. After dinner, instead of whisky (which he detested) or more wine, I meant to present our ex-President with a cup of *slemp*. He must have drunk a lot of *slemp* when he was in the Low Countries while in search of those loans that were so badly needed by the young American republic he had just helped to found.

When I was young, *slemp* was still a very popular beverage in winter. On cold nights, we used to drink it all evening long, and it was especially popular when we went skating. There were little "*slemp* tents," flying a big Dutch flag, all over the frozen landscape, and as the stuff was completely harmless, we drank it by the bucketful.

Not finding the recipe in the modern cookbooks, I went to

consult Lucie, who was an inexhaustible fountain of information upon every culinary subject connected with the days of our ancestors. She asked to be excused a moment, went into her parlor, and almost immediately reappeared with a recipe for *slemp* which she remembered having seen in a cookbook her great-great-grandmother had started to write in the year 1746, when all great ladies were also supposed to be great cooks. She copied it and gave it to me, and here it is:

2 quarts of milk
a pinch of saffron
1 tablespoonful of tea
8 cloves
3 inches of stick cinnamon
a pinch of mace
1/6 pound of sugar
2 tablespoons of cornmeal

Put all the spices and the tea into a small bag like an ordinary tea bag. Drop the bag into the milk and start it boiling very slowly. From time to time, take the spice bag between two forks and squeeze the juice out of it. After about half an hour, add the cornmeal and the sugar. Then let everything simmer for another five minutes and serve it in teacups.

Of course, Jefferson might have a terrific aversion to this concoction. However, as it was easy to make and much cheaper than hard liquor, he would undoubtedly be interested in this beverage as something that might have been introduced among his Virginia neighbors to wean them away from the dangerous products of their stills. He had spent the latter half of his life looking for such substitutes but never, I am afraid, had found them.

When you are going to entertain a man of as wide tastes as Thomas Jefferson had been, the subject of music too had to be thought out with more than usual care. Our guest had been a very competent fiddler before he had suffered that accident on horseback which left him with a perpetually stiff arm. But even after he had ceased to play himself, he had kept up his interest in music and, by ordering all the best compositions that were published in London and Paris, he had always been well informed about all the latest novelties for both the violin and the pianoforte.

But how far back had he gone? Had he known Bach and Handel? Or the great Italians of the seventeenth century? I thought he probably had and I asked Hein to start our evening's concert with Bach's motet, *Jesu, meine Freude,* and let this be followed by the first two records of Handel's *Water Music.* Then the first part of Karl von Dittersdorf's String Quartet No. 6, in A major, and Haydn's "The Heavens are telling," from *The Creation.*

But I remembered that he could not possibly have heard a great deal of orchestral music. Even today the government which resides in the capital of the greatest nation on earth does not consider it necessary to support a symphony orchestra and leaves this matter to private initiative. Therefore, I felt that it would be perhaps wiser to let the rest of the program consist of very simple melodies, such as records of parts of Bach's Italian Concerto, the first part of his Toccata in D major, Haydn's Minuet in C-sharp minor, and Castagnetta's rendition of Bach's "Chromatic" Fantasia and her three short pieces from *The Well-Tempered Clavichord,* which she had sent me a short time before.

I also promised myself that if possible I would get our guest to talk a little upon the subject of music as part of a program of public well-being. He was, as far as I can remember, our only President to whom music had meant something more than a hymn and *I've Been Working on the Railroad.* It would be nice to find out what he felt upon the subject.

I did not look forward to any spectacular mode of approach on the part of Mr. Jefferson. I expected that he would come on horseback, and so he did, riding a fine Virginia mare which he examined most carefully after his arrival.

"There was so much snow," he explained, "that she slipped several times, but I don't think that any harm has come to her. By the way, I notice that you have a stable boy ready to take care of her." (I had asked our local livery-stable man to be at Frits' house at seven o'clock.) "That was very thoughtful of you, but how could you guess that I would come on horseback?"

"I remembered the fourth of March of the year 1801," I answered.

"Oh, that silly story about my inauguration! As a matter of fact, I did not even go on horseback, as people still seem to say. I walked. It was much the safer way. I could, of course, have taken my coach, but with Pennsylvania Avenue one long mud puddle, it seemed much wiser to go on foot. And also, I needed the exercise. Later, I needed it even more, for being President of the United States is hard work. You are never master of your own time. Just when you want to go out for a little fresh air, some bore is sure to walk in, and, of course, you've got to see him, and he promises you that he will take only five minutes of your valuable time, but he stays five hours! In the end, you are no wiser than you were before he came, but you have lost your chance at the fresh air. You are quite sure they will know how to take care of my horse? I am devoted to the animal."

"My dear sir, these people have taken care of horses and have loved them for the last three hundred years, so you really need not worry. And now, won't you please come in? It is cold, and you must feel tired after your long ride."

Erasmus and Frits were waiting for us, and we had (encouraged by our party of the week before) taken the liberty of inviting Lucie and Jimmie. I knew that Jimmie would appeal to the former President because of her gift for figures and her love of facts and on account of that practical common sense which was perhaps her most outstanding quality, whereas Lucie, who was a direct flareback to the eighteenth century, would remind him of all the many charming women by whom he had been surrounded during most of his life. Lucie even bore (at least, I thought so) a slight resemblance to his beloved Martha. In this

Veere in winter.

I had guessed right, for just before we went to table, he took her gently by the hand and said, "It will not only be an honor but a pleasure for me, madam, to spend an evening sitting by your side. You remind me of one whom I held dearer than life itself, for you have Martha's smile. There were not any Wayleses among your ancestors, were there?"

"I'm sorry," Lucie answered. "All my people were either Dutch or French. There is not a drop of English blood in my veins."

"Then it is only my great good luck that you should be the way you are," and he handed her into her chair with such exquisite elegance that I could well understand why the awkward Adamses had always disliked him so thoroughly and had denounced him for his so-called aristocratic leanings.

On a social basis Monticello and Quincy had never been able to understand each other. At times they had dropped their private differences to work for the common good of the republic, but as for inviting each other to dinner—no, that had been out of the question if it possibly could have been helped.

Jo's Zeeland costume greatly interested our guest, and he asked Lucie to tell him in detail how it was arranged.

"It takes thirty-eight pins to put it on the correct way," Lucie informed him.

"Thirty-eight pins! Every morning! Doesn't that mean a lot of time just wasted and isn't it horribly unpractical?"

"It could not possibly be less practical," Lucie agreed.

"Then why do women go on wearing it?"

"Your Excellency knows why," Lucie answered.

"You may as well call me Mr. Jefferson, ma'am."

"I know that I have your permission, sir, but I have not got my own."

"That is curious! And why not?"

"Does Your Excellency see that Rembrandt etching on the wall over there?"

"I do, ma'am."

"How would it look in a cardboard frame?"

"Not so well, I'm afraid. It seems to need just that kind of frame."

"There Your Excellency has his answer," Lucie continued, "both why I shall go on giving you a title which provides you with the right frame and why these girls continue to wear their impractical clothes."

"They make them look lovely. Is that what you meant to imply, ma'am?"

"Your Excellency reads my mind like a book."

"And a delightful book it is, Madame Lucie, and· in exactly the right kind of binding."

"Thank you, Monsieur Thomas."

"Your very good health, Madame Lucie."

"*Merci,* Monsieur Thomas, and yours."

But it was not only with Lucie that Jefferson was right away at home. He had been delighted to make the acquaintance of Erasmus, whose *Colloquies* and *Praise of Folly* he had read at college. With Jimmie, he at once got lost in a serious discussion of the metric system, which, however, did not lead very far, as both of them fully agreed that America had made a terrible mistake when immediately after the French Revolution it had failed to adopt the metric system and had stuck to the cumbersome old English method. But the metric system had been devised by revolutionaries, as Jefferson observed, and that, of course, had been enough to make it highly suspicious in the eyes of all good patriots who had prayed day and night for the defeat of the wicked regicides in Paris.

What made the author of the Declaration of Independence such an ideal guest was the fact that he was one of the most observant men we had ever met. He noticed everything, absolutely everything. He immediately remarked upon the macaroni in the soup, and this led to a discussion of the best way to feed the poorer classes, especially in the more backward frontier regions, where it was very difficult to avoid an almost unbearable monotony.

The olives in the duck's stuffing caused him to explain his own efforts to grow olive trees on his estate in Virginia. And the champignons made him regret the conservatism of most people in the matter of food, which prevented them from eating all sorts of cereals and fruits which would have been excellent for them from every point of view if only they had been able to overcome their foolish prejudices.

"Now take rice," he said. "It has marvelous food values. I experimented with rice all my life. It grows in the valley of the Po, and so there is no reason why it should not grow equally well in Virginia and in Georgia and in Kentucky. But our people would not eat it. They would rather starve than eat it. Take French endives. I imported them from France to take the place of the salads which do not grow so well in our hot climate. But it was hopeless. I did my best to make each of our farmers raise a few endives in their own gardens. They refused—every single one of them. None of that 'foreign fodder' for freeborn Americans.

"Then there was broccoli—a fine substitute for cauliflower. I raised some of it in Monticello, but my neighbors would not touch it. And there was this macaroni, which the Italians had found to be an excellent staple for those who had large families and were too poor to buy anything else. But even the poorest of my day laborers would have none of it. And think of the wines we could have grown! Wine, to my way of thinking, is one of the necessities of life and it is also the best antidote for the bane of whisky, that vile stuff which has killed more of our young men than all the wars we ever fought. I used to take my neighbors over my place and show them my vineyards. Then they went home and built themselves another still.

"And finally, there was a practical and handy kind of democracy I tried to introduce. It consisted of equal rights for all and special privileges for none. It was ideally suited for our soil, and I am convinced that we could have made it work too, if we had seen to it that each man had got his own little plot of land, for that is the only way to make any kind of democracy work. Give every man and woman a bit of soil they can call their own, and at the same time you will instill into them a feeling of responsibility for the whole of the community.

"Look at those big cities in France and England! I visited all of them when I was in Europe. I was not in a hurry. I spent considerable time in most of them. I studied them carefully. Ninety per cent of the people who lived in those towns had nothing, never had had anything, and never would have anything they could call their own. Why should they have been interested in what happened to the other ten per cent or in the country as a whole? But the moment you gave them a few acres of land—even less—which they could really call their own, they were eager to work for it, willing to fight for it, and, if necessary, to die for it. I tried to make my friends in Congress see it that way, but as soon as I began to ride my hobby, they would smile vaguely and tell me they had a very important appointment and would I please excuse them. And off they would be, and I would not see them again until a week later."

Here Mr. Jefferson halted abruptly and, turning to Lucie, said, "But I am afraid that all this must bore you, my dear ma'am, almost as much as it used to bore poor Alexander Hamilton."

Lucie smiled at him. "I thought that Your Excellency told me a moment ago that he did not like Mr. Hamilton. Or did I read that in the book our host gave me last night?"

"Again, ma'am, you win. Pray forgive me for being so clumsy, and remember that I am a bit out of practice. It is a long time since I was engaged in one of these pleasant verbal duels. And now, if you will pardon me, I would like to propose a toast."

I got up and addressing him directly I said, "And if you will pardon me, sir, it is I and not you who will propose that toast. But I am sure it will be the same toast as you would have given, and so it does not really matter which of us speaks."

Then lifting my glass I said, "To the nation you founded, sir. May it some day become what you hoped to make it—a beacon of justice and fairness to guide all mankind toward a happier future."

Jefferson thanked me with a slight bow of the head. Then he remained silent for quite a while, but soon his ideas had become formulated. "I thank you for your gracious words, my dear fellow citizen," he said, raising his own glass, "for with all my respect for your native land, which taught me much, I still feel that no greater honor can befall any man than to be called a citizen of our beloved republic. Yes indeed, I thank you and from the bottom of my heart. You remarked a moment ago that I had helped to found a nation which you hoped might some day become a beacon of justice and righteousness. I noticed that you used the qualitative clause. Let me change that just a little. Let me express the firm conviction that it will actually do so, and ere long. And now enough of this, for here I am talking again as if I were delivering a speech in Congress and, as you know, I never was a believer in long orations. They are a waste of time and they settle nothing. So let us spend the rest of the evening trying to remember that God gave us this world for the express purpose of our being happy in it—all of us!

"You told me when I arrived that you had some special music for me. If the ladies won't mind, would you play it for me?"

At all our former parties we had begun the dinner with music so as to break the ice and make everyone feel at ease. But tonight the talk had been so animated from the very beginning that I had told Hein to forget about his gramophone. I now asked him to turn it on and to start with Handel's *Water Music* while Jo passed the waffles. They had been brought by a boy on a bicycle, and the poor lad was half frozen after his long trip through the snow, so we put him in the kitchen to get thawed out and to have his share of waffles, for although he delivered them every day, he rarely got a taste of his master's products. As for the rest of the party, we were in a mood of such perfect contentment with ourselves and with the world at large that we did not bother to move over to the fire but merely pushed our chairs back a little to make ourselves entirely comfortable and remained where we were.

In this way we passed the next hour, and then Hein turned on Bach's *Well-Tempered Clavichord.* Jefferson listened intently. "What charming melodies!" he said. "I never heard them

before. I don't know how they escaped my attention. That first piece—it is so simple. I would have liked to play an obbligato to it."

"Perhaps you would care to do so now," I said.

"But you only have a piano, and I can't play it. I used to be a fiddler, but with that bad arm of mine, there is not much left I can do. Just the same, this is so much like olden times, I wonder whether you have a fiddle in this delightful house, where you seem to have everything else needed to make life happy and beautiful?"

"I have two violins here."

"You have? How wonderful! Will you let me see them? What are they?"

I took my violins out of their cases. I had brought them with me because I had anticipated—or rather, I had hoped—that something like this might happen. Mr. Jefferson was especially

Thomas Jefferson tried out my best fiddle.

delighted with the Amati, a very early one and therefore somewhat smaller than the later models. Not very powerful of tone, but with a most agreeable voice, like that of an Italian singer who has not been spoiled by the Scala or the Metropolitan.

"This one would suit me best, but my fingers must be terribly stiff after a hundred years without any practice."

The fingers proved to be less unobliging than he had expected, and he took the utmost delight in trying to discover how much he had lost and how much he had retained, and when the gramophone stopped he was so carried away by his own enthusiasm that he went on playing the simple tunes he remembered from his childhood days. I knew most of them too, and taking the other violin, the modest Serafino, I played the second parts (making them up as best I could), and our concert might have gone on until the hour of departure, but at half-past eleven the telephone rang.

This was a most unusual occurrence, for the postmaster always went to bed at ten and never got up except in case of high emergency. All of us therefore felt that something very unusual must have happened and, as always on such occasions, we held our breath and while we pretended not to be listening, we tried to catch every word that was being said.

The call seemed to come from Amsterdam, and apparently it was Frits' partner who was talking. Their conversation did not last long, and then Frits told us that his partner had called him up to inform him that according to the news on the Exchange that afternoon, Hitler would become Reichsführer the day after next or just as soon as old Hindenburg would be well enough to go through the necessary ceremonies.

Jefferson noticed our consternation and discreetly inquired whether anything very serious had happened. Perhaps we had lost a friend or relative?

"No, sir," I told him, "not exactly a relative, but a very dear friend. She is still alive, but God only knows how much longer we shall have her with us."

Then I hesitated. Should I tell him that the name of this

friend was Liberty? Or should I spare him the grief of knowing that that ideal, for which he himself had so valiantly fought all his days, was on the point of being destroyed in every country of this earth and that it could not possibly survive unless our own beacon began to burn brighter than ever and right away, too.

I looked at Lucie. She understood. "Won't Your Excellency play us once more that tune he had just begun when he was interrupted?" she asked. Jo too, with her fine sense for the right thing at the right moment, felt that something must be done to allay his suspicion that something had gone very much wrong. She suggested a third round of waffles, but there were not any. The hungry boy had eaten them all, and he was now fast asleep. But there was still plenty of *slemp,* and the hot drink took Jefferson back to the days he had spent in the Low Countries, trying to raise funds for the Revolution, and he entertained us most amusingly with stories about the great-grandfathers of the men and women with whom we ourselves had grown up and in whom we recognized many of the characteristics of their ancestors.

That was all. As Veere houses had been built in the days before ventilation had been invented, the air in the room was growing pretty bad. We therefore opened the door. Outside, the night was of a particularly clear beauty. Millions of stars were shining brightly. Our beloved village looked more peaceful than ever. Just before midnight, Thomas Jefferson once more picked up my Amati.

"Do you by any chance remember this melody?" he asked, and he played us an old version of *Drink to Me Only with Thine Eyes.* I did remember it and once more played the second part while Lucie and Frits hummed the words.

A few minutes before twelve o'clock the bells of the tower chimed in with Valerius' *Hymn of Thanksgiving.* The violin began to sing softer and softer while the bells gradually increased in strength. In this way, Thomas Jefferson once more slipped out of our lives. The clock struck twelve and we were alone with our thoughts. The noblest champion of freedom the world has ever seen was gone while the dread specter of tyranny was rapidly descending upon earth.

Four days later I was on my way to America. Exactly five weeks later, I was back in Veere. Nothing had happened. Outwardly everything was as it had always been. But a change had come over the world, and neither Frits nor I felt in the mood to go on with our dinner parties. At least, not for the moment. Some other day perhaps, but not now.

"The music has gone out of our lives," as Jo so aptly put it when one day we were sitting in her kitchen and were finishing the last few drops of the cognac that had been left after Thomas Jefferson's visit.

"But no more weeping, if you please," she added. "Do you remember what our ancestors used to say when everything went wrong? *Ende desespereert niet.* Whatever we do, let us never despair. So here is to good health and here is to our love for each other and here is to hope."

Jimmie, Lucie, Frits, and I looked at each other and repeated Jo's prayer. "Here is to hope!"

Here Is a List of Our Guests, Together with the Chapters in Which They Make Their Appearance in This Book.

found time to lecture, draw cartoons against Hitler, keep his former fellow countrymen informed about the war by means of short-wave broadcasts in Dutch, serve with countless groups devoted to the alleviation of suffering—and, for relaxation, to play his beloved fiddle.

His next book, on which he is already at work, will be his long-awaited story of Ludwig van Beethoven.

The new method of writing history established by Hendrik Willem van Loon has now become an integral part of the teaching method of most civilized countries, and his works on history, geography, and the arts have appeared in 147 different translations in 21 languages.

The country of his birth has knighted him. His adopted country has honored him by the affectionate devotion of millions of readers who, without his writings, might never have been tempted to take an interest in history or the arts. By and large, he feels that he has received more than he deserved, and, being a person capable of gratitude, he also is a fairly happy one. And that is as much as he cared to tell us about himself.

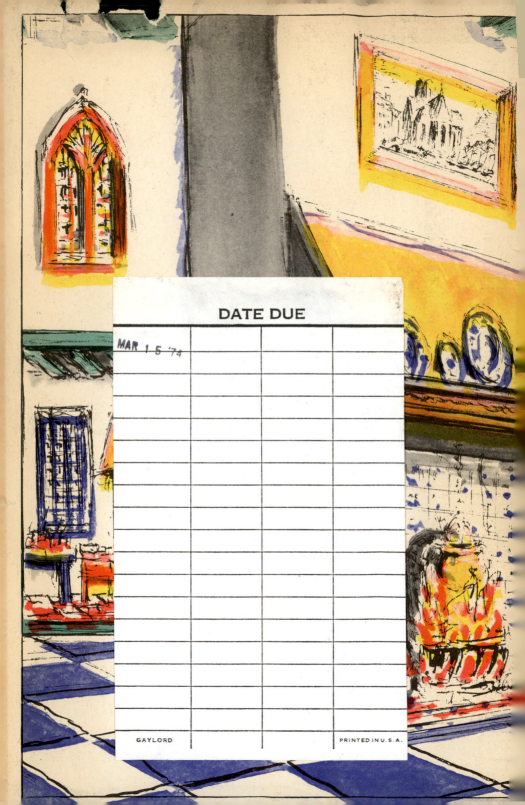

DATE DUE

MAR 1 5 '74			